ROBERT H. HAMMOND, Lt. Colonel, U.S. Army, is Associate Professor of Advanced Engineering Fundamentals at the U. S. Military Academy. He is Chairman of the Division of Engineering Graphics of the American Society for Engineering Education. Colonel Hammond formerly taught at Purdue University.

CARSON P. BUCK is Administrator of the Engineering Graphics Program and Assistant Dean of the College of Engineering of Syracuse University. He has been Chairman of the Department of Engineering Graphics there and Associate Professor in the Department of Engineering Drawing at the University of Notre Dame. Dean Buck is Chairman of the Future Development Committee of the A.S.E.E. Division of Engineering Graphics.

WILLIAM B. ROGERS, Lt. Colonel in the U. S. Army Corps of Engineers, is Associate Professor of Engineering Fundamentals at the U. S. Military Academy, and Circulation Manager of the *Journal of Engineering Graphics* of the American Society for Engineering Education. He formerly taught at the University of Florida.

GERALD W. WALSH, JR., is Associate Professor of Engineering Science at Jefferson Community College. Formerly, he was Assistant Professor of Mechanical Engineering and Engineering Graphics at Syracuse University, and Development Engineer for the Carrier Corporation.

HUGH P. ACKERT is Associate Professor of Mechanical Engineering at the University of Notre Dame. Professor Ackert was formerly Head of the Industrial Arts Department of Southern State Teachers College.

ENGINEERING

for design and

THE RONALD PRESS

GRAPHICS
analysis

ROBERT H. HAMMOND
United States Military Academy

CARSON P. BUCK
Syracuse University

WILLIAM B. ROGERS
United States Military Academy

GERALD W. WALSH, JR.
Jefferson Community College

HUGH P. ACKERT
University of Notre Dame

COMPANY • NEW YORK

PREFACE

This book reflects the growing needs of the engineer for a greater breadth of comprehension of graphics as a powerful tool in the design process. Its principal purpose is to provide the student with an understanding of the complete role the graphic language plays in the conception, analysis, and communication of ideas. Emphasis is on the theory of projection and on analysis rather than merely on the techniques and skills required in preparing a production drawing. The development of skill is also stressed as it affects the concepts of accuracy in the use of graphics for analysis. At the same time sufficient material is presented to enable the student to understand basic production drawings and to provide the background for the understanding of more complex drawings. The authors have used this material in their various classes and believe that it accomplishes its purpose in the light of the present needs in engineering education.

Spatial relationships required for the analysis of three-dimensional problems are presented in a way that permits the student to develop his own solution for any particular problem. Of special interest is the large number of step-by-step illustrations supplementing the text discussion. It should also be noted that no concept is applied in any solution until the theory of that concept has been developed for the general case.

Many engineers and scientists, when required to analyze a situation, rely on the use of symbolic mathematics. However, almost all symbolic mathematics can be represented and manipulated in graphic form. In this form problems are very often easier to understand and the effects of varying conditions more clearly visualized than through the more abstract manipulation of symbolic mathematics. Thus the engineers and scientists are, in effect, crippled in their use of rapid tools for analysis unless they have an understanding of graphic as well as symbolic mathematics. The use of the computer has hastened the need for an understanding of graphic solutions since before a computer output can be accepted as factual it must be checked initially against some known solution. Though not as precise as symbolic solutions, graphic solutions will often provide a time-saving check sufficiently precise for the purpose of a test solution.

An undertaking of this sort must of necessity depend on the contributions of a host of people. It is impossible to thank all personally and individually but the authors do wish to express their gratitude for any and all assistance. The authors wish to acknowledge in particular the contributions of Mr. R. Ford Pray in the preparation of the majority of the illustrations and his assistance in the critical evaluation of the material presented. The authors wish further to acknowledge the good advice and most constructive criticism of Dr. Andrew Longacre of Syracuse University. Acknowledgment is also given to the American Standards Association for the illustrations and tables extracted from their standards by permission of the publisher, the American Society of Mechanical Engineers.

Some of the figures in this book were drawn and adapted from material in *Basic Engineering Drawing* by Turner, Buck, and Ackert. Two co-authors of the present volume, Carson P. Buck and Hugh P. Ackert, especially wish to express their appreciation and gratitude to their former teacher, mentor, and colleague, William Wirt Turner, former Head of the Department of Engineering Drawing at the University of Notre Dame, for his assistance, guidance, and encouragement over the years.

To our wives and immediate colleagues go our very special thanks for their help and patience.

ROBERT H. HAMMOND
CARSON P. BUCK
WILLIAM B. ROGERS
GERALD W. WALSH, JR.
HUGH P. ACKERT

March, 1964

CONTENTS

II.   Projection Drawing

III.   Spatial Analysis

IV.   Graphical Mathematics

V.   Applications

Appendix

ENGINEERING GRAPHICS

1

INTRODUCTION

1-1. COMMUNICATION

Man's progress through the ages has been measured by his ability to convert his ideas into realities. Initially, alone, or with little help, he translated his creative thoughts directly into a finished product. He made his own tools and weapons, built his own houses, and fashioned his own transport vehicles. Verbal expression and example sufficed to accomplish the transmission of the little direction that was needed to effect the completion of his projects.

As communities were established and projects became more complex, the need grew for recording ideas and transmitting instructions—frequently at a distance. As a result, man gradually developed graphical means of expressing himself and thereby communicating with others, who also understood the meaning of the symbols used. It is natural that these early symbols were crude representations of objects, sounds, and ideas.

Graphical expression has developed in several forms. We have on the one hand man's artistic expression in the form of drawing and painting, etc. Then we have the development of letter symbols which in turn have given us our written languages.

Next there has been the development of numbers and other mathematical symbols that provide a vehicle for the efficient development of commerce as well as providing a means by which man analyzes and expresses concepts of his spatial environment.

Concurrently with the development of the use of mathematical symbols there has been the development of what is known today as *Engineering Graphics*. This is the science of the use of points, lines, and planes combined with principles of projection to present visually the accurate mathematical representation of physical or energy concepts and systems. Because of the mathematical relationships that exist, this latter mode of communication also serves as a vehicle for analysis.

1-2. HISTORICAL DEVELOPMENT

Isaac Newton once said, "If I see as from a mountain, it is because I stand on the shoulders of giants." In order to have a better frame of reference and to gain a more complete understanding of the graphical methods used by the engineer in representation and analysis, one should have an appreciation for the historical development of the science.

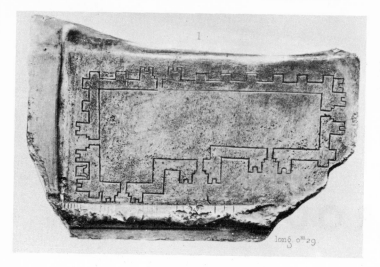

Fig. **1–1.** Statue of Gudea, Chaldean engineer, holding plans for a building (2200 B.C.). (From Ernest de Sarzec, *Découvertes en Chaldée,* 1891. Courtesy Yale University Library.)

The first plan of an irrigation system, a building, or other structure became the first graphical engineering communication. Initially there was no use of projection per se, though many of the earliest known technical drawings are plan views of structures. In the Louvre is perhaps one of the earliest known examples. It consists of a plan of a building, possibly a fort, engraved on a stone tablet. The plan was made for Gudea, a Chaldean engineer. There is also a statue of Gudea seated and holding the tablet on his lap. This statue dates back to approximately 2200 B.C. (Fig. 1–1).

Perhaps the first person to realize the possibilities of associating plan and elevation drawings in a mathematical fashion while using the same scale was Marcus Vitruvius (63 B.C.–14 A.D.). He was an architect and built, among other structures, a basilica at Farno in Umbria, Italy.

In the latter part of the fifteenth century and the early part of the sixteenth century drawings showing three views of an object were in use. The drawings were made in what is now referred to as first angle projection[1] and were based on orthographic projection. Examples of these are found in the works of Pierro della Francesca (1410–1492) and Albrecht Durer (1471–1528).

Leonardo da Vinci (1475–1516) was another famous historical figure who contributed greatly to the beginnings of the engineering profession. He was equally famous as an artist and an engineer. Many of his ideas for inventions, which give evidence of a keen imagination, have been preserved for us by his very complete sketches (Fig. 1–2). He also wrote an exposition on the theory of perspective, which probably gave direction to many subsequent efforts in this field.

It remained, however, for Gaspard Mongé (1746–1818) to synthesize the work of his predecessors and develop the science of descriptive

[1] Projection angles and theory are discussed in detail in Chapter 5. It is sufficient to note here that in first angle projection the object is considered to be in front of the projection planes; in third angle projection, the object is considered to be behind the projection planes.

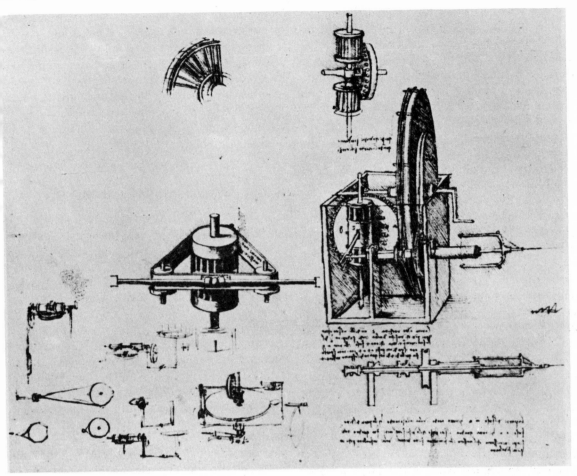

Fig. 1–2. Design sketches by Leonardo da Vinci for a proposed machine device. (Courtesy of the IBM Corporation.)

geometry. Descriptive geometry is the science of the application of orthographic projection to the construction of related views of objects and particularly to the solution of spatial problems.

Mongé is known as the "father of descriptive geometry." While a young man at military school at Mézières, he developed and advanced the application of orthographic projection to the solution of spatial problems. His initial efforts were concerned with military fortifications, and for a time a cloak of secrecy shrouded his work. In 1795 he published "Leçons de Géométrie Descriptive," a series of lecture notes, and in 1800 the first text on the subject.

In 1816, Claude Crozet introduced descriptive geometry to the United States. At the time Crozet was assistant professor of engineering at the United States Military Academy, West Point, New York. In 1821 he wrote the first descriptive geometry textbook published in the United States.[2] Because there were no descriptive geometry textbooks printed in English available when Crozet started teaching at West Point, an interesting development resulted. Teaching geometry to a class without the aid of pictures was impractical. As a result, he made use of an idea he was familiar with from the École Polytechnic in France. He built an oversized schoolboy's slate of wood covered with black paint, and thus was born the first classroom use of a blackboard in the United States.

[2] CROZET, Claude, *Descriptive Geometry*, 1st ed. (New York: A. T. Goodrich Co., 1821).

During the balance of the nineteenth century, texts in descriptive geometry in the United States showed the basic European influence by using first angle projection as the basis of presentation of the subject. With the advent of the twentieth century, texts began to appear based on third angle projection. Professor W. S. Hall of Lafayette College was the first to do this.[3]

The early years of the twentieth century also saw the beginnings of the modern "direct" or auxiliary view method for the graphical solution of spatial problems. Professor J. A. Moyer's text[4] was the first one giving evidence of the use of this method, which is now the common method of presentation. The terms "direct" and "indirect" arise from the fact that in the former approach solutions to spatial problems are accomplished by projecting onto auxiliary planes of projection that show directly the desired relationships. In the use of the indirect method the spatial situation is first referred to the principal planes of projection and then the views are revolved until the solution is obtained. In 1926, Professor G. J. Hood of the University of Kansas published the first text[5] that combined the "direct" method and third angle projection throughout. This approach is the commonly accepted one in the U.S. today.

At this point, we have traced the development of projection methods which form the basis of both graphical representation and spatial analysis. Perhaps an additional note should be made relative to graphical representation. The development of a knowledge of the principles of projection was paralleled with greater application of these principles to all the phases of graphical representation. From the time of Mongé on, great strides were made in graphical presentation. Applications to many fields such as architectural, structural, map, and machine drawing, were developed and perfected.

Machine drawing, which concerns the representation of machine parts and assemblies and related material, and whose formal beginnings might be attributed to James Nasmyth (1808–1890) about 1839, developed to the point where in recent years it made up the bulk of most engineering drawing courses in schools of engineering. The last decade has seen a drastic revision of graphics course content based on a reappraisal of the function of graphics in the engineering curriculum. It is now felt that a more comprehensive understanding of graphics in all of its phases, including analysis as well as representation, is needed by the engineer.

1–3. GRAPHICS AND THE ENGINEER

Essentially, engineering is the art of applying scientific knowledge in the process of efficiently converting natural resources to the service of mankind. In doing so the engineer follows a process which consists of transforming a conceptual design through the stages of "bread board" model and prototype to finished design. He makes use of the scientific method in analyzing and perfecting his concept, and throughout the process of conceptualization the science of engineering graphics aids him in the analysis of his design and in the presentation of information (Fig. 1–3).

The engineer has through the ages been characterized by his ability to visualize and analyze spatial concepts. His ability to work graphically with such concepts is most advantageous to him as the means of expressing himself and directing his ideas to fruition. To this extent the often used phrase that engineering graphics is "the language of the engineer" is true. One of the principal functions of the engineer is to develop and design systems and products useful to humanity. This text presents the graphics tools necessary for this work. The balance of this chapter will give a brief summation of the phases of engineering graphics to be treated in this text and their importance to the engineer.

1–4. ENGINEERS AND DRAFTING SKILL

The question frequently arises as to how much proficiency, if any, is necessary for the practicing engineer to have with drafting instruments. The crowded curriculum of the engineering college affords little time for the development of manipulative skills, either with the drawing instruments or

---

[3] HALL, William S., *Descriptive Geometry*, 1st ed. (New York: D. Van Nostrand, 1902).

[4] MOYER, James A., *Engineering Descriptive Geometry*, 2d ed. (New York: John Wiley and Sons, 1905).

[5] HOOD, George J., *Geometry of Engineering Drawing, Descriptive Geometry by the Direct Method*, 1st ed. (New York: McGraw-Hill Book Co., Inc., 1926).

Fig. 1–3. Engineers design new products, devise production methods, and develop the unique equipment used in many manufacturing operations in the Apparatus and Optical Division of the Eastman Kodak Company in Rochester, N. Y.

other technical tools.   In practice, the services of a trained engineer are far too valuable to be utilized at routine drawing board tasks which can be better handled by a skilled technician.   However, neither of these conditions relieves the engineer of the *responsibility* for developing a reasonable skill in the use of drawing instruments. The engineer, lacking a reasonable facility with drawing instruments, will often overlook a relatively simple graphical solution to a problem in favor of a more difficult and time-consuming (hence expensive) approach simply because he lacks confidence in his ability to achieve satisfactory results on the drawing board.   A nominal skill should be acquired as early as possible.   This is why graphics courses are given early in college programs.   Development of draft-

ing skill is continuous throughout the engineer's career; the degree of development depends upon the amount of drawing board work his chosen specialty requires.

In practice, an experienced engineer may personally develop the initial basic conceptual design layout of a project.   He will then turn over to the technician, or in some cases a less experienced engineer, the task of turning out the detailed representational drawings.   While the engineer may seldom actually make such representational drawings himself, he will supervise those who do, and is responsible for their work.   He assigns tasks to others working under his supervision, judges the results of their work, and approves the final product.   This requires a knowledge of drafting skill, the capabilities and limitations of the instruments, an understanding of the time required to perform a given task, and the recognition of quality in the finished drawing. Such appreciation of the draftsman's problems can best be acquired as a result of the engineer's own experience with the drawing instruments. When drafting work falls short of the engineer's requirements, the engineer should be capable of picking up the instruments and showing just what he wants and how it can best be accomplished.

Part I of this text presents the basic graphic techniques necessary to the proper and effective use of drafting instruments and the skillful execution of freehand work and lettering. The material has been presented with particularly painstaking simplicity, because it is assumed that little if any time will be devoted to these topics in the college classroom. Many students arrive at college with some degree of proficiency in the use of drafting equipment. Those who do not will be expected to develop and perfect this necessary proficiency on their own. Part I can serve as a self-teaching unit or as a ready reference review.

1–5. REPRESENTATIONAL DRAWING

Projection theory, developed in Part II, serves as the means for the creation of representational drawings. Such drawings provide a means of communication between the engineer, who conceives and describes an idea, and the individuals who convert the engineer's "instructions" into a reality. These drawings must describe a particular item or project accurately, definitely, and completely and in addition provide such supplemental information as is necessary to carry the concept to completion.

Pictorial drawings or sketches used by the engineer can lend understanding about a particular engineering project to the layman, who may not be versed in the theory of orthographic projection. In engineering circles, they can supplement instructions relative to some rather complicated design which is not clearly delineated by orthographic views. Furthermore, pictorials, which are capable of being scaled, add an opportunity for the engineer to alter design measurements and at the same time have a reasonably accurate picture, pictorially, of what is happening as he does so.

The engineer can be handicapped in the process of transforming a design from concept to finished product if he cannot make use of pictorial sketches and drawings to aid him in the development of his ideas. It is with such sketches that the engineer *communicates with himself.* There are very few, if any, engineers who can develop a design entirely by mental effort; by far the great majority rely upon sketches to aid them in the development of their design concepts.

1–6. GRAPHICAL ANALYSIS

Graphical methods often provide comparatively simple solutions to engineering problems which may be quite difficult or even impossible to solve by other means. To make practical use of the graphical approach to the solution of engineering problems, the engineer must have a thorough understanding of both the problem involved and the fundamental principles of graphical techniques and their applications. This understanding further implies an appreciation for the capabilities and limitations of the graphic method.

In his dealings with the physical world, the engineer is concerned with three-dimensional space. As a result, most engineering problems are three-dimensional in nature. They can be solved by reference to a set of coordinate axes or planes. Symbolic mathematics makes use of the principles of analytic geometry, which refers problems to the principal XYZ coordinate axes. Descriptive geometry refers problems to principal coordinate planes, which in turn are defined by the principal axes. Thus both mathematical systems are directly related and it is possible to work from one to the other. Capable engineers make use of both systems in problem analysis, employing the system most suitable for the particular problem at hand. Part III on Spatial Analysis discusses the various principles of descriptive geometry and their application to three-dimensional problems.

The engineer, in dealing with his physical world, is also concerned with quantitative problems. Many of these are discrete as to nature of units, particularly when the problem concerns economics (something the engineer is vitally interested in relative to all his work) or quantity to be produced, etc. Many problems are based on quantity as a continuous function, as in the measurement of length, weight, or time. Both types of problems lend themselves to graphical solutions, the latter particularly so.

Except to the adept mathematical mind, symbolic mathematics does not generally give to its user the transitional picture of what is occurring while it is being employed to develop a solution involving continuous functions. Furthermore, solutions are generally given in discrete units even in the case of continuous functions. Graphical solutions to algebraic equations offer the advantage of graphically picturing the relationship of the functions involved in a problem, and thereby lend themselves to the quick determination of desired parameters. In other words, graphical methods can enable the engineer to "see" what is occurring in a problem as the values of the functions vary. Part IV, concerned with graphical mathematics, develops a number of the areas in which the graphical approach in the solution of quantitative problems can be advantageous.

1-7. FUTURE TRENDS

From concept to finished product or process is still a relatively slow procedure. True, through the years this procedure has been stepped up, until now, in some cases, the time lag from scientific discovery to completed engineering application has been reduced from, say, roughly 20 years at the turn of the century to a matter of months. Nevertheless, the dream frequently expressed is for the engineer somehow to acquire an Aladdin's lamp.

While we never may be able to approach the instantaneous perfection of Aladdin's genie, we are rapidly approaching the wedding of the designer and the finished product through the aid of the computer and automation.

Experimentally it is possible today: 1) with the aid of an oscilloscope "drawing board" joined to a computer, to make three-view orthographic drawings, having correct spatial relationships, more accurately and far quicker than it is possible to perform the identical task on the drafting board; 2) by means of handbook information stored in the computer, one can automatically design and draw structural members almost instantaneously that will correctly serve the functions for which they are intended; and 3) by tying the computer to machines, to fabricate and mass-produce parts according to specifications "created" on the computer "drawing board."

In essence then, it is going to be possible to associate directly the creative mind of the engineer with the finished product. We are several steps away as yet from the complete accomplishment of this concept on an industrial basis, but it is only a question of time.

Under the circumstances, one might well question the need for any formal education in graphics. Also, won't this eventually do away with the need, too, for draftsmen? The answer is, "Hardly," in either case. From the standpoint of the engineer, it is going to be more essential than ever that he have a working knowledge of graphics, its capabilities and its limitations. One who will be working directly in a graphical frame of reference will need to be versatile in his understanding of this frame of reference.

I
EQUIPMENT AND TECHNIQUES

2

DRAWING WITH INSTRUMENTS

2-1. INTRODUCTION

Drawing instruments are used by the engineer for the mechanical rendering of technical drawings. A good *mechanically rendered drawing* is the result of the correct use of precision instruments. Anyone can learn to draw with the drawing instruments. The ability to produce a good instrumental drawing has little to do with artistic talent. Considerable care should be taken to learn, at the beginning, the correct methods of handling the drawing instruments, and these details of technique should be constantly practiced. Initially, the correct details of technique must be consciously performed, and some effort may be necessary to make the hand do what the mind dictates. After some facility has been acquired in the use of the drawing instruments and the student has confidence in his ability, these drawing techniques become effortless and are performed without conscious thought. Good habits are as easily acquired as bad ones, provided correct methods are learned and conscientiously followed. Any deviation from approved techniques should be attempted only after the approved methods have been thoroughly mastered. Individual styles or shortcuts developed by the student in his early experiences usually result in bad habits which reduce his drafting efficiency and haunt him throughout his career.

2-2. THE DRAWING INSTRUMENTS

Good drawing instruments are precision tools, expensive to manufacture and to purchase. However, quality instruments, if given reasonable care, will produce excellent results even after many years of use. Cheap drawing instruments are a poor investment, and should be avoided. It is a mistake to attempt to "get by" with cheap and inferior instruments with the intention of purchasing better equipment later. Poor equipment is a constant annoyance, resulting in unsatisfactory work and lack of confidence in all drawing instruments. This does not mean, of course, that the beginner should buy for himself one each of the most expensive items offered in the instrument manufacturer's catalog. Money can be saved by buying only the basic equipment, and by "shopping around" for quality instruments at a reasonable price. The best assurance of quality in drawing instruments is the warranty of a reputable manufacturer. Before buying, the advice of draftsmen and engineers, who use drawing instruments in their daily work, should be sought. The graphics professor in the engineering college should be particularly helpful, since he is usually informed about products, prices, and new trends, and will probably have in his file the catalogs of several different manufacturers.

The items of basic drawing equipment listed below and illustrated in Fig. 2-1 and succeeding illustrations should satisfy the requirements for a college course in graphics, and prove adequate to handle most graphical problems which will be encountered. It will also provide an excellent beginning to the collection of professional equipment needed by the practicing engineer.

1. LEAD HOLDERS (three desirable with a supply of F, 2H, and 6H lead); see Fig. 2-7.
2. PENCIL POINTER (sandpaper pad, file, or mechanical pointer); see Fig. 2-6.
3. ERASER (a soft pencil eraser is best); see Fig. 2-8.
4. ERASING SHIELD (stainless steel); see Fig. 2-8.
5. DRAWING PAPER (white or buff colored; tracing paper or cloth as required).

6. DRAFTING TAPE (roll).
7. DRAWING BOARD AND T-SQUARE; see Fig. 2-3; or DRAWING BOARD equipped with a PARALLEL STRAIGHTEDGE; see Fig. 2-4.
8. 45° TRIANGLE (plastic).
9. 30°-60° TRIANGLE (plastic).
10. INSTRUMENT SET; see Fig. 2-2.
11. SCALES (triangular architect's scale and triangular civil engineer's scale or equivalent); see Figs. 2-30 and 2-32.
12. PROTRACTOR (plastic); see Fig. 2-21.
13. IRREGULAR (FRENCH) CURVE; see Fig. 2-53.
14. LETTERING INSTRUMENT (Braddock lettering triangle or Ames lettering instrument or equivalent); see Figs. 4-5 and 4-6.

The instrument set (item 10) is the most expensive single item required. It consists of a matched set of compasses, dividers, ruling pens, and accessories assembled in a fitted case. The instruments are made of steel, nickel-silver, plated brass, or aluminum alloy, the material depending upon both the design function of the instrument and the intended selling price of the set. A variety of

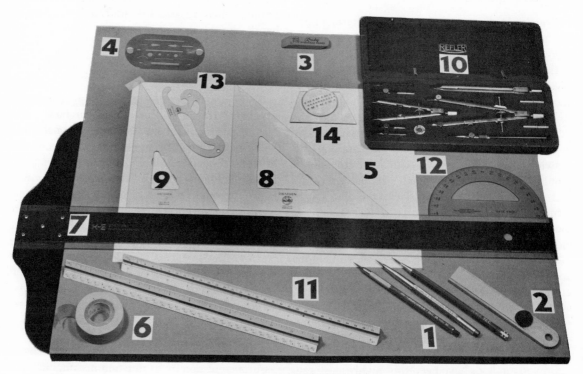

Fig. **2-1.** Basic drawing equipment.

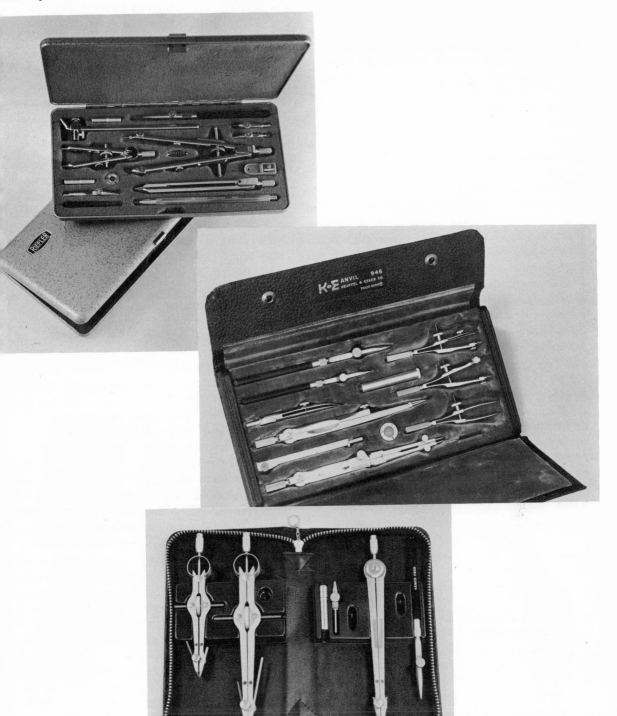

Fig. **2–2.** The instrument set. (Photographs courtesy of: Gramercy Import Co.,
Denver, Colo.; Keuffel & Esser Co., Hoboken, N. J.; V & E Mfg. Co., Pasadena, Calif.)

instrument designs and case styles are available. Typical instrument sets from several different manufacturers are illustrated in Fig. 2–2.

2–3. DRAWING SURFACES

Several types of drawing surfaces are commonly used for instrumental drawing. These are opaque paper, transparent paper, coated cloth, and glass cloth or plastic film.

Opaque drawing paper is usually white, buff, or light green in color. It should have a hard, fairly smooth, surface capable of taking both pencil and ink lines and with good erasing qualities for both pencil and ink. Opaque paper is generally used for original design layouts and for graphical solutions to problems. Buff or light green colors are often used to reduce eyestrain. Patent Office drawings, drawings for display or presentation purposes, and drawings which are to be photographed for printed reproduction in reports, technical publications, textbooks, etc., are usually drawn with ink on white paper.

Transparent drawing paper, usually referred to as tracing paper, is not really transparent, as a pane of clear glass is transparent, but is actually translucent. However, when tracing paper is placed in contact with a pencil drawing, the lines of the drawing are easily visible through the paper. Time was when drawings were first laid out in pencil on opaque paper and then traced on thin, rather fragile, tracing paper from which blueprints or other types of prints were made. Today, good quality tracing paper is tough, durable, and dimensionally stable, and the usual practice is to make the drawing directly on the tracing paper, thus saving considerable time and expense.

Tracing cloth is a high grade of finely woven cloth coated to provide a drawing surface for both pencil and ink. One side may be glazed, with the other side having a dull finish which takes a clean, sharp pencil or ink line, or both sides may have a dull finish. Tracing cloth is easy to work on, more transparent than paper, tough and durable. It is also expensive, subject to insect damage if not protected, and expands and shrinks with changes in relative humidity. Because of improved quality, good tracing paper has all but replaced cloth in the preparation of engineering drawings.

Glass cloth or *plastic films* have overcome the disadvantages of both paper and cloth. These are relatively new materials utilizing cloth woven of glass fibers or translucent plastic film. Both of these materials are more transparent than tracing cloth, offer a superb drawing surface which erases easily for both pencil and ink, are dimensionally stable and, with reasonable care, practically indestructible. Glass cloth or plastic films provide the ideal surface for instrumental drawing; however, their high cost restricts their use to assignments where a high degree of dimensional stability and/or extreme durability is required. These materials are particularly suited for the solution of graphical problems which must be drawn with great precision to a large scale.

Tracing paper, cloth, glass cloth, and plastic are all obtainable in either sheets or rolls, and are sold under various trade names.

Original engineering drawings are usually carefully filed in the drafting office where they are prepared. From these original drawings, full-size copies called *prints* are made. These prints are then distributed to the shop, prospective bidders, subcontractors, and others concerned with production, construction, purchasing, advertising, and the like. Additional prints can be prepared as required while the original drawing remains clean and undamaged for further use. When changes are made, they are made on the original drawing and properly recorded. The use of a transparent original is necessitated by the methods employed for making the prints or reproductions from the original drawings. The most common method now in use for reproducing engineering drawings is the dry diazo process. In this process, the copy is made on paper coated with a light-sensitive chemical. The sensitized copy paper is placed with its coated side in contact with the transparent original and a strong light is directed through the transparent original to the sensitized paper. Where the copy paper is exposed to the light, the sensitized coating is neutralized leaving only the white paper. Where the light is held back by the pencil or ink lines of the drawing, the chemical coating remains active. The copy is then separated from the original and "developed" in dry ammonia fumes produced by a container of aqua-ammonia. The ammonia fumes cause the sensitized areas of the copy paper which were not exposed to the light to turn black (or some other color depending on the choice of sensitized paper). The black lines that appear on the copy reproduce the lines drawn on the original. This process requires only a few minutes time, and the copies are dry and ready for immediate use.

2–4. DRAWING BOARDS AND STRAIGHTEDGES

The drawing board provides a smooth working surface to which the paper is fastened. Drawing boards are usually made of white pine or basswood, laminated to prevent warping, with wood or metal end ledges added to the left and right sides to provide true edges for the T-square. Wooden cleats are sometimes screwed to the underside of the board to add strength. Drawing boards vary in size from about $12'' \times 17''$ to as large as $60'' \times 120''$. The larger boards are often mounted

vertically, and are used in the production of full-size layouts of large objects. The size of the drawing board is dictated by the size of the drawing to be made on it. A medium-size board ($23'' \times 31''$) is usually adequate for student use. A board this size is about $\frac{3}{4}''$ thick, fairly light, and can be conveniently carried under the arm. It is a good idea, before using a new board, to cover the surface with heavy brown wrapping paper or a heavy plastic-coated paper specially made for this purpose. This will provide a smoother working surface, and preserve the board. Use of a light green cover will reduce eyestrain. The paper cover can be taped or stapled in place. Care should be taken that neither paper nor tape protrudes beyond the left or right edges of the board to interfere with the free movement of the T-square.

The T-*square* is used with the drawing board, and the two are usually considered together (Fig. 2–3). The T-square is used as a straightedge for drawing long, straight lines. At least one end ledge

Fig. **2–3.** Drawing board and T-square.

of the drawing board must be straight and true to provide a base for the head of the T-square. (To accommodate both right- and left-handed draftsmen, both the left and right end ledges of the drawing board should be true, although these two edges are not necessarily parallel.) The T-square is made in two parts, the head and the blade, joined firmly together with glue and screws at near 90°. (Exact perpendicularity between the head and the blade is not necessary as long as the angle is fixed.) The best T-squares are constructed with a thin hardwood blade with transparent plastic edges set in grooves along the wooden blade. These plastic edges are thinner than the blade so as to allow a slight space between the straightedge and the paper. This prevents the plastic from becoming scratched and losing its transparency. It also keeps the tip of the ruling pen, when inking against the T-square, from being in contact with the straightedge, a condition which often results in the ink's being drawn out of the pen and under the blade by

capillary attraction and causing a disastrous blot. T-square blades vary in length from 18″ to 72″, the length used depending upon the size of the board on which the T-square is to be employed. The T-square should have a blade long enough to reach almost all the way across the long dimension of the board.

In place of a T-square, the drawing board may be equipped with a *parallel straightedge* (Fig. 2–4). The parallel straightedge is a long blade similar to the T-square blade made to fit the length of the long dimension of the drawing board. Parallel motion is automatically maintained through a cord and pulley arrangement. On large drawing boards, the parallel straightedge is preferable to the T-square, which becomes unwieldy and difficult to control precisely in the longer lengths. The parallel straightedge is often attached directly to the top of a drawing table. This is usually the case with the larger sizes where the drawing table top doubles as a drawing board.

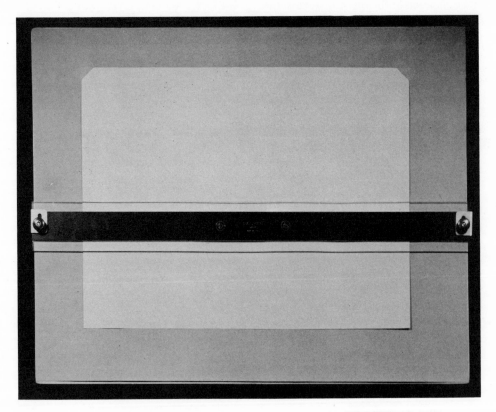

Fig. **2–4.** Drawing board with parallel straightedge.

2–5. PLACING THE DRAWING PAPER ON THE BOARD

Right-handed draftsmen should place the sheet of drawing paper generally in the left and upper two-thirds of the board area (Fig. 2–3). Left-handed draftsmen, who guide the head of the T-square against the right edge of the board, should place the paper in the upper right area of the drawing board. The degree of precision of the T-square diminishes toward the end of the blade, so the edge of the paper should be placed about two inches from the head. The paper must be placed high enough on the board to permit all or most of the T-square head to be guided by the edge of the drawing board when the blade has reached the bottom of the paper. When using the parallel straightedge, the paper can be centered on the board and need only be high enough for the top edge of the straightedge to reach the bottom of the paper. Advantages of the parallel straightedge are that it is uniformly rigid throughout its length, and permits fuller utilization of the drawing board area. When the paper has been located on the board in the proper area and approximately squared away, the top edge of the paper is carefully aligned with the top of the T-square blade or parallel straightedge. When using the T-square, care must be taken to insure that the head is bearing firmly against the true end ledge of the drawing board. The upper left and right corners of the paper are then fastened to the board with drafting tape. On small drawings, only the upper corners should be fastened down. This will be sufficient to keep the paper firmly in place, and will permit the paper to be raised for sweeping away eraser dust and foreign particles which inevitably find their way under the paper. Larger drawings, however, must be fastened down at all four corners and sometimes in between. The use of tape is recommended for fastening the paper to the board since it holds firmly, can be easily removed, and does not damage either the drawing paper or the board. Special drafting tape should be used for this purpose. Transparent cellophane tape is not good; it is difficult to remove and leaves a sticky residue. Drafting tape should be cut into short pieces about one inch long for fastening the corners of the paper to the board. Tearing the tape results in ragged and wrinkled tape edges which tend to catch the instruments and can thus cause mistakes.

2–6. PENCILS AND LEAD HOLDERS

Lines are drawn on the drawing paper with a drawing pencil, or more specifically, the "lead" of the pencil. Pencil lead is a mixture of powdered graphite and clay. The clay serves as a binder and at the same time regulates the blackness of the line. The proportion of clay and graphite determines the grade or hardness of the lead. The *soft* lead grades contain higher proportions of graphite, and produce blacker lines. Being literally softer, these soft grades wear faster and require more frequent sharpening. The *hard* lead grades contain more clay, and are capable of producing long, fine lines without re-pointing. Drawing leads are available in eighteen degrees of hardness identified by number and letter, ranging from 7B, the softest and blackest, to 9H, the hardest. The following table classifies the pencil grades into three groups (*hard, medium,* and *soft*) according to hardness, and indicates the best use of the pencils in each group.

Hard	9H	8H	7H	6H	5H	4H
Graphical calculations and other work requiring great accuracy.						
Medium	3H	2H	H	F	HB	B
Representation drawing, sketching, lettering, and most general-purpose work.						
Soft	2B	3B	4B	5B	6B	7B
Art work, shading on architectural renderings, large freehand sketches, etc. Too soft for instrumental work.						

Drawing leads may be cased in wood (usually cedar) or held in a lead holder to facilitate handling. Wooden casings for drawing pencils are hexagonal in cross section to reduce the probability of the pencil's rolling from a tilted drawing board. If wood pencils are used, the wood must be cut back from the lead with a sharp pocket knife or a special draftsman's pencil sharpener [Fig. 2–5(a)]. In order to retain the identity of the lead grade, the pencil should always be sharpened on the unlettered end. About $\frac{1}{2}$ inch of lead should be exposed. The lead must then be shaped, using a

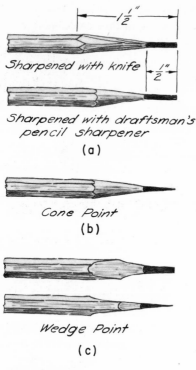

Sharpened with knife

Sharpened with draftsman's
pencil sharpener

(a)

Cone Point

(b)

Wedge Point

(c)

Fig. 2–5. The draftsman's point.

pad of sandpaper, a file, or a mechanical lead pointer (Fig. 2–6), to a long, conical point [Fig. 2–5(b)]. Some draftsmen prefer a wedge point [Fig. 2–5(c)], and for some purposes it may be useful. The wedge point must be shaped with a sandpaper pad or file.

While a few draftsmen still prefer the wood drawing pencil, the *lead holder* (Fig. 2–7) is recommended. The lead holder is easier and faster to use, and results in less mess and bother. A large variety of weights, sizes, and styles of lead holders are available, and the one best suited to the tastes of the individual draftsman should be chosen. Most are quite well made and durable, and with minimum care will last a long time. While the draftsman can use only one lead holder at a time, it is convenient to have three, so that hard, medium, and soft leads are always immediately at hand.

2–7. ERASERS, ERASING SHIELD, AND DUST BRUSH

Lines, once drawn, must sometimes be removed because of a mistake or a change in design. A soft

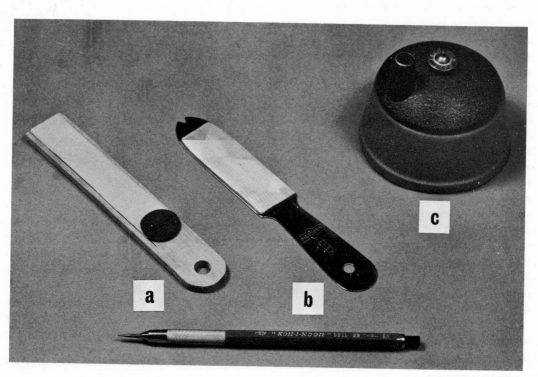

Fig. 2–6. Lead pointers. (a) Sandpaper pad. (b) File. (c) Mechanical lead pointer.

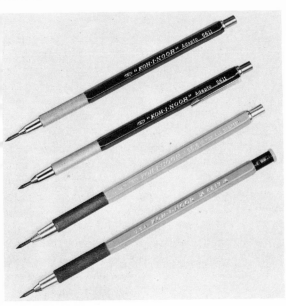

Fig. **2–7.** Lead holders. (Photograph courtesy of Koh-i-noor, Inc., Bloomsbury, N. J.)

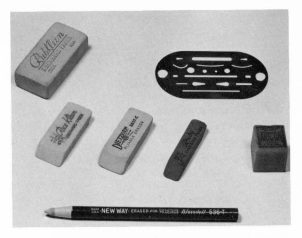

Fig. **2–8.** Erasers and erasing shield.

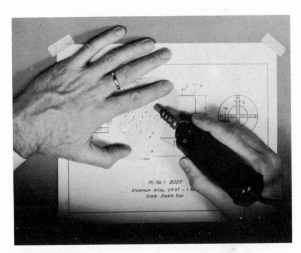

Fig. **2–9.** Electric erasing machine.

rubber eraser should be used to remove both pencil and ink lines. The soft eraser, called a pencil eraser, is slower working, but will not destroy the drawing surface. Hard, gritty erasers, the ink erasers, will remove lines faster, but will damage the paper surface. Maintaining the drawing surface undamaged is important when changes are being made and new lines are to be drawn over erased areas.

Pencil erasers are available in several forms, the most common having a rectangular cross section with wedge-shaped ends (Fig. 2–8). Those referred to by the trade names of "Pink Pearl" and "Ruby" are particularly good. One type of pencil eraser is in the form of a long rubber cylinder about one-fourth of an inch in diameter cased in a paper wrapping which can be peeled off to expose the eraser as needed (Fig. 2–8).

When there is an appreciable change to be made in a drawing and time is important, the *electric erasing machine* (Fig. 2–9) is a useful accessory. A short cylinder of rubber eraser is gripped in the chuck of the erasing machine and rapidly rotated by means of an electric motor. When properly operated, the electric erasing machine will remove pencil and ink lines cleanly and efficiently. However, care must be taken to use light pressure and

to keep the eraser tip constantly moving over the area or a hole will be burned in the paper or cloth.

The *erasing shield* (Fig. 2–10) should be used when only a small portion of a line is to be removed or when several lines are close together and only one line is to be removed. An opening of the appropriate size and shape is placed over the line or portion of line to be removed, and while the erasure is made through the opening, the adjacent area is protected by the shield. Erasing shields are made either of stainless steel or plastic sheet several thousandths of an inch thick. Those of stainless steel are recommended.

The dust brush (Fig. 2–11) is used mainly for removing eraser dust from the drawing paper after

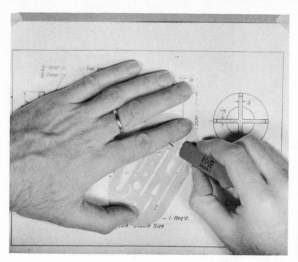

Fig. 2-10. Use of the erasing shield.

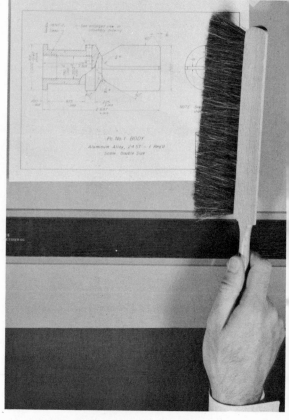

Fig. 2-11. The dust brush.

erasing. The dust brush is a flat, wood-handled brush having soft bristles 2 to $2\frac{1}{2}$ inches long. Several passes over the drawing area with the dust brush will remove eraser dust, lint, and other residue from the drawing area.

2-8. INSTRUMENTAL DRAWING

Any instrumental drawing, simple or complex, whether the representation of a physical object, an engineering design concept, or the graphical solution to a problem, is composed entirely of straight lines, circles and circle arcs, and curves of an irregular form, all precisely located and mechanically rendered with the aid of suitable drawing instruments. In the articles that follow, techniques will be described for drawing horizontal, vertical, and inclined straight lines, circles and circle arcs, and irregular curves, with a discussion of the instruments used for locating, measuring, and laying down on paper each type of line.

2-9. HORIZONTAL LINES

Horizontal lines are drawn by guiding the pencil along the top edge of the T-square blade or the parallel straightedge (Fig. 2-12). When using the T-square, the left hand checks to make sure the head is pressed firmly against the left end ledge of the drawing board. (This explanation is for a right-handed draftsman. Left-handers reverse the

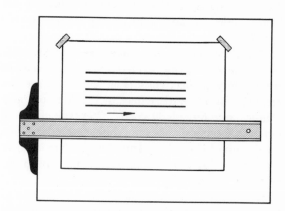

Fig. 2-12. Horizontal lines.

procedure.) The fingers of the left hand then move to the right stopping close to the center of the line to be drawn, and continuing to apply pressure down and to the right to hold the blade in place with the head against the edge of the board.

Fig. **2-13.** Position of the hands when drawing horizontal lines.   (Inset) Holding the pencil.

(When using the parallel straightedge, only downward pressure is used to fix the straightedge in place.) The pencil is held in the right hand by the thumb and forefinger [Fig. 2–13 (inset)]. The thumb grips the pencil about an inch behind the point. The pencil crosses the second joint of the forefinger. The last three fingers rest lightly against the surface of the straightedge. Movement of the pencil in drawing a horizontal line is from left to right. The pencil should be maintained in a plane perpendicular to the drawing board and angled at about 60° to the straightedge, leaning in the direction of motion (Fig. 2–13). The pencil point is carefully placed on the paper at the starting point of the line to be drawn and moved quickly to the right in one continuous sweep of the arm. (The last three fingers slide easily along the top surface of the straightedge.) The arm movement should

be stopped just before the pencil point reaches the ending point of the line, and the last half-inch or so finished with a movement of the fingers. If a conical point is being used, the pencil should be rotated between the fingers to insure uniform thickness throughout the length of the line. For light lines, such as construction lines, which may be erased later, only light pressure should be applied to the pencil point. For permanent lines, such as the outlines of an object after their final position has been established, the light lines are traced over using a softer pencil and bearing down on the point with enough pressure to lay down a good black line which may slightly groove the paper. If one is sure of the beginning and ending points of the line, it may be drawn permanently the first time without first drawing the light construction line.

After the line is drawn, the straightedge is moved into position to draw the next line. In moving the T-square from one place to another, it is a good idea to press down on the head to raise the blade slightly so as not to smear the pencil lines and move dirt about on the paper with the underside of the blade. The horizontal lines of a drawing are generally drawn first, working from the top of the sheet to the bottom. This procedure is a must when inking to avoid sliding the straightedge through a wet ink line, and it is a good idea to develop the habit when working with a pencil. Working from the top down enables the draftsman to see the finished work as the drawing progresses, and is the beginning of a systematic drafting technique which should be developed early and followed until it becomes habitual.

The pencil must be re-pointed frequently or the lines will become progressively thicker. Several short lines can be drawn without dulling the pencil point appreciably, but when drawing long lines such as border lines, the pencil must be re-pointed after every line. Hard leads used for drawing light lines will retain their sharp points much longer than the softer leads used in laying down the darker, permanent lines. The experienced draftsman watches the lines he draws, and re-points the pencil before the gradually thickening lines become noticeable. Re-pointing the lead promptly avoids erasing a line, once drawn, because it is obviously too thick. On the other hand, re-pointing too frequently wastes time.

2–10. VERTICAL LINES

Vertical lines are drawn with either the 45° or 30°–60° triangle. One side of the triangle is supported by the top edge of the straightedge while the other side provides a guide for the pencil (Fig. 2–14). The T-square (or parallel straightedge) is positioned just below the lower end of the line to be drawn. The left hand checks the position of the head of the T-square against the end ledge of the drawing board and moves across the blade to a position just below the triangle, pressing down and pulling to the right along the T-square blade. This keeps the head firmly against the drawing board and prevents the blade from slipping. The small finger and thumb of the left hand continue

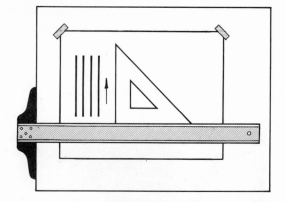

Fig. 2–14. Vertical lines.

Fig. 2–15. Position of the hands when drawing vertical lines.

to push down and pull to the right on the T-square blade while the three inside fingers are placed on the horizontal side of the triangle (Fig. 2–15). These fingers keep the horizontal side of the triangle pressed firmly against the straightedge and are used to move the triangle slightly to the left or right as necessary to align the vertical side with the point through which the line is to be drawn. The pencil is held in the right hand in the same manner as for drawing horizontal lines. The vertical line is drawn by reaching across the left hand

and, with the pencil point guided by the vertical edge of the triangle, drawing the line from bottom to top (Fig. 2–15).

Additional vertical lines are drawn by shifting the fingers of the left hand to the right as required to move the triangle to the next position. Vertical lines are usually drawn after all horizontal lines have been drawn, working from the left side of the sheet toward the right.

The left hand plays an important role in the drawing of vertical lines. It must hold the T-square in place with the head squarely against the edge of the drawing board. At the same time, the left hand must keep one leg of the triangle in firm contact with the horizontal straightedge while the fingers remain free to move the triangle a short distance to the left or right. This requires a certain amount of digital dexterity which is developed only through conscious practice of proper procedures.

Other techniques for manipulating the triangle and the horizontal straightedge when drawing vertical lines may occur to the student; however, the temptation to deviate from the procedure described above must be resisted. "Original" techniques, seemingly more comfortable and convenient at the moment, will almost certainly result in inaccurate and sloppy work and the development of poor habits.

2–11. INCLINED LINES

Lines at 45°. Lines inclined at 45° to the horizontal or vertical are drawn with the *45° triangle*. One side of the triangle is supported by the T-square or straightedge, and the 45° line is drawn along the hypotenuse (Fig. 2–16). The triangle can be reversed for drawing lines inclined at 45° in the opposite direction.

Lines at 30° and 60°. Lines inclined at 30° and 60° to the horizontal or vertical are drawn with the *30°–60° triangle*. One leg of the triangle is supported by the horizontal straightedge, and the 30° or 60° line is drawn along the hypotenuse (Fig. 2–17). By reversing the position of the triangle, lines can be drawn inclined at 30° or 60° in either direction.

Fig. **2–16.** Inclined lines at 45°.

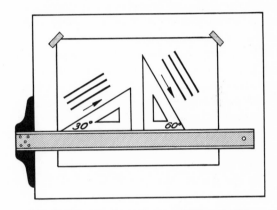

Fig. **2–17.** Inclined lines at 30° and 60°.

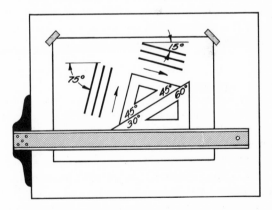

Fig. **2–18.** Inclined lines at 15° and 75°.

Lines at 15° and 75°. Lines inclined at 15° and 75° to the horizontal or vertical can be drawn by combining the 45° and 30°–60° triangles as illustrated in Fig. 2–18. Some practice is required to skillfully manipulate the triangles for drawing

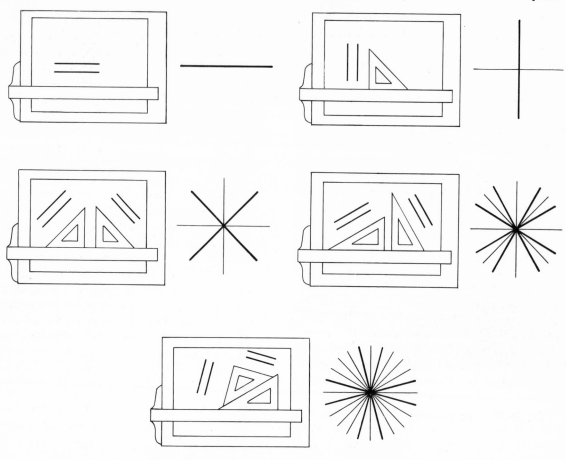

Fig. **2–19.** Drawing radial lines at 15° intervals.

these 15° and 75° lines. The fingers of the left hand must be able to slide both triangles short distances with respect to each other and to the horizontal straightedge, at the same time maintaining the alignment of the sliding edges and keeping the T-square firmly against the edge of the drawing board. Then, when the correct position of the upper triangle has been determined, the two triangles and T-square or straightedge must be fixed in place while the line is drawn.

Using the T-square or parallel straightedge (for horizontal lines), and the two triangles singly (for vertical, 45°, 30°, and 60° lines) and in combination (15° and 75° lines), lines can be drawn at 15° intervals from 0° to 360° (Fig. 2–19). This technique is useful for dividing the circumference of a circle into four, six, eight, twelve, or twenty-four parts.

Adjustable Angle Triangle. Most of the lines encountered in instrumental drawing will be horizontal, vertical, or inclined at 15°, 30°, 45°, 60°, or 75° to the horizontal, and can be drawn as previously described. However, lines do occur at other angles, particularly in the area of graphical calculation. A convenient device for drawing these lines is the *adjustable angle triangle* (Fig. 2–20). The adjustable angle triangle combines a protractor scale with a triangle. The protractor scale is usually graduated in half-degree increments. Lines inclined at any angle between 0° and 360° can be drawn with this instrument by setting the protractor scale to the desired angle (or its supplement) and turning the appropriate leg in the proper direction. Like the 45° and 30°–60° triangles, one leg of the adjustable angle triangle is supported by the horizontal straightedge.

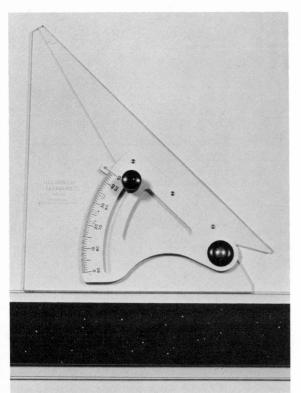

Fig. 2–20. The adjustable angle triangle.

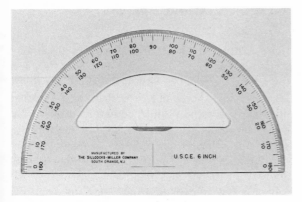

Fig. 2–21. The protractor.

Protractor. The desired angle for inclined lines can be laid off with the *protractor* (Fig. 2–21). The most common protractor design is a plastic, semicircular instrument about six inches in diameter graduated around its circumference in degrees of arc. Protractors of this type are usually graduated every one-half degree of arc. A line is

scribed on the protractor joining the 0° and 180° graduations. This line is called the *base line*. The base line may be the actual straightedge base of the instrument, but this is not always the case. A line dropped from the 90° graduation perpendicular to the base line intersects the base line at a point called the *index*.

An angle can be laid off only with respect to an existing line or implied line (such as the horizontal or vertical). The point of intersection of the two lines forming the angle must be known. Suppose a line, *CD*, is to be drawn from *C* making an angle of 37° with an existing line, *AB* (Fig. 2–22). The protractor is placed so that the base line coincides with line *AB* and the index is at point *C*. (It may be necessary to extend line *AB* to insure accurate alignment of the base line.) A tick mark, *D*, is carefully made opposite the required graduation (37°) on the protractor. The required line is then drawn with a straightedge (T-square, triangle, or the straightedge of the protractor, depending on its length) from point *C* through the tick mark, *D*. The line may be extended if necessary.

Long, Inclined Lines. Inclined lines too long for the triangles can be drawn by locating two points on the line and connecting these two points with the straightedge of the T-square (Fig. 2–23). The T-square is turned over so its head will not be blocked by the drawing board. The straightedge is carefully lined up with the two previously located points. The blade must be fixed firmly in place by the fingers of the left hand while the line is being drawn.

2–12. PARALLEL LINES AND PERPENDICULAR LINES

A line can be drawn parallel or perpendicular to a given line by either of two methods. One method is by geometric construction. The draftsman usually employs a more rapid and convenient procedure for drawing parallel and perpendicular lines using the T-square and a triangle or two triangles. This procedure is often called the *draftsman's method*, and is illustrated in Fig. 2–24. The hypotenuse of one of the triangles (either the 45° or 30°–60° triangle) is placed against the T-square blade, and the two are moved together until one leg of the triangle is in precise alignment

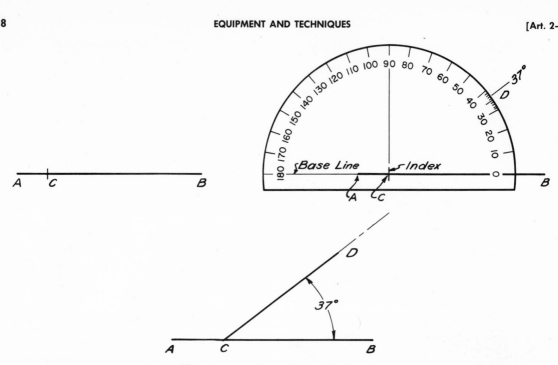

Fig. **2–22.** Laying off an angle with the protractor.

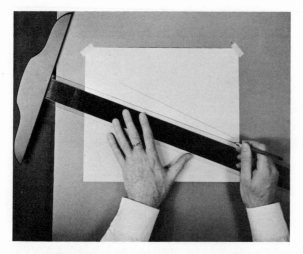

Fig. **2–23.** Drawing a long inclined line.

with the given line. The T-square blade is then held in place while the triangle is slid to the proper position to draw the required parallel line [Fig. 2–24(top)]. Additional parallel lines can be drawn by sliding the triangle up or down the blade. The other triangle can be used instead of the T-square blade as a base for the sliding triangle [Fig. 2–24 (bottom, left)]. Perpendicular lines are drawn in

like manner along the other leg of the triangle [Fig. 2–24 (bottom, right)].

2–13. THE DRAFTING MACHINE

The *drafting machine* performs the same functions as the combination of the T-square (or parallel straightedge), the 45° and 30°–60° triangles, and the adjustable triangle. With the aid of the drafting machine, horizontal, vertical, and inclined lines can be rapidly and accurately drawn. By using straightedge arms having an appropriate scale, linear measurements can be made in any desired direction. The drafting machine is precisely constructed and relatively expensive. Although a few student drafting rooms are equipped with drafting machines, it is usually thought of as a tool of the professional draftsman.

In general, the drafting machine consists of two straightedges fixed at right angles to one another. This pair of right-angled straightedges can be moved anywhere on the drawing board, with the mechanism insuring parallelism between succeeding positions of the straightedges. A protractor scale with a locking device is provided so that the straightedges can be fixed at any desired angle.

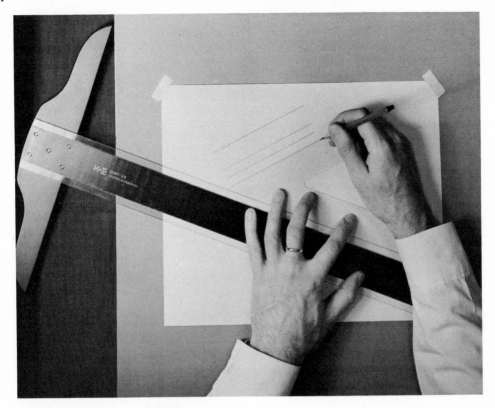

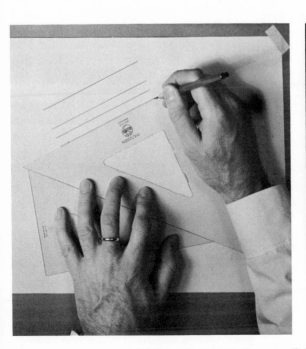

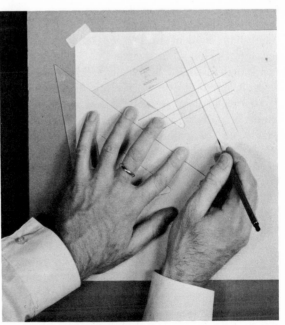

Fig. **2–24.** Drawing a line parallel or perpendicular to a given line.

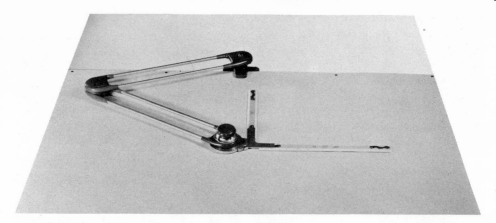

Fig. **2–25.** Drafting machine employing parallel motion mechanism. (Photograph courtesy of Keuffel & Esser Co., Hoboken, N.J.)

Drafting machines employ either a parallel motion mechanism (Fig. 2–25) or a pair of right-angled tracks (Fig. 2–26) to maintain parallelism in succeeding positions of the straightedges. Drafting machines are available in sizes small enough to fit a small drawing board or big enough to cover a large wall-mounted drawing area.

2–14. LINEAR MEASUREMENT

To the geometrician, a line is determined by any two points and may continue to infinity. The draftsman deals with *line segments*. He must lay off a line segment to a given length; he must measure the length of a given line segment. The instrument used for laying off a line segment to a given length and for measuring the length of a given line segment is called a measuring scale or simply a *scale*. (The term *scale* is also applied to the size of a drawing, photograph, or model relative to the actual size of the object represented.)

Measuring scales are made of wood, usually boxwood, and are slightly more than twelve inches long. (Pocket-size scales are about six inches long.) Graduations are in inches and subdivisions of an inch. (Metric scales are available, but are not common in the drafting rooms of the United States.) Standard scales are made in four different cross-sectional shapes: triangular, flat with two bevels, flat with opposite bevels, and flat with four bevels (Fig. 2–27). Each shape has its advantages and its adherents. The triangular scale offers six faces for graduations, hence many scale combina-

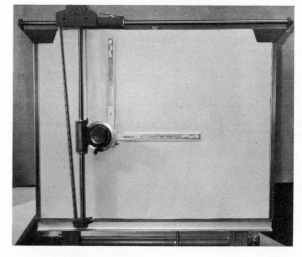

Fig. **2–26.** Drafting machine mounted on right-angled tracks. (Photograph courtesy of Keuffel & Esser Co., Hoboken, N. J.)

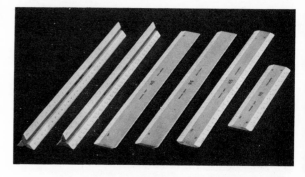

Fig. **2–27.** Scale shapes. (Photograph courtesy of Keuffel & Esser Co., Hoboken, N. J.)

tions are conveniently available on one instrument. The flat scales are usually preferred by the professional draftsman since the scale face being used on a given drawing is always readily discernible without turning and seeking. The two-bevel scale has the advantage of a wide base, and the two scale faces are always visible without turning the scale over. The opposite-bevel scale can be more easily picked up from the surface of the drawing table, and, while only one scale face is visible at a time, the face being used is easily located. The four-bevel cross section is commonly used on the six-inch pocket scales since it provides for four scale faces on one small instrument.

Scale Graduations. While the inch is the basic unit of linear measurement in the drafting room, there are many ways of dividing this inch into smaller units and good reasons for each method of subdivision. The most familiar method of subdividing the inch is that used on the school ruler, household yardstick, and sewing basket tape measure. Here, the inch is divided, by graduation marks of varying lengths, into quarters, eighths, sixteenths, and, in the case of the draftsman's measuring scale, thirty-seconds (Fig. 2–28). Another way of subdividing the inch is by decimal parts with graduations every 0.1 inch [Fig. 2–29(a)]. It would be desirable, when dealing with decimal parts of an inch, to further subdivide the 0.1-inch increments into ten 0.01-inch parts. However, 0.01 inch is too small a division to be accurately marked on the scale face. The decimally divided inch is usually graduated in fifty parts making the value of the smallest division on the scale face one-fiftieth or two-hundredths (0.02) of an inch [Fig. 2–29(b)]. Interpolations to 0.01 inch can be made. The draftsman's measuring scale is about twelve and a half inches in overall length providing space for twelve inches of graduations. To protect the end readings from damage, the zero and twelve-inch graduations are set in about one quarter of an inch from the end of the scale face. Pocket scales are about six and one half inches in overall length with graduations from zero to six inches.

Drawing Scales. A scale face on which the inch is subdivided in thirty-two parts is referred to and identified on the instrument as a *32 scale*. In like manner, the scale face on which the inch is sub-

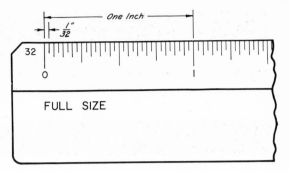

Fig. **2–28.** Scale with 32 divisions per inch.

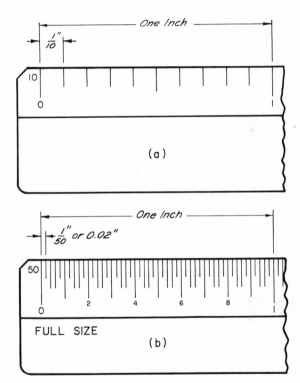

Fig. **2–29.** Decimal scale.

divided into fifty parts is often referred to and identified on the instrument as the *50 scale*. Both the 32 scale and the 50 scale are used when making full-size measurements. These scales are to be used when measurements are transferable from the drawing to the object in a one-to-one ratio. Drawings which are the same size as the object represented are called *full-size* drawings, and a note to this effect (SCALE: FULL SIZE) is placed on the drawing. Since the objects represented by an

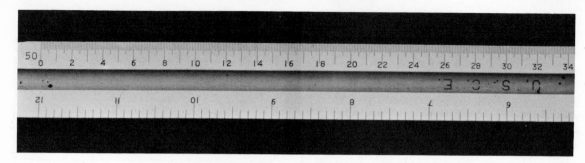

Fig. **2-30.** The civil engineer's scale.

engineering drawing are frequently too large (a portion of the earth's surface, a piece of machinery, or a building) to be conveniently drawn full size, drawings in such instances are made proportionately smaller than the object itself. The scale of the drawing is reduced.[1] Drawings of machine parts under about seventy-two inches in overall size are usually reduced to three-fourths, one-half, one-fourth, or one-eighth actual size. In making a reduced-size drawing, one could mentally calculate three-fourths, one-half, one-fourth, or one-eighth of each dimension and lay off the result with the 32 scale; however, there is a better way. A scale graduated for this purpose permits making reduced scale measurements directly without any calculation required. Consider a drawing to be made three-fourths size (SCALE: $\frac{3}{4}'' = 1''$). This means that $\frac{3}{4}''$ on the drawing represents $1''$ on the object. The measuring scale for this three-fourths size drawing scale is divided into $\frac{3}{4}$-inch increments with each increment *representing* one inch. This reduced "inch" is subdivided into fourths, eighths, sixteenths, and thirty-seconds, each subdivision representing that fraction of an inch to the reduced scale.

When making drawings to a reduced scale, it is rarely necessary to perform any calculations to determine the reduced measurements. A drawing scale should be chosen which will fit one of the available measuring scales, and used to measure the drawing directly in its reduced size.

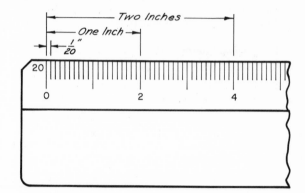

Fig. **2-31.** The 20 scale (civil engineer's scale).

Civil Engineer's Scale. The civil engineer's scale, or simply the *engineer's scale* (Fig. 2-30), is a triangular measuring scale with twelve inches of graduations on each of its six faces. The basic unit is the inch which is divided on the six faces, respectively, into 10, 20, 30, 40, 50, and 60 subdivisions. The scale face on which the inch is subdivided into ten parts is referred to and identified on the instrument as the *10 scale*. The other scale faces are similarly referred to and identified on the instrument as the *20 scale, 30 scale*, etc. These scale graduations are also available arranged in pairs on flat two-bevel and opposite-bevel instruments, or with four scale faces on four-bevel pocket instruments. Except on the 10 scale, the inch is not identified as such. The scale values indicate the number of subdivisions (tenths, twentieths, thirtieths, etc.) from the zero graduation. The 20 scale, illustrated in Fig. 2-31, is representative of the graduations on the engineer's scale.

---

[1] Here, scale refers to the ratio of drawing size to object size. The dual definitions of scale can sometimes be confusing. The measuring scale is the instrument used for making linear measurements. The drawing scale is the ratio of drawing size to object size.

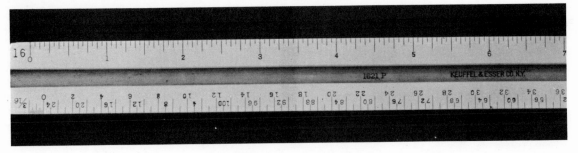

Fig. **2–32.** The architect's scale.

The engineer's scale is used on drawings where considerable reduction in size is necessary. The civil engineer deals with long distances measured on the ground in feet and decimal parts of a foot. These long distances must be proportionately reduced and laid out on a topographic drawing (map).

Typical drawing scales for topographic drawings are:

SCALE: 1″ = 10′   Measurements are made with the 10 scale with the smallest scale division (0.1 inch) representing one foot on the ground.

SCALE: 1″ = 50′   Measurements are made with the 50 scale with the smallest scale division ($\frac{1}{50}$ of an inch) representing one foot on the ground.

The engineer's scale, with its variety of decimal subdivisions of an inch, is particularly useful in the preparation of graphs, in making graphical calculations, and in other applications where a given distance must be uniformly divided.

Architect's Scale. The architect's scale (Fig. 2–32) is a triangular measuring scale accommodating eleven scales on its six scale faces. This is accomplished by overlapping two sets of graduations on five of the six available scale faces. The sixth scale face is a full-size scale, graduated from zero to twelve inches, with each inch subdivided into quarters, eighths, sixteenths, and thirty-seconds (the 32 scale).

The architect deals with building construction and landscaping where measurements are made in feet and inches. Measurements on reduced-size architectural drawings are made with a

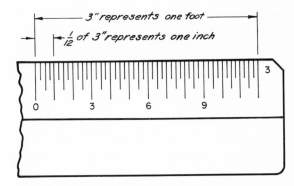

Fig. **2–33.** Measuring scale for a drawing scale of 3″ = 1′0″ (architect's scale).

measuring scale reading directly in feet and inches but proportionately reduced. Ten such measuring scales, corresponding to ten common drawing scales, are provided on the architect's scale. On each of these measuring scales, a convenient distance, three inches for example, represents a foot (Fig. 2–33). This distance representing a foot is subdivided into twelve equal parts representing inches. Each of these twelve parts is further subdivided as far as practicable into halves, quarters, and eighths. Drawings made with this measuring scale, where a distance of three inches represents a foot, have a corresponding drawing scale which is noted on the drawing (SCALE: 3″ = 1′-0″). This particular measuring scale is identified by the number 3 on the scale face. The other scales are similarly identified by a number corresponding to the number of inches or fraction of an inch which represents one foot. Measuring scales for use with the following drawing scales are part of the architect's scale:

Scale Face Identification	Drawing Scale	Ratio of Dwg. Size to Obj. Size
32	FULL SIZE	1:1
3	$3'' = 1'-0''$	1:4
$1\frac{1}{2}$	$1\frac{1}{2}'' = 1'-0''$	1:8
1	$1'' = 1'-0''$	1:12
$\frac{3}{4}$	$\frac{3}{4}'' = 1'-0''$	1:16
$\frac{1}{2}$	$\frac{1}{2}'' = 1'-0''$	1:24
$\frac{3}{8}$	$\frac{3}{8}'' = 1'-0''$	1:32
$\frac{1}{4}$	$\frac{1}{4}'' = 1'-0''$	1:48
$\frac{3}{16}$	$\frac{3}{16}'' = 1'-0''$	1:64
$\frac{1}{8}$	$\frac{1}{8}'' = 1'-0''$	1:96
$\frac{3}{32}$	$\frac{3}{32}'' = 1'-0''$	1:128

Each of the above scale faces is available on flat two-bevel and opposite-bevel scales and on four-bevel pocket scales. On the triangular architect's scale, the 32 scale occupies one scale face alone. The other ten measuring scales share a scale face as follows: 3 and $1\frac{1}{2}$, 1 and $\frac{1}{2}$, $\frac{3}{4}$ and $\frac{3}{8}$, $\frac{1}{4}$ and $\frac{1}{8}$, $\frac{3}{16}$ and $\frac{3}{32}$. The zero marks for the two overlapping scales are at opposite ends of the instrument, and the foot marks between are shared. Graduation marks are read in the direction of increasing scale values.

Combination Scale and Mechanical Engineer's Scale. Scales are available which combine the most used scale faces of both the engineer's and architect's scales.

Measuring scales for use with drawing scales of $\frac{3}{4}'' = 1''$, $\frac{1}{2}'' = 1''$, $\frac{3}{8}'' = 1''$, and $\frac{1}{4}'' = 1''$ (generally referred to as: three-quarter size; half size; three-eighths size; and one-quarter size), are found on the *mechanical engineer's scale*, and may also be incorporated in a combination scale.

Scale Divisions. Measuring scales may be either *fully divided* or *open divided*. On the fully divided scale, each unit is fully subdivided into the smallest scale division throughout the length of the scale. The civil engineer's scale (Fig. 2–30) is fully divided. On the open divided scale, only the major units are marked. An additional unit is provided beyond the zero mark which is fully divided into the smallest subdivision. The architect's scale (Fig. 3–32) is open divided, except for the 32 scale which is fully divided.

2–15. TRANSFERRING A DISTANCE

General. The requirements of instrumental drawing demand a convenient and precise method for transferring a given distance from one place on the drawing to another. The instruments designed for transferring distance on an instrumental drawing are called *dividers*. Two types of divider design are in general use: the larger *friction head dividers* [Fig. 2–34(a)], and the smaller *bow dividers* [Fig. 2–34(b)]. Both instruments are made of metal, usually nickel-silver or nickel plated brass, with steel needle points. The springs of the bow instrument are made of steel.

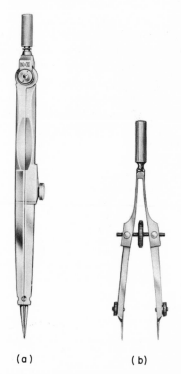

(a)   (b)

Fig. **2–34.** (a) Friction head divider with hairspring. (b) Bow divider. (Photograph courtesy of Keuffel & Esser Co., Hoboken, N. J.)

Friction head dividers look something like a compass used for drawing circles but have no scribing point. The dividers consist of two legs about 6 inches long joined at the top by a friction joint. This friction joint permits the legs to be readily opened and closed, but at the same time holds the legs firmly in place when set. This joint is self-lubricating, and should not be oiled. A tension screw is provided to adjust the tightness of the friction joint. At the top of the instrument is a knurled cylinder for gripping. A sharp steel needle point is fixed to the end of each leg. On some dividers, one leg is split and provided with a hairspring and a setscrew for making fine adjustments. Instruments of this type are called *hairspring dividers* [Fig. 2-34(a)].

In use, the dividers are held in one hand in such a manner that the legs can be adjusted by opening and closing the fingers. Fig. 2-35 illustrates the

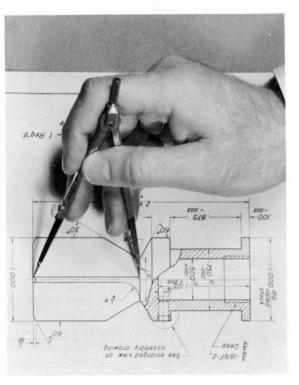

Fig. **2-35.** Handling the dividers.

proper method of holding the dividers. The dividers are set by eye to the approximate distance to be transferred. One needle point is carefully placed at the near point, and the opposite leg is adjusted, using the hairspring if necessary, until the two needle points precisely span the given distance. The distance is then moved to the desired location and laid down by pricking the paper slightly with the needle points. The prick marks should be ticked immediately with a sharp pencil. When picking up or laying down a distance with the dividers, the side of the hand should rest on

the surface of the drawing board. By supporting the hand, the instrument is steadied, and adjustments are more easily made.

Bow Dividers. The bow dividers are one of a family of three similar instruments, the bow dividers, bow compass, and bow pen. These latter two will be discussed later. The bow instruments are made in two designs, the ringhead type [Fig. 2-36(a)], and the flat spring type [Fig. 2-36(b)]. Both types are available with a central thumbscrew [Fig. 2-36(a)] or a side thumbscrew [Fig. 2-36(b)].

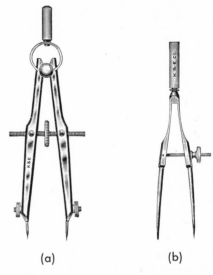

(a)　　　　　　(b)

Fig. **2-36.** (a) Bow divider, ringhead, central thumbscrew. (b) Bow divider, flat spring, side thumbscrew. (Photograph courtesy of Keuffel & Esser Co., Hoboken, N. J.)

While both these spring designs and thumbscrew arrangements have their advantages, the ringhead bow with a central thumbscrew is the most widely used. The bow dividers are used to span relatively short distances (from zero to a little over an inch) which are transferred as previously described for the friction head divider. The instrument is held as illustrated in Fig. 2-37(left) so that the thumbscrew can be easily adjusted with the thumb. When transferring a distance, the bow dividers are gripped by the knurled cylinder at the top [Fig. 2-37(right)]. Although the bow dividers can only be applied to short spans, the given distance can be set and fixed on the instrument with the thumbscrew, then used many times without get-

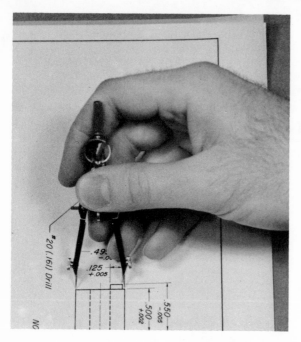 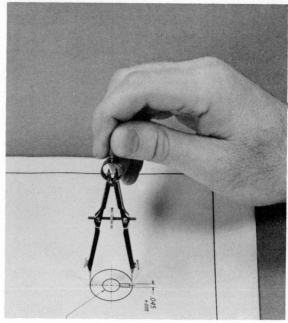

Fig. **2-37.** Handling the bow dividers.

ting out of adjustment. The friction head dividers are easily knocked out of adjustment since the legs are not locked in place.

2-16. DIVIDING A DISTANCE INTO A SPECIFIED NUMBER OF EQUAL PARTS

Divider Method. The dividers can be used for "dividing" a given distance into a specified number of equal parts. Hence the name, divider. If a line segment, *AB* [Fig. 2–38(a)], is to be divided into five equal parts, the dividers are first set by eye to what appears to be one-fifth the given distance. Starting at one end of the line segment, *A*, the distance set on the dividers is "walked off" along the line *AB* [Fig. 2–38(b)]. If the eye has judged well, the five steps along *AB* should bring the needle point to rest precisely on *B*. However, there will probably be a small error [Fig. 2–38(b)]. If the needle point is short, open the divider legs by one-fifth the error, again judging this distance by eye. If the needle point is over, close the divider legs by one-fifth the error. Repeat this procedure until the error has been reduced to zero. The divisions can be stepped off once again, this

time pricking the paper slightly and ticking the prick marks with a pencil [Fig. 2–38(c)]. A circle or circle arc can be similarly divided into a given number of equal arcs with the dividers.

Scale Method. Dividing a line segment into a specified number of equal parts with the dividers is a trial and error procedure, time-consuming and of questionable accuracy. A better method for dividing a line segment into a specified number of equal parts makes use of the scale and the proportional relationship of similar triangles. Consider again the line segment, *AB* [Fig. 2–39(a)], and the requirement to divide *AB* into five equal parts. From either end of the line segment, *A* in this case, draw a fine line of indefinite length at any convenient angle with *AB* [Fig. 2–39(b)]. Using the scale, lay off along this line, starting with *A*, five equal divisions [Fig. 2–39(c)]. It is possible to use the dividers to lay off the five divisions, but the scale is recommended. The engineer's scale is particularly suited for this purpose because of its variety of graduations. From the last division, 5, draw a fine line, 5-*B*, to the end of the given line segment [Fig. 2–39(d)]. Draw additional lines from points 4, 3, 2, and 1, parallel to line 5-*B* and

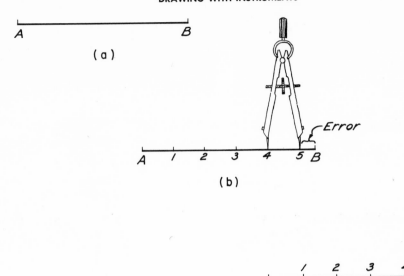

Fig. **2-38.** Dividing a line segment with the dividers.

intersecting *AB* [Fig. 2–39(e)], thus dividing *AB* into five equal parts. Use the two-triangle method described in Art. 2–12 for drawing the parallel lines.

2-17. PROPORTIONAL DIVIDERS

Proportional dividers (Fig. 2–40) are used for reducing or enlarging a given distance by a specified ratio. Proportional dividers are available in several sizes with legs 6″, 8″, and 10″ long. Both ends of both legs terminate in steel needle points. The legs are joined by a slide which can be fixed in place by tightening a thumbscrew. The legs are graduated, and by setting the index mark on the slide to the proper graduation, a specified ratio is established between the span of the needle points on one end of the instrument and the span of the needle points on the opposite end. Depending on the design of the instrument, ratios vary from 1:1 to 1:10 with any desired ratio, between the two extremes of the instrument, possible. Special ratios such as the ratio of the diameter of a circle to its rectified circumference, the ratio of feet to meters, etc., are graduated on some proportional dividers, or they may be listed in a table accompanying a given instrument. Other special ratios not graduated or tabulated can be computed and the slide set to the proper graduation. Proportional dividers are not usually included as a part of the set of drawing instruments, but must be purchased as a separate accessory.

2-18. THE COMPASS

General. Circles and circle arcs are drawn with the compass. The compass is similar to the dividers except one leg of the compass is provided with a lead holder instead of a needle point. The circle or circle arc is scribed by the lead revolving around the needle point which is fixed at the center of the circle. Several different types of compass designs are available to facilitate drawing circles varying in radius from the very small to the very large.

Friction Head Compass. The friction head compass (Fig. 2–41) is almost identical in appearance to the friction head divider. In some instrument sets, the friction head compass doubles as a divider by replacing the lead in the lead holder with a needle point. Some compasses are provided with a hairspring and a setscrew for making fine adjustments. For drawing circles in ink, the lead holder can be removed and replaced with a pen insert.

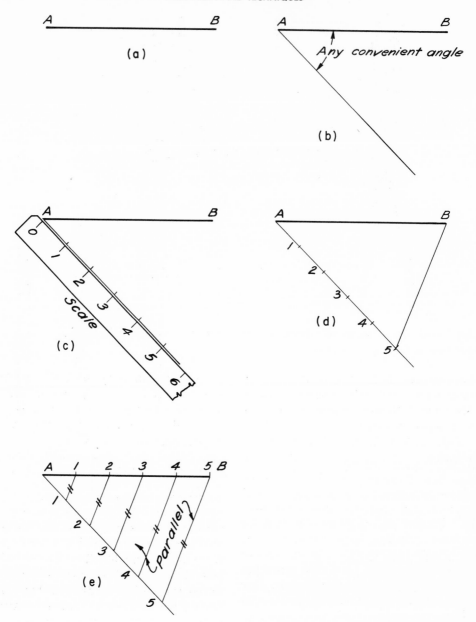

Fig. **2–39.** Dividing a line segment into a specified number of equal parts.

This compass (Fig. 2–41) is used for drawing circles in the medium range with radii from about 1″ to 4″. Most compasses are made with "knuckle joints" which increase their radial capacity to about 8″ (Fig. 2–42). A lengthening bar (Fig. 2–42), provided with the compass, adds another 3″ to 4″ to its radial capacity making it possible to draw a circle arc of about 12″ radius.

Bow Compass. The bow compass is the second member of the bow instrument family. Like the bow divider (Fig. 2–36), it may be either of flat spring or ringhead design and either type may be adjusted with a thumbscrew in the center or on the side. One leg of the bow compass ends in a needle point; the other leg is a lead holder for the scribing lead. The bow compass is capable

Fig. **2–40.** Proportional dividers. (Photograph courtesy of Keuffel & Esser Co., Hoboken, N. J.)

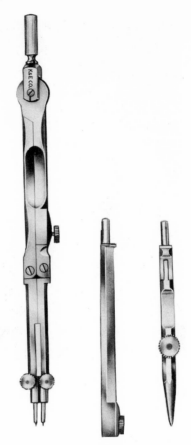

Fig. **2–41.** Friction head compass with lengthening bar and pen insert. (Photograph courtesy of Keuffel & Esser Co., Hoboken, N. J.)

of fine adjustments, using the thumbscrew, and once set, the radius is fixed for repeated use.

The bow compass is used for small circles with radii from about $\frac{1}{8}''$ to $1\frac{1}{2}''$, depending on the size of the instrument.

The Large Bow Compass. Many present-day sets of drawing instruments contain, instead of the friction head compass and the three small bow instruments (dividers, compass, and pen), a large ($6\frac{1}{2}''$) ringhead bow compass (Fig. 2–43) with interchangeable needle point, pencil, and pen inserts. This large bow compass will span a distance up to about 6″, and extension bars are provided to extend this span another 6″. These instruments are both rugged in construction and precise in operation, and are designed to meet the requirements of modern pencil drawing. A set of instruments of this style often contains a smaller ($4\frac{1}{2}''$) bow compass in addition to the large compass.

Drop Bow Compass. The drop bow compass (Fig. 2–44) may be included as part of the set of drawing instruments, but usually must be purchased as a separate accessory. The drop bow compass is provided with interchangeable lead holder and pen inserts.

This instrument is used for drawing very small circles with radii from slightly greater than zero to about $\frac{1}{4}''$. It is particularly useful when many small circles of the same diameter must be drawn. Drawing the rivet heads in a structural steel drawing is a typical task for the drop bow compass.

Beam Compass. Circle arcs which exceed the radial capacity of the friction head or large bow compass with added lengthening bar must be drawn with the beam compass (Fig. 2–45). The beam compass consists of a long bar (the beam) on which are mounted at right angles two holders, one for the lead, the other for the needle point. The needle point holder is provided with a micrometer screw for making fine adjustments. The beam may be wooden, but is usually nickel-silver, aluminum, or plated brass or steel. For convenience, the

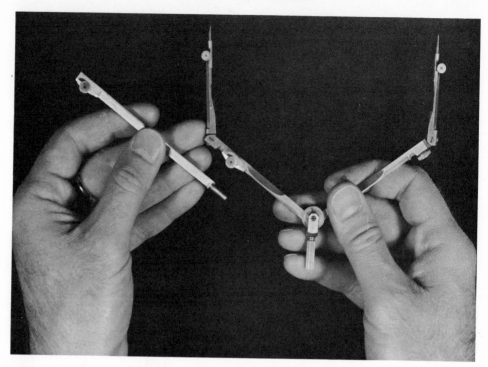

Fig. **2–42.** Extending the compass radius with the knuckle joints and lengthening bar.

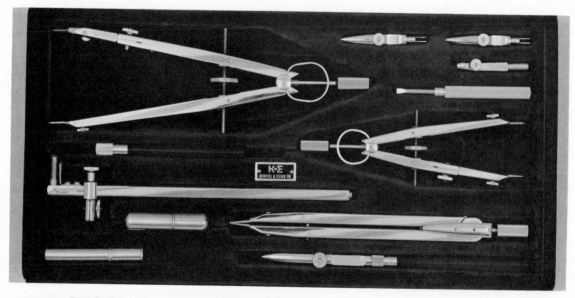

Fig. **2–43.** Instrument set featuring the large bow compass. (Photograph courtesy of Keuffel & Esser Co., Hoboken, N. J.)

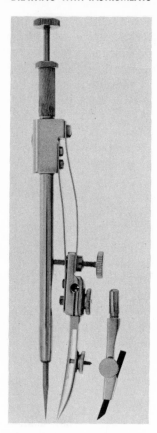

Fig. **2–44.** The drop bow compass.   (Photograph courtesy of Keuffel & Esser Co., Hoboken, N. J.)

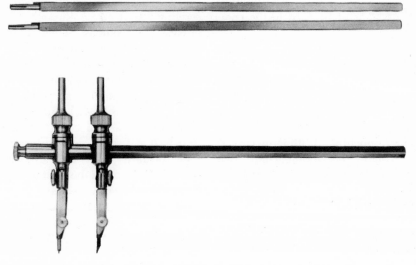

Fig. **2–45.** The beam compass. (Photograph courtesy of Keuffel & Esser Co., Hoboken, N. J.)

beam is usually 8″ to 12″ in length. Greater radial capacity is obtained by joining additional beam sections. Interchangeable lead holders and pen inserts are provided with the instrument. The beam compass must be purchased as a separate accessory, since it is not ordinarily included in the set of drawing instruments.

While the radial capacity of the beam compass is limited only by the practical length of a given beam design, the usual range of the beam compass is between 8″ and 42″.

2–19. CIRCLES

Accurately drawn circles and circle arcs of uniform thickness throughout their length depend on two factors, a well-sharpened compass lead of the proper degree of hardness, and an accurately measured radius. Compass leads are available in five degrees of hardness, HB, H, 2H, 3H, and 4H. Other degrees of lead hardness can be obtained by breaking the long leads prepared for the lead holder into short lengths. Special leads for the compass are about $1\frac{1}{4}″$ long, and come packed by the dozen in small tubes.

The compass lead should be one grade softer than the lead used for the straight lines on the same drawing. This is because more pressure is usually applied to the pencil than to the compass, and if the straight lines and circles are to be of uniform thickness, a softer lead must be used in the compass.

Sharpening the Compass Lead. Compass leads are sharpened to a long wedge shape with the sandpaper pad or file. The wedge-shaped lead retains its keen edge longer than a cone point, and is easier to touch up and keep sharp. The compass lead must be sharpened frequently. With large circles, the lead usually requires re-sharpening after one complete circle. Fig. 2–46 shows how to sharpen the compass lead, and illustrates the correct shape of the lead after sharpening.

Measuring the Radius. For the finished circle to be of the required diameter, an accurate measurement of the radius must be made. The center

lines of the circle should be drawn first. (See Fig. 2–80 for an illustration of the proper line symbol for the center line.) The center lines are two perpendicular lines, usually a horizontal and a vertical line, intersecting at the center of the proposed circle. The center lines are drawn slightly longer than the diameter of the circle. Using an appropriate scale, the diameter of the circle is laid off along one of the center lines (Fig. 2–47). It is best to place the scale with the midpoint of the specified diameter at the center and lay off the half diameter in either direction. With the center located, and the diameter marked on the center line, the circle can now be drawn.

Drawing the Circle. Most compasses have removable needle points. One end of the needle point has a long tapering point; the other end has a short shoulder point [Fig. 2–46(a)]. The shoulder point should be used when drawing circles. It should be adjusted so that it is slightly longer than the lead [Fig. 2–46(b)]. The shoulder point is now carefully located at the center of the circle, and the compass is adjusted to the previously marked half-diameter. Before drawing the circle, the compass lead should be swung around and the radius set on the instrument checked against the opposite half-diameter. This will check the centering of the needle point. The compass is held by the pads of the thumb and forefinger, and the scribing leg revolved through 360° drawing the circle. The compass should be revolved in one direction only, and only one turn should be made. Reversing the direction of revolution may change the radius slightly because the chisel point is not necessarily perpendicular to the plane of the legs. Additional turns thicken the line as the lead wears dull. When several concentric circles are to be drawn, it is best to draw the smallest circle first, then the next larger, etc. As the hole made by the needle point at the center of the circle grows in size from wear, it becomes increasingly difficult to draw accurately the smaller circles. The compass used should be appropriate to the size of the circle being drawn. Figs. 2–48 through 2–52 illustrate the techniques used for drawing circles with the various compasses.

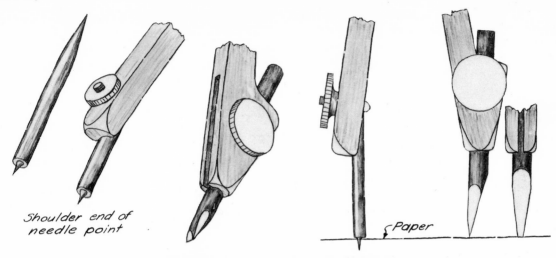

Shoulder end of
needle point

Paper

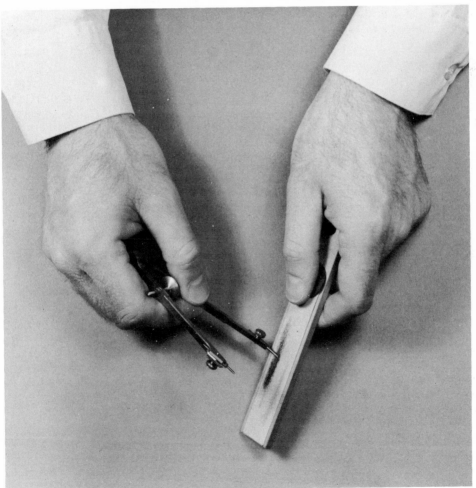

Fig. **2-46.** Sharpening the compass lead and adjusting the needle point.

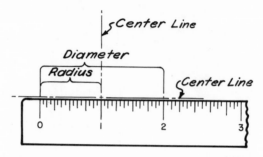

Fig. **2-47.** Laying off the radius for drawing a 2"-diameter circle.

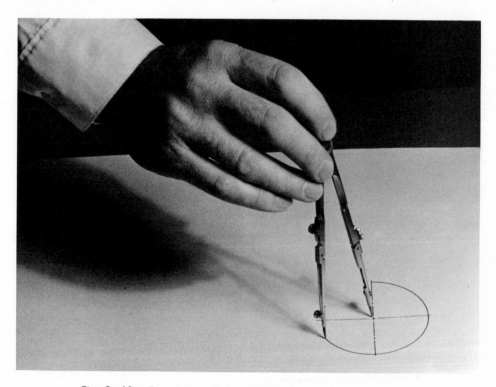

Fig. **2-48.** Drawing a circle with the friction head compass.

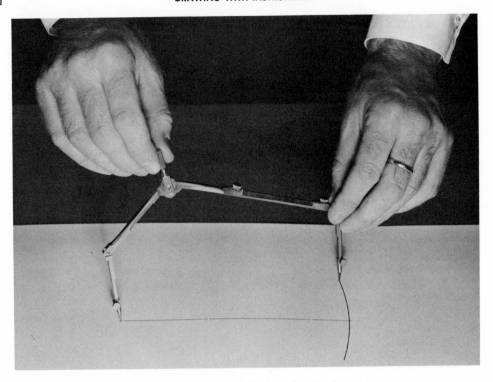

Fig. **2-49.** Use of the lengthening bar.

Fig. **2-50.** Using the bow compass.

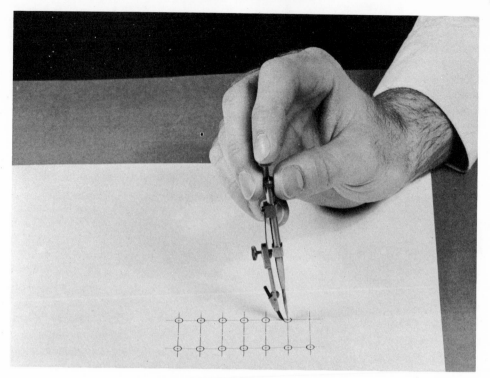

Fig. **2–51.** Using the drop bow compass.

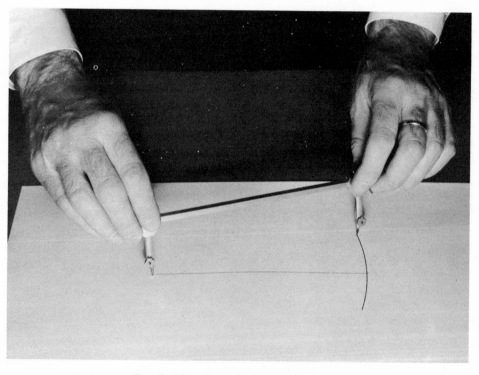

Fig. **2–52.** Using the beam compass.

2–20. IRREGULAR CURVES

The instrumental drawing of smooth curves which are not circle arcs is accomplished with the aid of an instrument known as the *irregular* (or *French*) *curve* (Fig. 2–53). Irregular curves are flat

Fig. **2–53.** Irregular curves.

plastic instruments available in a great variety of shapes and sizes. The curves making up the edges of the instrument are segments of the ellipse, parabola, and hyperbola. Curves for special applications may be obtained in sets ranging in size from very small curves to large curves, each separate instrument varying only slightly in size and curvature from adjacent instruments of the set. Railroad curves, ship curves, and mechanical engineer's curves are examples of such sets.

Before the irregular curve can be successfully employed as a guide for drawing curved lines, a number of points through which the curve is known to pass must be accurately plotted. Enough points must be located to define the curve adequately, and it must be assumed that the curve is continuous without abrupt changes in direction between the plotted points.

Fig. 2–54 illustrates the use of the irregular curve. After the points have been plotted [Fig. 2–54(a)], a light, smooth line may be sketched through the points as an aid in aligning the instrument [Fig. 2–54(b)]. Beginning at one end of the curve, the instrument is aligned with the sketched curve until as many points as possible lie along the edge of the instrument [Fig. 2–54(c)]. This portion of the curve can now be drawn with the pencil guided against the edge of the instrument. The line should be stopped *before* the last point in alignment with the instrument is reached. The instrument is then shifted until a position is found that lines up with the adjacent portion of the previously drawn segment and a continuing series of the plotted points [Fig. 2–54(d)]. This portion is then drawn, carefully picking up and continuing the segment of the curve already drawn. This procedure is repeated until the curve is completed. Irregular curves are easier to draw if the paper is not taped to the board but is free to be rotated and moved about. The direction of curvature of the edge of the instrument must always correspond generally to the direction of curvature of the curve to be drawn. In connecting successive segments of the curve, sufficient overlap must be allowed in placing the instrument to permit smooth tangents without humps, points, or failure of the overlapping ends to line up.

The plastic irregular curve is not well suited for drawing long, flat curves. Adjustable curves in several designs are available and can be used as a guide in drawing long, flat curves. Adjustable curves made of rubber and metal, and flexible splines used with spline weights are illustrated in Fig. 2–55.

2–21. COMBINING STRAIGHT LINES, CIRCLE ARCS, AND IRREGULAR CURVES

Several typical combinations of straight lines, circle arcs, and irregular curves repeatedly occur in instrumental drawing. These combinations are

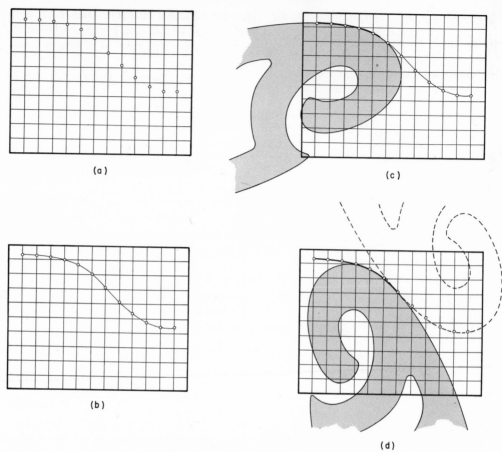

(a)

(b)

(c)

(d)

Fig. **2-54.** Use of the irregular curve.

Fig. **2-55.** Adjustable curves. (Photograph courtesy of Keuffel & Esser Co., Hoboken, N. J.)

usually incidental to the drawing as a whole, being part of the "grammar" of the graphic language. Familiarity with these combinations will contribute considerably to the ease and speed of the individu-

al's execution of graphical work. The articles and illustrations that follow describe and illustrate some of the most often used combinations of straight lines, circle arcs, and irregular curves.

2-22. TO CONSTRUCT THE PERPENDICULAR BISECTOR OF A GIVEN LINE, AB, USING A STRAIGHTEDGE AND COMPASS (FIG. 2-56)

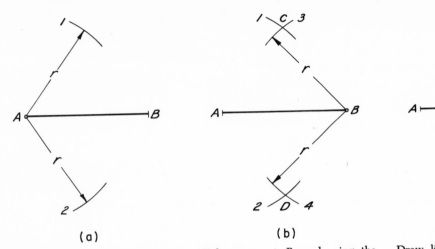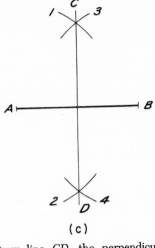

(a)

(b)

(c)

With center at A, and using any appropriate radius, r (about $\frac{2}{3}$ AB), draw arcs 1 and 2.

With center at B, and using the same radius, r, draw arcs 3 and 4 intersecting arcs 1 and 2 at C and D.

Draw line CD, the perpendicular bisector of line AB.

Fig. 2-56. To construct the perpendicular bisector of a given line, AB, using a straightedge and compass.

2-23. TO CONSTRUCT THE PERPENDICULAR BISECTOR OF A GIVEN LINE, AB, USING T-SQUARE AND A TRIANGLE (FIG. 2-57)

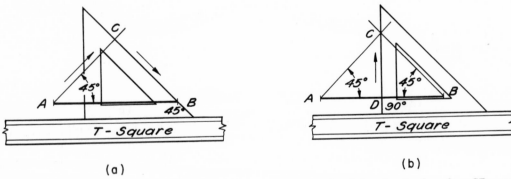

(a)

(b)

Using the 45° triangle (or the 30°-60° triangle), draw inclined lines from A and B, making equal angles with AB, intersecting at C.

With the side of the triangle, draw line CD perpendicular to AB. CD is the perpendicular bisector of AB.

Fig. 2-57. To construct the perpendicular bisector of a given line, AB, using a T-square and a triangle.

2-24. TO DIVIDE A GIVEN LINE, AB, INTO THREE EQUAL PARTS USING A T-SQUARE AND 30°-60° TRIANGLE (FIG. 2-58)

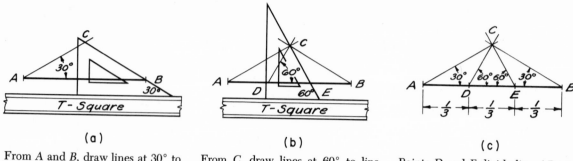

(a)

From A and B, draw lines at 30° to line AB, intersecting at C.

(b)

From C, draw lines at 60° to line AB, intersecting line AB at D and E.

(c)

Points D and E divide line AB into three equal parts, AD, DE, and EB.

Fig. 2-58. To divide a given line, AB, into three equal parts using a T-square and 30°-60° triangle.

2-25. TO CONSTRUCT AN ANGLE, ROS, EQUAL TO A GIVEN ANGLE, ABC (FIG. 2-59)

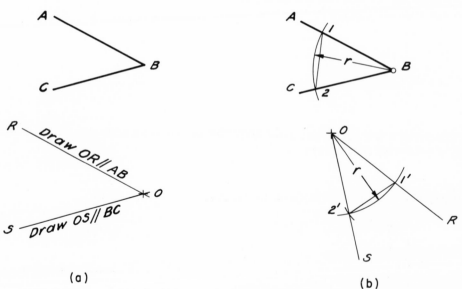

(a)

(b)

PARALLEL LINE METHOD: From O, located at any desired point, draw OR parallel to AB and OS parallel to BC. The angle ROS is equal to angle ABC.

CHORD METHOD: From O, located at any desired point, draw OR in any desired direction. With center at B, and using any appropriate radius, r, draw an arc intersecting BA and BC at 1 and 2 respectively. With O as center, using radius, r, draw an arc intersecting OR at 1'. Lay off chord distance 1'-2' equal to chord distance 1-2. Draw line O-2' and extend to any desired length (S). Angle ROS is equal to angle ABC.

Fig. 2-59. To construct an angle ROS equal to a given angle, ABC.

–26. TO CONSTRUCT A GIVEN ANGLE FROM ITS TANGENT (FIG. 2–60)

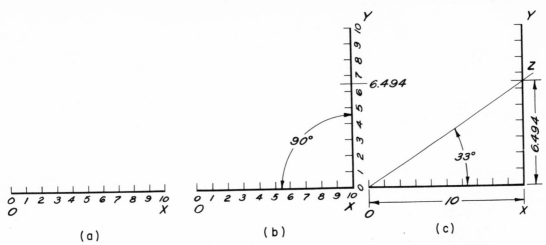

(a)   (b)   (c)

Let the given angle be 33°. From a table of trigonometric functions, tan 33° = 0.6494.

Multiply the tangent of the given angle by 10. (0.6494 × 10 = 6.494.) Along one side of the angle lay off ten equal units, OX.

Erect a perpendicular to OX at X. Lay off 6.494 units along the perpendicular, XY.

Draw line OZ. The angle ZOX is the required angle, 33°.

Fig. 2–60. To construct a given angle from its tangent.

2–27. TO CONSTRUCT THE BISECTOR OF A GIVEN ANGLE, ABC (FIG. 2–61)

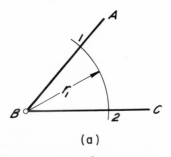
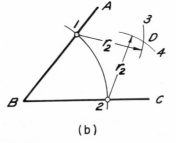

(a)   (b)   (c)

With center at B, and using any appropriate radius, r_1, draw an arc intersecting BA and BC at 1 and 2.

With centers at 1 and 2 and using any appropriate radius, r_2, draw arcs 3 and 4 intersecting at D.

Draw line BD, which will bisect the angle, ABC.

Fig. 2–61. To construct the bisector of a given angle, ABC.

2-28. TO BISECT THE ANGLE BETWEEN TWO GIVEN LINES, AB AND BC, WHEN THEIR POINT OF INTERSECTION IS INACCESSIBLE (FIG. 2-62)

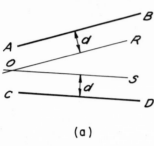

(a)

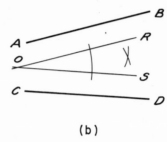

(b)

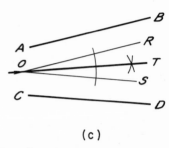

(c)

Draw intersecting lines *OR* and *OS* parallel to and at an appropriate distance, *d*, from *AB* and *CD* respectively.

Bisect the angle *ROS* by the method described in Art. 2-27.

Draw line *OT* which will bisect the angle between lines *AB* and *CD*.

Fig. **2-62.** To bisect the angle between two given lines, *AB* and *CD*, when their point of intersection is inaccessible.

2-29. TO DRAW A LINE THROUGH A GIVEN POINT, P, AND THE POINT OF INTERSECTION OF TWO GIVEN LINES, AB AND CD, THE POINT OF INTERSECTION BEING INACCESSIBLE (FIG. 2-63)

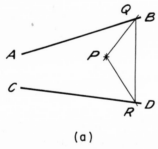

(a)

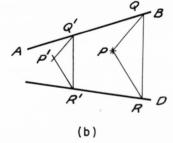

(b)

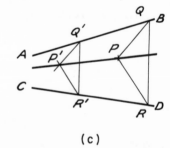

(c)

From any convenient points, *Q* and *R*, on lines *AB* and *CD*, complete the triangle, *PQR*.

Draw a triangle *P'Q'R'* similar to triangle *PQR* by drawing *Q'R'* parallel to *QR*, and *P'Q'* and *P'R'* parallel respectively to *PQ* and *PR*.

Draw line *PP'*, which, if extended, will pass through the inaccessible intersection of lines *AB* and *CD*.

Fig. **2-63.** To draw a line through a given point, *P*, and the point of intersection of two given lines, *AB* and *CD*, the point of intersection being inaccessible.

2–30. TO CONSTRUCT A TRIANGLE, ABC, GIVEN THE THREE SIDES, AB, BC, AND CA (FIG. 2–64)

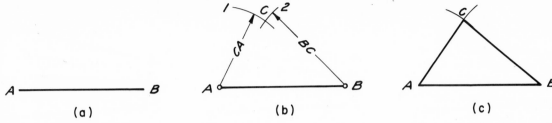

(a)

Draw line *AB* equal in length to one side, *AB*, of the required triangle.

(b)

With *A* and *B* as centers and radii equal respectively to the other two sides, *CA* and *BC*, draw arcs 1 and 2 intersecting at *C*.

(c)

Draw lines *CA* and *BC* to complete the required triangle, *ABC*.

Fig. **2–64.** To construct a triangle, ABC, given the three sides, AB, BC, and CA.

2–31. TO CONSTRUCT A SQUARE WITH A GIVEN SIDE, AB (FIG. 2–65)

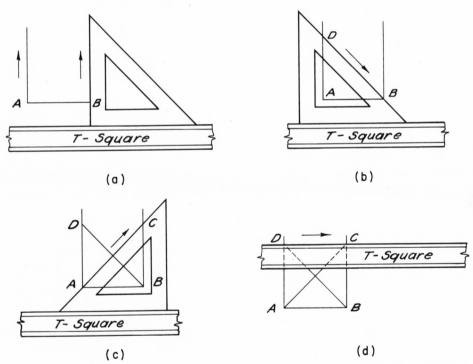

(a)

(b)

(c)

(d)

(a) With the 45° triangle, draw perpendiculars at *A* and *B*.

(b) From *B* draw a diagonal construction line at 45° intersecting the perpendicular from *A* at *D*.

(c) From *A* draw a diagonal construction line at 45° intersecting the perpendicular from *B* at *C*.

(d) Draw a line from *D* parallel to *AB*. This line should pass through point *C*, thus checking accuracy of construction. *ABCD* is the required square.

Fig. **2–65.** To construct a square with a given side, AB.

2–32. TO DIVIDE THE CIRCUMFERENCE OF A GIVEN CIRCLE INTO FIVE EQUAL PARTS (TO CONSTRUCT A PENTAGON OR A FIVE-POINTED STAR) (FIG. 2–66)

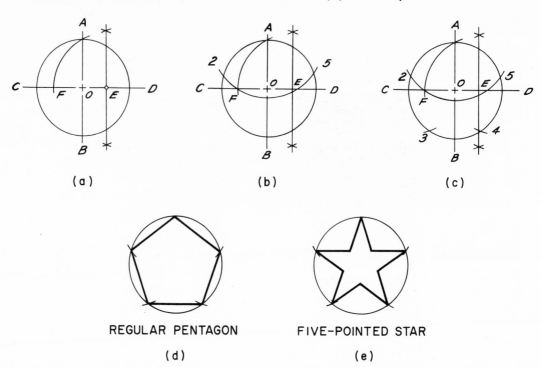

Draw the diameters, *AB* and *CD*, intersecting at *O*. Bisect *OD*, and with the midpoint, *E*, as center, and *EA* as a radius, draw arc, *AF*.

With *A* as center and a radius, *AF*, draw arc 2–5. Arcs *A*–2 and *A*–5 are each ⅕ the circumference.

Step off arcs 2–3, and 3–4 to divide the circumference into five equal parts.

Figs. 2–66(d) and 2–66(e) show how the five equally spaced points can be joined to form a regular pentagon and a five-pointed star.

Fig. 2–66. To divide the circumference of a circle into five equal parts (to construct a pentagon or a five-pointed star).

–33. TO CONSTRUCT A REGULAR HEXAGON WITH A GIVEN DISTANCE, d, ACROSS FLATS (FIG. 2–67)

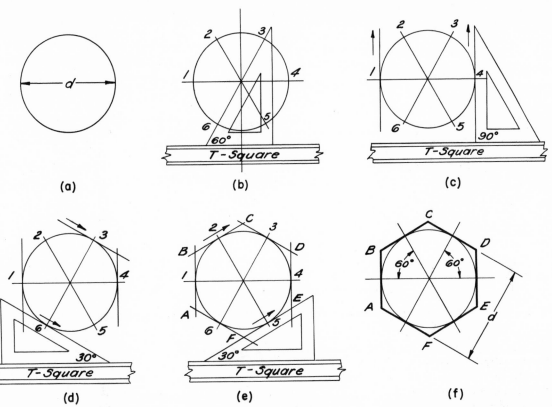

(a)	(b)	(c)
(d)	(e)	(f)

a) Draw a construction circle with a diameter, d; and

(b) Using the 30°–60° triangle, divide the circumference into six equal parts, 1, 2, 3, 4, 5, and 6.

(c)–(e) Using the 30°–60° triangle, draw tangents, AB, BC, CD, DE, EF, and FA, at points 1, 2, 3, 4, 5, and 6.

(f) $ABCDEF$ is the required regular hexagon with a distance across flats equal to the given distance, d.

Fig. 2–67. To construct a regular hexagon with a given distance, d, across flats.

2–34. TO CONSTRUCT A REGULAR HEXAGON WITH GIVEN DISTANCE, *d*, ACROSS CORNERS (FIG. 2–68)

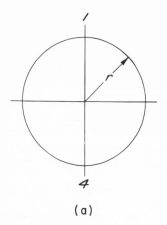
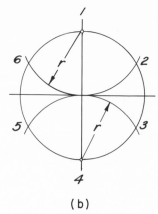
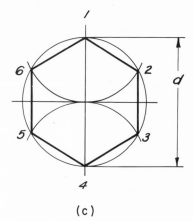

(a)   (b)   (c)

Draw a construction circle with radius, r ($d/2$). Draw the diameter, 1–4.

With 1 and 4 as centers and radius, r, draw arcs intersecting the construction circle at 2 and 6 and 3 and 5, respectively, dividing the circumference into six equal parts.

Join the points, 123456, in order, with straight lines. 123456 is the required hexagon with a distance across corners equal to the given distance, d.

Fig. **2–68.** To construct a regular hexagon with a given distance, *d*, across corners.

2–35. TO CONSTRUCT A REGULAR POLYGON WITH A GIVEN NUMBER (SEVEN) OF SIDES OF A GIVEN LENGTH, *AB* (FIG. 2–69)

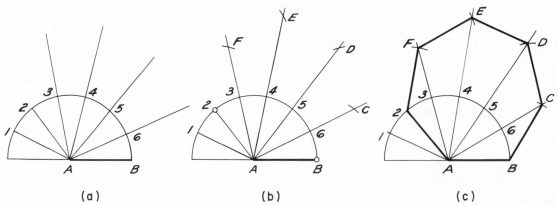

(a)   (b)   (c)

With center at A, and a radius, AB, draw a semicircle, and using the dividers, divide it into seven equal parts. Draw radial lines from A through each of the six numbered points, extending A–3, A–4, A–5, and A–6 as shown.

With centers at 2 and B and a radius, AB, draw arcs intersecting A–3 at F and A–6 at C. With centers at F and C, and the same radius, AB, draw arcs intersecting A–4 at E and A–5 at D.

Draw lines BC, CD, DE, EF, F–2, and 2–A joining the points thus located. $ABCDEF2$ is the required regular polygon with seven sides equal to AB.

Fig. **2–69.** To construct a regular polygon with a given number (seven) of sides of a given length, *AB*.

2-36. TO DRAW A CIRCLE ARC WITH A GIVEN RADIUS, r, TANGENT TO TWO GIVEN STRAIGHT LINES (FIG. 2-70)

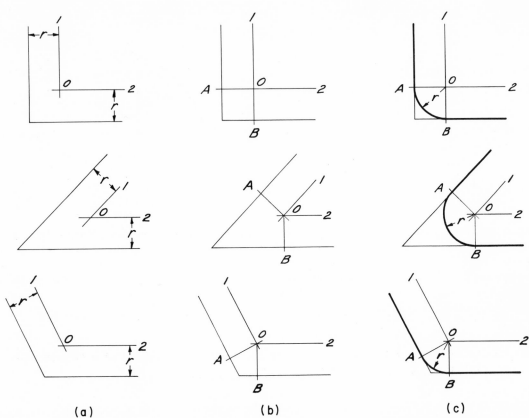

(a)

(b)

(c)

Draw lines 1 and 2 parallel to and at a distance, r, from the two given lines. Lines 1 and 2 are the loci of the centers of all circle arcs r distance from the given lines. O, the intersection of lines 1 and 2, is a point r distance from both the given lines, the center of the required circle arc.

Draw perpendicular lines from O to locate points A and B, the tangent points of the required circle arc.

With the center at O and radius, r, draw arc AB, the required circle arc having a radius, r, and tangent to the two given straight lines.

Fig. **2-70.**   To draw a circle arc with a given radius, r, tangent to two given straight lines.

2–37. TO DRAW A CIRCLE ARC THROUGH THREE GIVEN POINTS, A, B, AND C (FIG. 2–71)

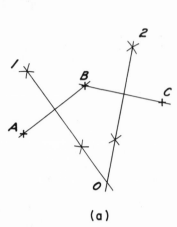

(a)

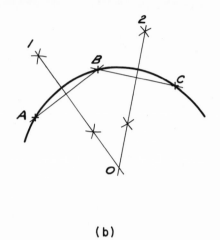

(b)

Draw lines *AB* and *BC*, chords of the required circle arc. Draw the perpendicular bisectors, 1 and 2, of the chords *AB* and *BC*. Bisector 1 is the locus of all points equidistant from *A* and *B*. Bisector 2 is the locus of all points equidistant from *B* and *C*. *O*, the intersection of the perpendicular bisectors of the chords *AB* and *BC*, is therefore a point equidistant from points *A*, *B*, and *C*, and the center of a circle arc passing through the three points.

With the center at *O* and radius *OA*, draw the required circle through the given points, *A*, *B*, and *C*.

Fig. **2–71.**   To draw a circle arc through three given points, A, B, and C.

2–38. TO LOCATE THE CENTER OF A GIVEN CIRCLE ARC (FIG. 2–72)

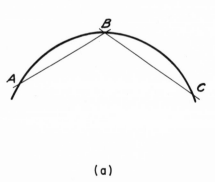

(a)

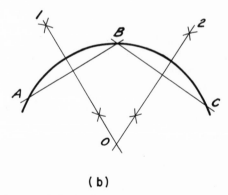

(b)

Choose any three points, *A*, *B*, and *C*, on the given circle arc, and draw chords *AB* and *BC*.

Draw the perpendicular bisectors, 1 and 2, of the chords *AB* and *BC*. Point *O*, the intersection of the perpendicular bisectors of the chords *AB* and *BC*, is the center of the given circle arc.

Fig. **2–72.**   To locate the center of a given circle arc.

2–39. TO DRAW A CIRCLE ARC WITH A GIVEN RADIUS, r, TANGENT TO A GIVEN STRAIGHT LINE AB, AND A GIVEN CIRCLE ARC, C (FIG. 2–73)

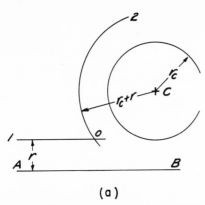

(a)

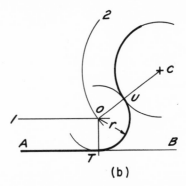

(b)

Draw line 1 parallel to and r distance from AB. This line is the locus of the centers of all circles of r radius tangent to AB. Draw arc 2 with center at C and a radius equal to r_C plus r. This arc is the locus of the centers of all circles of r radius tangent to the circle arc C. Point O, the intersection of line 1 and arc 2, is the center of the circle arc tangent to both the straight line AB and the circle arc C.

Draw a line OT perpendicular to AB. Draw a line OC intersecting circle arc C at U. Points T and U are the tangent points of the required circle arc. With center at O and radius r, draw an arc from U to T. This is the required arc, with radius r, and tangent to line AB and circle arc C.

Fig. 2–73. To draw a circle with a given radius, r, tangent to a given straight line, AB, and a given circle arc, C.

2–40. TO DRAW A CIRCLE ARC WITH A GIVEN RADIUS, r, TANGENT TO TWO GIVEN CIRCLE ARCS, A AND B, WITH RADII OF r_A AND r_B (FIG. 2–74)

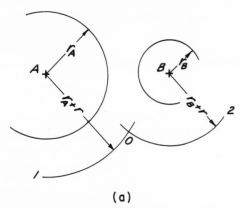

(a)

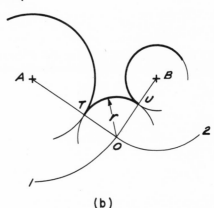

(b)

With center at A and a radius equal to r_A plus r, draw arc 1. This is the locus of the centers of all circle arcs of r radius tangent to arc A. With center at B and a radius equal to r_B plus r, draw arc 2. This is the locus of the centers of all circle arcs of r radius tangent to arc B. Point O, the intersection of arcs 1 and 2, is the center of the required circle arc tangent to both arcs A and B.

Draw lines OA and OB intersecting circle arcs A and B at T and U, the tangent points. With center at O and a radius r, draw an arc from T to U. This is the required circle arc, with radius, r, tangent to circle arcs A and B.

Fig. 2–74. To draw a circle arc with a given radius, r, tangent to two given circle arcs, A and B, with radii r_A and r_B.

2-41. TO DRAW A REVERSE (OGEE) CURVE TANGENT AT B AND C TO TWO GIVEN PARALLEL LINES, AB AND CD (FIG. 2-75)

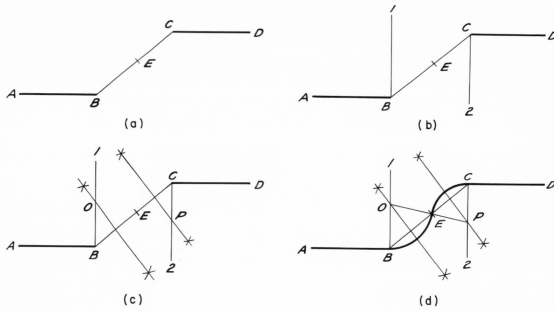

(a) Draw line BC, and assume a point E, on line BC through which the curve must pass.

(b) Draw lines 1 and 2 perpendicular to AB at B and CD at C respectively. Line 1 is the locus of the centers of all circles tangent to AB at B. Line 2 is the locus of the centers of all circles tangent to CD at C.

(c) Construct the perpendicular bisector of BE. This is the locus of the centers of all circle arcs passing through B and E. Construct the perpendicular bisector of CE. This is the locus of the centers of all circle arcs passing through C and E. Points O and P, the intersections of lines 1 and 2 with the perpendicular bisectors, are the centers of circle arcs tangent to AB at B, tangent to CD at C, and passing through E.

(d) With center at O and a radius OB, draw arc BE. With center at P and a radius CP, draw arc CE, completing the reverse curve. The two arcs will be tangent at E. This can be proven by drawing a line OP, which will always pass through E.

Fig. 2-75. To draw a reverse (Ogee) curve, tangent at B and C, to two given parallel lines, AB and CD.

2-42. TO CONSTRUCT AN APPROXIMATE ELLIPSE WITH GIVEN MAJOR AND MINOR DIAMETERS, AB AND CD (FOUR-CENTER METHOD) (FIG. 2-76)

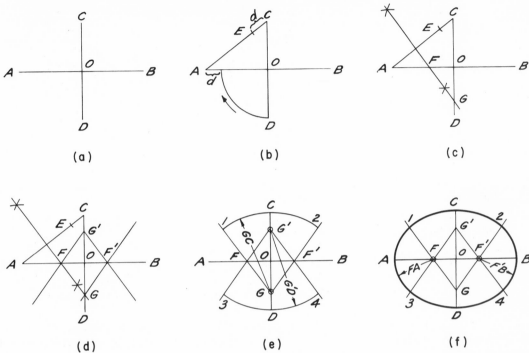

(a) Given major and minor diameters AB and CD intersecting at O.

(b) Draw line AC and mark off CE equal to the difference between AO and DO.

(c) Draw the perpendicular bisector of AE and extend it cutting AB at F and CD at G.

(d) Lay off OF' and OG' equal respectively to OF and OG. Draw lines $G'F$, GF', and $G'F'$.

(e) With center at G and a radius equal to GC, draw the circle arc 1–C–2. Similarly, with center at G' and a radius equal to $G'D$, draw the circle arc 3–D–4.

(f) Complete the approximate ellipse by drawing circle arc 1–A–3 with center at F and a radius equal to FA, and circle arc 2–B–4 with center at F' and a radius equal to $F'B$.

Fig. 2-76. To construct an approximate ellipse with given major and minor diameters, AB and CD (four-center method).

2-43. TO CONSTRUCT AN ELLIPSE WITH GIVEN MAJOR AND MINOR DIAMETERS, AB AND CD (CONCENTRIC CIRCLE METHOD) (FIG. 2-77)

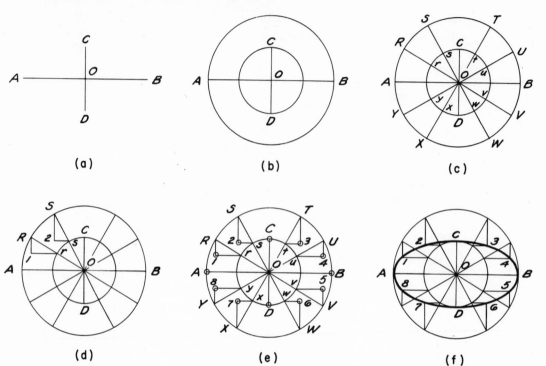

(a)   (b)   (c)

(d)   (e)   (f)

(a) Given major and minor diameters, AB and CD intersecting at O.

(b) With center at O, draw concentric construction circles with AB and CD as diameters.

(c) Divide the circumference of the two concentric circles into a number of parts by drawing OR, OS, OT, etc.

(d) From R and S on the larger circle, draw lines parallel to the minor axis which will intersect at points 1 and 2, similar lines drawn from r and s on the smaller circle parallel to the major axis.

(e) Repeat the construction described in (d) in all four quadrants. Points A, B, C, D, and 1, 2, 3, 4, 5, 6, 7, and 8 all lie on the required ellipse. Additional points can be located if desired.

(f) Using the irregular curve, draw the required ellipse through the established points.

Fig. 2-77. To construct an ellipse with given major and minor diameters, AB and CD (concentric circle method).

2-44. TO CONSTRUCT A PARABOLA WITH A GIVEN SPAN, AB, AND A GIVEN RISE, OP (PARALLELOGRAM METHOD) (FIG. 2-78)

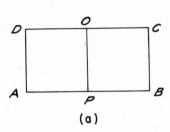

(a)

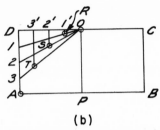

(b)

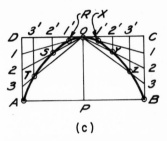

(c)

Complete the parallelogram, *ABCD*, with base *AB* and altitude *OP*.

Divide *DA* and *DO* into the same number of equal parts. Draw rays *O*-1, *O*-2, and *O*-3. From points 1', 2', and 3' drop perpendiculars to *OD* intersecting the rays *O*-1, *O*-2, and *O*-3 at *R*, *S*, and *T*. Points *O*, *R*, *S*, *T*, and *A* are points on the required parabola.

Repeat the construction of (b), locating points *X*, *Y*, and *Z*. Using the irregular curve, draw the parabola through the points thus located.

Fig. 2-78. To construct a parabola with a given span, *AB*, and a given rise *OP* (parallelogram method).

2-45. TO CONSTRUCT AN EQUILATERAL HYPERBOLA ASYMPTOTIC TO THE GIVEN AXES, OA AND OB, AND PASSING THROUGH A GIVEN POINT, P (FIG. 2-79)

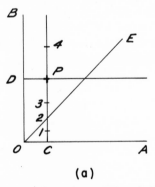

(a)

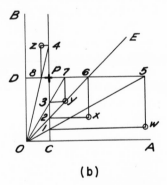

(b)

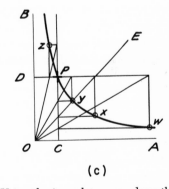

(c)

From *P*, draw lines *PC* and *PD*, perpendicular respectively to *OA* and *OB*. Draw line *OE* bisecting angle *AOB*. Line *OE* is the line of symmetry of the hyperbola. Mark off a number of points, 1, 2, 3, and 4, along the line *PC*.

Draw rays *O*-1, *O*-2, *O*-3, and *O*-4 intersecting line *PD* at points 5, 6, 7, and 8. From each of the numbered points, draw perpendiculars to *PC* and *PD* intersecting at points *w*, *x*, *y*, and *z*. Points *w*, *x*, *y*, *P*, and *z* are points on the required hyperbola.

Using the irregular curve, draw the hyperbola through the points thus located.

Fig. 2-79. To construct an equilateral hyperbola asymptotic to the given axes, *OA* and *OB*, and passing through a given point, *P*.

2-46. CONVENTIONAL LINE SYMBOLS

The line symbols illustrated in Fig. 2-80 are recommended by the American Standards Association for use on engineering drawings. These conventional line symbols apply to both instrumental drawings and freehand sketches. The three line thicknesses used are designated *thick*, *medium*, and *thin*. The actual thickness of the line will vary somewhat with the scale of the drawing, but there should be a distinct contrast between thick and medium lines and medium and thin lines. Thick lines should be as thick as practicable for pencil work. For good reproduction, lines of all thicknesses should be a dense black.

1. Visible Outline. Thick solid lines are used for representing the visible edges or contours of an object. The visible edges should be the most obvious lines of the drawing, contrasting clearly with all other lines.

2. Hidden Outline. Medium dashed lines are used for representing the invisible or hidden edges or contours of an object. The dashes are about $\frac{1}{8}''$ in length with spaces of about $\frac{1}{32}''$ between dashes. Spacing is by eye.

3. Center Lines. Intersecting center lines locate the centers of circles. Single center lines locate the axes of circular cylinders and cones, and indicate the axes of symmetry of symmetrical parts. Center lines are thin lines drawn as alternately long and short dashes. The long dashes may vary in length from $\frac{3}{4}''$ to $1\frac{1}{2}''$ or more depending upon the size of the drawing. The short dashes should be about $\frac{1}{16}''$ to $\frac{1}{8}''$ long. Spaces between dashes are about $\frac{1}{32}''$.

4. Cutting-Plane Line. The cutting-plane line is a thick line representing the edge view of a cutting plane. It is used when sectioning to indicate the location of an imaginary cutting plane. The symbol is a long dash, $\frac{3}{4}''$ to $1\frac{1}{2}''$ long, alternating with two short dashes, about $\frac{1}{8}''$ long. Spaces between dashes should be about $\frac{1}{16}''$. The ends of a cutting plane are bent at right angles and terminated by arrowheads which indicate the direction of sight for viewing the section. For good contrast, cutting-plane lines are usually drawn slightly thicker than visible outlines.

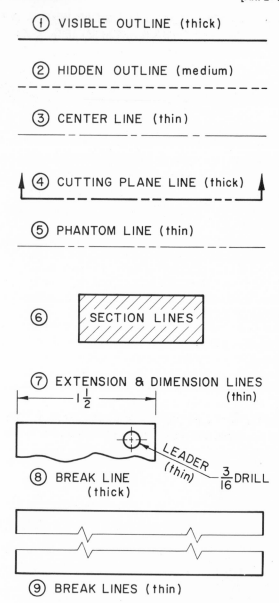

Fig. 2-80. Conventional line symbols.

5. Phantom Lines. Phantom lines are thin lines composed of long dashes, $\frac{3}{4}''$ to $1\frac{1}{2}''$ long, alternating with two short dashes, about $\frac{1}{8}''$ long. Spaces between dashes should be about $\frac{1}{16}''$. Length of the dashes varies depending upon the size of the drawing. Phantom lines are used to represent alternate positions of moving parts, adjacent positions of related parts, and repeated detail.

6. Section Lines. Section lines are thin solid lines used to indicate surfaces in a sectional view. Parts of an object cut by an imaginary cutting plane are represented by section lines. Section lines are evenly spaced, by eye, from $\frac{1}{16}''$ to $\frac{1}{8}''$ apart, depending upon the size of the drawing.

7. Extension Lines, Dimension Lines, and Leaders. These lines are used in dimensioning. Extension lines extend out from the extremities of an object. Dimension lines are drawn at right angles to extension lines, and are used in conjunction with dimension figures to indicate the distance between extension lines. Leaders are used to direct notes, symbols, or identification numbers to various parts or features of a view.

8. Break Lines (thick). Break lines are thick lines used to limit a partial view or to represent the break in a broken section. Break lines are drawn freehand the same thickness as a visible outline. This form of break line is recommended for short breaks.

9. Break Lines (thin). This form of break line is recommended where the break is long. It is particularly applicable to structural drawing. The symbol is a thin solid line broken at intervals with Z-shaped jags.

2–47. INKING

Only a few years ago engineering drawings which were to be reproduced were first laid out in pencil and then carefully traced in ink on tracing cloth. Inking is a tedious and time-consuming (hence expensive) operation, requiring a high degree of skill. Using present-day reproduction techniques, inking is seldom required. Excellent reproductions can be made from pencil lines drawn directly on transparent paper, cloth, or film. Some inking is still done, but ink work comprises only a small fraction of the total output. Patent Office drawings, drawings prepared for presentation or display, and drawings which are to be reproduced in a book (by the photo-lithographic process) must be inked.

Ink lines are drawn with the ruling pen (Fig. 2–81), one of the instruments of the set of drawing instruments. The ruling pen, fitted in a handle as

Fig. **2–81.** The ruling pen. (Photograph courtesy of Keuffel & Esser Co., Hoboken, N. J.)

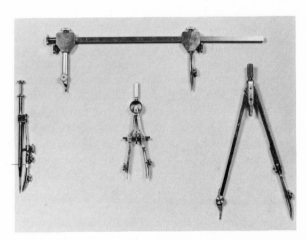

Fig. **2–82.** Compasses equipped with ruling pens.

illustrated in Fig. 2–81, is used for drawing straight lines against the T-square, parallel straightedge, and triangles, and for drawing irregular curves against the French curve. The bow compass, friction head compass, drop bow compass, and beam compass can all be fitted with a ruling pen in place of the lead holder for inking circles and circle arcs (Fig. 2–82).

The ruling pen is filled with a black, opaque drawing ink from a special bottle equipped with a dropper in the cap. A small amount of ink (about $\frac{1}{4}''$) is carefully placed between the nibs of the pen

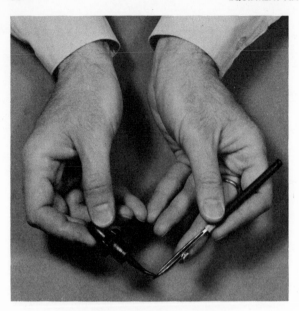

Fig. **2–83.** Filling the ruling pen.

Fig. **2–84.** Position of the pen nibs in relation to the straightedge.

(Fig. 2–83) making sure that no ink overflows or drops on the outside of the nibs. If any ink is spilled on the outside of the nibs, the pen must be wiped clean with a cloth and refilled. If too much ink is put in the pen, its weight will force all the ink out at once depositing a large blob on the paper. If not enough ink is put in, the pen will run out of ink before the line to be drawn is completed. Stopping a line and picking it up again after refilling the pen is difficult and frequently results in an obvious irregularity in the line.

The thickness of the inked line is determined by the distance between the nibs of the ruling pen. For a fine line, the nibs are close together. Thicker lines are obtained by opening the nibs. This adjustment is made by means of a knurled screw on the side of the nibs. After an adjustment has been made, a short trial line should be drawn on a piece of scrap paper similar to the paper of the drawing. Further adjustments are made and new test lines drawn until a line of the desired width is obtained.

The ruling pen is never used freehand. It is always guided against a straightedge or the irregular curve. The handle of the ruling pen should be leaned slightly back from the straightedge so that the inner pen nib is actually guided by the upper edge of the straightedge (Fig. 2–84). If the nibs are pointed in toward the bottom of the straightedge,

the ink will flow out of the pen and under the straightedge. If the pen nibs are leaned too far away from the straightedge, only one nib will be in contact with the paper, and the line will be ragged.

Ink lines are drawn from left to right (if one is right-handed) along the top edge of the T-square or parallel straightedge, and from bottom to top along the vertical edge of the triangles. It is important that horizontal lines be completed from the top of the drawing down and vertical lines from the left of the drawing to the right. This procedure will reduce the probability of sliding the straightedge or triangle across a wet ink line with smearing results. Long, straight lines should be inked in one continuous motion of the arm, finishing the last inch or so with a wrist and finger movement. Short lines can be inked with hand and finger motion.

Inked circles and circle arcs are drawn in the same manner as pencil circles. The pen should be filled with enough ink to finish a given circle without refilling. Only once around the circle is enough; additional turns will thicken the arc. In inking a drawing, it is good practice to ink the circles and circle arcs first, beginning with the smallest circles. This is particularly important when drawing straight lines tangent to circle arcs. It is much easier to ink a smooth tangent when the circle arc is drawn first and the straight line then drawn tangent to the circle.

For drawing long lines and unusually wide lines such as border lines, specially designed pens—long-line and wide-line pens—are available. These pens, called *Marathon* pens by their manufacturer (Fig. 2–85), hold large amounts of ink, and are capable of drawing several long lines without refilling. The nibs are pre-set insuring a constant width line. Marathon pens come in sets with pens of different settings for drawing lines in various widths.

Fig. 2–85. Long line and wide line ruling pens. (Photograph courtesy of Keuffel & Esser Co., Hoboken, N. J.)

Ink should flow freely from the nibs of the pen. If the ink has dried on the end of the nibs, flow can sometimes be started by touching the nibs to the back of the finger. If this does not start the flow, the pen should be wiped dry and refilled. Drying of the ink in the nibs is most likely to occur when the nibs are close together. When drawing fine lines, rapid work is essential to avoid constant refilling of the nibs. After use and before each refilling, the nibs should be wiped clean of all old ink. A damp cloth will usually remove dried ink, although sometimes a pen-cleaning fluid is necessary to remove thickly caked ink which has been allowed to dry in the pen. With proper care, this condition should not occur. Some pen nibs either hinge open like a jackknife blade or pivot open to facilitate cleaning. These pens, if carefully handled, can be opened for cleaning and closed again without disturbing the setting of the nibs.

Ink lines which must be removed because of a mistake or change in the drawing should be erased with the *pencil eraser*. So-called ink erasers are hard and gritty, and will damage the surface of the paper so that a new line cannot be drawn through the erased area without blotting. The electric erasing machine greatly speeds the work of erasing ink lines. After the line has been erased, the erased area should be burnished with the fingernail to restore the gloss to the paper before a new line is inked. A sharp knife or razor blade is helpful in removing short bits of line such as an overrun corner or slightly ragged edge; however, they must be used with considerable care, scraping or cutting only deep enough to remove the ink without damaging the paper.

2–48. CARE OF THE DRAWING INSTRUMENTS

If treated with proper care, quality drawing instruments will give many years of satisfactory service. Improper handling, through ignorance or carelessness, can cause damage to the equipment which results in constant annoyance and inaccurate work. The correct handling of the drawing instruments should be understood and applied. If occasional damage does occur, in spite of proper care, the damaged instrument should be repaired or replaced.

Drawing Board. The drawing board should be flat and unwarped. The edges should be tight and straight. Dropping the board results in damaged edges which prevents the T-square from being properly aligned. To avoid punching holes in the board, tape should be used rather than thumbtacks for fastening down the paper. A drawing board filled with thumbtack holes is a needless handicap. Drawing boards should be stored flat or on edge away from excessive heat or dampness.

T-square. The T-square should be handled with reasonable care. It should not be used as a hammer for pounding thumbtacks, as a foil in an impromptu fencing match, or as a paddle for a friendly assault on the posterior of a classmate. Dropping the T-square should be avoided, but if dropped, it should be examined for loosening of blade and head. If tightening the screws does not fix a loose head, the screws should be removed completely, the head and blade re-glued, and the screws replaced. The plastic straightedge should not be used as a guide for a knife or razor blade when cutting paper. This will surely nick the straightedge, and result in lines with a little wiggle at the point where the pencil or pen jumps across the nick. Nicks can be detected by sliding the edge of the fingernail lightly along the straightedge. A T-square thus damaged is best replaced by a new one. The T-square should not be washed in water, but may be wiped with a damp cloth. The blade should always be wiped with a dry cloth before using. Stubborn dirt which accumulates on the underside of the blade can be removed with a soft pencil eraser. When not in use, the T-square is best stored if it is hung from the hole in the blade or laid flat to prevent warping.

Triangles. The plastic triangles should not be used as a guide for a knife or razor blade. Like the plastic straightedge of the T-square, they nick easily. The triangles can be washed with cold or lukewarm water and soap. Adjustable triangles should not be washed in water, but are best cleaned by wiping with a dry cloth. Triangles should be hung or stored flat when not in use.

The Instrument Set. The dividers, compasses, and ruling pens which comprise the instrument set deserve special care, since they are the most expensive and precisely made items of equipment used by the draftsman. Instruments should be kept in the case when not in use. Wiping each instrument with a soft cloth before replacing it in the case will prevent tarnish.

The friction head dividers and compass are equipped with set screws for adjusting the tightness of the head. They should be loose enough to permit free movement yet tight enough to remain fixed while in use. The set screws are adjusted with the small instrument screw driver provided with the set, being careful not to damage the screw driver slot in the head of the set screw. Dropping the dividers or compasses will result in broken or bent needle points. If the points are removable, they can be replaced; otherwise they must be re-sharpened with a pocket stone. When sharpening divider points, both points must be sharpened so that they are of equal length.

The nibs of the ruling pens must not be tightened beyond their point of contact. Pen nibs which open for cleaning must not be "snapped shut," but

should be closed carefully. The nibs of ruling pens are made of hard carbon steel and are easily broken. Ink should be wiped out immediately after use and not allowed to harden. Ruling pens not properly cleaned will rust. The nibs of the ruling pens should be opened completely to relieve the tension on the springs when stored in the case.

2-49. CLEANLINESS

Cleanliness is most important in the production of a good engineering drawing. Dirt can be removed from the drawing with the pencil eraser, but it is simpler to keep the drawing as clean as possible while work progresses. The draftsman should wash his hands with soap and water before beginning work. The board should be dusted with the brush, and the T-square and triangles wiped with a cloth. The triangles should be washed occasionally with soap and water. When sharpening the pencil or compass leads, do not work over the drawing area. Graphite dust on the fingers and instruments will soon spread all over the drawing. Touching the drawing paper leaves invisible grease spots which are collectors of dirt. A spot of eraser dust under the paper or a wrinkle in the paper will pick up dirt. The T-square and triangles should be lifted and moved rather than slid about on the drawing surface. By bearing down slightly on the head of the T-square, the blade can be moved up and down without sliding on the drawing surface. When working on a large drawing, the finished area can be kept clean by covering it with paper, exposing only the small portion being worked on. When cleaning up a finished drawing, either pencil or ink, scrubbing over the lines with art gum or eraser should be avoided as this will dull the lines and result in poor reproduction.

2-50. SKILL WITH THE DRAWING INSTRUMENTS

Good drawing ability entails both *accuracy* and *speed*. The two are inseparable. Speed without accuracy is time wasted, while accuracy at the expense of speed has little commercial value. One without the other is always expensive. In addition to speed and accuracy, *legibility* and *neatness* are of prime importance. Accuracy, legibility, and neatness are the products of good habits. Speed is not the result of hurrying, but develops as the correct use of the drawing instruments becomes natural and effortless.

2-51. QUALITY

How good must a drawing be? The answer, of course, depends upon the use to be made of the finished drawing. A representational drawing, made for the use of someone else, must be so clear and legible that no supplementary written or verbal instructions are necessary. What of the details of technique? Must corners and tangents meet precisely? Must the lines on a dimensioned drawing be measured with great accuracy? Is it worth the time involved to rule guide lines for lettering, or carefully space the views, or maintain uniform line work by continually sharpening the pencil? One might as well inquire, is it worth the time required to put on a clean shirt, to have the suit pressed and the shoes shined, or to brush the hair? An engineer is most frequently judged by the quality of the drawings he or his organization produces. A good drawing is as easy to make as a poor one, and, in the final cost accounting, less expensive. A sloppy drawing is indicative of careless work, lack of organization, and poor drafting habits. A potential client, viewing a drawing with overrun corners, gapping tangents, and lettering with a downhill slope, may wonder, with some justification, if engineering computations and cost estimates have not been performed with comparable carelessness. If the job is such that an instrumental drawing is required, it should be of the highest quality. The professional should be satisfied with nothing less than the best. Work which does not warrant the time and expense of an instrumental drawing can usually be accomplished with a freehand sketch.

2-52. ACCURACY

Dimensioned representational drawings are seldom scaled. Size determinations are made from the dimension figures and notes. In fact, one basic drawing may be used for similar objects of different sizes, with only the dimension figures altered to indicate differences in size. Drawings of objects which are to be made to tolerances of several thousandths or ten-thousandths of an inch are drawn to a nominal size close to the actual size and dimensioned with figures describing to the machinist the tolerances required.

In making representational drawings, it is not usually necessary to measure or lay out distances with extreme precision. However, in making drawings for the purpose of determining numerical answers to engineering problems, great care must be observed in laying out and measuring distances and in accurately drawing lines through precisely plotted points. It is in the area of graphical calculation that the engineer needs all the drafting skill he can command to derive maximum results from his precision instruments. It is in the graphical solution that the engineer achieves full professional status. He has made a decision based on a thorough analysis of the problem and his judgment of the best means of solution, and is exercising the manipulative skills necessary to obtain answers which provide the basis for other decisions and the issuing of orders to his subordinates. Accuracy in graphical calculations is of prime importance. The drawing may not be of presentation quality with neatly ruled borders and carefully lettered notes; it may not be as complete in its detailed information as the representational drawing; the line work may not be suitable for good reproduction, but it must be accurate, producing precise numerical answers.

2-53. CONCLUSION

In instrumental drawing, as in all phases of his professional development, the engineer should strive to achieve a high degree of knowledge and skill, working on his own to fill the unavoidable gaps in his formal education. Standards of quality and accuracy should be as high as possible commensurate with the nature of the assignment and the time allowed for its completion. Unskilled and indifferent work on the drawing board is unworthy of either the aspiring or practicing engineer.

Problems

2-1. Draw the squares illustrated in Fig. 2-86 to the dimensions given.

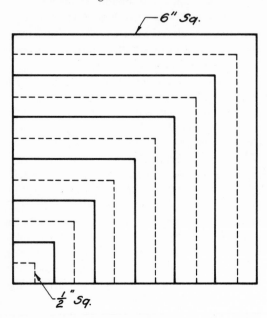

Fig. **2-86.**

2-2. Draw the diagonal line design illustrated in Fig. 2-87 to the dimensions given.

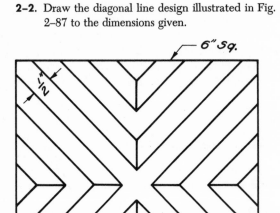

Fig. **2-87.**

2-3. Draw the radial line and circle exercise illustrated in Fig. 2-88 to the dimensions given.

*Circle diameters are $6\frac{1}{2}$", 6", 1", $\frac{3}{4}$"
Radial lines at 15° intervals*

Fig. **2-88.**

2-4. Draw the five-pointed star illustrated in Fig. 2-89 to the dimensions given.

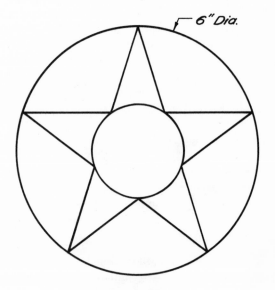

Fig. **2-89.**

2–5. Draw the hexagon design illustrated in Fig. 2–90 to the dimensions given.

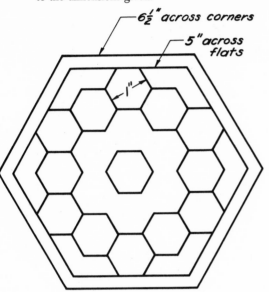

Fig. **2–90.**

2–7. Draw the tangent circle arrangement illustrated in Fig. 2–92 to the dimensions given.

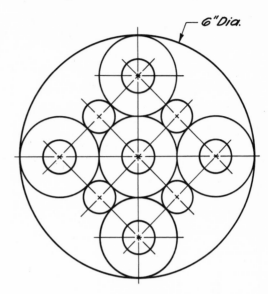

Fig. **2–92.**

2–6. Draw the concentric circles illustrated in Fig. 2–91 to the dimensions given.

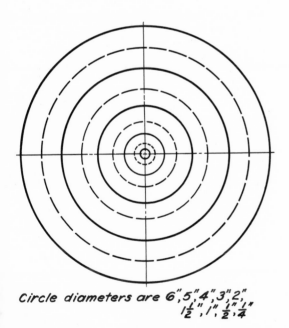

Circle diameters are 6",5",4",3",2", 1½",1",½",¼"

Fig. **2–91.**

2–8. Draw the straight line and circle arc exercise illustrated in Fig. 2–93 to the dimensions given.

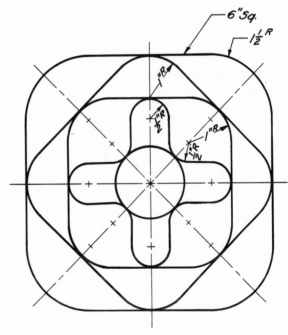

Fig. **2–93.**

2–9. Draw the centrifugal pump gasket illustrated in Fig. 2–94 to the dimensions given.

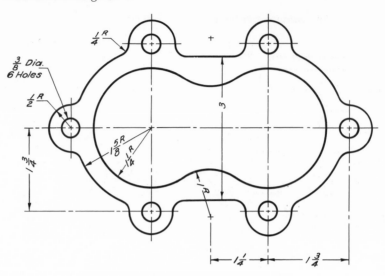

Fig. **2–94.**   Centrifugal pump gasket.

2–10. Plot the sine curve illustrated in Fig. 2–95 to the dimensions given.   Using the irregular curve, connect the plotted points with a smooth curve.

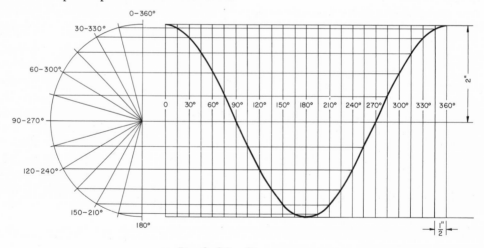

Fig. **2–95.**   Sine curve.

3

SKETCHING

3-1. INTRODUCTION

Skill with the drawing instruments is a valuable asset to all those concerned with technical communication. Of even greater importance to both the student and the practicing engineer is the ability to express ideas through the use of understandable sketches, rapidly drawn, *without* the aid of instruments.

The engineer uses sketches to develop an idea. These early developmental sketches may be nothing more than a few almost unintelligible lines hastily blocked out on a scratch pad. As the idea takes form (Fig. 3–1), the sketches become more detailed, and several possible solutions may be outlined and discarded before the basic requirements of the design or product have been satisfied. The sketch now becomes a means of communication between the engineer and the draftsman or between the engineer and the shop. The completed sketch, with sufficient construction detail included (Fig. 3–2), may go directly to the shop for the building of a prototype, or it may be turned over to a junior engineer, technical assistant, or draftsman, who will prepare the required instrumental drawings.

The amount of detail included in a sketch or its degree of completeness depends upon how and by whom the sketch is to be used. A designer preparing sketches which he knows will be used by an experienced assistant working at a drafting table a few yards away, permitting frequent observation and immediate consultation, may choose to communicate his ideas through sketches containing a minimum of detail, and depend on short conferences and hasty supplementary sketches as the work progresses to supply any missing information or to modify the original conception. However, the original sketch or a copy may be used by the shop in lieu of an instrumental drawing for the construction of prototypes or production models. Consultation between the designer and shop personnel may be neither convenient nor possible. For shop use, the sketch must be completely understandable without further explanation and include all necessary details of construction. It is not unheard of for a factory to go into full production working from sketches only, with the finished instrumental drawings being prepared for permanent record after the product has been marketed.

Sketches may be either pictorial or in the form

73

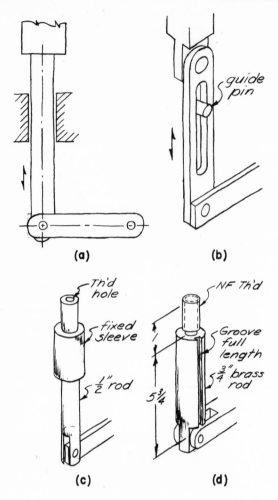

Fig. **3–1.** Development of an idea.

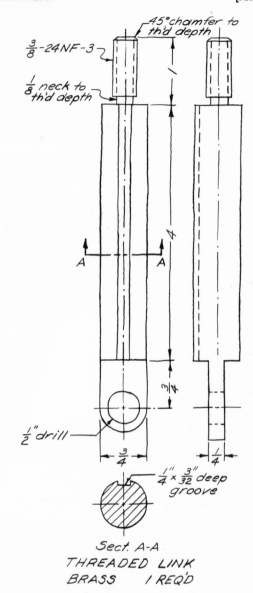

Sect. A-A
THREADED LINK
BRASS   1 REQ'D

Fig. **3–2.** A detail sketch.

of single or multi-view projections (Fig. 3–3). In either case, the same principles of shape and size description and the same conventional practices which apply to instrumental drawings must be understood and applied to the sketch. The term "sketch" in no way implies careless or incomplete work; neither should an undue amount of time and effort be spent in creating a "work of art." The sketch of the engineer is technical in nature and utilitarian in use. It is produced solely as a means to an end. The quality and completeness of the sketch should be commensurate with the time available and the purpose for which the sketch is intended.

Sketching, like instrumental drawing, is not dependent upon artistic ability. Anyone who will take the trouble to learn a few simple techniques and practice these techniques can produce acceptable freehand sketches. In the paragraphs that follow, the basic techniques of sketching are described and illustrated. Reading about these techniques will be of little benefit. Only practice and more practice will develop sketching ability. The value of an ability to sketch rapidly and well is worth the effort required. It is the engineer's most useful means of graphic expression.

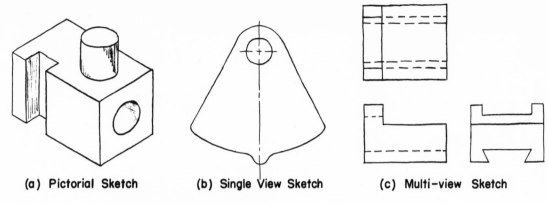

(a) Pictorial Sketch   (b) Single View Sketch   (c) Multi-view Sketch

Fig. **3-3.** Types of sketches.

Fig. **3-4.** Sketching equipment.

3-2. EQUIPMENT

Sketching requires little equipment. A pencil, an eraser, and paper (Fig. 3-4) are all that is necessary. A medium soft pencil, with lead grade H, F, or HB, is recommended for sketching. The lead may be either in a wood casing or held in a lead holder. The lead holder is preferable since it facili-

THE PENCIL IS IMPORTANT -

Do not use a short
stubby pencil with
a dull point .....

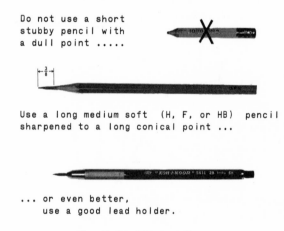

Use a long medium soft (H, F, or HB) pencil
sharpened to a long conical point ...

... or even better,
use a good lead holder.

Fig. **3-5.** The pencil.

tates the frequent sharpening required and permits easy adjustment of point length. The eraser should be a soft pencil eraser which will not smudge.

Pencils used for sketching (Fig. 3-5) should be sharpened to a long, conical point extending about $\frac{3}{8}''$ beyond the wood casing or lead holder. The pencil point must be sharpened frequently (Fig. 3-6) with a sandpaper pad, file, or one of the mechanical lead-pointing devices. After sharpening, it is a good idea to dull or round the point slightly on a piece of scratch paper to reduce the tendency of the sharp needle point to chip off.

The paper used for sketches is usually in pad form with sheets $8\frac{1}{2}'' \times 11''$ or somewhat larger. The surface should be rough enough to take pencil marks well, and tough enough to erase easily with-

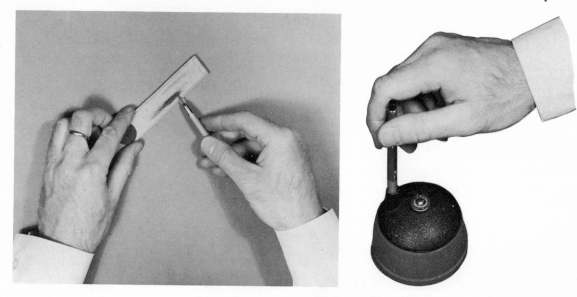

Fig. **3-6.** Sharpening the point.

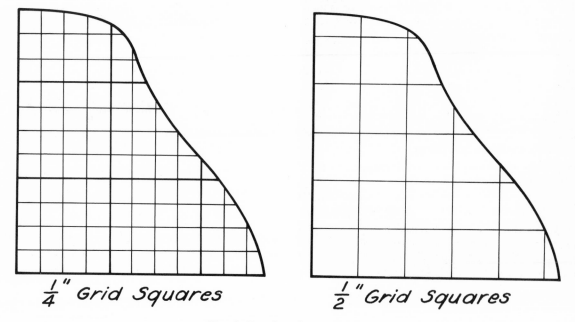

$\frac{1}{4}''$ Grid Squares $\frac{1}{2}''$ Grid Squares

Fig. **3-7.** Coordinate paper.

out smudging or damage. Sketching paper is available in plain white or ruled with light blue or green grid lines dividing the sheet into $\frac{1}{8}''$, $\frac{1}{4}''$, or $\frac{1}{2}''$ squares (Fig. 3–7). Coordinate paper is helpful in sketching straight lines, estimating lengths, and obtaining proper proportion. If printed lines on the completed sketch are undesirable, a grid of heavy black lines can be placed under a sheet of translucent sketch paper to serve the same purpose. Black printed grids are sometimes provided with sketch pads to slip under each successive sheet of the pad. If the sketch is to be reproduced, coordinate paper is available with lines that will not reproduce. High quality office bond or typewriter paper makes good paper for technical sketches, and is frequently used. The sketcher, in practice, is not inhibited by lack of proper materials; he uses whatever is at hand, the back of an envelope, a menu, a leaf torn from a pocket notebook or calendar pad, sketching while the idea is fresh.

3–3. SKETCHING TECHNIQUE

Any sketch is composed of straight and curved lines. The straight lines may be horizontal, vertical, or inclined. Curved lines are usually circles or circle arcs, ellipses or arcs of ellipses. Other types of curved lines are less frequently encountered in technical sketches and will not be considered in detail. Straight lines should look like straight lines and should begin and end at the proper place. Perpendicular lines should appear perpendicular; parallel lines should be parallel throughout their length. Circles and circle arcs should look like circles without obvious flats or humps. The major and minor axes of ellipses should be perpendicular and in the proper proportion. The curve of an ellipse should be smooth without flats, humps, or abrupt changes in direction.

Probably the most important single factor in sketching is *proportion*. Proportion deals with the relative length of lines and with the relative size of objects. Good proportion (Fig. 3–8) is achieved when a square is sketched with the four sides equal in length; when a rectangle is sketched with the correct ratio of long side to short side; when the center of a circle is placed in the proper position relative to the whole sketch and the radius is kept in the proper ratio; when ellipses have the correct ratio between the major and minor axes. Good and bad proportion are illustrated in Fig. 3–9, using a familiar object, the tennis racquet, as an example. Fig. 3–9(a) shows the tennis racquet as one is accustomed to seeing it—it is in its *correct proportion*. In Fig. 3–9(b), the racquet looks a bit strange; the object is recognizable, but the handle is too long— the handle is *out of proportion*. The object looks more like a squash racquet than a tennis racquet. Fig. 3–9(c) is sketched with the correct overall shape and dimensions, but certain interior details have been slightly altered: the wood of the frame has been thickened; the handle has been increased

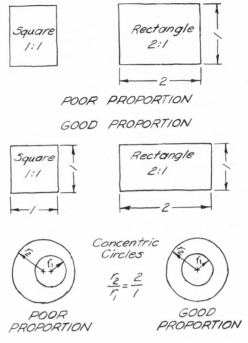

Fig. **3–8.** Proportion.

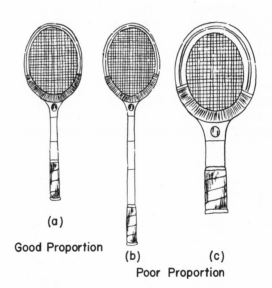

(a)

Good Proportion

(b)   (c)

Poor Proportion

Fig. **3–9.** Effects of good and bad proportion.

in size. Poor proportion in these features has resulted in a sketch which is almost unrecognizable. The familiar tennis racquet has become a ping-pong paddle with strings. Correct proportion can be established using the pencil or a strip of paper as a guide for laying off distances. The squares of coordinate paper are also a great aid to the beginner in obtaining proper proportion. The experienced sketcher judges proportion with the aid of a well-trained eye. As the "eye" for proportion is developed, less dependence on paper strips, coordinate paper, etc., is required, and both quality and speed are increased.

Shape is another important factor in technical sketching (Fig. 3–10). Squares and rectangles should be sketched with corners at right angles and opposite sides parallel. Circles should look like circles all the way around. Circles which appear to be distorted squares with rounded corners, and oval or egg-shaped circles should be avoided. Ellipses should be symmetrical about both the major and minor axes. Pointed ends, unsymmetrical halves, and flattened arcs result in "footballs," "eggs," and "weiners" instead of graceful ellipses.

Size must be considered, but it is of secondary importance to proportion and shape. A technical sketch should be big enough to show clearly all necessary details. Tiny, postage-stamp size sketches huddling in the corner or center of a large sheet of paper, or a sketch that grows to such outlandish size that it can no longer be confined within the borders of the paper, can sometimes occur when the size factor is overlooked. A line whose true length should be three inches, which by actual measurement on the sketch is two and three-quarters or three and a half inches, is of little concern provided other lines are in their correct proportion. Knowing that the length of the middle joint of the index finger is one inch long, or scratching a mark one, two, and three inches from the end of a favorite lead holder, or using coordinate paper will aid materially in the estimation of length. Again, the well-trained eye of the experienced sketcher can closely estimate length without the use of mechanical aids.

A sketch combines the manual skill necessary to sketch straight and curved lines with the ability to assemble these lines in the correct proportion, shape, and size to depict accurately an idea or product to another person. Both manual skill and the "eye" for proportion, shape, and size are developed only through continual practice in sketching—*thinking with the pencil and paper.*

The technique of sketching is largely a matter of individual preference; the finished sketch is of

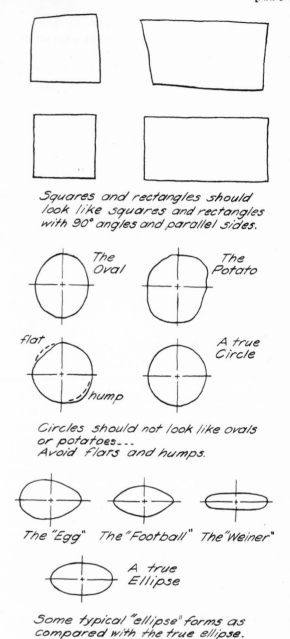

Squares and rectangles should look like squares and rectangles with 90° angles and parallel sides.

Circles should not look like ovals or potatoes...
Avoid flats and humps.

Some typical "ellipse" forms as compared with the true ellipse.

Fig. **3–10.** Shape.

greater importance than the steps taken to achieve it. However, the following instructions should prove helpful to the beginner. If these suggestions are understood and conscientiously practiced, a facility for freehand drawing will be quickly developed, and sketching will become a natural means of expression and communication.

3–4. STRAIGHT LINES

Begin with a sheet (or pad) of white paper about $8\frac{1}{2}'' \times 11''$, a soft (H, F, or HB) pencil, and a soft pencil eraser. For practicing straight lines, plain white paper without grid squares is best. Sharpen the pencil to a long, conical point with about $\frac{3}{8}''$ of lead exposed. The pencil should be fairly long (a lead holder is recommended). Do not begin to sketch with a short stub of a pencil (Fig. 3–5). A few turns of the pencil point on a sheet of scratch paper will "round" the needle point and prevent it from chipping off. The paper should not be taped down, but should be loose on the drawing table so it can be easily turned and moved about. Hold the pencil in a natural writing position with the forefinger about one to two inches above the point. The pencil should be held in a relaxed grip, firmly enough for good control, but not in a tight, cramped clutch. The entire forearm should be supported by the drafting table. (This, of course, is the "ideal condition." The skillful sketcher can sketch standing on his head if necessary, but why handicap the beginner?)

Horizontal Lines. It is quite difficult to sketch a long straight line with a single stroke. It is easier to sketch a short straight line. Therefore, a long straight line is drawn by breaking it into a series of short straight lines (Fig. 3–11). When sketching horizontal lines, the forearm is oriented at right angles to the direction of the line being sketched (Fig. 3–12). Short straight-line strokes about one inch long are drawn from left to right with the wrist held straight and the hand and forearm pivoting about the elbow. These strokes should be light and slightly overlapping, although occasional minute breaks are acceptable (Fig. 3–11). Before beginning to sketch a horizontal line, mark the left and right ending points of the line. As the line progresses in a series of short straight lines from the left starting point to the right ending point, direction (which is very important) is maintained by keeping the eye directed toward the right ending point rather than on the moving pencil point. After this first trial line has been completed, make corrections in the direction and straightness where necessary by adding shorter straight-line strokes correcting those previously laid down out of alignment. When the requirements for length, direc-

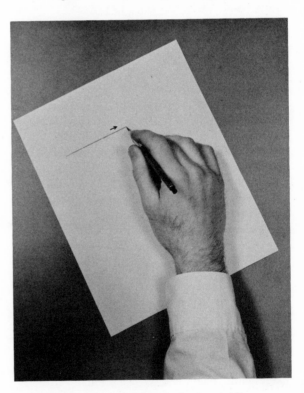

Sketching a long straight line between two points is rather difficult - - - - - - -

Sketching a short straight line is relatively easy - - - - -

So - - - - - -

A long straight line is sketched as a series of short straight lines - - - -

Either overlapping slightly - - - -

Or - - - - -

With minute breaks between strokes.

Fig. 3–11. Sketching a straight line.

Fig. 3–12. Sketching a horizontal line.

tion, and straightness have been satisfied, go over the line with a sharp pencil point, bearing down to produce a clean and distinct black line. If the initial strokes have been light, little or no erasing is probably necessary. However, there may be,

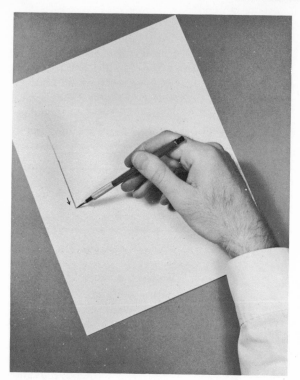

Fig. **3–13.** Sketching a vertical line.

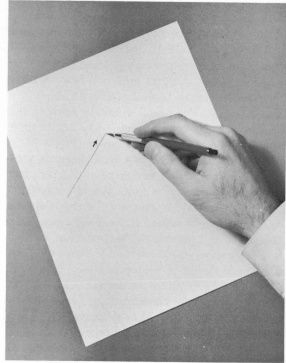

Fig. **3–14.** Sketching an inclined line—1.

particularly in the beginner's early attempts, considerable "brushiness" in the line. "Brushiness" should be, and can be, corrected by using the eraser to smooth out and remove incorrect attempts.

Vertical Lines. Vertical lines are drawn with the same short-line technique described for horizontal lines (Fig. 3–13).   The arm is oriented at a comfortable angle (anywhere from parallel to about 45°) to the direction of the line to be drawn.   The same relaxed, natural writing grip is maintained on the pencil with somewhat more pencil (about two inches) extending below the index finger. When sketching vertical lines, the line progresses from top to bottom, and the short straight lines are made with a finger and wrist motion.

Inclined Lines. Inclined lines which slope up from lower left to upper right (Fig. 3–14) are best drawn by keeping the wrist straight and pivoting the forearm and hand about the elbow.   Begin the line at the lower left and sketch up and to the right. The motion is similar to that used in sketching horizontal lines.   Inclined lines sloping down from the upper left to lower right (Fig. 3–15) are drawn

Fig. **3–15.** Sketching an inclined line—2.

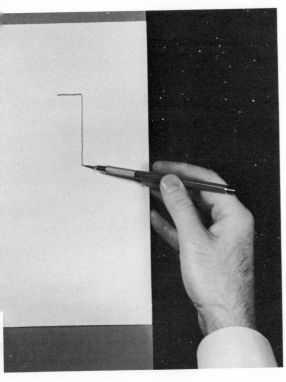

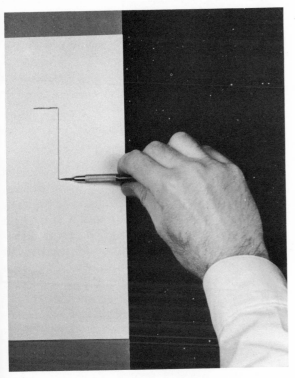

Fig. 3–16. Sketching long lines.

with a wrist and finger motion starting at the upper left and working down toward the right. The motion is the same as that used for vertical lines. For some individuals, vertical and inclined lines are more difficult to draw than horizontal lines. If horizontal lines are quicker and easier to sketch, the paper can be rotated so that all lines are sketched as horizontal lines. However, this practice is to be discouraged at the beginning since the technique of sketching a line in any direction should be learned. When sketching on a large sheet of paper taped to a drawing table (and this is sometimes necessary), rotating the paper may be impractical.

Long Lines. Long horizontal or vertical lines such as border lines, base lines, or long center lines can be quickly sketched using the edge of the sketch pad or drawing table as a guide. The pencil is extended until the point touches the starting point of the required line while the last two fingers rest lightly against the edge of the drawing table or sketch pad [Fig. 3–16(top)]. The pencil is moved down the paper with the fingers sliding along the edge of the drawing table or pad. The line sketched in this manner should be very light, serving only as a guide for the finished black line which will be drawn on top of it. Another way of holding the pencil when sketching long lines is illustrated in Fig. 3–16(bottom). Using this method, the thumb is guided along the edge of the table or pad. Either of these techniques is also useful when sketching parallel lines.

3–5. CURVED LINES

Circles. Several techniques may be employed in sketching circles. The one to use depends largely on the conditions of each individual sketch and the skill of the sketcher, although the size of the circle has much to do with the selection of the method of sketching it.

Small circles, up to about two inches in diameter, can be fairly easily delineated by first sketching a circumscribing square (Fig. 3–17). The center lines are drawn and the enclosing square is lightly sketched on the center lines. Each quadrant of the circle is then lightly outlined making the ends of each 90° arc tangent to the sides of the square at the midpoint. Extend the arc slightly at both

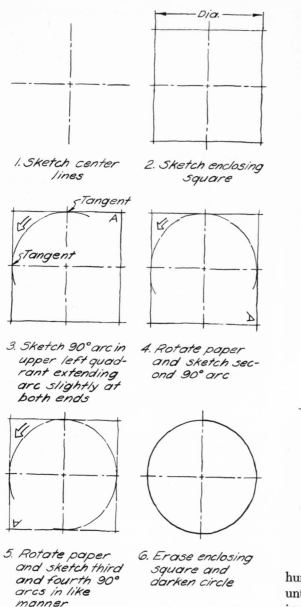

1. Sketch center lines

2. Sketch enclosing square

3. Sketch 90° arc in upper left quadrant extending arc slightly at both ends

4. Rotate paper and sketch second 90° arc

5. Rotate paper and sketch third and fourth 90° arcs in like manner

6. Erase enclosing square and darken circle

Fig. 3–17. Sketching a circle in a circumscribing square.

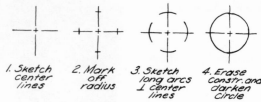

1. Sketch center lines *2. Mark off radius* *3. Sketch long arcs ⊥ center lines* *4. Erase constr. and darken circle*

Fig. 3–18. Sketching a small circle.

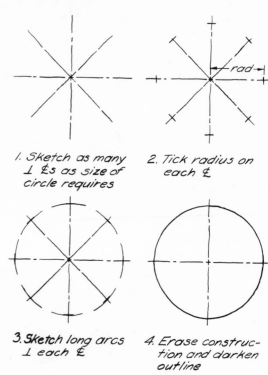

1. Sketch as many ⊥ ₵s as size of circle requires

2. Tick radius on each ₵

3. Sketch long arcs ⊥ each ₵

4. Erase construction and darken outline

Fig. 3–19. Sketching a large circle.

ends to facilitate continuity in drawing the complete circle. For a right-handed person, the upper left quadrant is usually the easiest to sketch. It is therefore a good idea to rotate the paper after each 90° arc is sketched, keeping an unfinished quadrant in the upper left position. After the complete circle has been lightly sketched, the

humps, flats, and irregularities should be corrected until a good circle is outlined. Any incorrect lines, including the circumscribing square, can now be erased and a clean black line traced over the light outline of the circle. This method may be abbreviated for circles under one inch in diameter by simply ticking off the radial distance along each center line instead of drawing the entire square (Fig. 3–18).

Instead of sketching an enclosing square, additional center lines may be drawn for larger circles (over one inch in diameter) and the radial distance ticked off on each one by eye or by marking the radius on a piece of scratch paper (Fig. 3–19).

ong arcs perpendicular to each center line are
en sketched through these tick marks thus out-
ning the circle.

Two other techniques particularly useful in
ketching large circles (three or four inches in
iameter) are the *trammel method* and the *two-
encil method*. In the trammel method (Fig.
–20), the radius is ticked off along the edge of a
trip of paper called a trammel. Center lines are
ketched, and with one marked point on the
rammel held at the center of the proposed circle,
uccessive tick marks are made every few degrees
round the periphery of the required circle. The
ircle is then drawn through these tick marks.

inclination to the paper. The paper is then carefully rotated through 360°; as it is pulled along
under the point of the tracing pencil the circle is
faintly outlined. An almost perfect circle, free
from irregularities, can be drawn by this method.
The faint line should then be traced to form the
finished circle.

Fig. 3–21. Sketching a circle using two pencils.

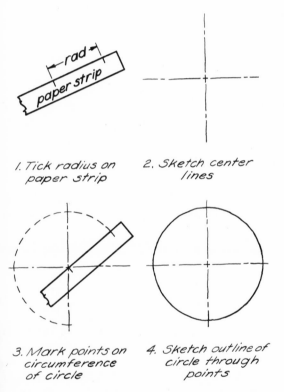

1. Tick radius on paper strip

2. Sketch center lines

3. Mark points on circumference of circle

4. Sketch outline of circle through points

Fig. 3–20. Sketching a circle—trammel method.

The two-pencil method uses a pair of pencils
to form a crude compass. The pencils are crossed
and held rigid as shown in Fig. 3–21. The point
of one pencil is held firmly at the center of the
required circle, and the point of the other pencil
(the tracing pencil) is adjusted at the correct radial
distance and held lightly touching and at a slight

Ellipses. A circle viewed at any angle between
zero and ninety degrees to its plane appears as an
ellipse. The proportions of an ellipse are determined by the relationship of the minor axis (short
diameter) to the major axis (long diameter). The
major and minor axes of an ellipse are perpendicular and mutual bisectors. An ellipse formed by
viewing a circle whose plane is inclined to the line
of sight has a major axis equal to the diameter of
the circle and a foreshortened minor axis. The
length of the minor axis is a function of the angle
of inclination of the plane of the circle to the line
of sight. The greater the angle of inclination, the
longer will be the minor axis until the angle of the
plane of the circle is perpendicular to the line of
sight. When the plane of the circle is perpendicular to the line of sight, the minor axis is equal
to the major axis, and the viewer sees a true circle.
The minor axis appears shorter and shorter as the
angle of inclination is decreased, and when the
plane of the circle is parallel (zero angle of inclina-

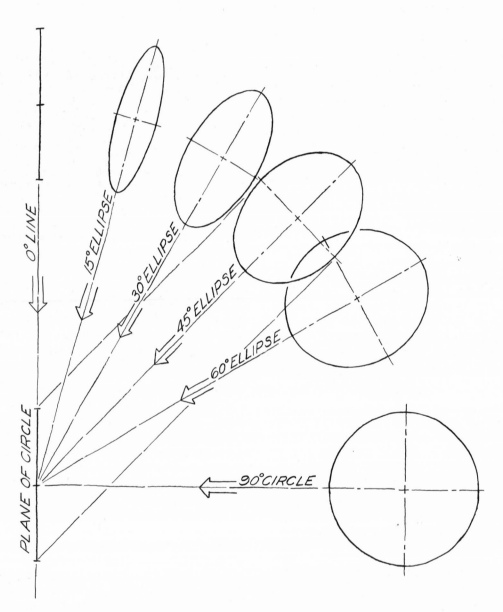

Fig. **3-22.** A circle viewed from an angle appears as an ellipse.

tion) to the line of sight, the minor axis has disappeared completely and the circle appears as a straight line whose length is equal to the major diameter. Fig. 3–22 illustrates the elliptical appearance of a circle when viewed from various angles.

In sketching an ellipse (Fig. 3–23), first sketch the major and minor axes making sure they are perpendicular and each divides the other in half. A rectangle is then sketched on the two diameters which will "box in" the ellipse. Sketch long arcs tangent to the long sides of the rectangle at the midpoints, and smaller, sharper arcs tangent to the short sides at the midpoint. Join these four arcs with smooth curves. It is important that symmetry be maintained about both the major and minor diameters. In sketching small ellipses, the "boxing-in" rectangle may be omitted.

Additional points on the periphery of the ellipse may be located by the method illustrated in Fig. 3–24. Divide half of the long diameter, AO, into four equal parts [Fig. 3–24(a)]. Divide half of the short side, AE, of the "boxing-in" rectangle into four equal parts [Fig. 3–24(b)]. (Any number of equal parts may be used, but for most ellipses, four equal parts will locate a sufficient number of additional points.) The intersections of lines sketched from both ends of the short diameter, B

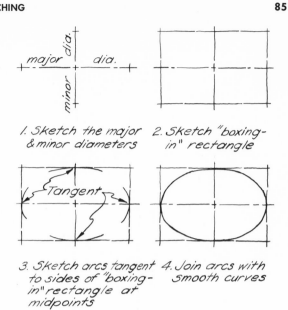

1. Sketch the major & minor diameters

2. Sketch "boxing-in" rectangle

3. Sketch arcs tangent to sides of "boxing-in" rectangle at midpoints

4. Join arcs with smooth curves

Fig. **3–23.** Sketching ellipses in a boxing-in rectangle.

and C, through these points will locate three additional points in one quadrant of the ellipse [Fig. 3–24(c)]. This construction can be repeated in each quadrant to locate a total of twelve additional points.

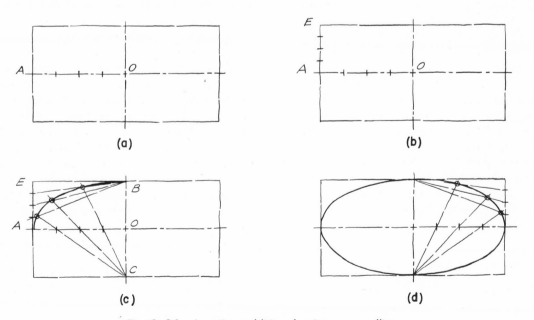

(a)

(b)

(c)

(d)

Fig. **3–24.** Locating additional points on an ellipse.

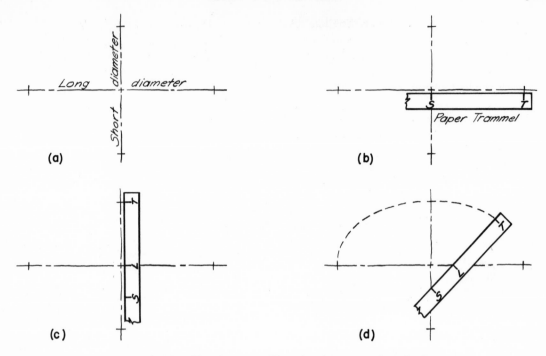

Fig. 3-25. Sketching an ellipse by the trammel method.

A method useful for sketching large ellipses is the *trammel method*. First, sketch the long and short diameters [Fig. 3-25(a)]. Then, using a paper strip or trammel, lay off half the long diameter, ST [Fig. 3-25(b)]. Place T at the end of the short diameter, and lay off half the short diameter, TL. Move the trammel a little at a time always keeping the mark at L on the long diameter and the mark at S on the short diameter. Mark a point on the paper opposite point T for each successive movement of the trammel. When sufficient points have been marked to define the ellipse, complete the outline by lightly sketching the curve through the plotted points. The trammel method is geometrically accurate, but is not worth the effort unless the ellipse to be sketched is large and considerable accuracy is desired.

3-6. SKETCHING HINTS

Bisecting a Line. Bisecting a short line can be accomplished quite accurately by eye. Bisecting a long line accurately by eye is more difficult. Fig. 3-26(a) shows how a long line can be bisected using a strip of paper or other simple measuring expedient such as the pencil and thumb. Mark the approximate center of the line by eye, and tick off the distance from one end on a strip of paper. Transfer this distance to the opposite end of the line and mark it off. If the first estimate is actually made at the middle of the line, the two marks will coincide. If the first estimate is in error, and this is usually the case, there will be a short distance between the two marks. The actual midpoint of the line will lie halfway between these two marks. This short distance can be accurately bisected by eye, thus bisecting the long line. If the line is short enough for its entire length to be ticked off on a paper strip of convenient size, the line can be bisected by folding the paper strip halfway between the two tick marks and laying off the half-length (determined by the fold line on the paper strip) from one end of the line [Fig. 3-26(b)].

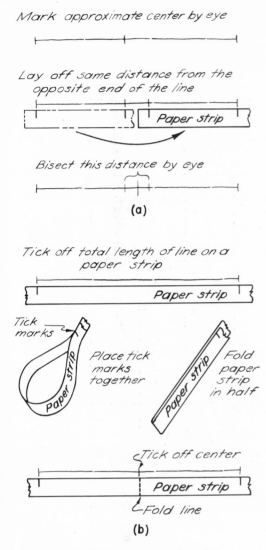

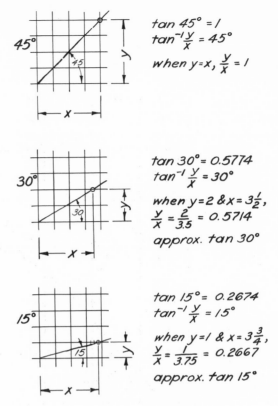

Fig. **3–27.** Estimating angles.

Fig. **3–26.** Bisecting a long line.

Estimating Angles. Inclined lines are usually sketched by first locating their end points and sketching the line between. However, it is helpful to have some means of estimating the more common angles occurring in technical sketching. Angles of 45°, 30°, and 15° (and similarly 60° and 75°) can be estimated by laying off the tangent of the angle as shown in Fig. 3–27. This is a most convenient method when sketching on gridded paper or when estimating angles in isometric sketches on isometric paper.

Copying by Proportional Squares. An intricate drawing composed of irregular curves can be enlarged or reduced by using the method of proportional squares (Fig. 3–28). Squares of convenient size are first ruled on the drawing to be copied. It is usually best to place a piece of tracing paper over the original drawing and rule squares on the tracing paper. Or, if much work of this type is to be done, a piece of transparent acetate can be permanently ruled and laid successively over each drawing to be copied. The copy (either enlarged or reduced) is then drawn on a sheet of coordinate paper whose squares are larger (or smaller) in the desired ratio than the squares superimposed on the original.

Thumbnail Sketches. Tiny sketches not much bigger than a postage stamp (or thumbnail) are an aid in planning technical sketches. These thumb-

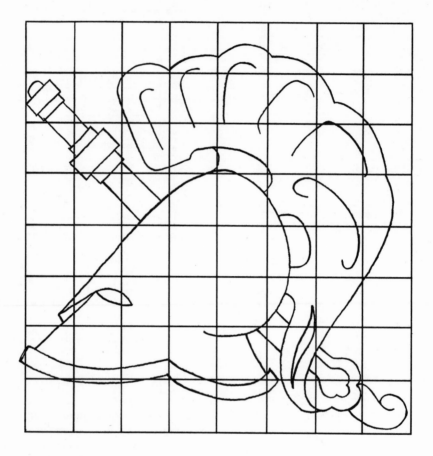

Fig. **3–28.**   Copying by proportional squares.

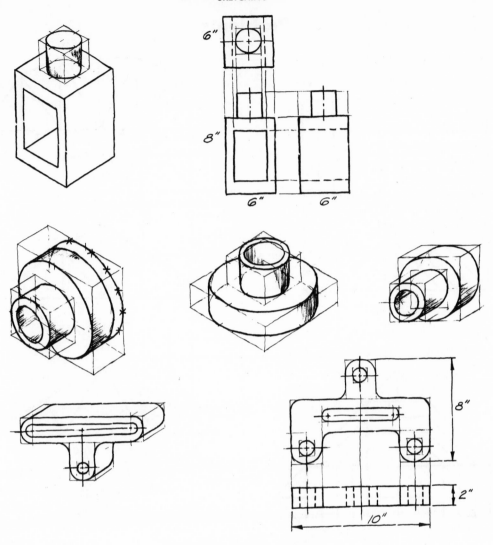

Fig. 3-29. Thumbnail sketches.

nail sketches (Fig. 3–29) can be quickly "doodled" on scratch paper showing the object oriented in various positions or forms of presentation. They are great timesavers and decision-making aids, and will avoid much use of the eraser or destruction of paper halfway through the sketch as a result of an initial poor decision or a change of mind.

Develop a Sketching Habit. The best way to learn to sketch is to sketch. Sketch small; sketch big; sketch often. Keep a pencil close at hand and sketch familiar objects. When the mind is idle and doodling seems in order, direct the doodling into useful sketching practice; sketch squares, circles, ellipses, oblique and isometric pictures; draw thumbnail sketches from memory; sketch the objects in view, the light fixtures, door knobs, chairs, etc. Learn to "think" with the pencil. Learn to communicate ideas to others clearly and unmistakably. Sketching is easily learned, and is an invaluable tool in the professional kit of the engineer.

Problems

3-1. Sketch the design illustrated in Fig. 3–30.

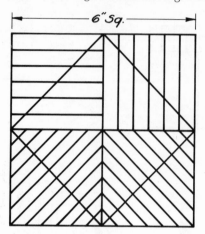

Fig. **3–30.**

3-2. Sketch the design illustrated in Fig. 3–31.

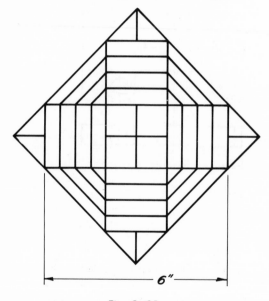

Fig. **3–31.**

3-3. Sketch the trusses illustrated in Fig. 3–32. The overall length of the truss on the sketch should be 6″. Proportion is indicated by the numbers adjacent to the truss members.

3-4. Sketch the pattern of circles illustrated in Fig. 3–33.

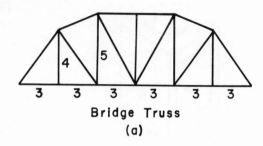

Bridge Truss

(a)

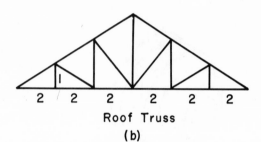

Roof Truss

(b)

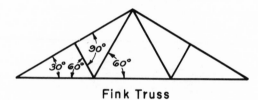

Fink Truss

(c)

Fig. **3–32.**

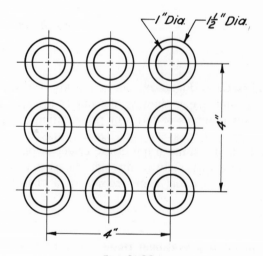

Fig. **3–33.**

3–5. Sketch the concentric circles illustrated in Fig. 3–34. Shade the inner circle by sketching diagonal lines in opposite directions spaced at about $\frac{1}{8}''$ as shown in the figure.

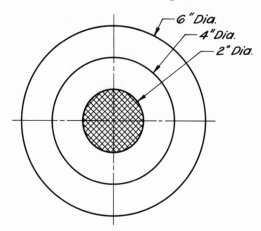

Fig. **3–34.**

3–6. Imagine the paper on which the circles of Problem 3–5 were drawn as being inclined and viewed as illustrated in Fig. 3–35. Sketch the circles as they would appear viewed along this inclined line of sight.

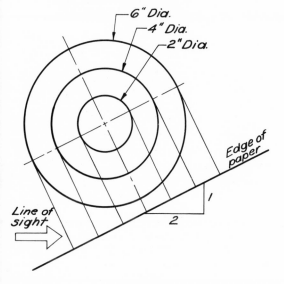

Fig. **3–35.**

3–7. Fig. 3–36 pictures a sheet metal cover for a toggle switch. A slot is provided in the top for the switch handle, and holes have been punched for the insertion of wires and for fastening the cover down. Sketch the cover as it would appear on a flat sheet after being cut but before being bent to shape. Indicate bend lines by long dashed lines on the sketch.

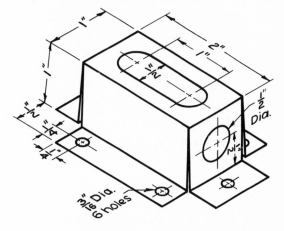

Fig. **3–36.** Switch cover.

3–8. Sketch the armature lamination illustrated in Fig. 3–37.

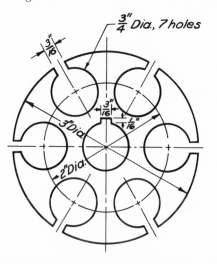

Fig. **3–37.** Armature lamination.

3-9. Sketch the pump gasket illustrated in Fig. 3–38.

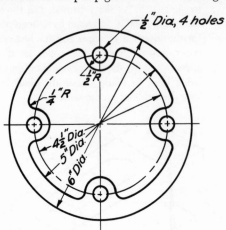

Fig. 3–38.   Pump gasket.

3-10. Imagine a length of tubing of circular cross section with an outside diameter of 2″ and an inside diameter of 1½″. The tubing is 3″ long and cut on both ends at right angles to its axis. Sketch the length of tubing as it would appear if viewed along a line of sight making an angle of 30° with its circular bases.

3-11. Using the method of proportional squares, enlarge the escutcheon and fleur-de-lis illustrated in Fig. 3–39 so that the width of the top of the escutcheon is 6″.

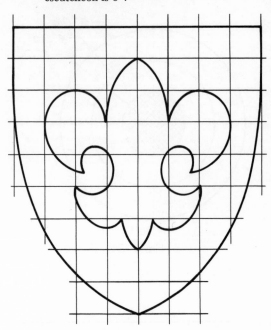

Fig. 3–39.   Escutcheon and fleur-de-lis.

4

LETTERING

4–1. INTRODUCTION

Lettering is the hallmark of the engineer. The engineer's ability to present his notes and instructions in clearly lettered form is one of the distinguishing features which separates his work from that of other professions.

Lettering is used on drawings for dimensions, notes, titles, and other information not completely presented in graphical form. If the information is to be correctly interpreted and mistakes in reading avoided, the lettering must be legible. Lettering is tedious and time-consuming; hence a letter style must be used which can be quickly learned and rapidly scribed by engineers and technicians. Lettering is most important to the overall appearance of a drawing. Good lettering can greatly improve the appearance of a mediocre drawing, while poor lettering can spoil the appearance of otherwise excellent work.

4–2. SINGLE-STROKE GOTHIC LETTERING

The lettering most often used in engineering is a style known as *single-stroke gothic*. "Single-stroke" means that the width of the stems of the letters is the same width as the pencil lead or pen point with which the letter is drawn. "Gothic" is a descriptive term applied in the United States to a square-cut letter without serifs. Fig. 4–1 contrasts the built-up, shaded-stroke Roman style lettering [Fig. 4–1(a)], characterized by serifs, with the single-stroke gothic lettering, without serifs [Fig. 4–1(b)]. The Roman style letter is widely used on the printed pages of books, magazines, and newspapers.

ROMAN
(a)

SINGLE STROKE GOTHIC
(b)

Fig. **4–1.** Comparison of single-stroke gothic and Roman letters.

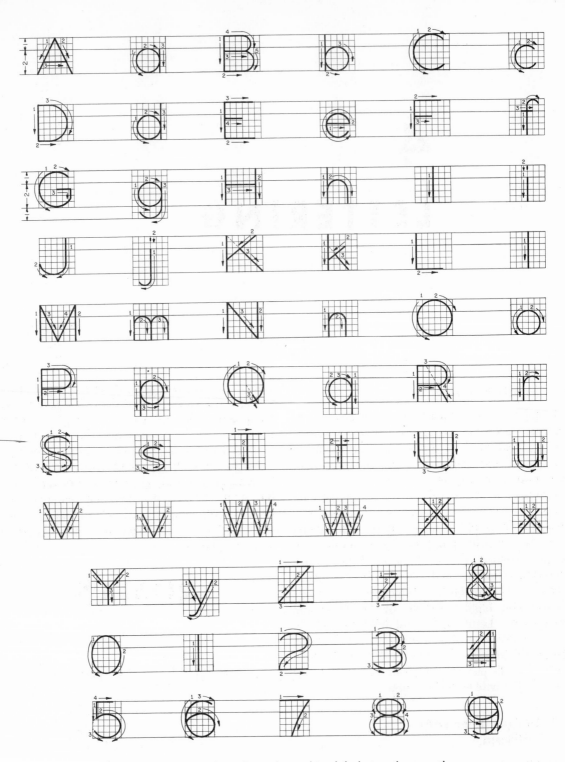

Fig. **4-2.**   Vertical single-stroke gothic alphabet and numerals.

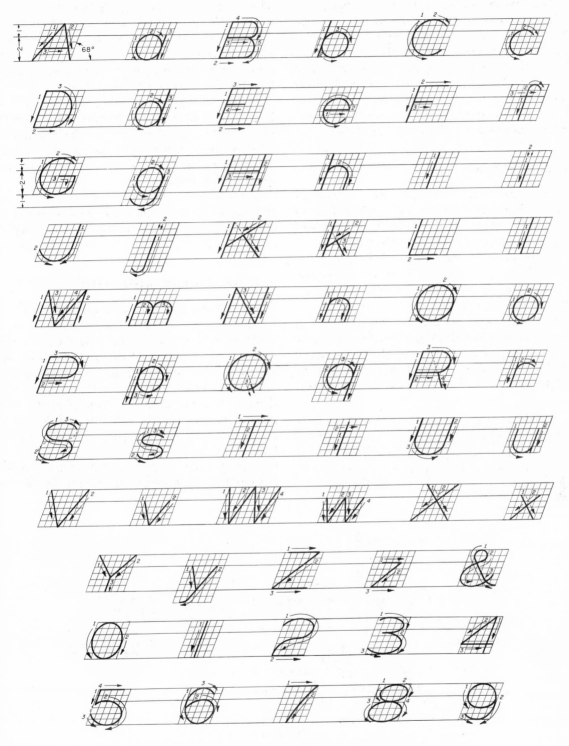

Fig. **4-3.** Inclined single-stroke gothic alphabet and numerals.

Single-stroke gothic lettering is simplified in form, easy to learn, and can be rapidly executed. It presents a neat, pleasing appearance and is legible and unmistakable to the reader. Two forms of single-stroke gothic letters are used, *vertical* and *inclined*. The vertical single-stroke gothic alphabet and numerals are illustrated in Fig. 4–2. The inclined single-stroke gothic alphabet and numerals are illustrated in Fig. 4–3.

4–3. GUIDE LINES

Horizontal guide lines are used to keep the letters of a single word and the words of a phrase in a straight line. It is absolutely essential that horizontal guide lines be used when lettering. If they are not used, the letters will be out of line and will vary in height. Letters drawn without horizontal guide lines present a poor appearance, and are difficult to read.

Four guide lines are used as illustrated in Fig. 4–4. The *base line* provides a base for the bottom of the letter. The *cap line* establishes the height of the capital letter. The *waist line* marks the height of the body of the lower case (small) letters.[1]

---

[1] In the printing trade, the tray of wood or metal divided into compartments in which the individual pieces of type are stored is called a *case*. The case is in two parts, an upper part and a lower part. Capital letters are kept in the upper case and small letters in the lower case; hence, the terms *upper case* applied to capital letters and *lower case* applied to small letters.

This height is two-thirds the height of the capital letter. The *drop line* locates the position of the tails of lower case letters such as j, p, and y. These letters drop below the base line a distance equal to one-third the height of the capital letter. In practice, the drop line usually is not drawn.

Vertical or slope lines may be drawn (Fig. 4–4) if desired to establish the vertical axis of vertical letters or the angle of inclination of inclined letters. These vertical or slope guide lines are drawn with the lettering triangle or lettering instrument, and are spaced at random.

Guide lines must be so light as to be almost imperceptible. These light guide lines need not be erased since they are inconspicuous on the original drawing and will not show up on reproductions.

4–4. THE LETTERING INSTRUMENT

Guide lines can be laid out using the scale or the dividers; however, it is usually faster and more convenient to use a lettering instrument for this purpose. Two types of lettering instrument, the *Braddock Lettering Triangle* and the *Ames Lettering Instrument,* are illustrated in Figs. 4–5 and 4–6. Each of these instruments is made of plastic with several columns of hole sets, each set spaced to correspond to the proper guide line proportions. Each hole is just large enough to accept a sharpened, cone-shaped pencil point. Each column on the Braddock Lettering Triangle is

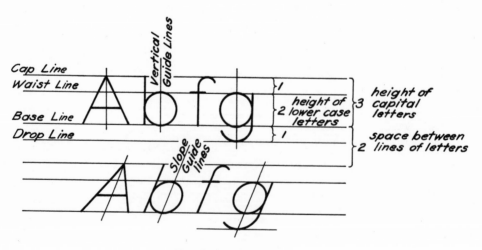

Fig. **4–4.** Guide lines.

numbered, the numbers indicating the distance in thirty-seconds of an inch between the base line and the cap line (the height of the capital letter). For example, if a capital letter height of $\frac{1}{8}''$ is desired, the number 4 column should be used ($\frac{1}{8}'' = \frac{4}{32}''$). (On the Ames Lettering Instrument, the number indicating the desired capital letter height is set opposite the index mark by turning the movable disk.)

The base of the lettering instrument must be guided by a straightedge, either the T-square or a triangle. To draw a series of guide lines, the pencil point is inserted in the top hole of a selected set in the desired column and light downward pressure is applied to the pencil. The pencil is then moved parallel to the guiding straightedge sliding the lettering instrument along the straight-edge and ruling a single line. The pencil point is then inserted in the next hole of the set and the pencil and lettering instrument moved back parallel to the straightedge in the opposite direction. This procedure is continued until a sufficient number of guide lines have been drawn. When the bottom hole in the column is reached, the straightedge and lettering instrument are moved until the top hole in the column is aligned with the last line drawn. With the lettering instrument re-aligned, the procedure is repeated as often as necessary. Spacing of the waist line and spacing between lines of lettering is provided for in the

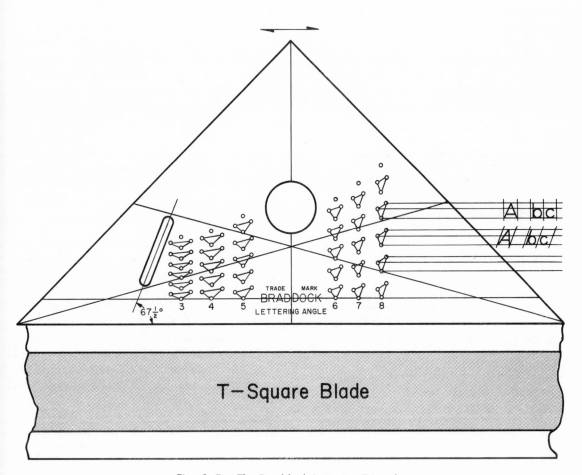

Fig. 4–5. The Braddock Lettering Triangle.

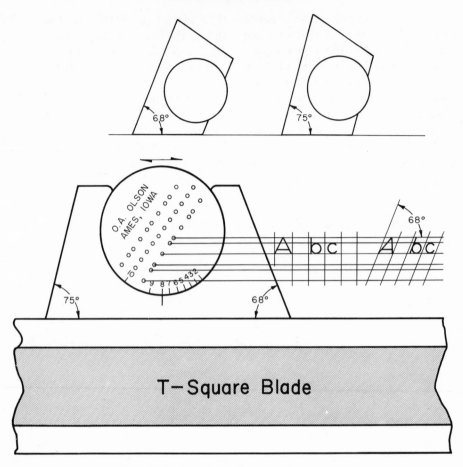

Fig. **4–6.** The Ames Lettering Instrument.

design of the lettering instrument, these spaces being proportional to the height of the capital letter.

Slope guide lines can be drawn along the sloping edges of the Ames Lettering Instrument (at 68° or 75°) (Fig. 4–6) or along the sides of the inclined slot in the Braddock Lettering Triangle (at $67\frac{1}{2}°$) (Fig. 4–5).

4–5. VERTICAL SINGLE-STROKE GOTHIC LETTERS

Vertical single-stroke gothic letters (Fig. 4–2) are drawn on vertical axes and are composed of straight lines and arcs of circles. The beginner

should draw vertical guide lines as an aid in maintaining a vertical axis for each letter. Each letter is drawn in one or more strokes, each stroke being a straight line or circle arc. (Certain letters and numerals—S, 2, 3, and 8, for example—are composed of arcs of ellipses.) The recommended order and direction of strokes for vertical letters are illustrated in Fig. 4–2. These strokes should be consciously followed by the beginner until they are easy and natural. Each draftsman, with experience, will develop individual variations, reducing or adding to the number of strokes for certain letters. However, the strokes recommended here will generally result in rapidly executed, well-proportioned letters.

Vertical lettering is generally preferred over inclined for the left-handed draftsman since inclined letters are often more difficult for the left-handed individual. Some modification of the recommended order of strokes is usually necessary when lettering with the left hand. These modifications are best worked out by the individual.

4–6. INCLINED SINGLE-STROKE GOTHIC LETTERS

Inclined single-stroke gothic letters (Fig. 4–3) are drawn on sloping axes. The precise angle of inclination is not fixed; however, the angle of inclination should be uniform on any drawing sheet. (The American Standards Association recommends an angle of $67\frac{1}{2}°$, the angle incorporated in the lettering instruments.) Slope guide lines should be drawn as an aid in maintaining a uniform angle of inclination. These slope guide lines can be drawn with one of the lettering instruments as explained in Art. 4–4, or a line at the desired angle of inclination can be drawn with the protractor and the slope guide lines drawn parallel to it using the two-triangle method for drawing lines parallel to a given line. The spacing of horizontal guide lines is the same for both vertical and inclined letters.

Inclined single-stroke letters are composed of straight lines and arcs of ellipses. The order of strokes and proportions of the letters for the inclined single-stroke gothic alphabet and numerals are illustrated in Fig. 4–3.

Since slight variations from a vertical axis are more noticeable to the eye than variations from an inclined axis, inclined letters can be more rapidly executed and present a more pleasing appearance than vertical letters. For these reasons, inclined letters are often preferred in engineering work. An exception to this generalization occurs in the case of left-handed individuals as discussed in Art. 4–5.

4–7. PROPORTIONS OF LETTERS

Drawing letters with proper proportions is important. Poorly proportioned letters reduce legibility and spoil the appearance of a drawing. Each letter and numeral in Figs. 4–2 and 4–3 has been superimposed on a grid to illustrate its correct proportion. These proportions should be carefully studied and remembered. Several points are worth noting relative to the shape and proportion of both the vertical and the inclined single-stroke gothic letters. The horizontal bar of the A is well below center, about one-third up from the base line [Fig. 4–7(a)]. The middle horizontal bar of the B, E, F, and H is slightly above center [Fig. 4–7(b)] while the lower horizontal bar of the P and R is slightly below center [Fig. 4–7(c)].

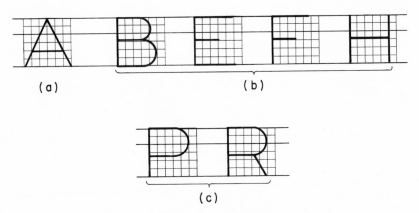

Fig. 4–7. Location of the horizontal crossbar.

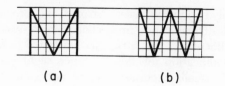

(a)   (b)

Fig. **4-8.** M and W proportions.

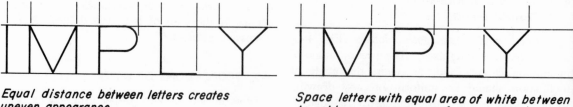

Equal distance between letters creates uneven appearance

(a)

Space letters with equal area of white between to achieve appearance of equal spacing

(b)

Fig. **4-9.** Spacing of letters.

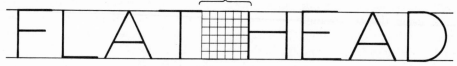

Leave space between words equal to height of capital letter

Fig. **4-10.** Spacing of words.

Placing the horizontal bar of these letters in the exact center results in an unbalanced appearance. The M and the W are often drawn incorrectly. The sides of the M are parallel; the center point drops all the way to the base line [Fig. 4-8(a)]. The W is the widest of the letters; it is only three-fourths as high as it is wide. Alternate legs of the W are parallel. The center point rises all the way to the cap line [Fig. 4-8(b)].

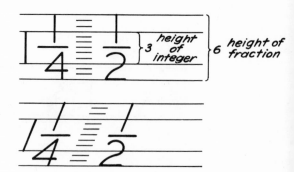

Fig. **4-11.** Fractions and mixed numbers.

4-8. SPACING OF LETTERS AND WORDS

Proper spacing of letters and words improves appearance and increases legibility. Good spacing is achieved by eye and is largely a matter of experience; however, several points must be noted. Equal linear spacing of letters [Fig. 4-9(a)] creates an uneven appearance, and results in words that are difficult to read. Letters should be spaced so that the *area* between letters is about equal [Fig. 4-9(b)]. Letters with adjacent straight sides such as I and M or M and P must be spaced wider apart than such letters as L and Y or A and T. The

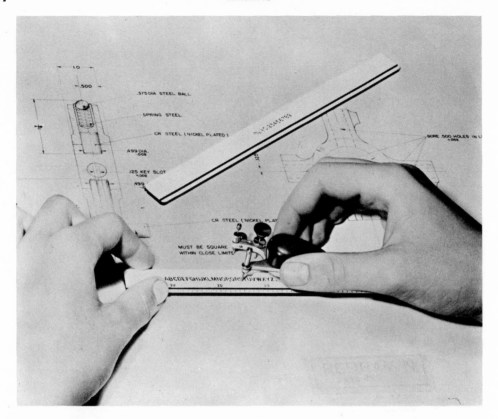

Fig. **4–12.** The Leroy Lettering Set. (Photograph courtesy of Keuffel & Esser Co., Hoboken, N. J.)

actual space between the extremities of these latter combinations of letters may be reduced to zero or some overlap may be necessary.

The spacing between words is generally equal to the height of a capital letter (Fig. 4–10). Some variations of this general rule may be necessary depending on the ending and beginning letters of the words in question.

The space between lines of letters should be two-thirds the height of the capital letter (Fig. 4–2). The distance between sets of holes in the lettering instruments provides this spacing.

4–9. FRACTIONS AND MIXED NUMBERS

Fractions and mixed numbers should be lettered to the proportions illustrated in Fig. 4–11. The total height of the fraction is twice the height of the integer. The integer is the same height as a comparable capital letter. The numerals comprising the fraction must be proportionately smaller than the integer.

4–10. MECHANICAL LETTERING DEVICES

Several devices are available to the draftsman which employ guides or templates for mechanically reproducing letters similar in appearance to single-stroke gothic letters. One of the oldest, best known, and simplest to operate is the Leroy Lettering Set illustrated in Fig. 4–12.

With only minimum practice, almost anyone can create mechanically perfect letters with one of these devices. However, lettering with a mechanical device is usually slow and the letters lack the character and individuality of hand lettering. Such devices are a valuable tool of the draftsman, but they do not make obsolete the hand lettering skill of the engineer.

II
PROJECTION DRAWING

5

PROJECTION
THEORY

5-1. INTRODUCTION

With the aid of Engineering Graphics one can, in effect, construct accurate scale "models" of objects or spatial problems. In the process, spatial information is transferred onto a system of reference planes. The resulting two-dimensional pictures may either serve to transmit information (pictorial views, detailed drawings, etc.), or may be used as a basis for solving spatial problems. Information is likewise transmitted, of course, in the problem-solving procedure, since both the analysis and solution are graphical.

The transfer of three-dimensional information to a two-dimensional system of reference planes is done by means of *projection*. As the term "projection" implies, points on the object are imagined to be transferred (projected) from the object to a plane of projection which might be considered as a translucent screen.

There are two fundamental types of projection: *convergent* and *parallel*. These classifications are based on the relationship that exists between imaginary straight-line projection rays, or projectors, extending from the object to the observer.

Each imaginary projector connects a point on the object with the *station point* (eye of the observer). Where this line, or ray, pierces the projection (picture) plane determines the location of the point in the projected view of the object. This process is similar to that which occurs when a photographic slide is projected onto a picture screen.

5-2. CONVERGENT PROJECTION

Fig. 5-1 illustrates the fundamentals of convergent projection. The projectors converge to a single point (the station point) at a *finite* distance from the object. The resulting image of the object on the plane of projection is referred to as a perspective view of the object. The small illustration at the lower right of the figure shows the perspective as viewed squarely from in front of the picture plane. The point denoted as *VP* (vanishing point) on the picture plane is the apparent vanishing point, in this case, of all lines perpendicular to the picture plane.

Perspectives are used to a considerable extent by architects, architectural engineers, and in

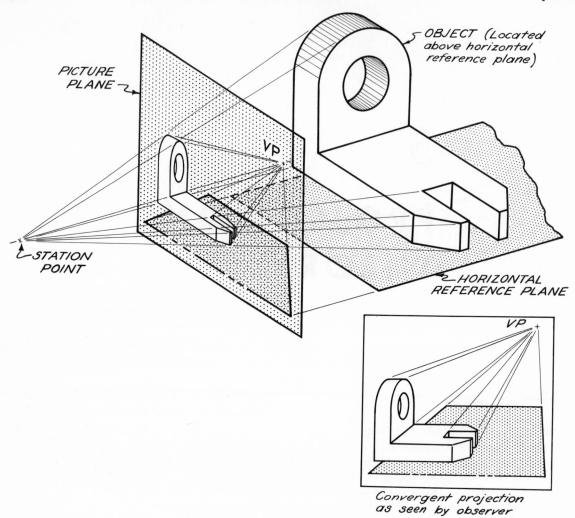

Fig. **5–1.** Convergent projection.

industry when true pictorial representation is essential. Additional applications exist where the large size of an object being shown pictorially would cause apparent distortion if other forms of pictorial representation were used. It should be noted that a perspective projection and a photograph made from the same station point will give the same resulting image insofar as the location of points of the object are concerned. The photograph, of course, adds qualities of shading and surface toning that a line drawing lacks.

Further observation will also reveal that the perspective view is generally smaller than the actual object being projected, but could be larger if the object were in front of the picture plane. Also, should the object straddle the picture plane, those portions of the object that occur in the picture plane would be "projected" in actual size. A more detailed discussion of perspective is contained in Chapter 8.

5–3. PARALLEL PROJECTION

If the station point is at infinity, the projectors become parallel to one another, and the result would be termed a *parallel projection*. There are two principal types of parallel projection: (a) the projectors make an angle other than 90° with the plane of projection (oblique projection); and (b) the projectors are perpendicular to the plane of projection (orthographic or orthogonal projection).

5–4. OBLIQUE PROJECTION

When the projectors are parallel and make an angle other than 90° with the plane of projection, a projection of an object is obtained which may have three-dimensional pictorial qualities. Such a projection is called an oblique projection and is illustrated in Fig. 5–2. Note that any face of the object which is parallel to the picture plane will

be projected onto the picture plane in exact shape and size. Other surfaces and lines are foreshortened in the oblique view. Additional information concerning oblique projections and drawings is given in Chapter 8.

5–5. ORTHOGRAPHIC PROJECTION

If the projectors are perpendicular to the plane of projection (Fig. 5–3), the projection is known as an orthographic projection (ortho = right, i.e., 90°; graphic = written). This form of projection is also referred to by some as orthogonal projection (i.e., right-angled). Orthographic projection is based on a system of geometry that is commonly

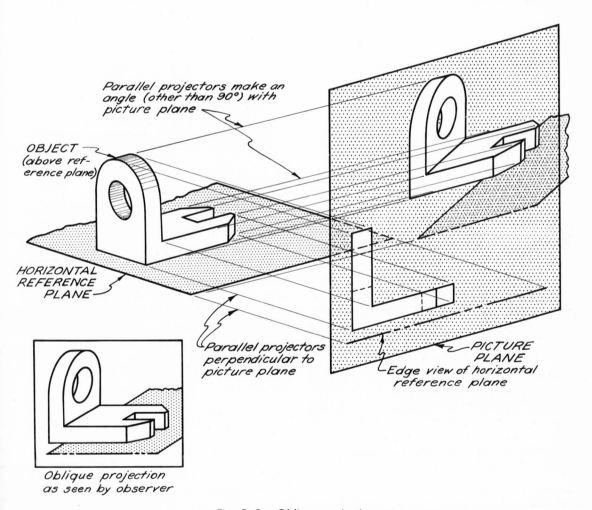

Fig. **5–2.** Oblique projection.

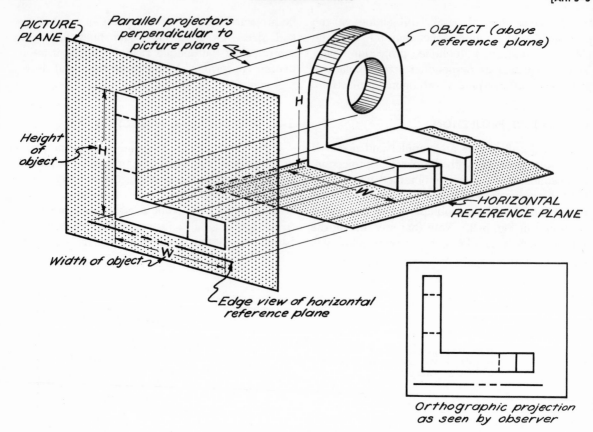

PICTURE PLANE

Parallel projectors perpendicular to picture plane

OBJECT (above reference plane)

H

Height of object

H

HORIZONTAL REFERENCE PLANE

Width of object

W

W

Edge view of horizontal reference plane

Orthographic projection as seen by observer

Fig. **5-3.** Orthographic projection.

referred to as *Descriptive Geometry*[1] (the geometry of description or representation). It is the method of projection used principally by the engineer because, as will be brought out in subsequent discussions, it lends itself readily to the accurate portrayal and manipulation of three-dimensional (spatial) information on a two-dimensional sheet of paper.

One of the principal advantages of orthographic projection relates to the measurements obtainable from an orthographic view. In Fig. 5-3 the object is aligned so that one of its principal faces is parallel to the given plane of projection. As indicated, height measurements (H) and width measurements (W) on the object, in this instance, are parallel to the plane of projection and are therefore

[1] Descriptive Geometry: the formal title customarily given to that portion of Engineering Graphics that deals with the solution of spatial problems by means of projection.

measurable in the projected view. Since the projection rays are parallel to one another and strike the plane of projection at right angles, they are able to transfer accurately to the plane of projection *any* measurement that is *at right angles to the directional path of the projectors.* In other words, *any distance on an actual object can be obtained from an orthographic view of the object as long as the measurement on the orthographic view is actually parallel to the distance desired on the object.*

5-6. AXONOMETRIC PROJECTION

Orthographic projection can also be used to construct pictorial views of an object. The object is simply tipped so that its principal axes make angles with the picture plane. The resulting projection is generally referred to as an *axonometric*

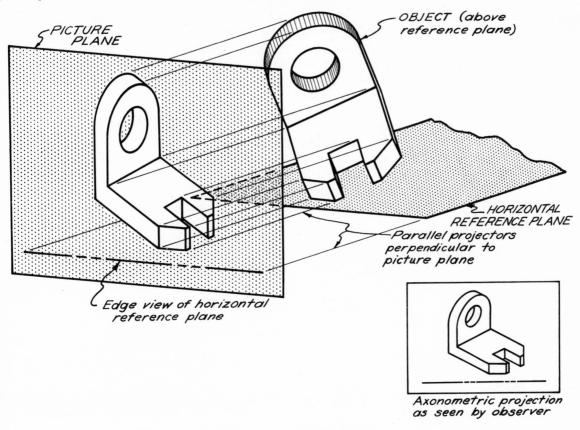

Fig. 5-4. Axonometric projection.

projection. (See Fig. 5–4.) There are three sub-divisions of axonometric projection known as *isometric*, *dimetric*, and *trimetric* projections. These terms have reference to particular relationships that may be established between the axes of the object and the picture plane. Axonometric projection is discussed further in Chapter 8.

5-7. PRINCIPAL PLANES OF PROJECTION

Fundamentally, an object or a spatial situation may be described completely by the use of the three basic dimensions of height, width, and depth.[2] These dimensions, based upon a system

of rectangular space coordinates, permit the location of any point in space with respect to any other.

As is shown in Fig. 5–3, a single orthographic view may accurately portray two of the basic dimensions of an object. In Fig. 5–3, the dimensions of height and width are accurately projected onto the given projection plane. The view shown might be thought of as looking at the "front" of the object and would be called a frontal view. The plane of projection would then be regarded as a frontal plane of projection. A second orthographic view taken at 90° to this frontal view would then accurately show any depth distances on the object. The second view might be a view looking directly down at the top of the object and would be referred to as a *horizontal* view.

In this manner, by means of two orthographic planes of projection arranged perpendicular to

[2] In this text, when referring to measurements on projection planes, the term "width" will be used in reference to horizontal measurements on the object parallel to the frontal, or picture plane. "Depth" will refer to measurements on the object perpendicular to the frontal plane.

one another it is possible graphically to describe completely the position of any point in space with respect to any other and, therefore, any object or spatial situation insofar as the location of its composing points is concerned. Two such orthographic views adjacent and at 90° to one another are generally referred to as *related* views.

The frontal and horizontal planes of projection are known as the fundamental planes of projection. The spatial situation, or object, which is to be projected is understood to be aligned with respect to these two planes (e.g., the height and width dimensions would be located parallel to the frontal plane). It is customary also to include a third plane, perpendicular to the first two and "related" to them, known as a *profile* plane. Fig. 5–5 shows such a reference system of planes which are generally referred to as the *principal planes of projection.* Here the frontal, horizontal, and profile planes have been continued vertically and horizon-

tally beyond their respective lines of intersection. While they are shown as being neatly bounded by straight lines, this is merely for convenience in illustration. In theory they may be considered as continuing indefinitely in all directions.

5–8. PROJECTION ANGLES

The frontal and horizontal principal planes (Fig. 5–5) divide a spatial area into four sectors known as *projection angles,* or quadrants. They are numbered as shown.

Fig. 5–6 shows four identical objects located in each of the four projection angles. Orthographic projections have been made upon the adjacent planes. The objects have been aligned in each case so that they are directly over one another and in horizontal alignment as indicated. This is done in order to illustrate that the frontal and horizontal projections for all four projection angles are the

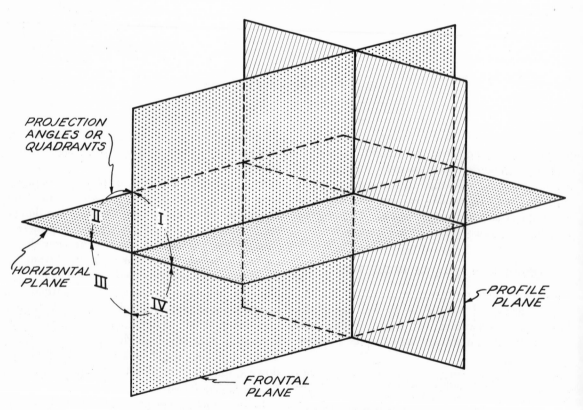

Fig. 5–5. Principal planes and projection angles (quadrants).

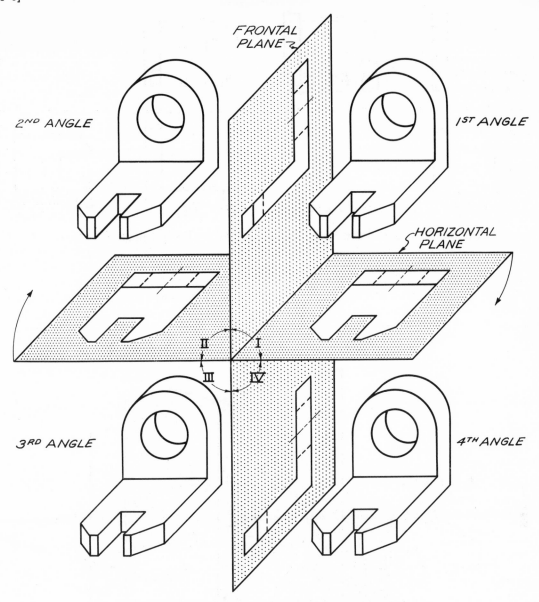

Fig. **5-6.** Four projection angles (quadrants).

same and that only their location relative to the object varies in each case. Though not shown in Fig. 5-6, the profile views of the objects, which would also be identical to one another, could each be located by projection onto the profile plane.

The principal projection planes may be moved so as to lie in a single plane. To do this, the horizontal and profile planes are revolved in a pre-scribed manner as indicated by the arrows at the edge of the planes in Fig. 5-6. For each projection angle this revolution would result in the arrange-ment of the horizontal and frontal views as shown in Fig. 5-7. It is apparent after a brief examination of Fig. 5-7, that only first or third angle projections are satisfactory projections for illustration purposes after the horizontal plane is revolved. The second

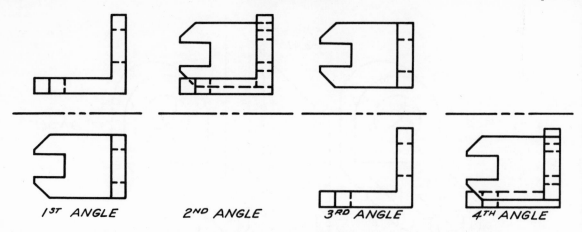

1ˢᵀ ANGLE   2ᴺᴰ ANGLE   3ᴿᴰ ANGLE   4ᵀᴴ ANGLE

Fig. **5-7.** Horizontal and frontal views (revolved) for the four projection angles.

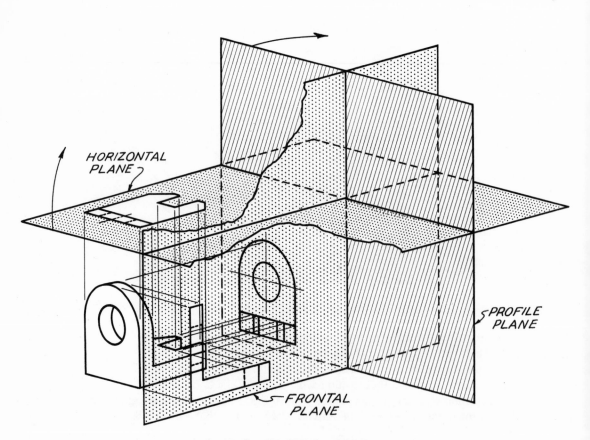

Fig. **5-8.** Third angle projection.

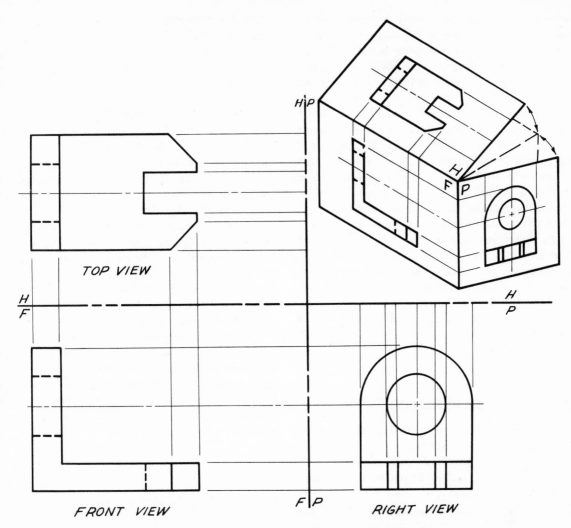

TOP VIEW

FRONT VIEW

RIGHT VIEW

Fig. **5-9.** Third angle projection—planes revolved.

and fourth angle projections are unsatisfactory because the horizontal and vertical views may overlap one another.

Since the relative position of the object may be located at random with respect to the planes of projection, there is ordinarily no real necessity for becoming involved in the use of problems in which an object would be located in the second or fourth quadrants, or for that matter, in more than one quadrant simultaneously. It is true that in the earlier, more formal, teachings of Descriptive Ge-

ometry, abstract as well as practical problems were often presented which involved several quadrants simultaneously.[3] It was felt by many early De-

[3] This practice in the teaching of Descriptive Geometry was a part of the Mongean method, after Gaspard Mongé (1746–1818). Mongé was the first to develop the science of Descriptive Geometry. He used it in solving problems involving sapping operations (tunnels under the enemy), and also, later, in the graphical design of cut stone (stereotonomy) for use in the construction of fortifications. Mongé's development was originally classified as a military secret. (See Art. 1–2.)

scriptive Geometry teachers that training in solving such problems developed the student's ability to visualize spatial concepts more readily. In fact, an engineering student who could not make a creditable grade in Descriptive Geometry was often considered a poor risk for more advanced engineering classwork. Whatever the validity of the argument, Descriptive Geometry is no longer taught for its own sake; instead, the emphasis is upon its practical problem-solving aspects. Little reference is now made to the second and fourth angles of projection except in discussions of the theoretical basis of the projection angles, as here. Aircraft manufacturers do make some use of second angle projection to save space when making full-size layouts. The space is saved because of the overlapping of views. Also, because of view proximity, drafting errors are sometimes more easily picked up than they would be on a large size third angle projection with the views widely separated.

5–9. THIRD ANGLE PROJECTION

If the object of Fig. 5–6 were located only in the third quadrant of our system of reference planes, and views were projected respectively onto the horizontal, frontal, and profile planes, the construction would look similar to Fig. 5–8. (Parts of the horizontal and frontal planes have been broken away for ease of visualizing the construction.)

Next, if the horizontal and profile planes were revolved, as indicated, until they were in alignment with the vertical plane, the result would be as shown in Fig. 5–9. The latter figure is classified as a three-view drawing in *third angle projection* of the given object. Engineers in the United States, with the exception of architectural engineers, use this angle of projection almost exclusively.

The lines marked *HF*, *HP*, and *FP* in Fig. 5–9 represent respectively the intersection lines of the horizontal and frontal planes, the horizontal and profile planes, and the frontal and profile planes. These lines may be referred to variously as reference lines, fold lines, hinge lines, ground lines, datum lines, axis lines, etc., depending upon any

particular individual's preference. At this particular point "fold line" seems most appropriate; however, in general, the term "reference line" will be used in this text. The discussion in the next chapter will bring out the reasoning for this choice. As we look at the frontal view of the object in Fig. 5–9, the line *HF* represents the edge view of the top plane and the line *FP* represents the edge view of the profile plane. Referring to the top view, the line *HF* represents the edge view of the frontal plane and the line *HP* the edge view of the profile plane. Referring to the right-side view the line *FP* represents the edge view of the frontal plane and the line *HP* the edge view of the horizontal plane.

The light projector lines shown in Fig. 5–9 are actually projections of the projectors shown in Fig. 5–8 which were used in creating the various views. Their inclusion in Fig. 5–9 serves to emphasize the vertical and horizontal alignment of the projected views after the revolvement of the planes.

The reader is encouraged to make a tracing or copy of Fig. 5–9 and fold it into the box shape indicated on the small pictorial in the upper right-hand corner of the figure. Doing this will aid in a better understanding of the spatial relationships of the various views, the object, and the revolved positions of the planes.

5–10. FIRST ANGLE PROJECTION

Figs. 5–10 and 5–11 are similar to Figs. 5–8 and 5–9 except that the object is located in the first quadrant. The resulting projections shown in Fig. 5–11 are termed a *first angle projection* of the object.

In first angle projections the object is between the eye and the projection plane, and the projected views show the side of the object seen by the eye. For example, the profile view in this case is actually a view of the left side of the object. The earliest drawings that give evidence of relating plane and elevation views were first angle projections.

Today, this angle of projection is used primarily in this country in architecture as it offers a logical relationship of plan and elevation views of buildings, etc. It is also the projection angle used in engineering in many countries in the world.

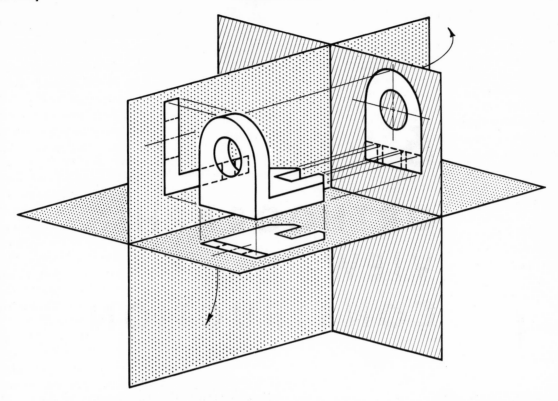

Fig. **5–10.** First angle projection.

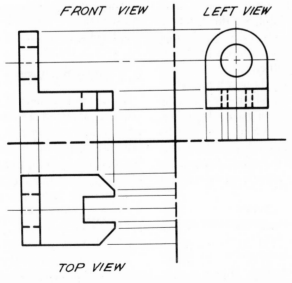

Fig. **5–11.** First angle projection—planes revolved.

6

ORTHOGRAPHIC VIEW CONSTRUCTION

6-1. GRAPHICAL REPRESENTATION

As previously noted in Art. 5–5, orthographic projection is a tool with the aid of which exact measurements on an object may be transferred to a projection plane that is placed parallel to the desired measurements. The term "object," here used in the broadest sense, implies a three-dimensional situation, which may be a single object or an entire spatial system involving a number of objects which are related to one another.

Projected views containing desired information and the projection planes on which the views lie are always considered to be imaginary. However, scaled reproductions of the projected views may be drawn (constructed) on some form of drafting surface (paper, metal, etc.). Views thus constructed form the *graphical representation* of the object they portray.

In order to describe completely in graphical form a three-dimensional object, only two related orthographic views are needed to establish the accurate location of any one point on the object with respect to any other point. (Refer to Art. 5–7.) Additional views, however, are frequently

needed to clarify the spatial model for the reader of the drawing. Therefore, if we are expected to reproduce the three-dimensional situation, we must have sufficient views (graphical representations) to describe completely the three-dimensional relationships of all points involved.

This chapter is concerned with the choice and construction of views that will provide accurate graphical representation of spatial situations.

6-2. PRINCIPAL VIEWS

These are the views (six in number) of an object that are projected onto the principal planes of projection and are generally named for them. As in the case of the fundamental planes of projection, the top (horizontal), front (frontal), and side (profile) *views* are referred to as the *fundamental views*.

Either side view, or both, may be used in giving the size and shape description of an object. If the choice as to which is to be used is immaterial, the right side view is customarily chosen.

In addition to the top, front, and side views, a rear view, projected on a plane that is parallel to the frontal plane but located to the rear of the

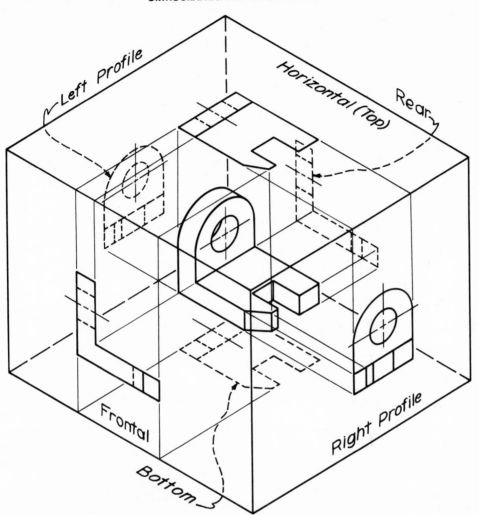

Fig. 6–1. Principal planes and views. Third angle projection.

object, and a bottom view, projected on a plane parallel to the horizontal plane but below the object, may be added as needed. These views are also considered as principal views. Fig. 6–1 shows the six principal planes of projection and the views projected on them. The total number of views used to describe any one object will naturally vary with the complexity of the object.

6–3. VIEW NOMENCLATURE

It has already been stated that the various views are generally named for the projection planes onto which they are projected. Other terms may also be applied to the principal orthographic views. The top view is sometimes referred to as a *plan* view in architectural drawings. A front view may be referred to as a front elevation. Side views are often called side elevations.[1] It should be emphasized that the right side view of an object refers to the object as viewed from the observer's right as *he faces* the frontal plane of projection.

[1] *Elevations* are those views that are projected onto a vertical plane.

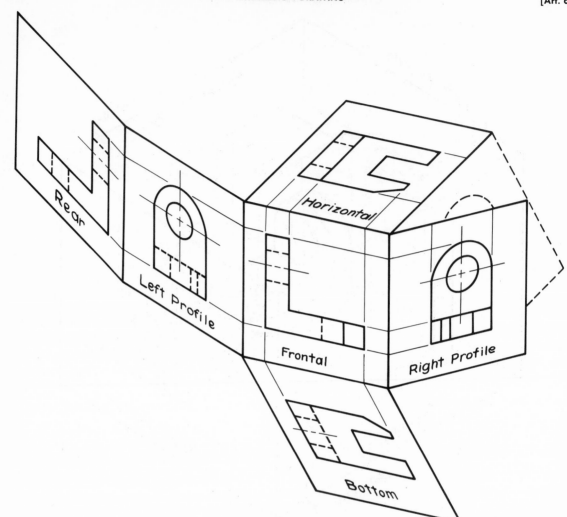

Fig. **6–2.** Principal views (planes) being unfolded.

6–4. VIEW ALIGNMENT

The drawings that an engineer creates generally concern objects that are non-existent at the time the drawings are prepared. In a sense, the drawing becomes the medium for recording a reproduction of the imaginary object on paper. What the engineer does with pencil and paper is analogous to what the sculptor does with clay.

Projection planes, in the sense of their actual existence in space, are imaginary. The sheet of drawing paper becomes the scaled reproduction of these planes as the individual constructs his drawing.

In order to systematically and consistently construct and work with the various views of an object, they are aligned on a single sheet of paper by theoretically "unfolding" the planes of projection. The method of unfolding is in keeping with the procedure described in Figs. 5–8 and 5–9. The complete set of six principal planes together with the views projected onto them are unfolded as shown in Figs. 6–2 and 6–3.[2] Note that there is a choice of position indicated in locating side

[2] The relative size of the principal views with respect to the principal planes of projection has been altered in these two figures from that in Fig. 6–1 in order to permit a more normal space relationship of views as they would occur on a finished drawing.

views. They are usually attached as shown, either to the front or top views. Attachment to the front view is the customary location. The choice of the alternate position is dependent on the nature of the object, spacing of the views on the paper, and the location of notes, title blocks, etc.

The arrangement shown in Fig. 6–3 is the standard one, and illustrates also an alternate not frequently used; however, the principal views may be grouped in many different ways, as long as the adjacent views bear the proper orthographic relationships to one another.

6–5. POINT LOCATION

As has been previously noted, two related orthographic views of an object (i.e., the top and front views) are sufficient to locate spatially any point on an object. Referring to Fig. 6–4, the actual location of every point on this object can be established by means of the top and front views. These two views give the width location as meas-ured in the top or front view, the height location (front view), and the depth location (top view) of any point. Such measurements may be made either (a) with respect to other points or surfaces on the object, (b) with respect to the planes of projection, or (c) with respect to established planes of reference located as desired.

For example, in Fig. 6–4, point A is a distance, X, to the right; a distance, Y, behind; and a distance, Z, above point B. Point B may be located as being a distance, R, to the right of the left profile plane of projection; a distance, S, in back of the frontal plane of projection; and a distance, T, below the horizontal plane of projection. Point C may be considered as being a distance, U, to the right of a vertical plane drawn through the "left" end of the object; a distance, V, in back of a plane through the front face of the object; and a distance, W, above a horizontal plane through the base of the object. Fig. 6–5 shows the above information on the horizontal and frontal planes after they have been revolved into vertical alignment.

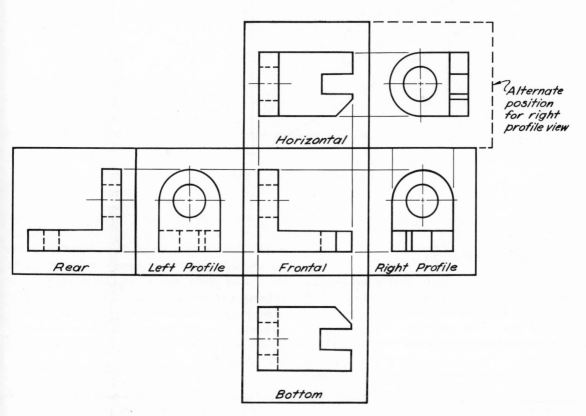

Fig. **6–3.** Principal views (planes) aligned in standard arrangements.

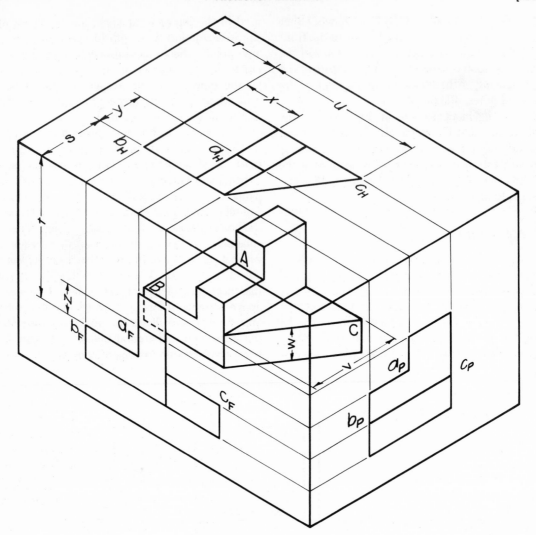

Fig. **6-4.** Location of points.

6-6. OBJECT ORIENTATION

While an object may be located in any position with respect to the principal planes of projection or vice versa, it is customary to "align" or orient the object so that its principal faces are respectively parallel to the horizontal, frontal, and profile planes of projection. Since many objects are regular in shape this procedure tends to reduce the number of views necessary for complete graphical description of an object.

The decision as to which face of an object is to be aligned with which specific reference plane (horizontal plane, etc.) is dependent on the consideration of several factors. First, insofar as possible, an object should be aligned to conform to its customary position in space. Thus, a table should be oriented so that its top would be parallel to the horizontal plane.

A second factor concerns what is known as the *principal view* of an object. This is the view that shows the *characteristic shape* of the object. The

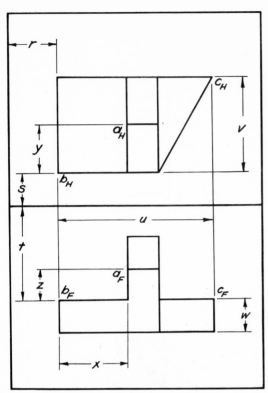

Fig. 6–5. Location of points.

characteristic shape of a chair, for example, is an h shape. The planes of projection are generally oriented so that the projection on the frontal plane will show the characteristic shape of the object.

A third consideration is the position the object will hold while it is being processed. A part to be turned on a lathe would preferably be oriented so that its axis of rotation is parallel to the horizontal and frontal planes, even though the part might occupy a vertical position in the finished object, particularly if the drawing were to be one used by the lathe operator.

A fourth consideration is the overall size of a part. The longest axis of an object will ordinarily be placed parallel to the frontal and horizontal planes of projection, providing none of the other previously mentioned factors controls the orientation of the object.

A fifth consideration is to orient the object so that the views used will employ a minimum of invisible linework.

In the alignment of an object, as many of the above five factors as possible are satisfied at one time. Preference is in the order in which they have been presented.

6–7. VIEW CONSTRUCTION

In constructing an orthographic drawing of a real or imaginary object, it is first necessary to determine what views of the object will be needed in order to give a complete size and shape description of it. The next step is to lay out these views on the drafting surface in keeping with the theories of orthographic projection, object orientation, and view alignment thus far discussed.

Fig. 6–6 illustrates one procedure for the construction of the necessary views of the relatively simple object shown previously in Figs. 6–4 and 6–5. A cursory examination of the object reveals its characteristic ⊥ shape. The view showing the characteristic shape is chosen to be the front view and the object is imagined to be aligned with the contour face parallel to the frontal plane of projection.

It must be assumed that the designer of this object has determined, or decided upon, all its dimensions in terms of some convenient unit of measure (e.g., inches). He then proceeds to draw the front view knowing the desired overall width and height dimensions, the thickness of the base, and the thickness of the upright portion of the object. The front view is shown in Fig. 6–6(a).

The top view is next constructed. It is drawn in vertical alignment with the front view. As was discussed in Chapter 5, the reason the top view is located vertically over the front view is that the views are "in projection." Both front and top views were theoretically "projected" simultaneously from the "object" onto their respective and perpendicular planes of projection. When the horizontal plane was "revolved" upward to become an integral part of the vertical plane, the views fell into vertical alignment.

Actual construction of the top view ordinarily proceeds similarly and simultaneously with that of the front view. The distance between the top view and the front view is purely arbitrary. Sufficient space is allowed between the two views so that a drawing will not look crowded or cluttered. An

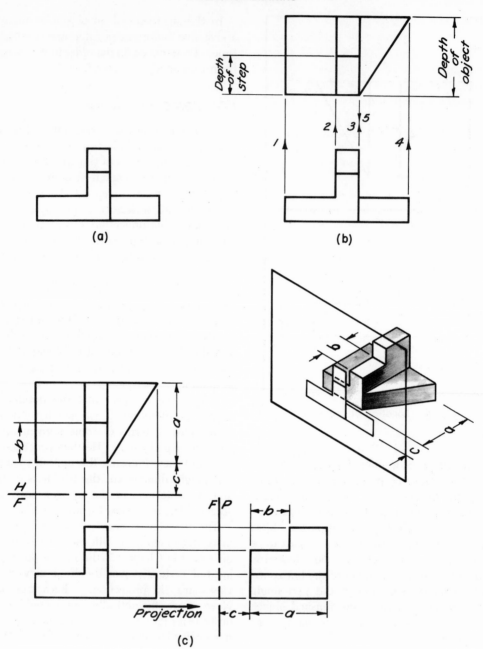

Fig. **6–6.** View construction.

additional consideration that affects the spacing of views is the use of dimensions and notes as will be discussed in Chapter 19. A well-executed drawing, from the standpoint of presentation, contributes to clarity of intent, thereby furthering understanding and promoting confidence in the work.

The width dimensions are transferred to the top view by projection. [See Fig. 6–6(b).] The four arrows pointing upward indicate the direction of projection and the principal points being projected; the numerals indicate a suggested order. The known depth of the object is laid off along the vertical projectors, which have been extended sufficiently far to cross the area in which the top view will be located. The depth of the step in the top view is known and laid off. Finally the diagonal cut-off on the right side is drawn. The intersection of the diagonal surface and the front plane of the object may now be projected (arrow 5) to the front view. The top and front views are now complete.

At this point the spatial position of every point on the object has been established. However, the true shape of the central upright portion of the piece is not shown in either the top or front views. A side view will be needed to provide this information.

The desired side view may be constructed in a manner similar to that just used in obtaining the top view. Essentially this procedure, which forms the basis of all orthographic view construction, consists of two steps: (a) projection, and (b) measurement. Projections are made from the view directly related and adjacent to the new view being constructed. They are made in the direction of the new view. The view from which projection is made thus becomes, in effect, a central view with two related views: the newly related view and the previously related view. Measurements for the new view are made parallel to the projectors to the new view and represent distances normal (at 90°) to the central view. These measurements are obtained from the previously related view and laid off in the newly related view. Care must be taken that the measurements are made in the same manner in all views. For example, if a measurement is obtained from the previously related view in a direction away from the central view, it must be laid off in the newly related view in a direction away from the central view. The view from which the new view is being projected may also be referred to as the projecting view, and the views related to the projecting views as the measuring views.

In the particular case at hand, projection is made from the front view as indicated by the projection arrow in Fig. 6-6(c). Measurements along the projectors, in this case, are measurements of depth. It is known that the top view likewise gives depth measurements. (The top view is the previously related view and the side view is the newly related view.) Thus measurements A, B, and C in the side view are the same distances indicated in the top view. The pictorial view in Fig. 6-6 may illustrate more clearly the reasoning behind the mechanics of view construction employed; the measurements in the top and profile views are one and the same. Both measure the depth in back of the reference plane (frontal in this case).

The object used in Fig. 6-6 is quite simple and the construction of the side view could easily be accomplished from a knowledge of the dimensions of the object and the proper view alignment. Where the object is at all complicated, the above described mechanics of view construction should be followed and can be relied upon to give the correct location of all points involved. In either case, for either simple or complicated objects, the basic theory is the same for the construction of any orthographic view.

It should be noted here that while the above discussion followed through a step-by-step, view-by-view construction procedure, an experienced individual, in laying out the three views of the object, would probably draw all three views simultaneously. Initially he would start by "blocking in" the three views. This refers to the construction of a rectangle on each view which would have the overall width and height, width and depth, etc., dimensions. Next, individual parts of the object could be constructed, with the same part being worked on simultaneously in all three views. This procedure is discussed in greater detail in Art. 6-20.

6-8. REFERENCE PLANES

In Fig. 6-6(c) measurements of depth were laid off from "reference planes" appearing as straight lines in the side and top views, which represent in each case the edge view of the frontal reference plane. This is illustrated in the pictorial view. The nomenclature and initial discussion of reference planes have been given in Art. 5-9.

Reference planes are always perpendicular to the projection rays between views and, conversely, projection rays are always perpendicular to reference planes. Reference planes may be located wherever convenient with respect to the object. Customarily they are placed as in Fig. 6-6(c). However, it is frequently advantageous to place the plane of reference so that it touches the object as in Fig. 6-6(b). This eliminates a measurement such as C in Fig. 6-6(c) and results in a more compact spacing of views, if desired, particularly in the case of multiple auxiliary views (Art. 6–10).

In the case of a symmetrical object, locating the reference plane through the plane of symmetry will reduce the number of measurements to be made and thereby simplify the construction of additional views.

6–9. REQUIRED VIEWS

Since the construction of views requires time, and time is expensive, the minimum number of views that completely describe an object should be used. Theoretically, two views establish the spatial relationship of all points on an object since the three space dimensions—height, width, and depth—are shown in any two adjacent principal views. However, two views often do not visually describe the object to the observer so that there is no possible ambiguity of shape. The engineer must therefore carefully analyze the object to determine the minimum number of views required.

6–10. THREE-VIEW DRAWINGS

The majority of objects will require the use of three related views. Fig. 6–7 shows an object which needs three views to describe exactly the shape of all features of the object. If any view were omitted, it could lead to a misinterpretation of

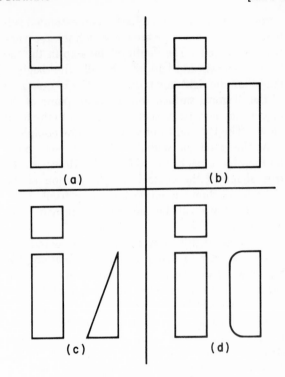

Fig. **6–8.** A two-view drawing.

the shape of some feature. Notice that no view of Fig. 6–7 could be singled out as the one that shows the most characteristic shape of the object. Other factors in this case determine the orientation of the object; e.g., the length of the part, which is placed parallel to the frontal view here.

6–11. TWO-VIEW DRAWINGS

Some objects are shaped so that two related views will completely describe the shape.

Fig. 6–8(a) shows the frontal (front) and horizontal (top) views of an object. From these views it could be assumed that the object is a rectangular prism, in which case the profile (side) view would be as in Fig. 6–8(b). Or the two views of Fig. 6–8(a) could be views of a triangular prism and the side view would be as in Fig. 6–8(c). Still another possibility offered by Fig. 6–8(a) is an object with a curved surface, and the side view could be as in Fig. 6–8(d). Therefore, while the two views of Fig. 6–8(a) do not completely describe the object, the side views suggested in Figs. 6–8(c) and 6–8(d)

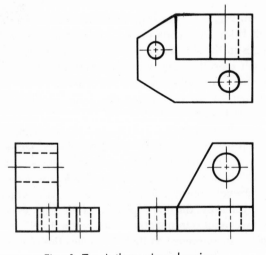

Fig. **6–7.** A three-view drawing.

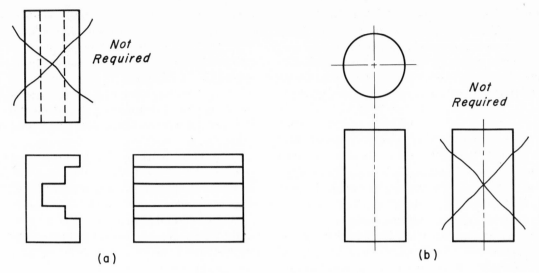

Fig. **6-9.** A two-view drawing.

give possible solutions to the complete shape description. The side view in both examples shows the characteristic shape (or principal contour) of the object. In Fig. 6–8(b), there is no one view that shows a unique characteristic shape that is different from the shape shown in any other view. Therefore, it can be said that simple objects can be completely shown by two related views if one of those views shows the characteristic shape of the object.

Fig. 6–9 shows two other objects that can be completely described using only two views. Notice in each example that one of the required views shows the characteristic shape of the object. In Fig. 6–9(a), it would be possible to use either the top (horizontal) or side (profile) views in conjunction with the front view. However, the side view is the preferred view because there are no hidden lines. Always select the views that show the fewest hidden lines.

6-12. ONE-VIEW DRAWINGS

When the object is made of uniformly thin material, a single view together with a note describing the thickness is all that is required. A typical example is a drawing of a gasket as shown in Fig. 6–10. Here the one view necessary shows the characteristic shape of the object; other views are

not needed because there can be no variance in the thickness.

6-13. AUXILIARY VIEWS

Even with careful orientation of the object relative to the planes of projection, it sometimes happens that the principal views alone will not give all the desired information about an object. Additional views are then required, taken at some angle with the principal planes, that will permit viewing the particular condition so as to see its true dimensions or relationships. Such views are known as *auxiliary views* and are represented on auxiliary planes.

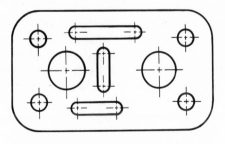

GASKET

Fig. **6-10.** A one-view drawing.

An auxiliary view may be defined as any orthographic view of an object projected on a plane other than one of the principal planes of projection (horizontal, frontal, and profile). Such a definition means that an infinite number of auxiliary views would be possible for any one object. For example, consider the exterior views (projections) that might be made of a house. In addition to the common elevation views (front, rear, sides) and the top (plan) view, an infinite number of angling views could be made from the ground or in the air. These additional views made from odd angles would fall under the classification of auxiliary views.

From a practical standpoint, auxiliary views are those described views which supplement the necessary principal views and aid in the completion of the description of an object or the solution of a spatial problem. In the example of the house given above, a practical auxiliary would be one which would show the true size of the side, or end of an angling wing of the house, or perhaps the true size of any of the sloping roof planes.

6–14. TYPES OF AUXILIARY VIEWS

As we have just seen, all auxiliary views are orthographic views, made by projectors which are perpendicular to the auxiliary planes. Furthermore, the mechanics of constructing any of them are the same as for any other orthographic view.

As a convenience for discussing auxiliary view problems, they may be classified under two general types: (a) *single* auxiliaries, and (b) *multiple* auxiliaries. Most problems necessitating the use of auxiliaries to determine a solution, such as finding the true length of a line or the true size of an *inclined* surface,[3] require only one auxiliary view to obtain an answer. Such a view would be called a single auxiliary. Problems containing oblique surfaces[4] generally necessitate the making of an auxiliary view projected from an auxiliary view. The second auxiliary view, projected from the first, may be referred to as a double auxiliary view.

A problem may demand the use of more than two auxiliary views projected in succession from a

given view. Often, even in these more compli cated situations, a thoughtful orientation of th object with respect to the principal planes of pro jection may reduce the number of auxiliary view needed for a solution.

In any case, regardless of the type classification the mechanics of constructing any of the auxiliar views are the same and are similar to the procedur outlined in Art. 6–7.

Fig. 6–11(a) shows an object with two inclinec surfaces. Fig. 6–11(b) shows the construction o the single auxiliary views which give the true size of the two surfaces. The auxiliary views show only the surface desired in each case since a view show ing the entire object would not yield any additiona information. It is common practice to use partia views in this manner.

Fig. 6–12 shows an object having two oblique surfaces. Study the figure carefully and note how the measurement x for the first auxiliary is taker from the front view and the measurements y and z for the second auxiliaries are taken from the top view. The projections in each instance are made from a related (adjacent) view. (In general, if projections are made from a projecting view, we may say that the measurements are taken from a measuring view preceding it.) Notice the location of the two reference lines in the top view. They have been placed in contact with the surfaces of the object which we wish to show in true shape in the second auxiliaries. This method may be used, if desired, in preference to that followed in Fig. 6–15. It saves space (i.e., distance d) in the location of the second auxiliary views in Fig. 6–12. Partial auxiliary views showing only the surfaces desired have again been used.

Fig. 6–13 shows a problem in which the entire object has been projected in each of the auxiliary views. The question of true shape of planes is dealt with in more detail in Chapter 9.

6–15. PROJECTION FROM VARIOUS PRINCIPAL VIEWS

Some individuals experience difficulty in projecting auxiliary views from different principal views. For example: one might be able to construct an auxiliary view projected from the top view with comparatively little trouble, but might

---

[3] *Inclined* surfaces are surfaces which are inclined to two of the principal planes of projection and perpendicular to the third.

[4] *Oblique* surfaces are those surfaces which are inclined to all of the principal planes.

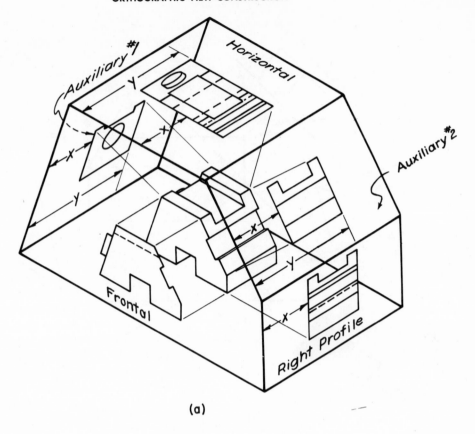

(a)

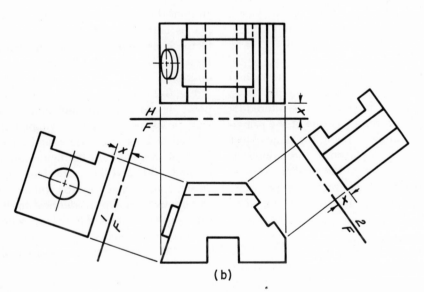

(b)

Fig. **6-11**.   Single auxiliary views.

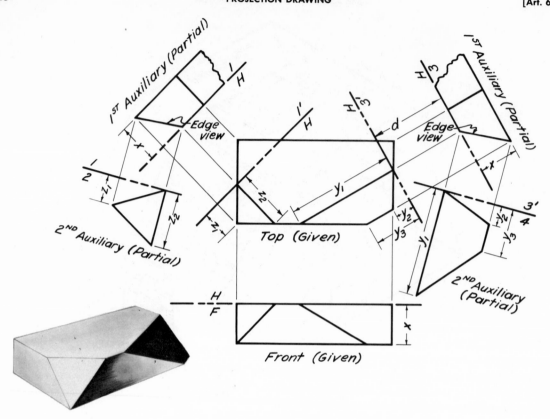

Fig. 6–12. Multiple auxiliary views.

experience quite a bit of trouble in projecting an auxiliary view from either the front or side views. The difficulty arises from erroneously thinking that auxiliaries projected from different views have to be treated differently.

Since all auxiliaries are orthographic views, and are constructed in the same way as principal views, view construction procedure will not be altered by projecting an auxiliary from any one of the principal views. To illustrate this point, the same object (see Fig. 6–14) has been placed in three different positions so that projection of the auxiliary view in each case is made from a different principal view. The ultimate result is the same in each case—i.e., the required view of the surface is the same.

Note that in each case in Fig. 6–14 the entire object is shown in the auxiliary view. Where the whole object is shown, the points (corners) of the parts that are foreshortened are, of course, located by the same construction procedure as the parts

that appear in true size. Also note in these illustrations the omission of the edge views of reference planes and planes of projection. These are aids to the construction of views and need not appear on a final drawing; the projectors, too, are usually omitted.

Fig. 6–14 also brings out another very important point or aid in visualizing and solving auxiliary view problems: any view may momentarily be considered to be a "top" view, and any related view a "front" view. Turn the figure around clockwise through 180° and 90° respectively as you look at illustrations (b) and (c). You will observe that these conditions both appear identical to illustration (a). The auxiliary views themselves, which show the true size of the inclined surface, may be thought of as "front" views. Turn Fig. 6–14 so that the word "Auxiliary" reads horizontally in each case, and the views which show the edge view of the surface will become "top" views. Many individuals can visualize an auxiliary view more easily if it is projected from some particular view—especially the top view. Where this is true, simply call the view from which the auxiliary is projected a "top" view, then the view being constructed will be a "front" view, etc.

6–16. VISIBILITY

In the process of constructing views, such as the second auxiliary view in Fig. 6–13, confusion is apt to arise as to what lines (edges) and surfaces of the object are visible, or conversely, what edges and surfaces are hidden. Fig. 6–15 will be of assistance in indicating the procedure that may be followed in determining the visibility of lines and surfaces of an object in any view.

For ease in initial visualization of the various views on the part of the reader, the "object" in this case is a simplified footstool. In constructing the first auxiliary view, projection is in the direction indicated, and measurements, x_1, x_2, etc., are obtained from the top view. In this fashion all the points (corners) of the object in the first auxiliary may be located. To determine the visibility in this first auxiliary, refer to the front view. As one looks at the first auxiliary, the direction of viewing of the object is indicated by the arrow marked "A" in the front view. This being so, the edge, 1–2, is closest to the observer and will therefore be a visible line in the first auxiliary. Surfaces R and S are attached to the edge, 1–2. Since nothing falls between them and the direction of sight, they are likewise visible in the first auxiliary. The drawing of the foreshortened views of these two surfaces actually completes the first auxiliary view. They cover the rest of the object. By checking other points, it will be seen that they fall either within the boundary of one of the two surfaces, or along the edges. Hidden linework may be added as desired. The reason for adding hidden lines to any view is to improve the clarity of the view and give a better understanding of the object being viewed. In industry, hidden lines may be omitted from auxiliary views when not required for clarity. However, in the classroom, hidden lines in auxiliary views are usually required in order to provide the student with additional practice in the theory of projection drawing.

In determining the visibility in the second auxiliary view, a similar procedure is followed as in the case of the first auxiliary. When the object is seen as shown in the second auxiliary the direction of sight is that indicated by the arrow, "B," in the first auxiliary view. Point 3 is therefore the closest to the observer in this case. This is a corner of the object. The three edges 3–2, 3–4, and 3–7 attached to this corner are therefore visible. The surfaces R, T, and U, which these three edges determine, are likewise visible. The establishment of these surfaces first in the construction of the second auxiliary will make the completion of the view a much easier task. Another rule that will materially aid in the completion of any view is the fact that: *Lines of an object that are actually parallel in space will appear parallel in all orthographic views of that object.*

From the above observations it can be stated that the visibility of points, lines, and planes in any

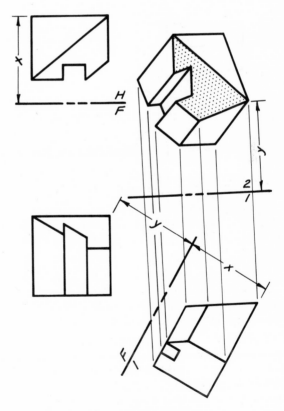

Fig. **6–13.** Multiple auxiliary views.

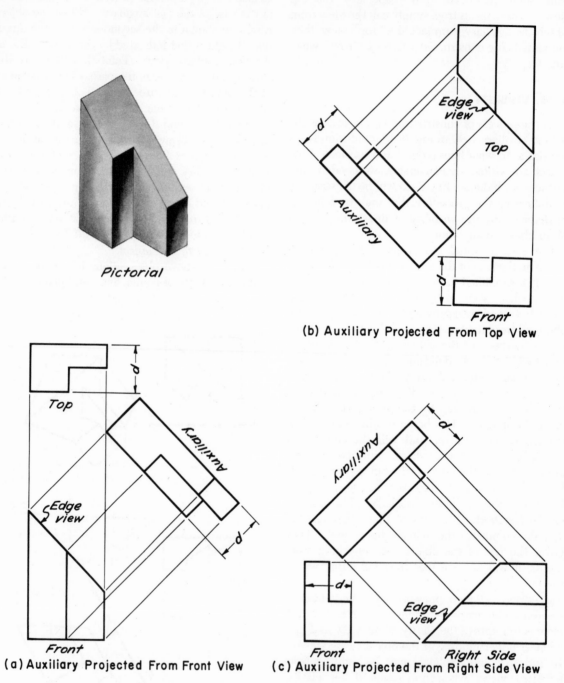

Pictorial

(b) Auxiliary Projected From Top View

(a) Auxiliary Projected From Front View   (c) Auxiliary Projected From Right Side View

Fig. **6–14.** Auxiliary views projected from various principal views.

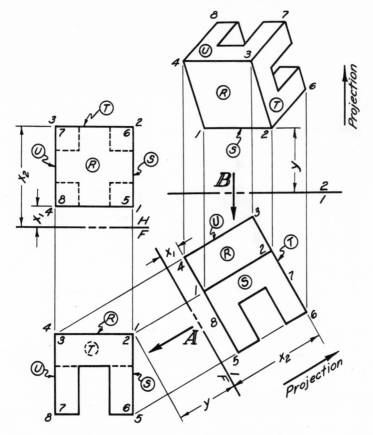

Fig. **6–15.** Visibility of lines and surfaces.

view is determined by their relative position in the related view from which the new view has been projected. Generally speaking, those unobstructed points and connecting lines in the adjacent view that are nearest the edge view of the reference plane will be visible in the new view.

6–17. INVISIBLE LINES

When invisible (hidden) lines, represented by dashed lines, occur in a drawing, care must be exercised to use them correctly; otherwise, the readability of the drawing will be seriously impaired. Fig. 6–16 illustrates the correct and incorrect use of these lines. The encircled conditions which are numbered on the drawing are correspondingly detailed below; the correct applications are shown by the group of figures at the left, and

the commonly made errors in application are shown at the right. These details may be itemized as follows:

Detail 1. When meeting at an angle, other than a straight or 180° angle, dash must touch line (see condition 1 in front view).

Detail 2. Intersection of hidden lines must form solid corners (see condition 2).

Detail 3. Multiple intersections must be solid (corners closed).

Detail 4. If a hidden line would appear to be the extension of a full line, a space should separate the two lines; otherwise, the full line will look too long.

Detail 5. Circle arcs start with dashes at tangent points unless they would appear to be the continuation of a full line, in which case the hidden arc starts with a space, as in Detail 4.

Detail 6. When invisible lines are near each other and are parallel, the dashes should be staggered.

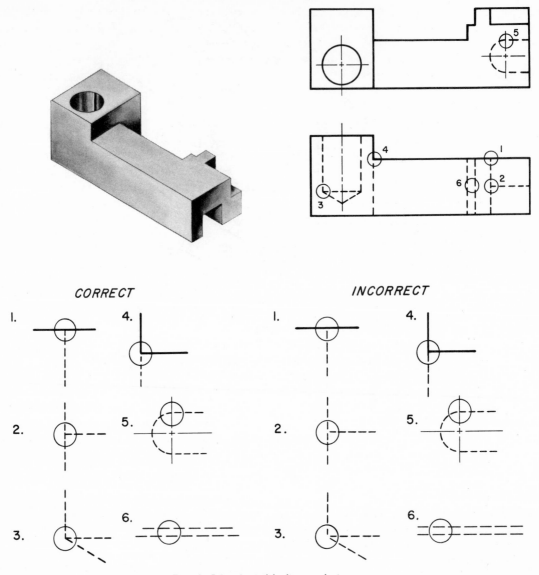

Fig. **6–16.** Invisible line technique.

6-18. READING THE DRAWING

Drawings are literally "read" point by point, line by line, or surface by surface. Theoretically, it is not possible to read a single orthographic view, or projection. One generally needs to make use of all the views available (with a minimum of two views) in determining the exact spatial orientation of each individual point, line, or surface area on an object. The procedure sounds laborious. Initially it may take some patience and perseverance, but once the knack of visualization is acquired, skill in reading a drawing will develop and can progress rapidly with practice.

Figs. 6–17 to 6–19 have been given here to aid in the acquisition of the ability to visualize points, lines, areas, and objects from orthographic views.

Points. Fig. 6–17(a) identifies several points on an object. Note the nomenclature that is used in identifying individual points on a drawing and in written material. This procedure will be followed throughout this text. For example, point A on the object is identified with a capital letter in the text and on the pictorial, since it identifies the actual point in space. The projections of points are identified with lower case letters. Subscripts denote the particular projection plane in which they are located. Check through the location of these five points (A, F, D, H, and K) in the pictorial and the projections of the points in each of the three views. Each point represents the intersection of two or more lines.

Fig. 6–17(b) is identical with Fig. 6–17(a), with the exception that the object outlines have been removed, leaving just the points located in space. Comparing the two drawings will be helpful in enabling an individual to acquire, or develop, a spatial perception of abstract situations consisting simply of points, lines, or planes, or combinations thereof.

Lines. In Fig. 6–18(a), three lines are identified. AF is an *oblique* line. As seen in the top view, the view of AF represents the intersection of two surfaces. As seen in the front view, the view of AF represents, in addition, the edge view of the plane ACF. As seen in the side view, the view of

AF represents, in addition, the edge view of surface AFG. All three views of AF are foreshortened views.

EH is an *inclined* line. The front view of EH represents the intersection of two surfaces. The top view of EH represents, in addition, part of an edge view of the front surface of the object. In the side view, the view of EH likewise represents, in addition, part of an edge view of the front surface of the object. The views of EH are *foreshortened* in the top and profile views—*true length* in the front view. It is given the special name of a *frontal* line. These special lines are discussed in more detail in Chapter 9.

KJ is a *horizontal* line. In the top view the projection of KJ is actually hidden behind the view of line DH and together with the view of DH represents an edge view of the plane DJKH. The front view of KJ is seen end-on and appears as a point. The side view of KJ represents an edge view of the bottom surface of the object. KJ is a horizontal line. It projects as a true-length view in both the side and top views.

Fig. 6–18(b) is identical with Fig. 6–18(a) with the exception that those object outlines not emphasized have been removed. Again, as with Fig. 6–17(b) the individual can refer from one to the other as an aid in better visualizing abstract situa-

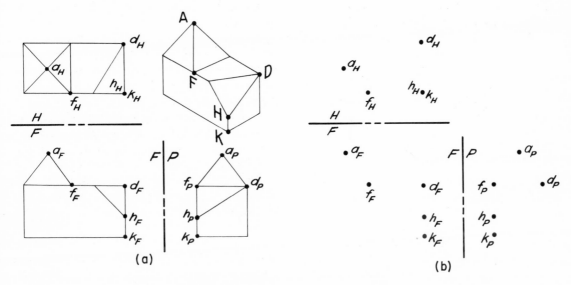

Fig. **6–17.** Reading the drawing—points.

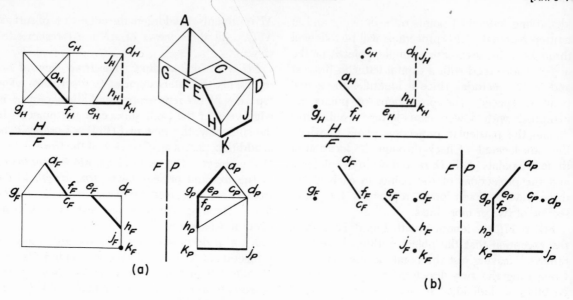

Fig. 6–18. Reading the drawing—lines.

tions in space. Fig. 6–18 illustrates that an object line on a drawing may represent the intersection of two surfaces (*AF* as seen in the top view), or the edge view of a surface (*KJ* as seen in the side view).

Object lines may also represent a third condition, as illustrated in Fig. 6–19. In the front view, the visible outlines, numbered *1*, *2*, and *3*, and all the invisible lines are limiting surface elements of cylindrical surfaces. Note that such limiting (tangent) surface elements are indicative of a condition as seen from a particular vantage point

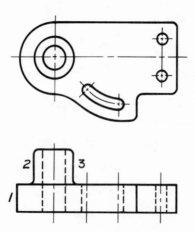

Fig. 6–19. Reading the drawing—tangent lines.

and do not necessarily project as the limiting elements from view to view. Refer to Fig. 6–20. Tangent element *AB* in the top view is *not* a projection of tangent element *CD* in the front view, even though on occasion the elements might appear to line up. The end points of these elements lie, respectively, on a horizontal and frontal diameter of the cylinder.

Surfaces. In Fig. 6–21(a), three surfaces are identified.

Surface *AGF* is an inclined surface seen foreshortened in the top and front views and as an edge (line) in the side view. Note the profile views of lines *AF*, *AG*, and the surface *AGF* are denoted by the same line in the view.

Surface *CDEF* is a *horizontal* plane. Being parallel to the horizontal plane of projection, it is seen in true shape in the top view, and is seen as an edge (line) in the front and side views.

Surface *EDH* is an oblique surface. It is foreshortened in all principal views, and therefore is not represented by a single line in any principal view.

Fig. 6–21(b) is identical with Fig. 6–21(a) except that those object outlines have been removed that are not connected with one of the surfaces identified in Fig. 6–21(a). Again this gives an abstract

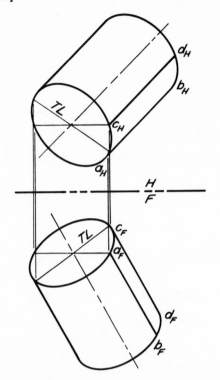

Fig. 6-20. Reading the drawing—tangent lines.

type situation, which the individual should be readily capable of visualizing three-dimensionally.

Care needs to be taken in reading (visualizing) surfaces when only two views are being considered. Note Fig. 6-22. Any one of the profile views would satisfy the given top and front views. *All* views must be considered in the process of visualizing the spatial model from the given orthographic views.

The top view in Fig. 6-23 indicates the manner in which it is customary to indicate tangent surfaces for varying degrees of curvature. Very sharp curves, as at *A*, may be shown by a single line. Curves less sharp, as at *B*, may be shown by two lines projected from tangent points. Curves, as *C*, should not be shown in the adjacent view by tangent lines. Tangent points, as at *D*, should not be shown. The above analysis holds for concave as well as convex curves.

6-19. LINE PRECEDENCE

When making drawings, one line will often fall directly over or coincide with another. The most frequent cases of line coincidence are between visible and hidden lines. That is, a visible line will coincide with, or blank out, a hidden edge line. A hidden line could never blank out a solid line, because a solid line represents an edge that

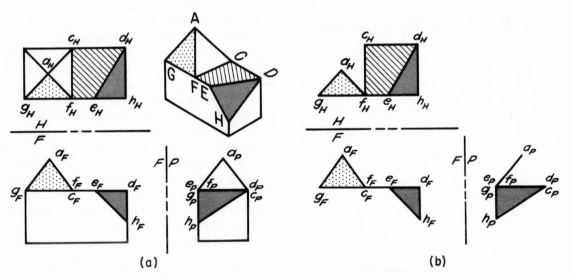

Fig. 6-21. Reading the drawing—surfaces.

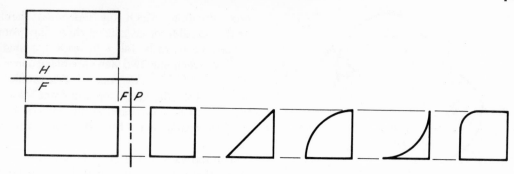

Fig. **6-22.** Alternate view solutions.

can be seen. Likewise, center lines or cutting plane lines may also coincide with visible or hidden linework. These likely conditions make it necessary to establish an order of precedence for the various lines; otherwise the correct reading of drawings would be difficult, if not impossible. Custom, guided by experience, has dictated the following order of precedence for lines which coincide:

1. A full line (outline of parts) takes precedence over any other line.
2. A hidden line (dashed) takes precedence over a center line or a cutting plane line.
3. A cutting plane line may have precedence over a center line.

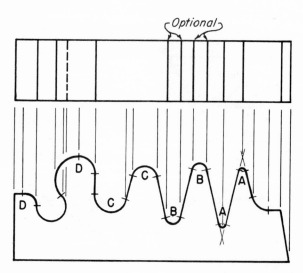

Fig. **6-23.** Showing tangent surfaces in a related view.

4. Center lines.
5. Construction and projection lines, if used.

6-20. CONSTRUCTING THE DRAWING

The theory and procedure for the projection and construction of individual orthographic views as discussed in Arts. 6-7 and 6-14 are followed in the construction of any drawing describing an object or spatial situation. However, in the process of constructing a drawing consisting of several views of an object or structure, time may be saved by blocking out the desired views on the drafting surface and then systematically and simultaneously constructing and completing all the views. Fig. 6-24 illustrates this procedure using the same object as in Fig. 6-1.

Initially the desired views are roughly "blocked in" with light construction lines using only the overall dimensions of the object; see Fig. 6-24(a). Reference lines are established as shown for the purpose of subsequent measurement. The purpose here is to secure a desirable balancing of the views on the sheet, while allowing sufficient room between the views themselves for the purpose of adding dimensions or notes as needed. At this time the proper arrangement of views is determined to give the desired orientation of the object relative to the principal views. (See Art. 6-6.)

Balancing of the views on the sheet is principally a matter of satisfying eye appeal. If no dimensions or notes are to be added to the drawing, the spacing between views and between the border lines and the views can be made uniform both horizontally and vertically. Where dimensions and/or notes

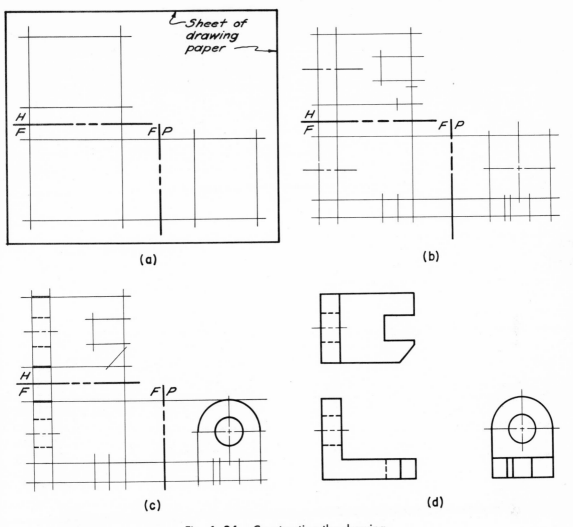

Fig. **6-24.** Constructing the drawing.

are added to the drawing, balance on the sheet must be adjusted to allow ample room for these to be worked in without crowding.

The next step [Fig. 6-24(b)] is to locate center lines and block out details of the object with light construction lines.

The third step [Fig. 6-24(c)] is to draw all circles and arcs and projections of them (as needed) in other views. These are then darkened.

The final step, completing the shape description of the object, is to darken all the remaining line-work. Time can be saved here, whether finished

pencil work or ink work is being used, by following the order of completing linework, as noted in Chapter 2, and by systematically drawing horizontal and vertical lines, working respectively from the top of the drawing sheet down and from the left edge of the drawing sheet to the right.

6-21. DEVELOPMENT OF THE MULTI-VIEW SKETCH

Multi-view technical sketches conform to the same principles and conventional practices as

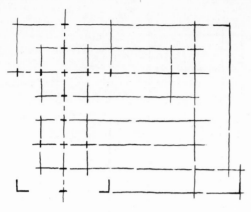

1. Lightly block in each view.

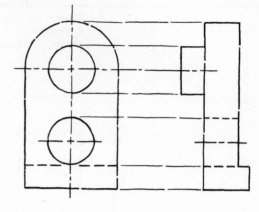

2. Sketch details in each view, projecting between views.

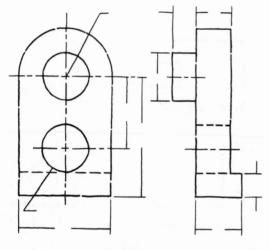

3. Locate extension and dimension lines and leaders for notes.

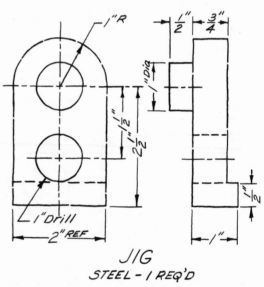

JIG
STEEL - 1 REQ'D

4. Complete arrowheads, dimension figures, notes and title.

Fig. **6-25.** Development of the multi-view sketch.

multi-view instrumental drawings. Technical sketching principles have been discussed in Chapter 3.

Before beginning to sketch, consider the object to be represented from the point of view of the person who will ultimately use the sketch. Determine the views required to describe the object completely, and decide how these views can best be arranged on the paper. Several small "thumbnail" sketches (Art. 3-8) quickly doodled on a bit of scratch paper may be helpful in making these decisions. First, as in instrumental drawing, lightly block in the views, sketching center lines or long base lines and marking the radii of circles and the extremities of the geometric shapes comprising each view. Sketch the details of each view, projecting from view to view as the work progresses rather than completing one view at a time. When all details have been properly located and outlined in their proper proportion and relation to other details, erase construction lines and darken the outlines of the object. It is usually best to darken circles and circle arcs first, then the straight lines. Pay due attention to the line symbols and conventional practices, using a fairly dull solid line for visible outlines, a somewhat sharper dashed line for the hidden-line symbol, and a fine, sharp, alternately long and short line for center lines. Add extension and dimension lines and leaders for notes, using a fine, sharp line. Complete the sketch by drawing arrowheads at the extremities of dimension lines and the terminals of leaders, and lettering the dimension figures, notes, and an appropriate title. Finally, check the sketch to make sure the object is completely described, and that no details, dimensions, notes, or other required information have been omitted. The steps in the development of a multi-view sketch are illustrated in Fig. 6–25.

Problems

READING EXERCISES

Problems 6–1 to 6–3 (Figs. 6–26 to 6–28) involve the ability to read orthographic views and associate the information with a pictorial view of the object, or vice versa. It is suggested that a table be completed for each problem as indicated in Fig. 6–26.

COMPLETION PROBLEMS

Problems 6–4 to 6–30 (Figs. 6–29 to 6–55) consist of orthographic drawings which are not complete. Some of the drawings are accompanied by pictorial views of the objects. In some cases, one or two individual orthographic views are complete. In each case complete the views by adding such visible and invisible linework as is necessary. Use an $8\frac{1}{2}'' \times 11''$ (A-size) problem sheet for each problem. Where exact dimensions are not given but must be secured from the drawing in the text, the precise duplication of measurements of various points on the objects is not critical to their solution as problems. (Corresponding points in related views must, of course, be in projection.)

Problems 6–4 to 6–8 (Figs. 6–29 to 6–33) are problems involving objects in the shape of buildings. Being somewhat familiar objects, they should assist the individual in his initial attack on this type of problem (completion). Place the problems four to a sheet as indicated. Scale of each object should be chosen accordingly.

Problems 6–9 to 6–22 (Figs. 6–34 to 6–47) may be considered to portray objects which are all basically about $2'' \times 2'' \times 4''$ in size. Place four problems to the sheet as indicated. Scale of each object should be chosen accordingly.

Problems 6–23 and 6–24 (Figs. 6–48 and 6–49) have an approximate graphic scale indicated. Here again, the precise duplication of measurement is not critical as long as points are correctly in projection.

CONSTRUCTION PROBLEMS

Problems 6–31 to 6–50 (Figs. 6–56 to 6–75) should be worked out on $8\frac{1}{2}'' \times 11''$ (A-size) sheets, one for each problem. The orientation of the object, and the choice and number of views, are to be determined in each case. Sufficient views to describe the object completely are required for each problem.

AUXILIARY VIEW PROBLEMS

Problems 6–51 to 6–57 are exercises in constructing auxiliary views. Use objects in Problems 6–31 to 6–37 respectively. In each case draw the given object at half-size. Then from the constructed top or front view, as assigned, project a first auxiliary view. The direction of projection is to be at an angle of 30° with a horizontal line on the drawing board. A second auxiliary view may be projected from the first as assigned. The angle for this should be at 60° with a horizontal line on the drawing board.

6–1.

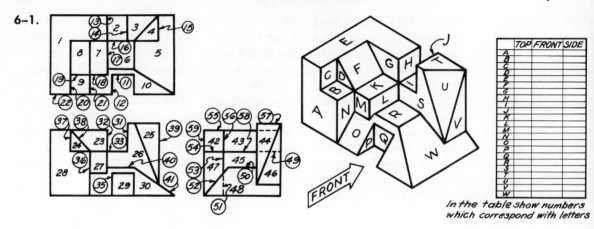

In the table show numbers which correspond with letters

Fig. **6–26.**   Reading exercise.

6–2.

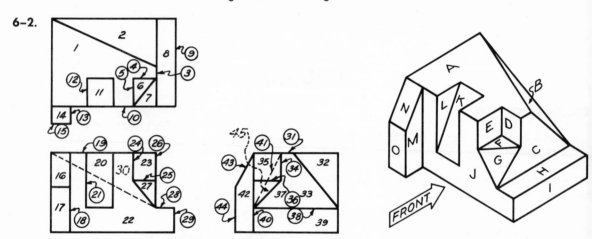

Fig. **6–27.**   Reading exercise.

6–3.

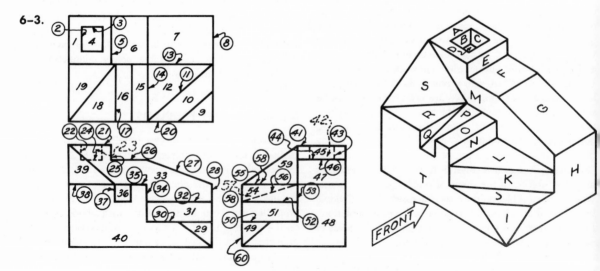

Fig. **6–28.**   Reading exercise.

6-4.

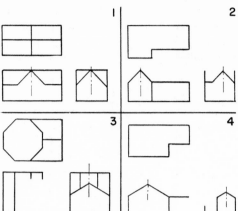

Fig. **6-29.**

6-7.

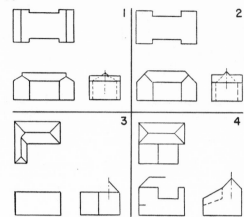

Fig. **6-32.**

6-5.

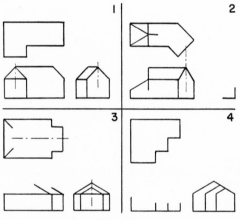

Fig. **6-30.**

6-8.

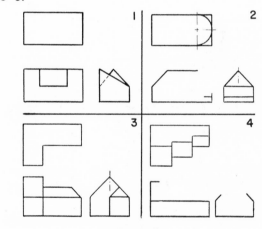

Fig. **6-33.**

6-6.

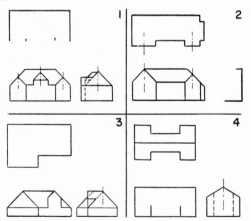

Fig. **6-31.**

Completion problems.

6-9.

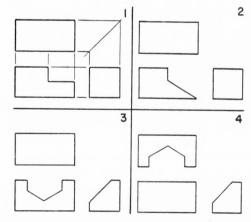

Fig. **6-34.**

6-10.

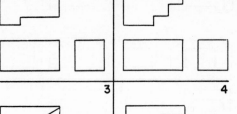

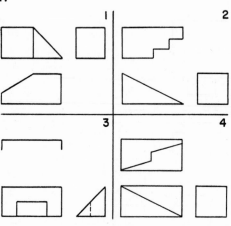

Fig. **6-35.**

6-11.

Fig. **6-36.**

6-12.

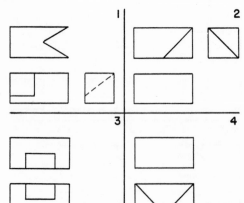

Fig. **6-37.**

6-13.

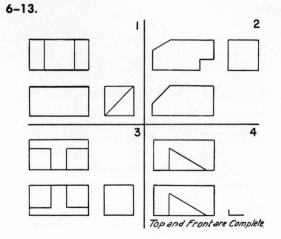

Top and Front are Complete.

Fig. **6-38.**

6-14.

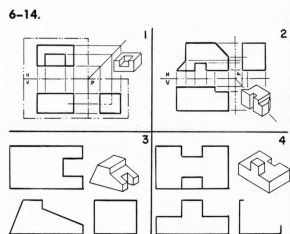

Fig. **6-39.**

6-15.

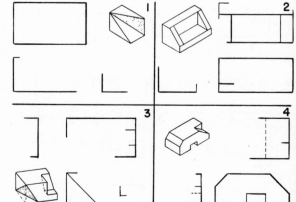

Fig. **6-40.**

Completion problems.

6–16.

6–19.

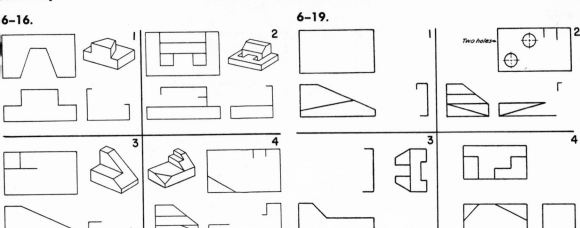

Fig. **6–41.**   Fig. **6–44.**

6–17.

6–20.

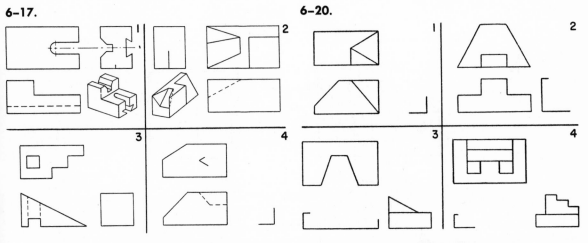

Fig. **6–42.**   Fig. **6–45.**

6–18.

6–21.

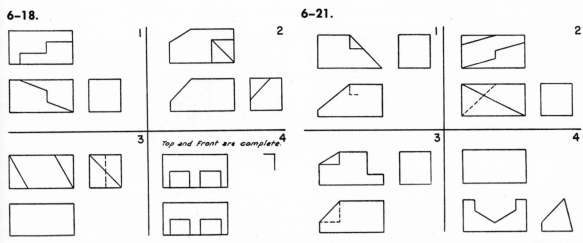

Top and Front are complete.

Fig. **6–43.**   Completion problems.   Fig. **6–46.**

6-22.

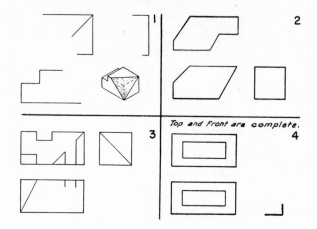

Fig. **6-47.** Completion problem.

6-23.

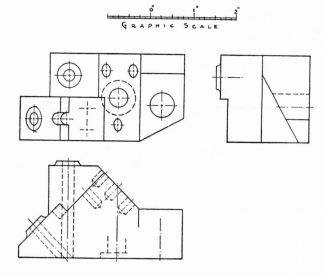

Fig. **6-48.** Centering block.

6-24.

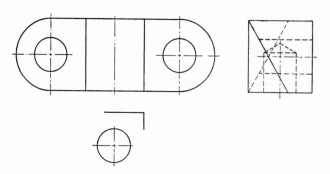

Fig. **6-49.** Spacer (use graphic scale on Prob. 6-23).

-25.

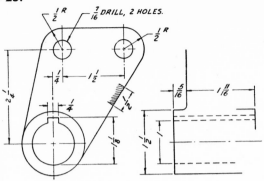

Fig. **6-50.** Anchor plate.

-26.

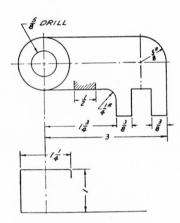

Fig. **6-51.** Latch finger.

6-27.

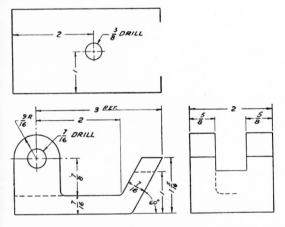

Fig. **6-52.** Lever stop.

6-28.

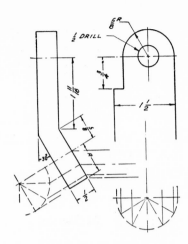

Fig. **6-53.** Angle clip.

6-29.

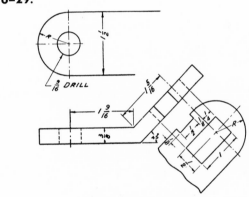

Fig. **6-54.** Engager tongue.

6-30.

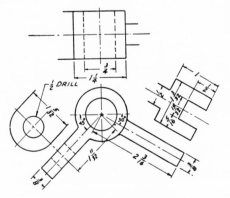

Fig. **6-55.** Angle spacer.

6-31.

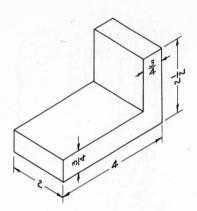

Fig. **6-56.** Bracket blank.

6-34.

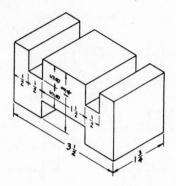

Fig. **6-59.** Gage block.

6-32.

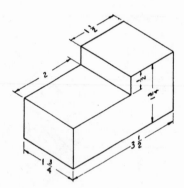

Fig. **6-57.** Gage block.

6-35.

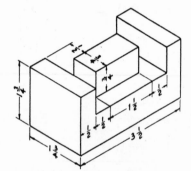

Fig. **6-60.** Gage block.

6-33.

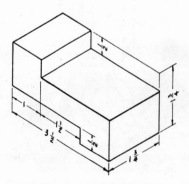

Fig. **6-58.** Gage block.

6-36.

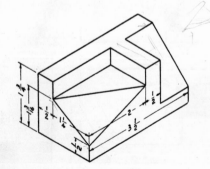

Fig. **6-61.** Gage block.

–37.

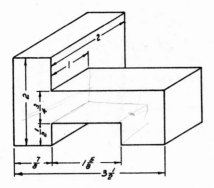

Fig. **6–62.** Stop guide.

6–40.

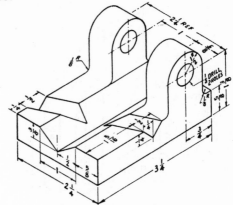

Fig. **6–65.** Angling V guide.

–38.

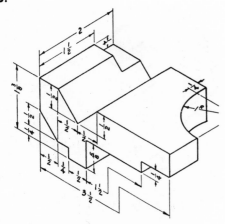

Fig. **6–63.** V slide stop.

6–41.

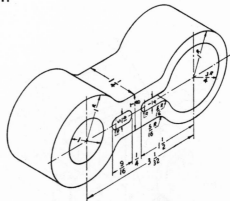

Fig. **6–66.** Connector link.

–39.

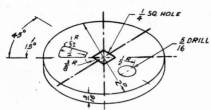

Fig. **6–64.** Valve cover.

6–42.

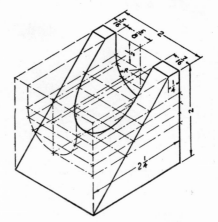

Fig. **6–67.** Wedge bearing.

6-43.

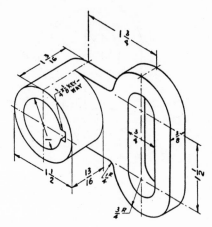

Fig. **6-68.**   Adjuster bracket.

6-46.

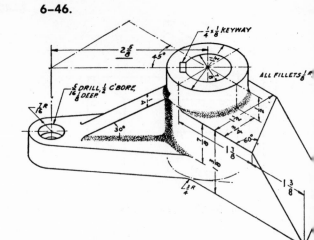

Fig. **6-71.**   Throw crank.

6-44.

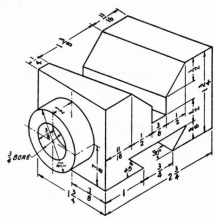

Fig. **6-69.**   Cross guide.

6-47.

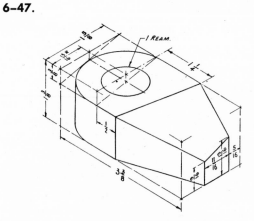

Fig. **6-72.**   Throw lever.

6-45.

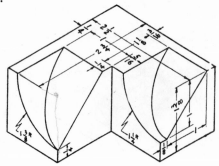

Fig. **6-70.**   Gage block.

6-48.

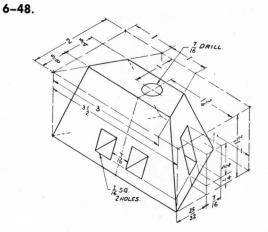

Fig. **6-73.**   Die block.

6–50.

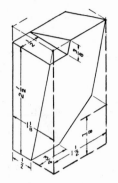

Fig. **6–74.** Gage block.   Fig. **6–75.** Gage block.

7

CONVENTIONS IN DRAWING

7-1. PURPOSE

The use of symbols and conventions in drawings is commonplace and serves to clarify and speed up both preparation and reading of the drawings. To this end many conventional practices have been standardized and approved by the standardizing agencies.

The practice of representing a complicated internal structure with sectional views is a conventional procedure. Drawings of objects and assembled parts having complicated internal structure are often confusing to read where hidden linework is the only means used to describe the design. Interpreting invisible linework as in Fig. 7-1 is difficult unless a clear understanding of the shapes is previously known. Sectional views may be made to clarify complicated or vague outlines and to speed up interpretation. Portions of the object are removed to show either internal or external design.

External contours of warped surfaces, such as air foils and other blended shapes, sometimes do not show clearly in the views of a drawing. Sec-

tional views, taken at critical positions, may aid to clarify these contours and hidden shapes.

7-2. ORIENTATION AND CONSTRUCTION OF SECTIONS

A sectional view (or sectioned view) shows the shape of the surface cut by passing an imaginary plane through an object or portion of an object. When sectional views are made we speak of *sectioning* or *taking a section*. Sections should not be used when internal shapes can be clearly indicated by the use of hidden lines. Illustrations in textbooks are often oversimplified for the reader and suggest sectioning views of objects which normally would be best shown by hidden lines. In the case of surface contours, sections should be used only when the contour is complicated. Standard items such as fasteners, where no interior detail must be shown and where the construction is understood, generally do not require sectioning.

To visualize a section, it is imagined that a cutting plane is passed through an object and that the portion of the object between the viewer and

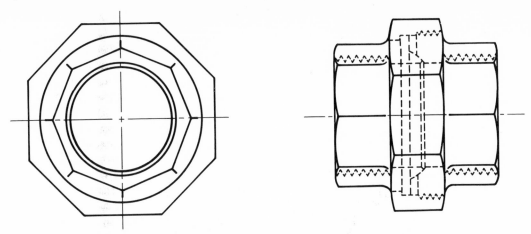

Fig. **7–1**. An assembled union.

the cutting plane is removed as in Fig. 7–2. The surface areas that would be cut and exposed by the plane are crosshatched with *section lining* to accentuate the outlines of the object. As many sections may be taken through an object as desired. They may be located on the drawing as principal views, or may be projected from principal views, or may be removed and oriented in correct projection. Sections are identified by labeling as shown in the illustrations of this chapter. Fig. 7–3 shows the location of the *cutting-plane line* in the orthographic views. The cutting-plane line is placed and labeled in the view showing the edge of the cutting plane. The direction of viewing the sectioned view is indicated by arrowheads at the ends of the cutting-plane line. The direction of the arrowheads and the projection must agree. Particular attention should be given to this factor if the section is other than a sectioned principal view. The sectional view is normally labeled directly below the view with bold lettering as *Section A-A*, *B-B*, etc. However, when the cutting plane passes through a line or plane of symmetry, or an obvious center line, and the sectioned view is a principal view, it is usually considered unnecessary to draw the cutting plane or line. In such cases the cutting-plane line, arrowheads, and labeling are omitted. Often the cutting plane is not continuous and may have offsets to meet specific needs, as will be explained later in discussing the several types of sections.

7-3. FULL SECTIONS

A full section is taken when a cutting plane is passed entirely across the object to be sectioned, as shown in Fig. 7–3. All visible lines behind the cutting plane are drawn to aid in fully describing the contour. Beginning students have a tendency to omit visible lines which show changes in internal diameters, as in Fig. 7–3. Be sure to show visible lines which are behind the cutting plane. Hidden lines behind the cutting plane are omitted, except when their addition will clarify the drawing, when they are needed for dimensioning, or when they eliminate a need for additional views. In Fig. 7–3 the sectioned view is one of the principal views. It is in projection with the adjacent view, and is the only sectional view on the drawing. There is no chance, in this case, for the location of the cutting plane and the identification of the section to be misinterpreted. It would therefore be correct to omit the cutting-plane line and identification of the section on this figure and on similar drawings.

7-4. HALF-SECTIONS

This type of section is used mainly in connection with symmetrical objects. The cutting plane passes through only half the object to reveal the interior, yet also shows exterior surfaces in the sectional view as shown pictorially in Fig. 7–4. In

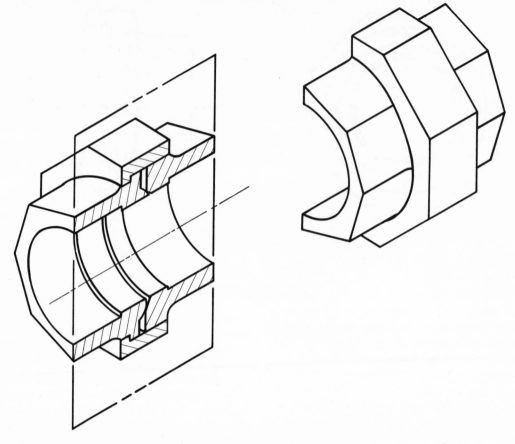

Fig. **7–2.** Cutting plane for a full section.

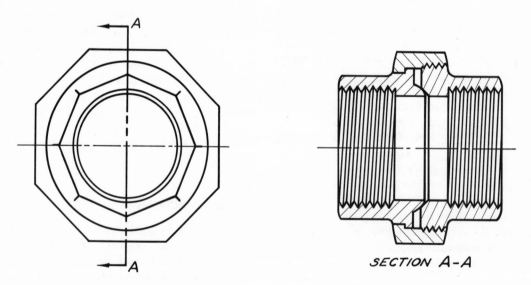

Fig. **7–3.** A full section.

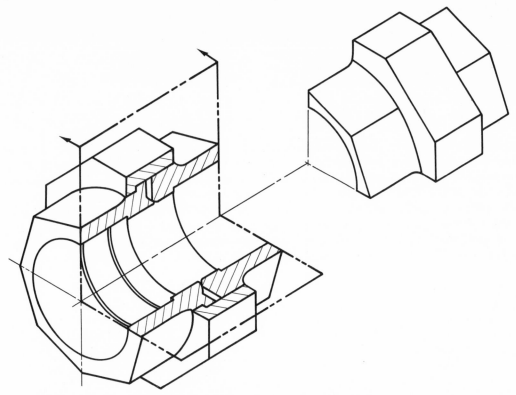

Fig. **7–4.** Cutting plane for a half-section.

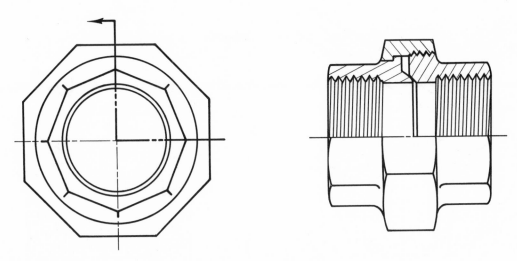

Fig. **7–5.** A half-section.

the orthographic views (Fig. 7–5) it would be permissible to show hidden lines in the exterior area, but in this case it would not add clarity and the hidden lines are correctly omitted. The line separating the sectioned and unsectioned parts in the sectional view may be drawn either as a center line or a solid visible outline. A center line is preferable.

7–5. OFFSET SECTIONS

Where the important features of the object to be clarified by sectioning do not fall in a single plane, it is good practice to jog the cutting plane forward or back to include desired details which can be combined into one sectional view. This is accomplished by offsetting the cutting plane as shown pictorially in Fig. 7–6. It will be noted that in this object the cutting plane passes through the small hole and is offset through the boss or reinforcement in the rim of the casting. In this type of section it is obviously necessary always to show the cutting-plane line and identify the section. Although there is a break or jog in the cutting plane, no indication of this is shown in the sectioned view (Fig. 7–7). In offset sections there

may be as many offsets as needed as long as clarity is maintained.

7–6. REVOLVED SECTIONS

At times it is possible to show the cross-sectional area of a shape without drawing an extra view. This is accomplished by passing a plane through the area, perpendicular to the plane of projection, and revolving the sectioned area until it is parallel to the plane of projection of the given view; see Fig. 7–8 at (a). In some instances the contour of the revolved section will be clarified if a broken-out area is provided as in Fig. 7–8 at (b). It will be noted that the cutting plane for the revolved section in the broken-out area is placed on a radial

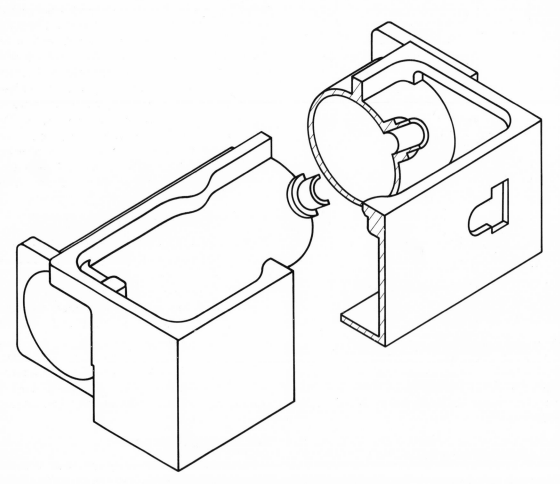

Fig. **7–6.** Offset section in pictorial.

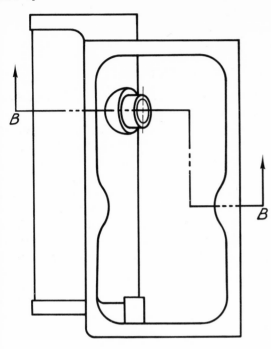

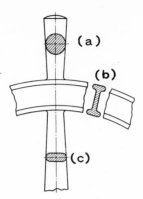

Fig. **7-8.** Revolved sections. (ASA 14.2; 1957.)

tain a position to read as indicated by the arrows at the end of the cutting-plane line. These are removed sections and must be identified by letter. Good form for section identification is illustrated in Fig. 7–9. From this drawing it will be observed that sections drawn to a size other than full scale should be so noted. When it becomes necessary to draw a view or an exterior portion of an object out of projection, a cutting plane may be placed outside the object to indicate the view taken. The removed view is identified as View A–A, etc. This procedure should not be encouraged for principal views, but is relatively common in representing irregular bosses, pads, and small detailed areas.

7-8. BROKEN-OUT SECTIONS

This type of sectional view is used where a portion of the object can conveniently be removed from an area to show wall thickness, contour, or the shape of an area exposed by the break-out as in Fig. 7–10. A broken-out section often eliminates the need for a full or half-section and is equally clear. The crosshatched area will be on a plane parallel to the plane of projection. The ragged break-out line is drawn freehand. The location of the break-out is generally so obvious that it is unnecessary to locate or identify the sectioned area.

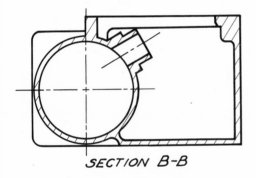

SECTION B-B

Fig. **7-7.** Offset section.

center line. Where the object tapers in size, as at (c), the section will be drawn to the size of the point chosen for the intersection of the cutting plane. Spokes, rims, wall thicknesses, and many structural shapes lend themselves to this type of sectioning.

7-7. REMOVED SECTIONS

Sections may be placed out of projection with the principal views on the drawing, but must re-

7-9. PHANTOM SECTIONS

Phantom sectioning, principally used in assembly drawing, has fallen into disuse but should be understood. In Fig. 7–11, which shows a phantom

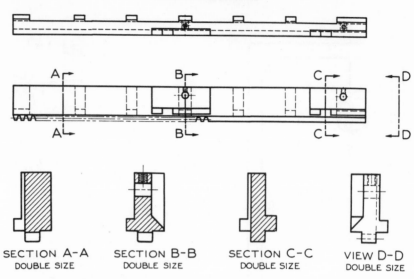

Fig. **7-9.** Removed sections and removed view. (ASA 14.2; 1957.)

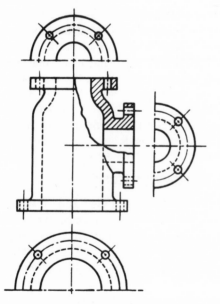

Fig. **7-10.** Broken-out sections. (ASA 14.2; 1957.)

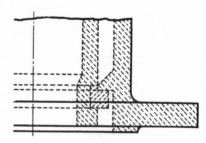

Fig. **7-11.** Phantom sections. (ASA 14.2; 1957.)

Although this shows both interior and exterior conditions, it frequently results in lack of clarity

7-10. THIN MATERIALS IN SECTION

It is standard practice, where material is too thin for effective section lining, to black-in sectioned areas showing materials such as sheet metal, packing, and gaskets. (See Fig. 7-12.) This is not, however, accepted practice in some automotive and aircraft manuals, and the individual should not be misled into the habit of blacking-in all thin areas until he is informed of the standards used in a particular industry. Blacked-in areas, if improperly used, may be mistaken for object shadings.

section, the drawing is made as it normally would be without sectioning, including the hidden edge lines. The individual pieces are then crosshatched with fine, dashed lines to show the relationship of the parts.

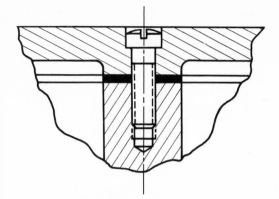

Fig. **7-12.** Thin materials.

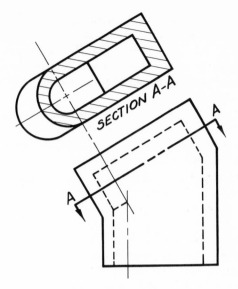

Fig. **7-13.** An auxiliary section.

7-11. AUXILIARY SECTIONS

Any auxiliary view in section is defined as an auxiliary section and should preferably be in direct projection with the indicated cutting plane. When located out of projection it must be placed on the drawing in such a manner that it is at the same angle and relationship indicated by the cutting plane. The identifying notation below the auxiliary section should read from the bottom of the drawing regardless of the angle at which the section is drawn, as should also the letters at the ends of the arrowheads on the cutting plane. Section A–A in Fig. 7–13 is an auxiliary section.

7-12. SECTION LINING

It is desirable, for clarity, to attract attention to the contour of sectioned areas by adding *section lining* or crosshatch lines to the cut surfaces. These lines are thin, as light as center lines, equally spaced, and preferably at 45° to the horizontal. Other angles must be used when 45° crosshatching becomes parallel or perpendicular, or nearly so, to other long lines of the object (Fig. 7–14). On adjacent pieces in an assembly drawing, the direction of the crosshatching should be changed to aid in identification of individual pieces as in Fig. 7–15. This condition requires the use of angles in addition to those at 45°. Sectioning sometimes causes the same part to appear in more than one area in a single view, particularly in symmetrical objects. The crosshatching for any single part

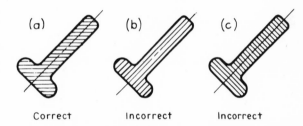

(a) Correct　　(b) Incorrect　　(c) Incorrect

Fig. **7-14.** Direction of section lining. (ASA 14.2; 1957.)

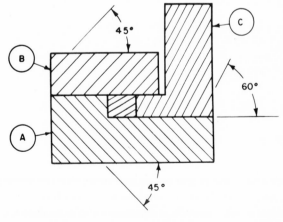

Fig. **7-15.** Sectioning adjacent parts. (ASA 14.2; 1957.)

must be the same slope, spacing, and type in all places where the part appears in section more than once in the same view. Fig. 7–3 illustrates the principle in which the crosshatching is the same in each piece above and below the center line of the sectioned view.

Section lines are ordinarily drawn approximately $\frac{3}{32}''$ apart. The spacing is estimated rather than measured. As the area to be sectioned increases or decreases the spacing of the section lines should be correspondingly increased or decreased. Students have a tendency to crowd the section lines much too closely, probably because illustrations in textbooks are reductions in size from the original drawings and section lines appear closer together than they should be on a drawing or a sketch.

Several patented mechanical devices and many tricks are employed by draftsmen and illustrators to produce uniform and attractive crosshatching lines. Light, sharp lines spaced by eye are satisfactory for engineering drawings.

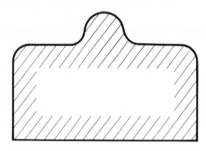

Fig. **7–16.** Outline sectioning.

Outline section lining, shown in Fig. 7–16, has merit as a timesaver on large drawings. It also tends to reduce clutter and thereby results in improved appearance of large surface areas.

7–13. SECTION LINING SYMBOLS

It is common practice to identify different types of materials in the sectioned views of assembled parts by the use of appropriate conventional section lining symbols. Symbols recommended by the American Standards Association for this purpose are shown in Fig. 7–17. In drawings of single

parts or details, it is common practice to use the general crosshatching symbol (the symbol for cast iron) on the part regardless of the actual material. The type of material is then noted in an appropriate area on the detail drawing. This procedure saves time. Fig. 7–18 shows that standard symbols may be used on exterior views as well as on sectioned views to denote the materials.

7–14. CONVENTIONAL PRACTICES IN SECTIONING

Aligned sections, as illustrated in Fig. 7–19, are used to eliminate the need for drawing extra views and to show the true size of a sectioned area for purposes of clarity and dimensioning. The surface cut by the cutting-plane line A–A is revolved (aligned) into the plane of projection of the frontal view. The offset auxiliary Section B–B is also aligned by revolving a portion of it into the auxiliary plane of projection. Changes of position in the cutting-plane line are not indicated in the crosshatching. Often, cutting-plane lines will fall on important center lines, making it necessary to show only the arrows and the plane line changes of direction by using heavy lines at the offsets. Aligning by revolving is frequently applied to levers and unsymmetrical arms.

Clarity in sectioning through ribs is obtained by leaving the rib area unsectioned even though the cutting plane passes through it longitudinally. The reason for this procedure is illustrated in Fig. 7–20, which shows both a solid conical object and an object with symmetrical ribs supporting a hub. In Fig. 7–20(a) the conical object is shown in full section. In Fig. 7–20(b) the ribbed object is shown in full section, with section lining appearing everywhere the object is cut by the cutting plane. The sectional views of the two objects are then identical, giving a misleading impression of the shape of the ribbed object. When the rib area is left unsectioned, as in Fig. 7–20(c), an impression of the true shape is conveyed to the viewer. Fig. 7–21(a) and (b) further illustrate this convention. Fig. 7–21(c) is an accepted method in which alternate section lines are omitted to identify the rib area.

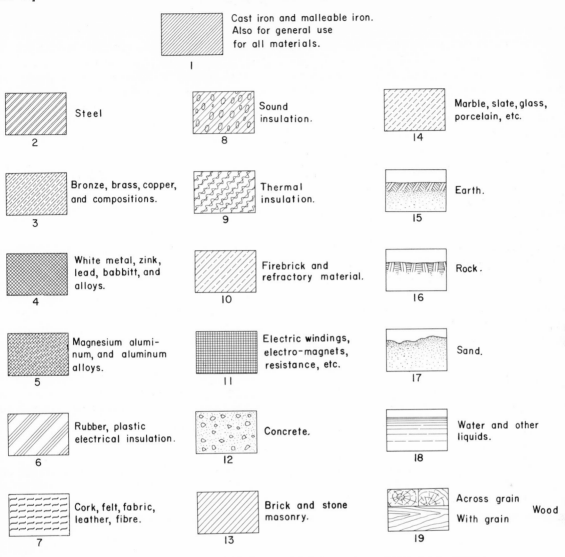

Fig. **7-17.** Standard symbols for materials in section.   (ASA 14.2; 1957.)

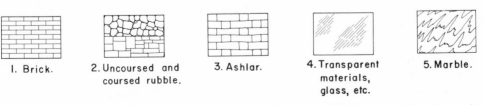

Fig. **7-18.** Standard symbols for exterior views.   (ASA 14.2; 1957.)

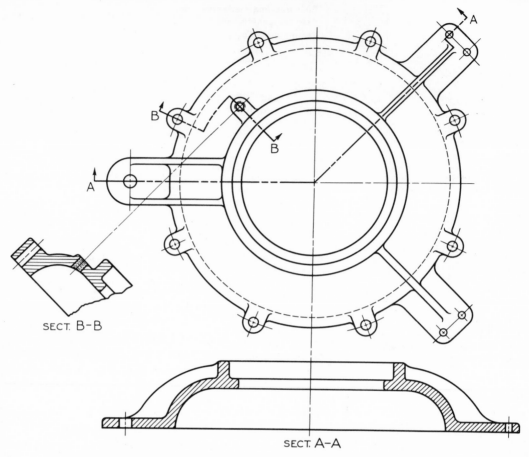

SECT. B-B

SECT. A-A

Fig. **7-19.** Auxiliary and aligned sections. (ASA 14.2; 1957.)

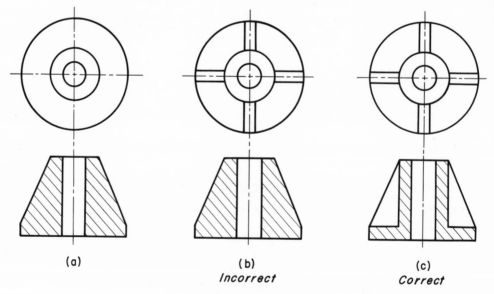

(a)

(b)
Incorrect

(c)
Correct

Fig. **7-20.** Rib conventions.

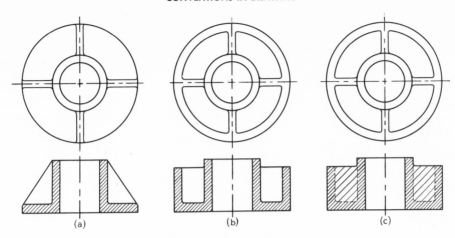

Fig. **7–21.** Sectioning through ribs.

Conventional breaks may be used to reduce lengths as in Fig. 7–22. The break lines are made freehand and for metals are relatively smooth lines; only wood appears jagged.

7–15. RADIALLY ARRANGED HOLES, RIBS, AND SPOKES

Fig. 7–23(a) illustrates the true and the conventional methods of drawing a series of radially arranged holes. The circular view shows the size and arrangement of the holes. The rectangular (side) view drawn in true projection is difficult to interpret because the lower holes are not shown in their true distance from the center of the piece. When the holes are drawn using conventional practice, all holes are theoretically rotated into positions parallel to the plane of the adjacent view and projected to the adjacent view from that position. The side view drawn conventionally shows clearly that the holes are all the same distance from the center of the piece or, in other words, are radially arranged. Fig. 7–24 demonstrates vividly the effectiveness of this conventional practice. The side view drawn in true projection is a meaningless jumble of hidden lines, while the side view drawn conventionally shows clearly that there are two concentric rings of holes.

Fig. 7–23(b) illustrates conventional practice when illustrating radially arranged ribs. The side view drawn in true projection shows clearly one

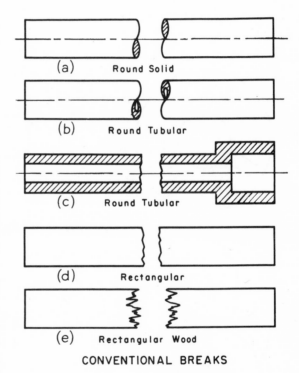

(a)   Round Solid

(b)   Round Tubular

(c)   Round Tubular

(d)   Rectangular

(e)   Rectangular Wood

CONVENTIONAL BREAKS

Fig. **7–22.** Conventional breaks.

rib, but the other rib is difficult to visualize and actually obscures some of the other detail. However, the view drawn conventionally shows the ribs clearly. In conventional practice the lower ribs were theoretically rotated until parallel to the profile plane of projection.

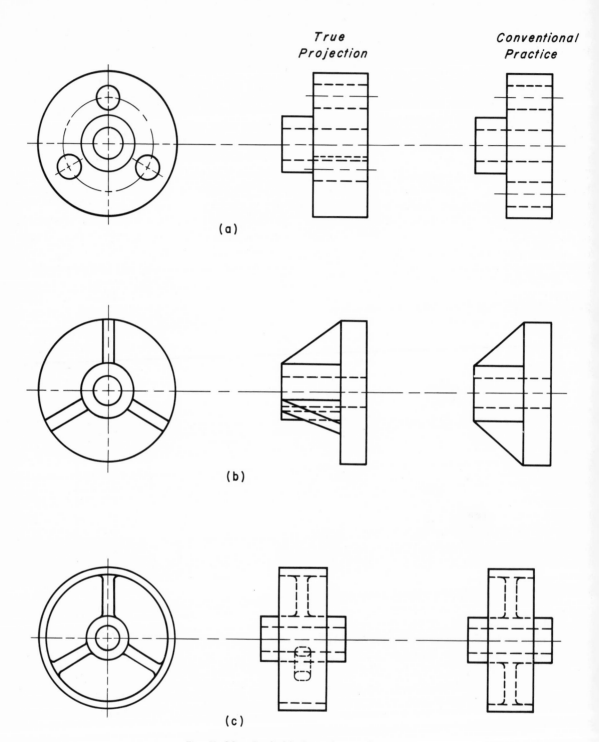

Fig. **7-23**.   Radial holes, ribs, and spokes.

Fig. 7-23(c) shows radially arranged spokes. The theory is the same as in Fig. 7-23(a) and (b) and the greatest clarity is gained by conventional practice.

7-16. INTERSECTIONS OF RELATIVELY SMALL HOLES OR BOSSES WITH CYLINDERS

Fig. 7-25(a) illustrates the intersection between relatively small holes and a cylinder, and Fig. 7-25(b) shows the intersections of relatively small bosses. The term "relatively small" means that the diameter, or the major dimension in the case of a rectangular hole, is less than half the diameter of the large cylinder. The simplicity and rapidity of construction gained through this conventional practice are self-evident.

7-17. INTERSECTIONS OF RELATIVELY LARGE CYLINDERS

Constructing the line of intersection between two relatively large cylinders is difficult and con-siderable time is consumed in drawing a true projection. The line of intersection, as shown in Fig. 7-26, is a smooth curve that must be con-structed by locating a series of points along the intersection by methods that are discussed in Chapter 13. The term "relatively large" means that the diameter of the smaller cylinder is equal to or greater than half the diameter of the larger cylinder. The conventional practice, illustrated in Fig. 7-26, is to replace the actual line of inter-section by an arc whose radius is that of the larger cylinder. This arc will cross over the vertical center line at the same point that the real line of intersection would have crossed over it. This conventional practice gives a rapid and acceptable approximation of the actual intersection. When this method is not acceptable for the purposes of the drawing, the methods that are discussed in Chapter 13 must be used.

7-18. FILLETS, ROUNDS, AND RUNOUTS

Interior corners on objects formed by the casting process are always rounded (or filled in) to prevent

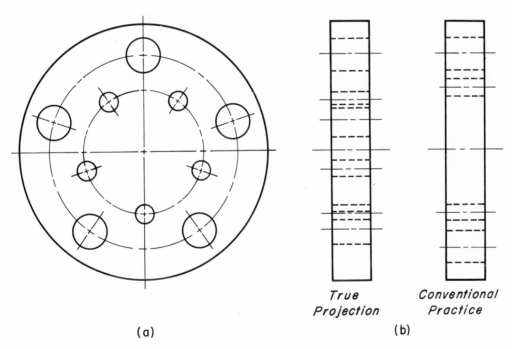

True Projection

Conventional Practice

(a)   (b)

Fig. **7-24.** Aligning radially arranged holes.

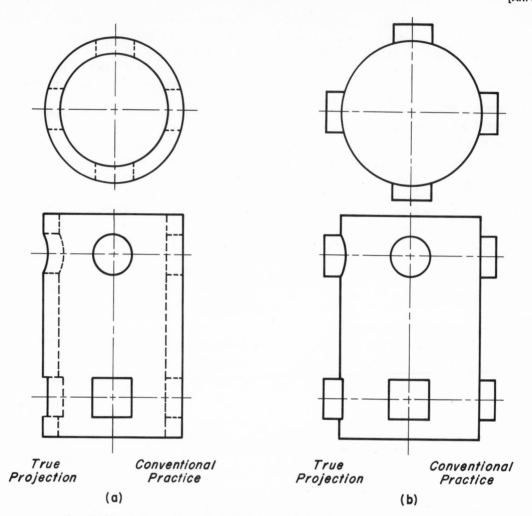

True Projection Conventional Practice

(a)

True Projection Conventional Practice

(b)

Fig. **7–25.** Intersection of relatively small holes or bosses with cylinders.

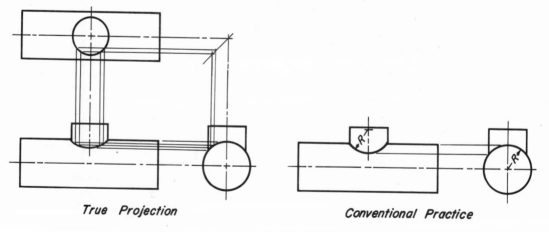

True Projection

Conventional Practice

Fig. **7–26.** Intersection of relatively large cylinders.

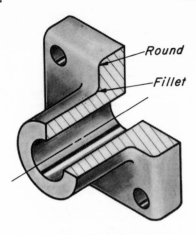

Fig. 7–27. Fillets and rounds.

the cracking and stress concentrations that occur with sharp corners due to unequal cooling rates. A rounded interior corner is known as a *fillet.* Exterior corners on castings are rounded off because a sharp corner in the cavity of the mold tends not to fill smoothly. A rounded exterior corner is called a *round.* Fig. 7–27 illustrates a fillet and a round.

Since fillets and rounds blend one surface into another surface, there is no actual intersection of surfaces to form a line, and the true projections of such an object often fail to convey the actual shape. Fig. 7–28 shows a hexagonal, dish-like object that could be an ashtray. Since all corners are rounded, the true projections of the front and

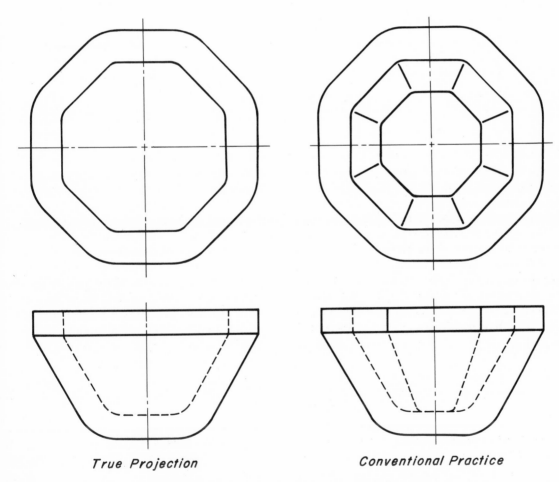

True Projection   Conventional Practice

Fig. 7–28. Conventional practice in rounded corners.

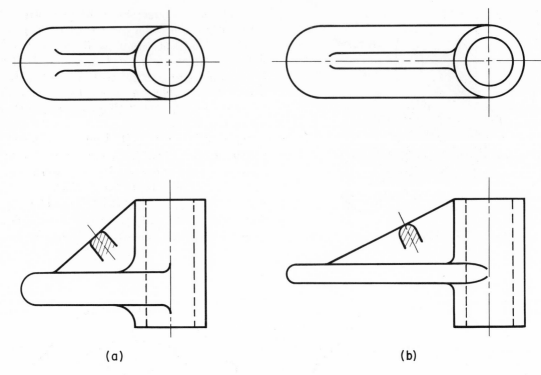

(a)   (b)

Fig. **7–29.** Runout lines.

top views show no lines except those representing the edge view of plane surfaces. The
result is two views that tell little about the actual
shape. Conventional practice is to show a line
where the surfaces would intersect if there were
no fillet or round. The true lines of intersection
are found by extending the plane surfaces. The
use of this conventional practice yields the views
as shown also in Fig. 7–28. These views are much
more descriptive of the real shape of the object.

The intersection of a round or fillet with a plane
or curved surface is difficult to show in true projection and hence has become conventionalized by

the use of runout lines as shown in Fig. 7–29. Fig.
7–29(a) shows conventional practice where the
cross section of the rounded portion would be a
rectangle with rounded corners. Here the lines
representing the edge views of surfaces terminate
in short arcs that curve outward from the surface,
ending at the line of tangency or intersection between the surfaces. These are called *runouts*.

Where the cross section of the rounded portion
would be more nearly an oval, these arcs at the
ends of the line turn inward as in Fig. 7–29(b).
However, they are still called runouts. In either
case, the runouts are normally drawn freehand.

Problems

7–1. Using a two-view drawing, show the front view
of the die-cast block in full section (Fig. 7–30).

7–2. Make a two-view sketch of the step pulley with
the front view in full section (Fig. 7–31).

7–3. Draw a third view in full section on a cutting
plane passing through the keyway (Fig. 7–32).

7–4. Using a two-view drawing, show the front view
in full section (Fig. 7–33).

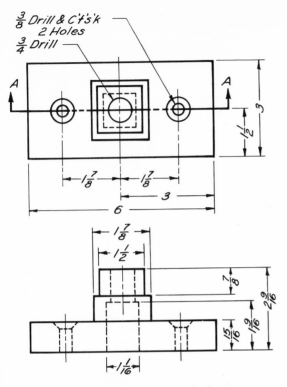

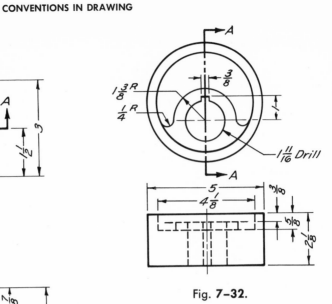

Fig. **7–32.**

Fig. **7–30.** Die-cast block.

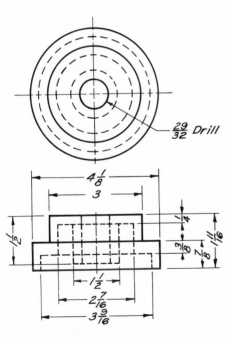

Fig. **7–31.** Step pulley.

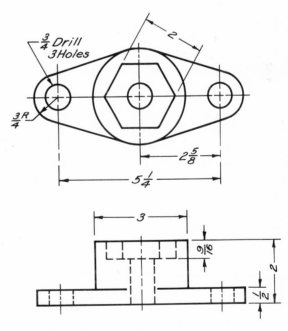

Fig. **7–33.**

7–5. Draw a half-section assembly of the bushing mount (Fig. 7–34).

7–6. Sketch two views of the cast iron (C. I.) block using the indicated offset cutting plane (Fig. 7–35).

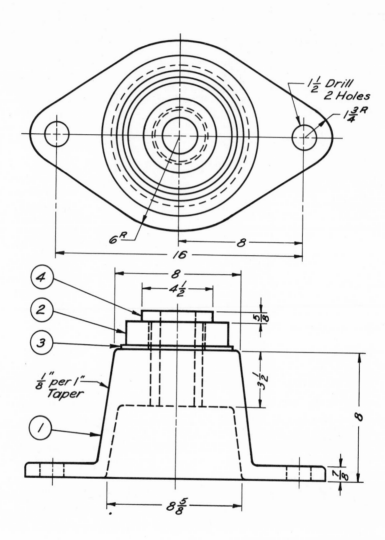

$1\frac{1}{2}$ Drill
2 Holes

$1\frac{3}{4}$R

6^R

8

16

4

2

3

8

$4\frac{1}{2}$

$\frac{5}{8}$

$3\frac{1}{2}$

$\frac{1}{8}$" per 1"
Taper

8

1

$\frac{7}{8}$

$8\frac{5}{8}$

BILL OF MATERIAL

PCMK	NAME	MAT'L	REMARKS
1	Housing	Cast iron	Fillets & rounds $\frac{1}{4}$R
2	Bearing washer	Steel	$6\frac{1}{2}$O.D. × $3\frac{1}{2}$ I.D. × $1\frac{1}{2}$
3	Washer	Fiber	7 O.D. × $3\frac{1}{2}$ I.D. × $\frac{1}{4}$
4	Bushing	Bronze	$3\frac{1}{4}$O.D. × $2\frac{1}{4}$ I.D. (See dwg.)

Fig. **7–34.** Bushing mount.

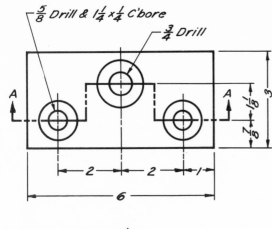

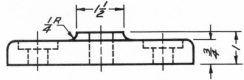

Fig. **7–35.** Cast iron block.

7-7. In a two-view drawing, represent the front view of the pulley in the form of a half-section (Fig. 7–36).

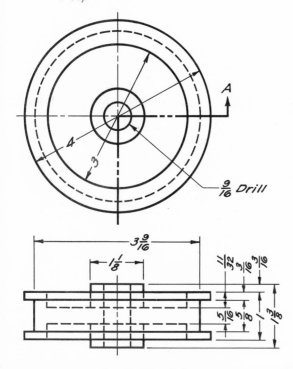

Fig. **7–36.** Pulley.

7-8. Make a two-view sketch showing the front view in section (Fig. 7–37). Use an offset section that will reveal all interior details.

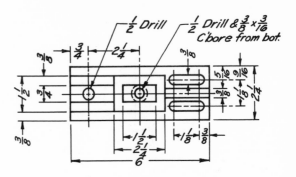

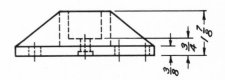

Fig. **7–37.**

7-9. Make a two-view drawing of the crank arm (Fig. 7–38). Show a revolved section that shows the I-shape of the arm.

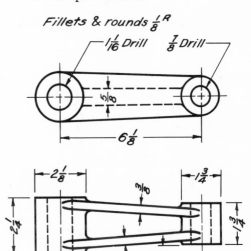

Fig. **7–38.** Crank Arm.

7-10. Make a two-view sketch showing Section *A–A* as a front view (Fig. 7–39). Then sketch Section *B–B* in its correctly projected position. Finally, show a revolved section at *C–C*.

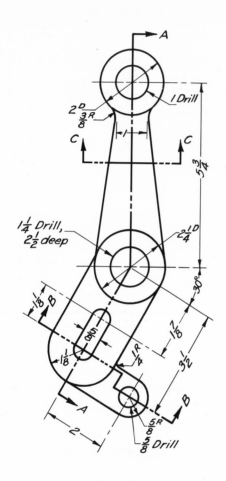

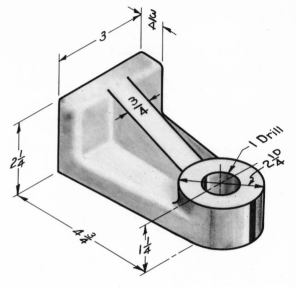

Fig. 7-40. Casting.

7-12. Make a two-view sketch of the bracket (Fig. 7–41). Show the correct positioning of the triangular shaped bracing ribs in the front view.

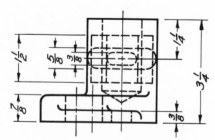

Fillets & rounds $\frac{1}{8}R$

Fig. 7-39.

7-11. Make a two-view sketch showing the front view of the casting in full section (Fig. 7–40).

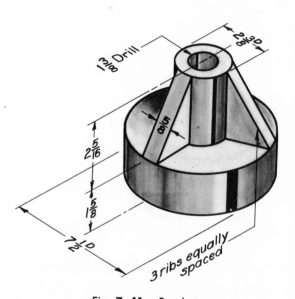

Fig. 7-41. Bracket.

7-13. Make a two-view drawing of the brace connector (Fig. 7–42).

7-14. Make a two-view sketch of the wheel (Fig. 7–43). Show the front view in section as indicated.

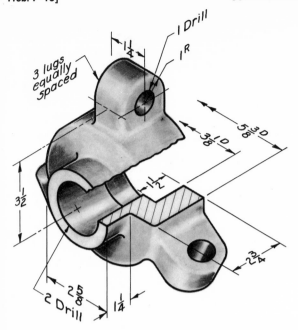

Fig. **7–42.**   Brace connector.

7-15. Make a two-view drawing of the casting, making the front view in section as indicated (Fig. 7–44).

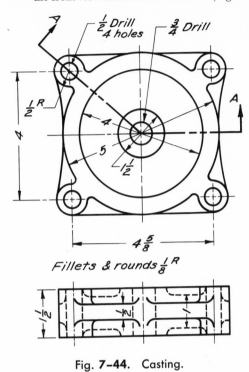

Fillets & rounds $\frac{1}{8}$ R

Fig. **7–44.**   Casting.

7-16. Make a two-view sketch of the alignment disk, showing the correct representation of the through holes in the front view (Fig. 7–45).

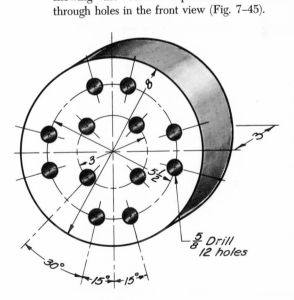

Fig. **7–45.**   Alignment disk.

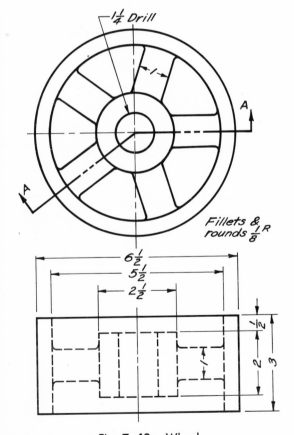

Fig. **7–43.**   Wheel.

7–17. Indicate by a sketch:
  a. A revolved section on a 1″-diameter cylindrical piece of steel bar stock. Break the ends
conventionally.

  b. A revolved section on a piece of 1″-square
steel bar stock. Break the ends conventionally.

  c. A break-out in a 1″-diameter piece of
wrought iron (W. I.) pipe.

7–18. Make a three-view drawing showing the right
side view in section as indicated (Fig. 7–46).

7–19. Make a three-view drawing of the intersecting
cylinders (Fig. 7–47).

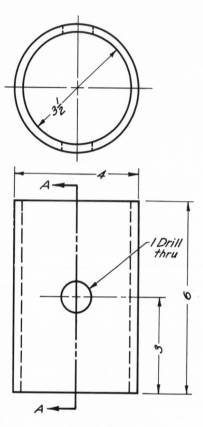

Fig. **7–46.**

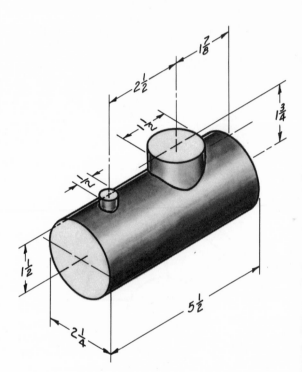

Fig. **7–47.**

8

PICTORIAL REPRESENTATION

8–1. INTRODUCTION

Multi-view projection as presented in Chapter 6 provides a means for accurately describing the true shape of complicated geometrical forms. Its use, however, is limited to those who understand orthographic projection theory. Frequently it is necessary to convey such information to persons unskilled in the reading of multi-view drawings. A form of graphics called pictorial representation is a means of accomplishing this. Somewhat similar in nature to photographs, these pictorial views show several surfaces of an object simultaneously.

While pictorials are used extensively in publications such as catalogs, sales literature, "do it yourself" assembly instructions, and maintenance manuals, they also frequently find technical application as a supplement to multi-view drawings. The engineer and designer often find the pictorial sketch a convenient means of visualizing their work as it progresses. It is of interest to note that the techniques described in this chapter form the basis for the construction of the majority of the pictorial drawings utilized throughout this text.

8–2. FORMS OF PICTORIAL REPRESENTATION

All pictorial representations may be classified into one of three broad divisions with further subclassifications as follows:

1. Axonometric
   a. Isometric
   b. Dimetric
   c. Trimetric
2. Oblique
3. Perspective
   a. One-point or parallel
   b. Two-point or angular
   c. Three-point

Pictorial representations may be constructed through the application of projection principles (auxiliary views or rotation), or they may be drawn directly, without the application of projection theory. In the former, the resulting pictorials are named *pictorial projections;* the latter are referred to as *pictorial drawings.*

Fig. 8–1 illustrates a simple cube as it might be drawn in each of the three divisions of pictorial

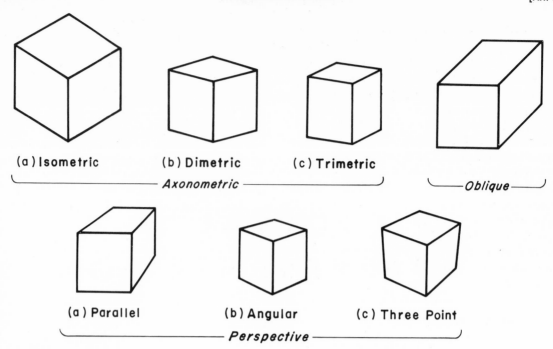

Fig. **8–1.** Divisions of pictorial representations.

representation referred to above. In actual practice several of the classifications have variations which result in differing representations of the cube. Such variations are discussed in detail in this chapter.

Selection of the form of pictorial representation to be used is dependent on the shape of the object, the space orientation desired, and how "true" or "pleasing" a pictorial is desired. While selection of the appropriate form of pictorial will be analyzed in detail in subsequent articles, some general observations are appropriate now.

Of the three forms of axonometric representation, trimetric results in the most pleasing pictorial, permits the greatest flexibility in spatial orientation, but is the most difficult to construct. Dimetric, while simpler to construct, is more restrictive in its orientation. Isometric is the simplest to draw, but has very limited object orientation possibilities, and is the least pleasing of the axonometric group.

Oblique representation, while permitting a wide variation in orientation, introduces much more distortion into the pictorial than any of the other classifications. However, when the object to be

represented has curved or irregular features in only one plane or in parallel planes, oblique is the simplest of the pictorial representations to construct.

Perspective provides the most pleasing and natural results, approaching that which a camera or the human eye sees. Perspective also permits the greatest flexibility in orientation of any of the pictorial representations. Of the three forms of perspective, parallel perspective is the most restrictive in object orientation, but is the simplest to draw. Three-point perspective is the most difficult to construct and, therefore, the least used. Angular (or two-point) perspective is the form most frequently used.

8–3. AXONOMETRIC PROJECTION

An axonometric pictorial projection may be defined as the resulting orthographic view when the three principal surfaces of the object are inclined to the projection plane. One method of accomplishing this is to rotate the object in space until it assumes a position similar to that of Fig. 5–4 on page 109. Then, the front projection becomes an axonometric pictorial. A second method is the establishment of an oblique projection plane known as an axonometric projection plane. The orthographic view on such a plane is an axonometric projection and can be obtained by drawing two successive auxiliary views.

Fig. 8–2 illustrates this latter technique, utilizing a cube for the object. For future reference, three edges of the cube have been identified as the principal axes of the object, and are specified in all orthographic views. The two auxiliary views are projected so that the angles α and β lie between 0° and 90°. There is an unlimited variety of possible axonometric projections dependent on values chosen for α and β. Only a selected few are normally used.

8–4. ISOMETRIC PROJECTION

Isometric projection is that form of axonometric projection in which the angles between each of the three principal planes of the object and the axonometric projection plane are equal. The result is that the three principal axes of the object form equal angles with the axonometric projection plane. Thus, the three axes are all foreshortened by the same ratio. To construct an isometric projection, utilizing the auxiliary view technique of Fig. 8–2, angle α must equal 45° and angle β must be 35° 16′. (Verification of these angles may be shown by trigonometry. The proof is based on the fact that a body diagonal of a cube must show as a point to obtain an isometric projection. Solution is left as a problem for the reader.)

The construction of an isometric projection of a simple object is illustrated in Fig. 8–3. In this, as in all isometric projections, the three principal axes are equally spaced with respect to each other. Thus, they are 120° apart. Any lines of the object drawn along the axes or parallel to the axes, are commonly referred to as *isometric lines*. The three planes formed by these axes, or any plane of the object parallel to them, are known as *isometric planes*. It can be shown that all of the isometric lines of an isometric projection are foreshortened in the ratio of approximately 0.81 : 1.00.

As illustrated in Fig. 8–3, hidden lines are omitted in a pictorial view. This is the normal

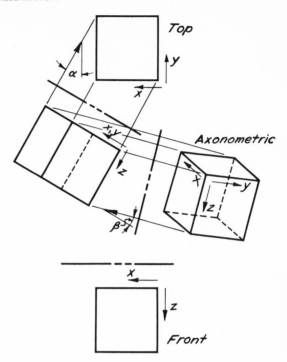

Fig. 8–2. Axonometric projection.

practice in all pictorial views, since the pictorial is an attempt to reproduce what is seen by the human eye or a camera.

8–5. ISOMETRIC DRAWING

In most applications of the isometric form of pictorial representation, projection techniques such as that of Art. 8–4 are not employed. The three equally spaced isometric axes may be laid out directly and used as a basis for construction. Also, the foreshortening effect is neglected and the isometric lines laid off true length along the isometric axes. This approach results in a pictorial similar to that of the isometric projection, except that the resulting pictorial is approximately 1.2 times as large as a comparable isometric projection. A pictorial constructed by this technique is known as an *isometric drawing*.

When it is necessary to consider foreshortening, the isometric drawing technique can still be used. However, lines along or parallel to the isometric axes must be laid off using an isometric scale which provides the 0.81 : 1.00 reduction in length. When

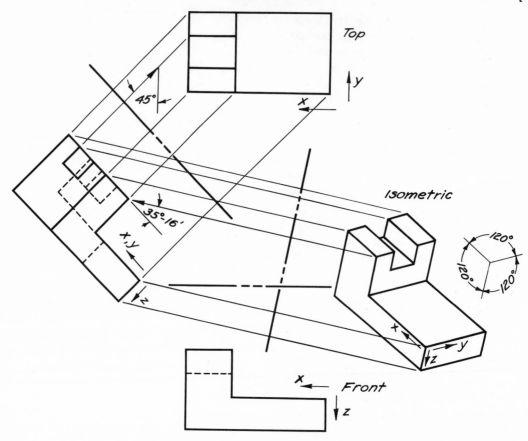

Fig. 8–3.   Isometric projection.

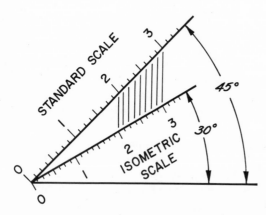

Fig. 8–4.   Isometric scale.

8–6. ISOMETRIC DRAWING OF A SIMPLE OBJECT

When constructing a pictorial, a multi-view drawing is usually available for obtaining size specifications. Fig. 8–5(a) presents the top and front views of a simple rectangular object of which an isometric drawing is to be made. The necessary steps in the construction of this isometric drawing are as follows. The three principal axes, x, y, and z, are first established on the multi-view drawings. Then, the corresponding, equally spaced isometric axes are drawn with the z-axis normally positioned vertically as shown in Fig. 8–5(b). Since the x- and y-axes are both inclined 30° to the horizontal, they may be drawn with the 30°–60° triangle. These axes (x, y, z) represent, respectively, the directions for measuring width, depth, and height. The three overall dimensions of the object are now laid off

such a scale is not available, it may be readily constructed following the procedure illustrated in Fig. 8–4.

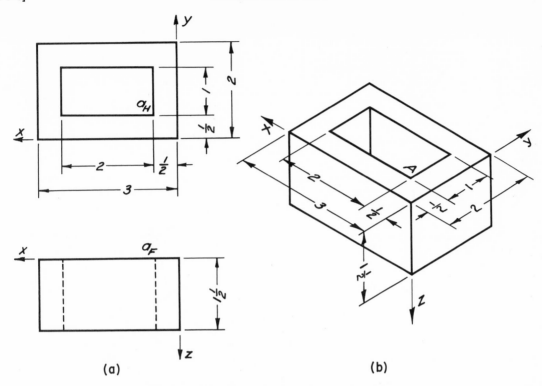

Fig. 8–5. Isometric drawing of rectangular object.

along these axes, and by drawing through the points so determined and parallel to the appropriate axis, the isometric drawing of the basic rectangular prism is obtained. Parallel lines on the object will always appear parallel in the isometric drawing. This principle will frequently simplify layout construction. To represent the rectangular hole, corner A is first located by laying off its width and depth coordinate distances on the pictorial drawing. Then through A, lines are drawn parallel to the isometric axes and equal to the width and depth of the hole. The hole is completed by drawing the remaining lines parallel to the proper principal axes. Hidden lines are omitted in the finished isometric drawing.

8–7. NON-ISOMETRIC LINES

As previously defined, an isometric line is any line of an object that lies either along or parallel to an isometric axis. Such lines appear in true length in the pictorial drawing. Any other line is

called a non-isometric line and does not appear in true length. It may appear longer or shorter than its actual length depending on its position. Since such lines do not appear in true length, the only way to construct them in an isometric drawing is to locate the two end points of the line, or any two points through which the line is known to pass, using the methods discussed in the next two articles.

8–8. BOX CONSTRUCTION METHOD

As an aid in laying out a pictorial, the object may be imagined as being contained in a rectangularly shaped box. The basic shape of the object is laid out on the surfaces of the box and the pictorial is completed. For example, assume an isometric drawing is desired of the octagonal prism with a square hole as shown in Fig. 8–6(a). The prism is first contained in a rectangular box, the boundaries of which are shown as dashed lines. Then a lightly penciled isometric drawing is made of this box, as

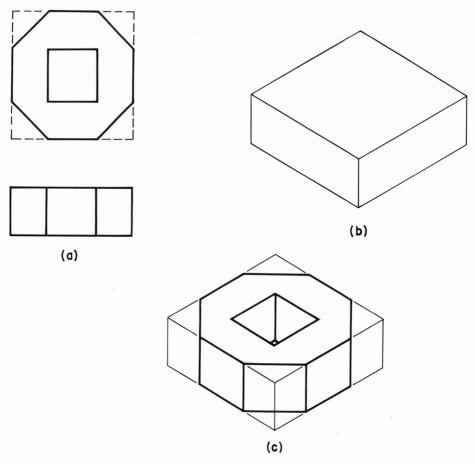

Fig. **8-6.** Box construction.

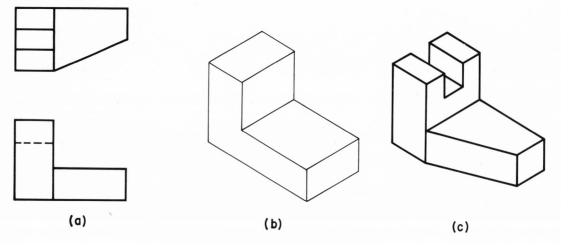

Fig. **8-7.** Composite box construction.

in Fig. 8-6(b). Since the edges of the box are iso-metric lines, the various corners of the octagonal prism may be readily located and its isometric pictorial drawn as in Fig. 8-6(c). A study of the completed pictorial drawing of this prism shows that the box method provides a technique for locating the end points of non-isometric lines. In some applications of the box method, it is more convenient to consider the object as contained in a combination of two or more boxes. Fig. 8-7(a) presents the top and front views of such an object. Fig. 8-7(b) shows the combination of boxes re-quired to contain this object, while Fig. 8-7(c) illustrates the completed isometric drawing.

The box method also serves as an aid in centering the pictorial on the paper. Since the object is entirely contained within the box, completion of the simple box construction shows the final location of the object before starting detailed construction.

8-9. OFFSET CONSTRUCTION METHOD

Certain objects do not lend themselves directly to the box method, and construction by offsets is more appropriate. Typical of such objects are those composed primarily of oblique planes or non-isometric lines. The offset method consists of determining the three coordinates (width, depth, and height) of various points with respect to an arbitrarily selected point, using these coordinates to locate the points, and then drawing the object by connecting the appropriate points.

Fig. 8-8(a) presents two orthographic views of an object appropriate for the offset method. To locate the base, ABC, of the pyramid in the pictorial, first establish x-, y-, and z-axes through the point C in both the orthographic and isometric views. The distances x_1 and x_2 are measured in the ortho-

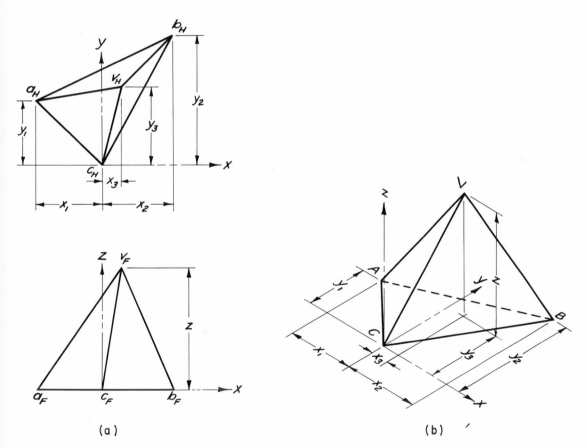

(a)   (b)

Fig. **8-8.** Offset construction.

graphic views and laid off along the corresponding axes in the pictorial as in Fig. 8–8(b). Offset distances y_1 and y_2 are next laid off similarly from the x-axis in the y-axis direction to locate points A and B. Since, in this example, all three points, A, B, and C, lie in the same horizontal plane, distances in the z-axis direction are zero. To locate the vertex V of the pyramid, the three coordinate distances, x_3, y_3, and z, are determined in the orthographic drawing and laid out parallel to the respective axes in the isometric drawing. The pyramid is completed by drawing lines VA, VB, and VC.

8–10. ANGLES IN ISOMETRIC

An angle projects in true size only when the projection plane is parallel to the plane of the angle. Thus, it is apparent that angles in the three principal planes of an isometric projection or drawing do not appear in true magnitude on the pictorial. Depending on their orientation, the angles may appear either larger or smaller than their true size.

To lay out an angle in an isometric drawing, the angle must be defined in terms of coordinates parallel to the isometric axes. The top and front views of Fig. 8–9(a) show certain features located in terms of angles. The object, exclusive of the angles in

question, may be laid out utilizing the box method as in Fig. 8–9(b). However, to construct the angles, coordinates a or b, and c must be determined from the multi-view drawing and transferred to the pictorial as in Fig. 8–9(c). Then the isometric view can be completed.

If it is necessary to construct many angles in isometric, isometric protractors are useful and they are available commercially. These protractors permit angles to be laid out directly on an isometric drawing, and the above construction is thereby eliminated.

8–11. IRREGULAR CURVES IN ISOMETRIC

Curves in an isometric drawing will not appear in true shape, and the offset method is readily adaptable to the isometric construction of these curves. Points are selected along the curve in the orthographic view and the coordinates of these points are determined. Then the coordinates are laid out on the isometric drawing, thus locating the points on the pictorial. Finally, these points are connected using an irregular curve. This procedure for constructing an irregularly curved surface is illustrated in Fig. 8–10. Arbitrary points 1 through 6 are selected along the front view of the

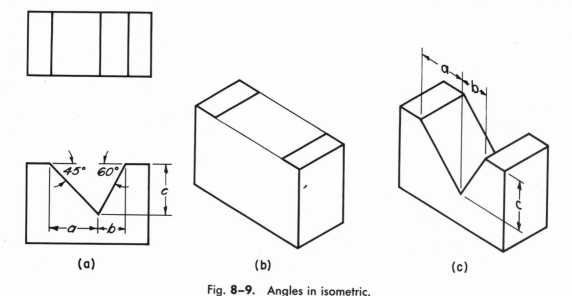

Fig. 8–9. Angles in isometric.

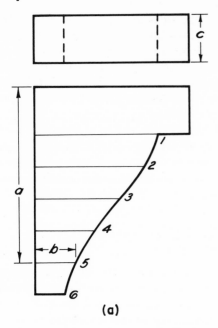

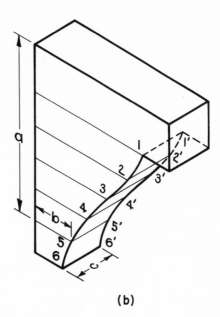

Fig. **8–10.** Irregular curves in isometric.

curve and their coordinates are determined. Typical coordinates a and b for point 5 are shown. All coordinates are transferred to the pictorial as shown, establishing the isometric curve 1–6. The back edge of the curved surface, 1'–6', may be plotted in the same way. However, it is simpler to lay off the thickness c of the object along an isometric line through each point to establish the curve 1'–6'.

8–12. CIRCLES AND ARCS IN ISOMETRIC

A circle, when drawn in isometric, appears as an ellipse. Construction of an isometric circle utilizing the offset method is illustrated in Fig. 8–11. Assume that the orthographic view [Fig. 8–11(a)] is the front view of a circle. To construct the isometric view [Fig. 8–11(b)], center lines are first laid

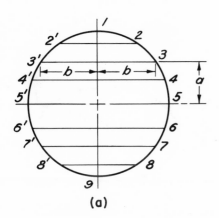

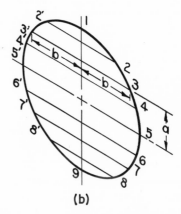

Fig. **8–11.** True isometric ellipse.

out. Since these center lines are isometric lines, any distance along or parallel to them is in true length. Random horizontal lines are drawn across the front view of the circle and transferred directly to the isometric, since height dimensions such as *a* are in true length. Then the horizontal distances, such as *b*, are transferred to the isometric to locate points on the circle. Using an irregular curve, the ellipse, representing the isometric circle, is drawn to complete the construction.

The true ellipse construction just described is seldom used in isometric drawings except when tangent circles are required. A method called the *four-center approximation* is usually substituted. This method, utilizing circle arcs drawn with a compass, is illustrated in Fig. 8–12. The circle to be drawn in isometric is shown in Fig. 8–12(a) (assumed to be a top view). A square circumscribing this circle is first drawn. The circle is tangent to the sides of the square at the midpoints. The square is next drawn in isometric and the mid-

points of the sides are located as shown in Fig 8–12(b). Perpendiculars to the sides are constructed from these midpoints as in Fig. 8–12(c) The points where adjacent perpendiculars cross establish centers of circle arcs with the radii as shown in Fig. 8–12(d). These circle arcs form the approximate ellipse.

In isometric drawings two of the points (centers) located by these perpendiculars from the midpoints lie at corners of the isometric square. However, in subsequent applications of this method to other forms of pictorials, this does not necessarily occur.

The similar constructions for isometric circles in the front and side isometric planes are shown in Fig. 8–13.

A comparison between the four-center ellipse and the corresponding true ellipse is depicted in Fig. 8–14. The four-center approximation is drawn with a solid line, while the true ellipse is shown by a dashed line. This difference sometimes results in undesirable conditions where the four-

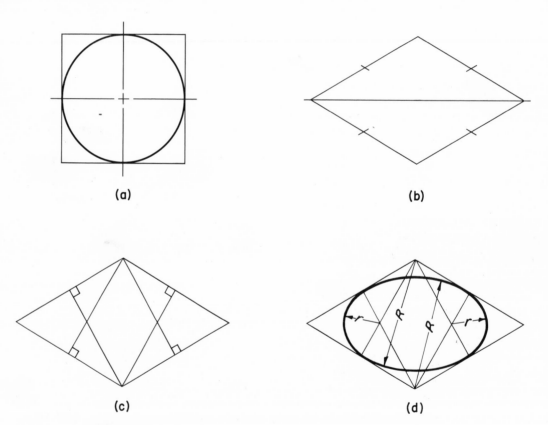

(a)   (b)

(c)   (d)

Fig. **8–12.** Isometric four-center ellipse construction—top view.

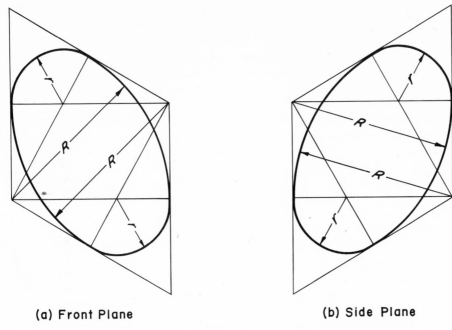

(a) Front Plane   (b) Side Plane

Fig. **8–13.** Isometric four-center ellipse construction—front and side views.

center approximation cannot be used. This occurs when two or more circles must be tangent to each other. Fig. 8–15 illustrates the results if the approximate construction is used under these circumstances.

Circle arcs are constructed in isometric using either of the methods described in this article. However, only that portion of the full circle is utilized which pertains to the specific application.

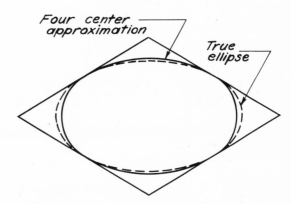

Fig. **8–14.** Comparison between four-center and true ellipse.

8–13. ALTERNATE POSITIONS FOR THE ISOMETRIC AXES

Occasionally it is desirable to view an object from a direction other than that presented by the usual arrangement of isometric axes thus far discussed. This is accomplished by rotating the isometric axes, but being careful to maintain the 120° equally spaced relationship among the three axes. Typical alternate positions for the isometric axes are shown in Fig. 8–16. In Fig. 8–16(a), the axes are positioned so as to view the object from underneath. This orientation of the axes is called the *reversed position*. Fig. 8–16(b) shows an axis orientation appropriate for an object of consider-

able length. This is known as the *horizontal position* of the axes.

8–14. ISOMETRIC SECTIONS

The primary intent of isometric drawings is to show exterior features, but occasionally a pictorial section can be advantageously employed to show interior details. A typical section is depicted in

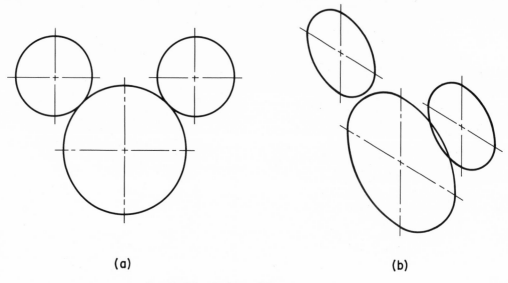

(a)   (b)

Fig. **8-15.** Failure of four-center ellipse.

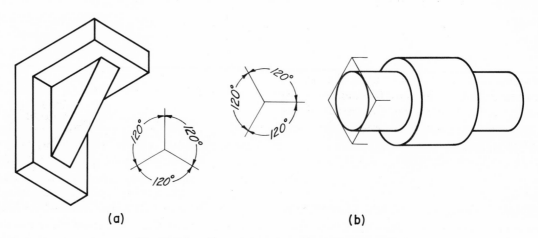

(a)   (b)

Fig. **8-16.** Alternate position for isometric axes.

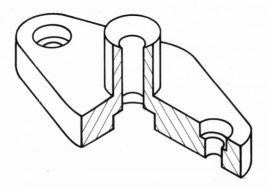

Fig. **8-17.** Section view in isometric.

Fig. 8–17. The cutting planes forming the section are usually isometric planes. Direction of the section lining is selected to achieve the best effect, but usually is in the direction of the longest diagonal of an imaginary square drawn on the cut surface.

8–15. DIMETRIC PROJECTION AND DRAWING

Dimetric projection is that form of axonometric projection in which two of the principal planes of the object form equal angles with the axonometric

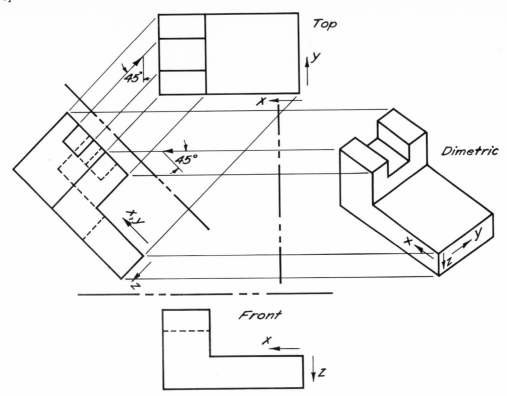

Fig. **8-18.** Dimetric projection.

projection plane, while the angle between the third principal plane and the axonometric plane is any other value. This object orientation results in only two of the three principal axes being equally foreshortened.

Dimetric projections can be constructed by successive auxiliary views using the method of Art. 8–3. There are many possible positions for the lines of sight which will result in equal foreshortening of two of the three axes. Fig. 8–18 presents a typical example where the value $\alpha = 45°$ assures the equal foreshortening of the x-axis and the y-axis. Angle β may be any angle other than 33°16′ (which results in an isometric projection). Larger values of β place greater emphasis on the horizontal surface of the object, while smaller values place greater emphasis on the side surfaces.

If the overall reduction in size obtained with the dimetric projection is not critical, the pictorial view may be constructed directly without the aid of auxiliary views. This construction, similar to that of the isometric drawing, is called *dimetric drawing*.

While the construction parallels that of isometric drawing, the three principal axes will not be equiangular. For each dimetric position a specified angular relationship exists among the three principal axes, as well as a specific foreshortening ratio for each axis. These properties have been determined, and tabled values are available for use in selecting appropriate dimetric drawing positions.[1] A few of the more convenient positions of the axes, along with the necessary foreshortening ratios, are illustrated in Fig. 8–19. A simple object is depicted in axonometric drawing in Fig. 8–20, utilizing position (c) of Fig. 8–19.

8-16. TRIMETRIC PROJECTION AND DRAWING

Trimetric projection is that form of axonometric in which the angles between the axonometric pro-

[1] Boehm, Paul F., *3 Dimensional Drafting*, "The Axonometric Universe" (John R. Cassell Co., Inc., 1953).

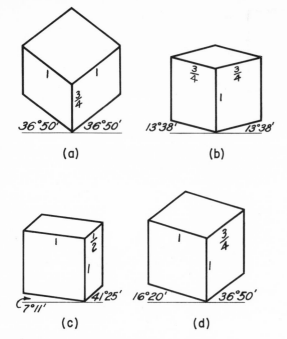

(a)   (b)

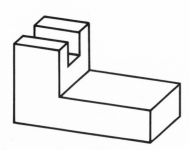

(c)   (d)

Fig. **8-19.** Typical positions for dimetric drawings.

Fig. **8-20.** Dimetric drawing.

jection plane and the respective principal planes of the object are all different. This orientation of the object results in a different foreshortening ratio along each of the three principal axes.

Construction of a trimetric projection follows the technique of Art. 8-3, as did dimetric projection. There are virtually an infinite number of possible positions for the lines of sight which will provide unequal foreshortening of the three axes. Decision as to which position to use is dependent on the surfaces of the object to be emphasized.

The construction of Fig. 8-21 is typical of a trimetric projection.

As with isometric and dimetric projection, trimetric projection has its counterpart, trimetric drawing. Angular relationships for the axes as well as foreshortening ratios for use in constructing a trimetric drawing have also been determined. These values are available in printed form.[2] Two of the more commonly used possible axes positions, and the corresponding foreshortening ratios, are shown in Fig. 8-22.

8-17. AXONOMETRIC PROJECTION DIRECTLY FROM ORTHOGRAPHIC VIEWS

Axonometric projection may be constructed directly from the original orthographic views rather than through the use of successive auxiliaries (or revolutions). This technique was originally developed by Professor L. Eckhart, of Vienna College of Engineering, in 1937.

To develop the theory for this technique, let us work backward and assume that the axonometric projection of a rectangular prism is given. From this projection the top, front, and side views of the prism and the orientation of these views with respect to the axonometric projection are to be obtained directly. Fig. 8-23 shows the axonometric projection of this prism with its principal edges coinciding with the x-, y-, and z-axes. The plane on which this axonometric projection is drawn is assumed to intersect the original top, front, and side projection planes along lines *BC*, *AB*, and *AC* respectively. These lines of intersection, *AB*, *BC*, and *AC*, are physically perpendicular to the y-, z-, and x-axes respectively in the illustration. (This perpendicular relationship is dependent on the properties of lines which are perpendicular in space, and is discussed in detail in Art. 10-4.) Thus, if the location of one of the three points *A*, *B*, or *C* is established on an axis, the remaining two points may be located by construction. Since lines *AB*, *BC*, and *AC* describe the axonometric plane, a variation in the location of this established point along its axis shifts the loca-

[2] *Ibid.*

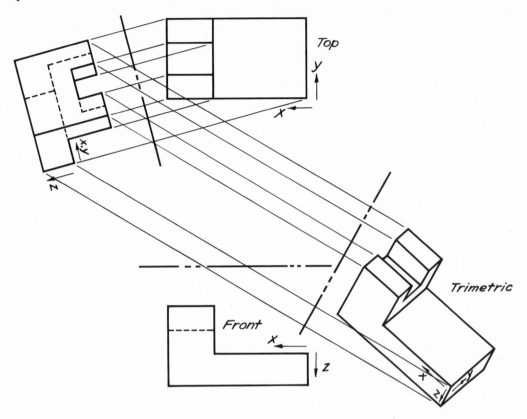

Fig. **8–21.**   Trimetric projection.

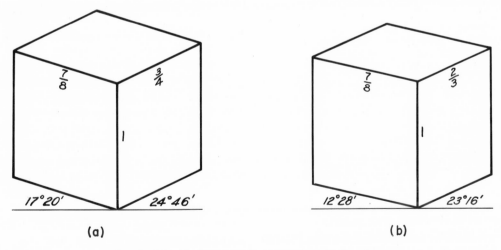

(a)   (b)

Fig. **8–22.**   Typical positions for trimetric drawings.

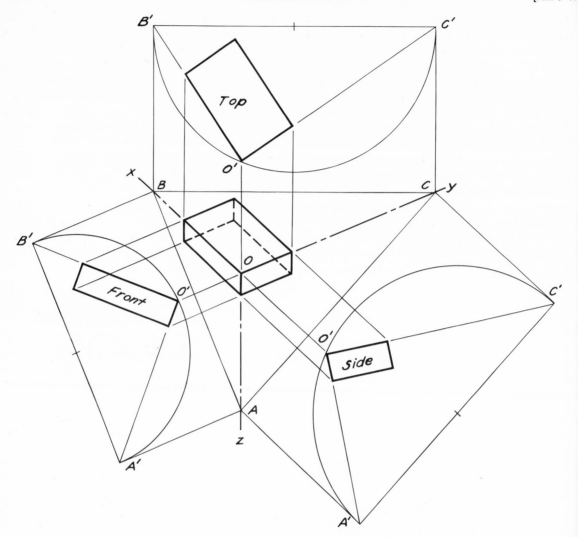

Fig. 8-23. Axonometric projection directly from orthographic views.

tion of the axonometric plane in space to a different, *but parallel*, position. Because the planes are parallel, such an arbitrary selection does not affect the pictorial projection.

The horizontal surface of the prism as shown in the axonometric projection appears in the same size and shape as would its projection on the horizontal projection plane, if this plane were shown in the axonometric view. Thus, it can be assumed that *OBC* is the horizontal projection plane and that the axonometric projection of the prism's horizontal surface is the image of the horizontal surface on *OBC*. To obtain a true-shape top view of the

prism, the plane *OBC* containing the horizontal projection must be shown in true size. Since plane *OBC* is in front of and above the axonometric plane, this true-size view is accomplished by rotating *OBC* downward about *BC* as an axis until it is in the axonometric plane. (To avoid overlapping of views, the axis *BC* has been redrawn at *B'C'* directly above its original position.) The x-axis and y-axis appear in true length in the revolved view, forming a 90° angle at *O'*. Thus *O'* is located on a semicircle having *B'C'* as a diameter. (Lines drawn from any point on a semicircle to the extremities of the diameter form a 90° angle.)

Axes $O'B'$ and $O'C'$ establish the orientation of the top view. Distances measured parallel to an axis of rotation remain constant during a revolution, hence the necessary points in the axonometric view may be projected perpendicular to the axes into the revolved view. The top view is completed by location of points on the axes $O'B'$ and $O'C'$, and by drawing lines parallel to these axes.

Following a similar procedure, the true sizes of the front and side views are also obtained as shown. Thus, a fixed relationship has been established between the basic orthographic projections of the prism and the axonometric projection for any given position of the principal, or x-, y-, and z-axes.

The reversal of this technique may now be applied to construct a pictorial projection directly from the suitably oriented orthographic views. The object of Fig. 8–3 will again be used to demonstrate the technique. First, the positions of the x-, y-, and z-axes must be arbitrarily selected, using judgment to emphasize the desired surfaces. One possible position for these axes is indicated in Fig. 8–24(a). Using these axes as a basis for construction, the following procedure establishes the necessary orthographic view orientation. Any point A is selected on the z-axis. Line AB is constructed so as to be perpendicular to the y-axis in the figure. In a similar manner, BC is drawn perpendicular to the z-axis, and CA is drawn perpendicular to the x-axis. To establish orientation for the top orthographic view, a semicircle is drawn using BC as a base and O is projected perpendicular to BC onto

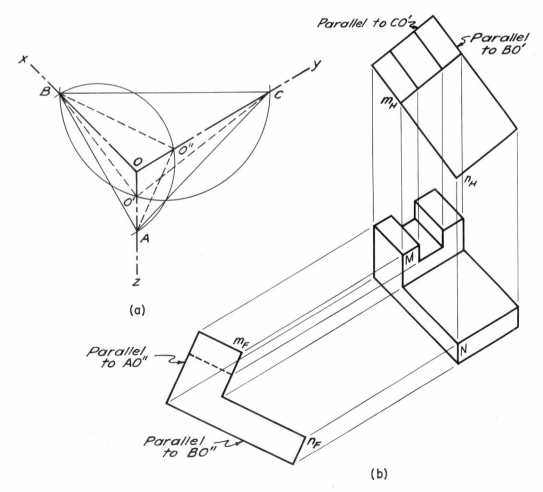

Fig. **8–24.** Axonometric projection.

this semicircle at O'. Lines BO' and CO' orient the top view. In a like manner, the front view orientation is determined by using AB as the base of a semicircle and projecting O perpendicular to AB onto the semicircle at O''. AO'' and BO'' now orient the front view. In a similar manner, the side view orientation could be determined, if necessary.

To construct the axonometric pictorial, the top and front views are now placed at convenient positions, as in Fig. 8-24(b). Orientation is as established previously. Any given point on the object is now projected from the front view parallel to the y-axis, and from the top view parallel to the z-axis. The intersection of these projectors locates the point on the pictorial view. Points M and N are typical examples. Repetition of this process will locate all points on the axonometric view to complete the pictorial.

If an object contains curved lines, they may be drawn by locating a series of points along the contour in the original orthographic views, projecting them into the pictorial, and connecting them with an irregular curve.

8-18. OBLIQUE PROJECTION

As stated in Art. 5-4, an oblique projection is formed when the projectors from the various parts of an object are parallel to each other but make an angle other than 90° with the picture plane. (Fig. 5-2 presents this concept.)

To construct an oblique projection, the top and side views of the object are necessary along with corresponding views of the picture (projection) plane as shown in Fig. 8-25. The direction of the parallel projectors in the top view is arbitrarily selected. All points in the top view are projected onto the picture plane parallel to the direction just established. The points where these projectors pierce the top view of the picture plane are now dropped vertically downward from the piercing points across the pictorial view area. In the side view, projectors are similarly drawn in an arbitrarily selected direction from all points of the object until they intersect the picture plane, and are then extended horizontally across the picture view area until they intersect the lines previously dropped from corresponding points. These inter-

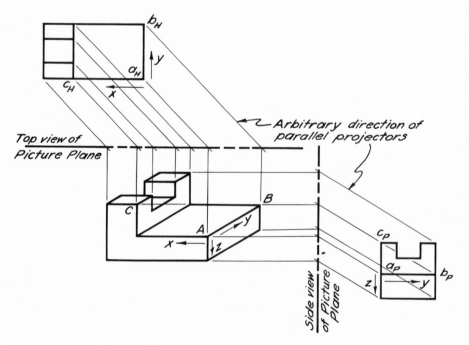

Fig. 8-25. Oblique projection.

sections form the oblique projection. Three typical points, A, B, and C, are identified on the drawing. Observe that distances and angles on the orthographic views parallel to the x-axis and z-axis also appear in true length (to scale) and true angle in the oblique projection, while distances in the y-axis direction are not necessarily true length and angles are distorted. Thus, any portion of the object parallel to the projection plane appears in true size (to scale) and shape in the oblique projection. The x-axis and z-axis will always intersect at a 90° angle in the pictorial, while the direction of the y-axis varies according to the directions selected in the top and side views for the parallel projectors. The projectors in the top and side views are not separate projectors but are in reality the top and side views of the same projectors. The arbitrarily selected angles are only the top and side views of the angle that the projector makes with the picture plane. The true size of this angle can be found by methods discussed in Art. 10-5. The selection of this angle, or, in actual practice the selection of the views of the angle, controls the angle with the horizontal of the y-axis and the amount of distortion in distances measured along it. Observe that in Fig. 8-25 the length of the depth axis appears to be exaggerated in the oblique view.

8-19. OBLIQUE (CAVALIER) DRAWING

Oblique projection construction may be made without the use of the projection technique described in the previous article. This is accomplished by drawing x-, y-, and z-axes so that the x-axis and z-axis are respectively horizontal and vertical (intersecting at 90°) while the y-axis (receding axis) is drawn at any angle with respect to the horizontal. Small angles for the y-axis emphasize profile surfaces of an object, while large angles emphasize horizontal surfaces. Distances along or parallel to the x-axis and z-axis are laid off in true length. Distances along or parallel to the y-axis are also laid off true length. (This is based on the fact that, when the true angle of the projectors with the picture plane is 45°, depth dimensions will project on the picture plane in true length.) An oblique drawing made in this manner is called a

cavalier drawing. By common usage, reference to oblique drawing is generally assumed to mean cavalier drawing unless otherwise stated.

8-20. OBLIQUE DRAWING OF A SIMPLE OBJECT

To illustrate the construction procedure for an oblique drawing, the orthographic views of the object of Fig. 8-5 (previously presented as an isometric drawing) are repeated in Fig. 8-26(a). An oblique drawing is required. Referring to Fig. 8-26(b), the x-axis and z-axis are first drawn perpendicular to each other. The y-axis is drawn at some convenient angle, in this example 45°, to the horizontal. True distances are laid off along the x-, z-, and y-axes respectively determining points which establish the width, height, and depth of the object. Appropriate lines drawn through these points and parallel to respective axes establish the rectangular outline of the object. To locate the rectangular hole, corner A is positioned by laying off its width and depth distances from the origin of the axes on the pictorial. Then, through A, lines are drawn parallel to the oblique axes and equal to the width and depth of the hole. The hole is then completed by drawing the remaining edges parallel to appropriate axes.

8-21. CIRCLES AND ARCS IN OBLIQUE

All lines, circles, arcs, or irregular contours of any object which lie in planes parallel to the oblique projection plane, will appear in true shape in the oblique drawing. If, however, they lie in any other plane they will not appear in true shape. Any irregular contour may be constructed in a receding plane by following the same offset technique described for isometric drawing in Art. 8-11, except that oblique axes are used.

If circles are required in either the xy (top) or yz (side) planes of an oblique drawing, they will appear as ellipses. In addition to the offset method, the four-center approximation, described in Art. 8-12, may be used. However, in the pictorial drawing the perpendiculars from the midpoints of the sides of the square do not necessarily intersect

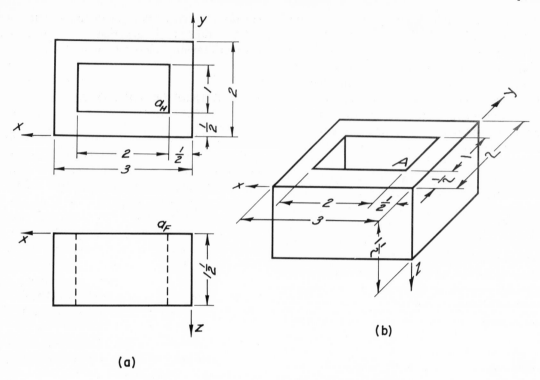

Fig. 8–26. Oblique drawing of rectangular object.

the corners of the square, as they do in isometric drawing. They may intersect either inside or outside of the square. Two typical examples are shown in Fig. 8–27. Fig. 8–27(a) shows the projection of a circle in the xy-plane; Fig. 8–27(b) shows the projection of a circle in the yz-plane. In both these examples, the y-axis (receding axis) is at 45° to the horizontal.

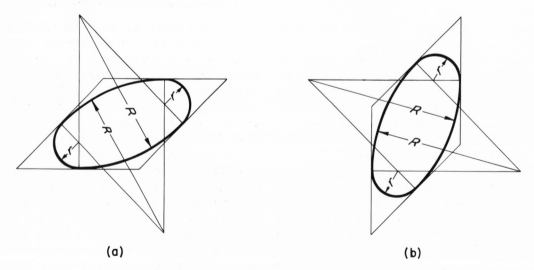

Fig. 8–27. Oblique four-center ellipse construction.

8-22. ORIENTATION OF OBJECTS IN OBLIQUE DRAWING

Oblique drawing provides more opportunities for possible alternate axes positions than does isometric. Fig. 8-28, utilizing a rectangular prism, shows the four basic positions and the resulting views. In any of these positions the angle which the receding axis makes with the horizontal can be varied to best represent a given object.

Care should be taken both in the selection of objects for representation in oblique, and in positioning the object in space for an oblique presentation. Objects having circles or irregular contours in one or in parallel planes are particularly appropriate for oblique, and should be positioned with the plane containing the irregular contours parallel to the projection plane, as in Fig. 8-29(a). If the object has irregular contours in more than one principal plane, or if such features must be placed in a receding plane for proper spatial orientation of the object, then an isometric drawing would result in a more pleasing presentation. A circle drawn in a receding plane appears distorted, as demonstrated by comparing Fig. 8-29(a) with Fig. 8-29(b). In positioning an object in oblique, the longest distance should be placed parallel to the projection plane so as to minimize distortion, as demonstrated in Fig. 8-30. While the object in each view has identical dimensions, Fig. 8-30(b) appears much longer than Fig. 8-30(a).

8-23. OFFSET PLANE METHOD FOR OBLIQUE DRAWING

Frequently an object is composed primarily of circular features located in parallel planes, as in Fig. 8-31(a). Such an object can best be constructed by drawing a center line in the y-axis direction and at appropriate locations laying off the centers for the various circles as in Fig. 8-31(b). Then, starting with the front surface of the object, the various circles are drawn using these centers as in Fig. 8-31(c). Finally, lines of tangency are drawn to the appropriate circles parallel to the receding axis to complete the object as in Fig.

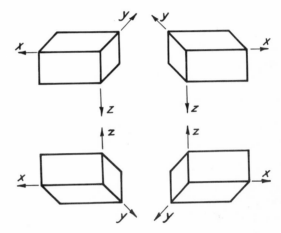

Fig. **8-28.** Basic axes positions for oblique drawings.

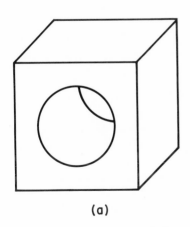

(a)

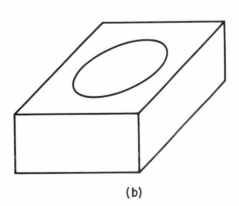

(b)

Fig. **8-29.** Position of object in oblique drawing—circles parallel to projection plane.

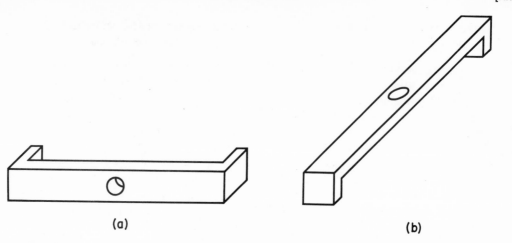

Fig. 8–30. Position of object in oblique drawing—longest axis parallel to projection plane.

8–31(d). Thus, the oblique drawing is constructed without the usual preliminary box construction.

8–24. CABINET DRAWING

Article 8–19 has discussed the construction of a cavalier drawing where the true angle between the projectors and the picture plane was 45°. In Fig. 8–32(a) a cavalier drawing is made of a wheel. If the angle the projectors make with the picture plane is greater than 45°, the resulting oblique projection will show the length of the receding edges of the object as less than their true length. This form of oblique projection has the advantage of reducing the distortion of apparent excessive thickness in the pictorial representation. When the reduction of receding distances becomes one-half, the resulting pictorial is known as a *cabinet projection*. Fig. 8–32(b) reproduces the same object as in Fig. 8–32(a), but shows it as a cabinet projection.

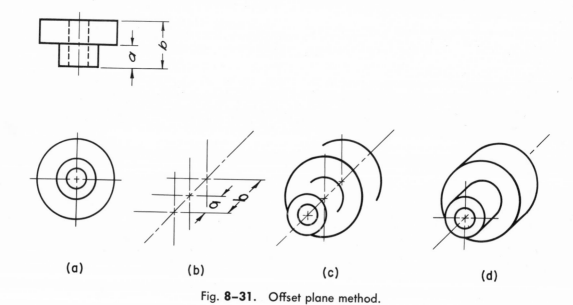

Fig. 8–31. Offset plane method.

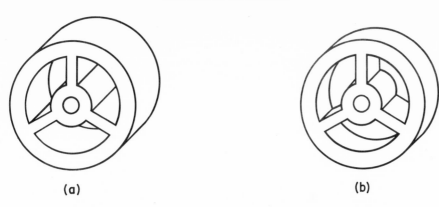

(a)   (b)

Fig. **8–32.** Comparison between cavalier and cabinet drawing.

In practice, instead of constructing the cabinet projection, a *cabinet drawing* is usually made. This is accomplished by following the procedure for construction of an oblique drawing with this one exception: all receding distances are laid off at one-half their actual values.

In some cases the one-half reduction just described for the cabinet drawing results in a pictorial which appears too thin. In such cases (in order to give a more pleasing appearance), reduction ratios ranging between 0.5 and 1.0 may be used as desired.

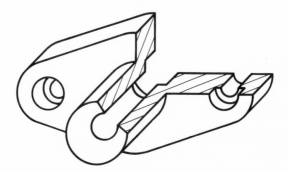

Fig. **8–33.** Section view in oblique.

8–25. OBLIQUE SECTIONAL VIEWS

As with isometric drawing, the primary intent of oblique pictorials is to show exterior details. Oblique sectional views, however, can often be used to advantage for showing interior details. As a typical example (Fig. 8–33), the same object previously drawn as an isometric section is now reproduced as an oblique section.

8–26. PERSPECTIVE DRAWING

Perspective is the truest form of pictorial representation, and the most pleasing since it reproduces the object as the human eye sees it. To better understand the principles of perspective projection, one might imagine himself looking through a picture window at an object. The window glass would represent a picture plane (P.P.) and the location of the eye is the center of projection (C.P.).

Lines of sight converge at the center of projection from all parts of the object and, in so doing, pierce the picture plane (window glass), thus creating an image of the object. This image is a perspective view. The farther an object is behind the picture plane the smaller the image appears, due to the convergence of the sight rays. In this respect, perspective produces the natural effect of objects appearing smaller as they move away from an observer. This is not true in other forms of pictorial projection.

Essentially, the construction of a perspective drawing is analogous to the construction of an oblique view except that convergent projectors are used rather than parallel projectors. Assume that the top and side views of an object, such as the rectangular prism of Fig. 8–34, are given. In each of these two views the picture plane appears as an edge. The top and side projections of the center of projection are selected and located in these views

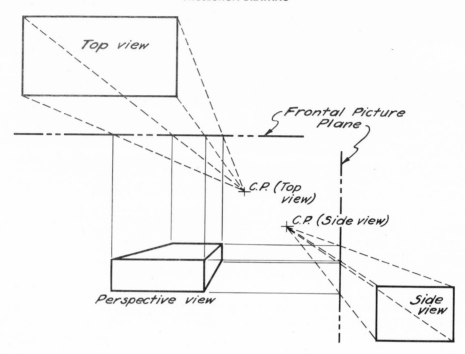

Fig. **8-34.** Perspective drawing.

as shown. Observe that, while the location of the center of projection is arbitrary, the center of projection must be the same distance in front of the picture plane in both the top and side views. Sight rays, shown by dashed lines, are drawn in each view to converge at the respective views of the center of projection. In each view, the points at which these lines of sight pierce the picture plane are extended across the perspective view, being drawn at 90° to the picture plane. The respective intersections of these extension lines locate points in the perspective view. As with most pictorial representations hidden lines are omitted.

8-27. BASIC CONCEPTS OF PERSPECTIVE DRAWING

Fig. 8-34 reveals certain basic principles inherent in any perspective pictorial. In this example, the object is behind the picture plane, and the resulting perspective representation is smaller than the actual object. A study of the drawing will show that, if the picture plane is placed so as to contain the front face of the prism, this face will

appear in true size in the pictorial. In fact, any portion of an object located in the picture plane will always appear in its true size and shape, since it is its own image. As features move back from the picture plane their perspective view is less than actual size. If any portion of the object should be in front of the picture plane, the perspective view of that portion is larger than actual size since rays from the center of projection strike the object and continue to diverge until they pierce the picture plane.

If any line lies in or parallel to the picture plane, its image maintains the same orientation as on the object (i.e., horizontal lines remain horizontal, vertical lines remain vertical, etc.). Any group of parallel horizontal lines on the object which are oriented other than parallel to the picture plane converge in the pictorial, and the lines, or their extensions, meet at a common point known as a vanishing point (V.P.). Groups of parallel horizontal lines have their vanishing point located on the horizon, an imaginary horizontal plane positioned at eye level. Each group of parallel horizontal lines has its own separate vanishing point. Parallel lines which are not horizontal also have vanishing points, but these points are not normally located on the horizon.

8–28. PERSPECTIVE NOMENCLATURE

To properly understand perspective theory, one must be familiar with the nomenclature associated with the points, lines, and planes used in the construction of a perspective drawing. Fig. 8–35 illustrates and identifies these various terms.

The *center of projection* (C.P.) is located at the eye of the observer. The *picture plane* (P.P.) is a vertical plane, usually located between the observer and the object. A horizontal plane through the center of projection is known as the *horizon plane.* The intersection of the horizon plane with the picture plane is the *horizon line* (H.L.). A horizontal plane, representing the surface of the ground, is called the *ground plane.* The intersection between the ground plane and the picture plane is the *ground line* (G.L.). A horizontal line of sight from the observer, perpendicular to the

picture plane, is called the *axis of vision.* Lines of sight from the observer to the object are *sight rays.* The piercing points of these sight rays with the picture plane produce the perspective view of the object. Two typical sight rays, in Fig. 8–35, show the location on the picture plane of the images, points 1′ and 2′, of points 1 and 2 on the object.

8–29. PERSPECTIVE OF A LINE

The ability to construct a perspective of a horizontal line is basic to drawing a perspective representation. One approach is similar to that of Fig. 8–34. Referring to Fig. 8–36, top and side views of a horizontal line *AB* are shown along with corresponding views of the center of projection, C.P., and the picture plane. By drawing sight rays in both views, finding where they pierce the picture plane, and extending these piercing points into the perspective view, the perspective view of *AB* is formed.

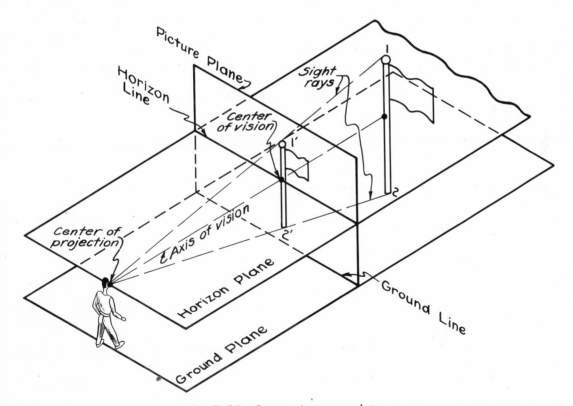

Fig. **8–35.** Perspective nomenclature.

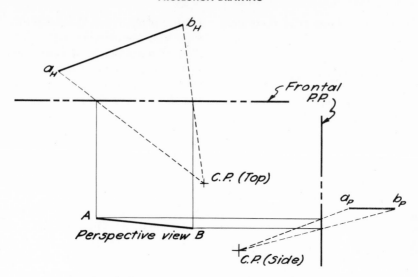

Fig. **8-36.** Perspective of a horizontal line.

An alternate approach is generally used to construct the perspective of a line. This approach eliminates the need for the side view of the picture plane and sight rays. This technique is illustrated in Fig. 8–37. The top view and an elevation view of the horizontal line AB are again shown along with the top view of the picture plane and the center of projection. Sight rays are drawn in the top view, and their piercing points with the picture plane are dropped down into the perspective view using construction lines perpendicular to the picture plane. Since AB is a horizontal line, if AB is prolonged infinitely beyond B, it will vanish at a point on the horizon called the vanishing point, V.P. Since the horizon line, H.L., represents the intersection of the horizon plane and the picture

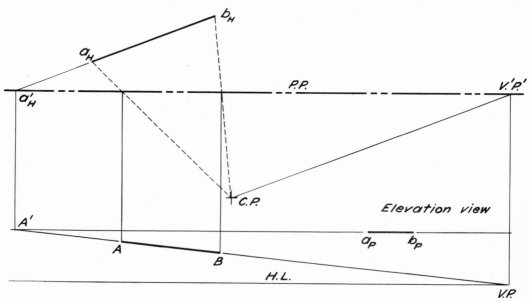

Fig. **8-37.** Perspective of a horizontal line—alternate method.

plane, it will appear in the perspective view as a horizontal line at eye level. The vanishing point of *AB* must lie on this horizon line. To determine the location of the vanishing point on the horizon line, a line is drawn in the top view through the center of projection and parallel to *AB*. This line has the same vanishing point as *AB* since parallel lines meet at a common vanishing point. Since the observer is at the center of projection, he can sight along this line and see the image of the line's vanishing point where the line pierces the picture plane. This is the top projection of the vanishing point and is labeled V.′P.′. This point is dropped down onto the horizon line in the perspective view, thus locating the perspective view of the vanishing point, V.P. This locates one end of the prolonged line *AB* in the perspective view. Now, if *AB* is prolonged forward from a_H in the top view, it intersects, or lies in, the picture plane at a'_H. This point

is dropped down into the perspective view. Since *A'* has the same elevation as point *A* on the object and also lies in the picture plane, its true elevation may be projected from the elevation view to obtain *A'* in the perspective view, which is the point where the prolonged line *AB* pierces the picture plane. The image of the prolonged line *AB* may be drawn in the perspective view from *A'* to the vanishing point, V.P. Points *A* and *B* in the perspective view now locate the perspective of the original portion of the line before its extension.

8–30. PERSPECTIVE OF A SIMPLE OBJECT

Assume that the object, picture plane, center of projection, and horizon line orientation shown in Fig. 8–38 are given, and the perspective view is desired. First, the sight rays are drawn from points

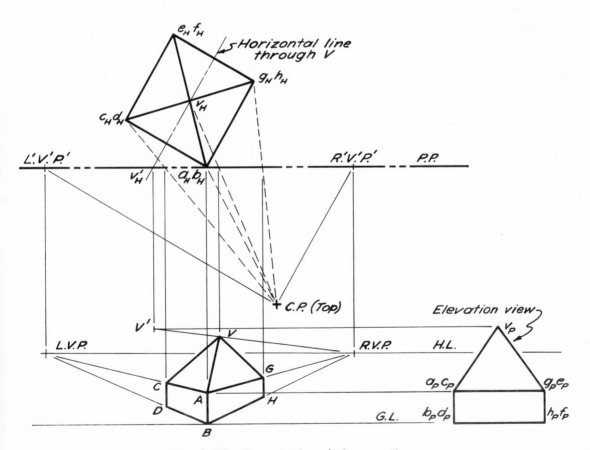

Fig. **8–38.** Two-point (angular) perspective.

in the top view to the center of projection (C.P.). The points where these sight rays pierce the picture plane are dropped into the perspective view. The precise location of the corresponding points of the object will later be established on these construction lines. The next step in the construction is to determine the necessary vanishing points. A line is drawn in the top view through C.P. and parallel to those horizontal lines of the object going back to the right. This line intersects the picture plane at the point labeled R.'V.'P.', and this intersection is dropped down onto the horizon line at point R.V.P., establishing the right vanishing point in the perspective view. In a similar manner the left vanishing point L.V.P., is determined for those parallel horizontal object lines going back to the left. While all object lines have vanishing points, the two just determined are sufficient for construction of this perspective.

Since the front edge, AB, of the object is located in the picture plane, it appears true length in the perspective view, and its elevation can be projected directly from the elevation view. Edges AC and BD converge at the left vanishing point and are so drawn. In a similar manner, edges AG and BH converge at the right vanishing point and are so drawn. Since points E and F are invisible in the final perspective, their location has not been determined.

To locate the vertex, V, a horizontal line is drawn in the top view through v_H and extended to the picture plane which it intersects at point v'_H. Since this horizontal line in the top view was drawn parallel to the family of horizontal lines that converge to the right vanishing point, this line will also pass through the right vanishing point. Point V' is located in the perspective view by dropping a construction line from v'_H and locating V' at its true elevation along this line. The perspective view of the horizontal line is then drawn from V' to the right vanishing point. V can now be located on this line. Pyramid edges VG, VA, and VC are now drawn to complete the picture.

This form of perspective construction is often called *two-point perspective* because it utilizes the two vanishing points. This construction is also called *angular perspective* since the top view of the object is oriented with no face parallel to the picture plane.

If the object is oriented as in Fig. 8–39 so that face $ACDB$ is parallel to the picture plane and the object is to the left of the center of projection, the left vanishing point will be located at infinity and lines AC and BD will appear parallel on the perspective view. Since such a construction results in only one vanishing point (in this example, the right vanishing point) it is known as a *one-point perspective*. Since one face of the object is parallel to the picture plane, it is also referred to as a *parallel perspective*.

8–31. PARAMETERS FOR A PERSPECTIVE DRAWING

When first laying out a perspective construction there are several variables to be arbitrarily selected, and these all have an effect upon the final appearance. First of these is the orientation of the top view. Rotation of this view for any given center of projection will vary the emphasis between side surfaces of the object; i.e., it will show one surface to better advantage than another. Shifting the center of projection left or right has much the same effect as does rotation of the top view.

Except for one restriction, the center of projection may be as close to or as far away from the picture plane as desired. Moving away from the picture plane moves the vanishing points further out on the horizon line, thus reducing the amount of foreshortening effect. In moving the center of projection toward the picture plane, the angle between the extreme lines of sight *must* not exceed 45° and preferably should be not more than 30°. A greater angle produces distortion.

Location of the horizon line is another variable. Usually it is placed at normal eye level above ground with respect to an elevation view. Raising the horizon line produces the effect of looking down on an object (bird's eye view); lowering it produces the effect of looking up at the object (worm's eye view).

8–32. PICTORIAL SKETCHING

The engineer and scientist find pictorial sketching a ready means for conveying ideas to other people. Pictorial sketches are also useful in the preliminary phases of design and as an aid in

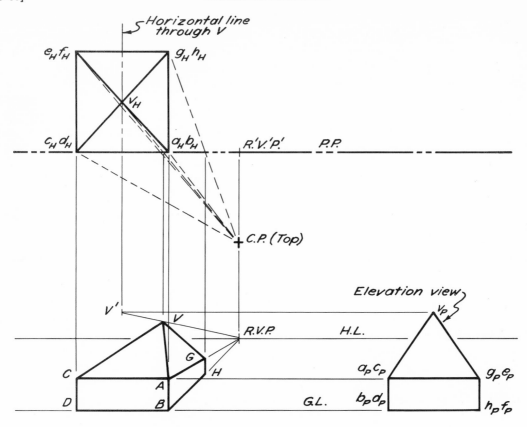

Fig. **8–39.** One-point (parallel) perspective.

making computations. Pictorial sketches may be made by utilizing any of the forms of pictorial representation presented in this chapter, but usually they take the form of isometric or oblique drawings. The principles of both of these forms of pictorial drawing have been presented in previous articles, and are equally appropriate for pictorial sketching. In the following two articles, these principles are briefly reviewed as they apply to sketching.

8–33. ISOMETRIC SKETCHES

The isometric sketch is constructed on three axes separated by 120°. Usually the height axis is vertical, with the width axis receding to the left and the depth axis receding to the right. If the upper face of the object is to be shown, the width and depth axes are drawn above the horizontal

as in Fig. 8–5(b). If the bottom face is to be shown, then the width and depth axes are drawn below the horizontal, resulting in the reversed axes position of Fig. 8–16(a). True width, height, and depth are laid off along the width, height, and depth axes respectively.

All three faces of the isometric sketch are distorted, and a circle in any of the three faces appears as an ellipse. These ellipses are made by first sketching the enclosing square in isometric, and then sketching the ellipse tangent at the midpoints of the sides of the square. Sketching the enclosing square first in isometric is necessary to insure the correct orientation of the ellipse in the proper plane. Fig. 8–40 illustrates a technique for sketching the ellipse in each of the isometric planes. Referring to Fig. 8–40, the first step is to sketch the enclosing square in the appropriate isometric plane. Next, locate the midpoints of each side of

²⁄₃ long; ¾ short

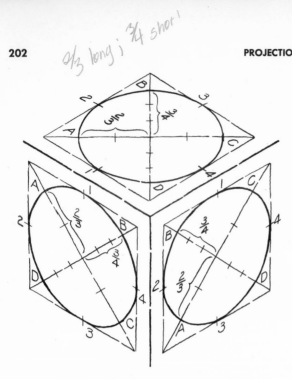

Fig. **8-40.** Sketching an isometric ellipse.

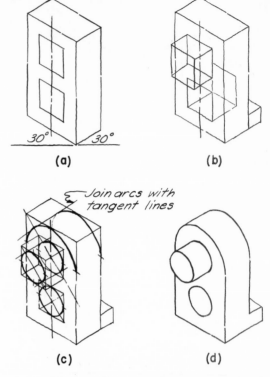

Fig. **8-42.** Development of an isometric sketch.

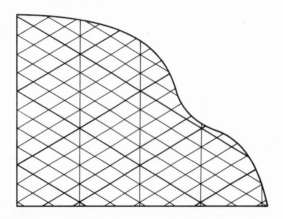

Fig. **8-41.** Isometric sketch paper.

the square, points 1, 2, 3, and 4. The ellipse will be tangent to the square at these four points. The diagonals of the square are lightly sketched. On the long diagonal the points A and C are located at $\frac{2}{3}$ of half of the diagonal. In a similar manner, locate points B and D at $\frac{3}{4}$ of half of the short diagonal. Long arcs are sketched through B and D, while short arcs are sketched through A and C.

These arcs are joined to complete a smooth ellipse. Isometric sketch paper, commercially available, has the isometric axes printed, usually at $\frac{1}{2}$- or $\frac{1}{4}$-inch intervals. Such paper, as shown in Fig. 8-41, is a great aid in sketching lines parallel to the isometric axes and in maintaining proper proportion.

The steps in the development of an isometric sketch are illustrated in Fig. 8-42. First, the object is blocked in as in Fig. 8-42(a), including the isometric squares for holes and bosses. The bosses, tongues, etc., are then extended out from the basic shape and the holes, grooves, etc., are depressed with boxing-in lines [Fig. 8-42(b)]. The various circles and circle arcs are outlined as ellipses in the appropriate isometric squares, and arcs are joined with tangent lines as in Fig. 8-42(c). Finally, construction lines are erased and outlines darkened to give the final isometric sketch, Fig. 8-42(d).

8–34. OBLIQUE SKETCHES

Objects which have an irregular or circular face, or several circular faces occurring in parallel planes, can usually be best represented by an oblique drawing. Since all faces parallel to the projection plane appear in true shape, irregular and circular faces of the object should be oriented parallel to the projection plane as in Fig. 8–29. Although of secondary importance to placing the circular face parallel to the projection plane, the object should also be oriented so that its long axis is parallel to the projection plane (Fig. 8–30). Considerable visual distortion occurs along the depth axis of an oblique drawing and this distortion can be reduced by turning the object so that the longest distance is either width or height with the least distance being laid off along the depth axis. Another way of reducing the visual distortion along the depth axis is by actually reducing the depth distance by one-half, as in cabinet drawings [Fig. 8–32(b)].

The oblique sketch is built on three axes (Fig. 8–28), usually with the width axis horizontal, the height axis perpendicular to the width axis (vertical), and the depth axis receding at any convenient angle above or below the horizontal to the left or right depending on the faces of the object to be emphasized. True width, height, and depth distances are laid off along the width, height, and depth axes respectively.

The steps in the construction of an oblique sketch are illustrated in Fig. 8–43. First, the object

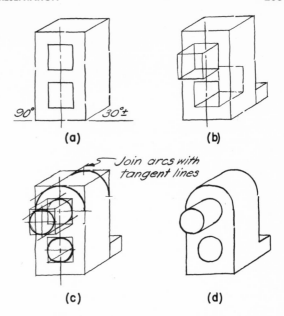

Fig. 8–43. Development of an oblique sketch.

is blocked in, including boxing-in squares for holes and bosses as in Fig. 8–43(a). The bosses, tongues, etc., are next extended out from the basic shape and the holes, grooves, etc., are depressed with boxing-in lines [Fig. 8–43(b)]. Circles and circle arcs are outlined in the boxing-in squares, and arcs are joined with tangent lines as in Fig. 8–43(c). Finally, construction lines are erased and the outline is darkened to give the final oblique sketch, Fig. 8–43(d).

Problems

Problems 8–1 through 8–19 (Figs. 8–44 through 8–62) are primarily intended for axonometric or oblique representation.

Selection of the appropriate division for presentation of the pictorial representation may be made by the instructor or left to the discretion of the student. In all problems, the object should be oriented so as to show its shape to best advantage, following the recommendations set forth in this chapter.

Problems 8–20 through 8–25 (Figs. 8–63 through 8–68) are primarily intended for perspective representation. For each problem the location has been given of the picture plane, horizon line, ground line, and center of projection.

8-1.

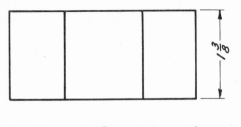

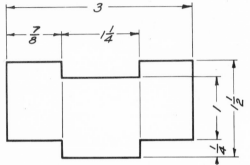

Fig. **8-44.**   Guide block.

8-3.

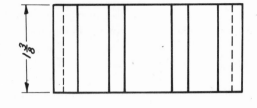

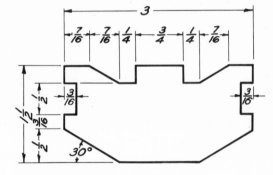

Fig. **8-46.**   Space gage.

8-2.

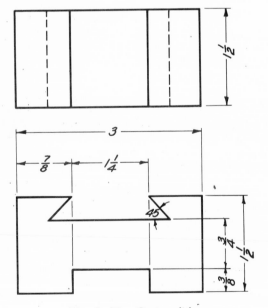

Fig. **8-45.**   Center slide.

8-4.

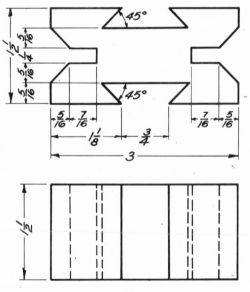

Fig. **8-47.**   V block slide.

8–5.

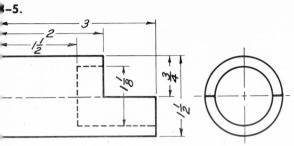

Fig. **8–48.**   Inset gage.

8–6.

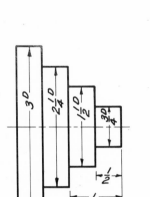

Fig. **8–49.**   Multiple stop gage.

8–7.

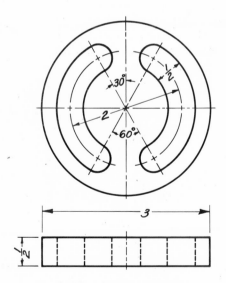

Fig. **8–50.**   Sector separator.

8–8.

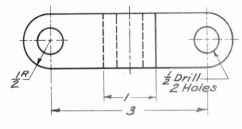

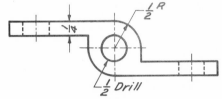

Fig. **8–51.**   Offset support.

8–9.

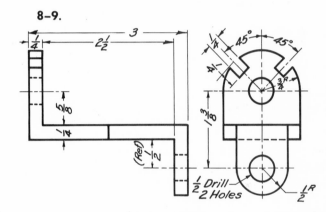

Fig. **8–52.**   Offset guide.

8–10.

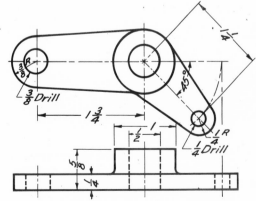

Fig. **8–53.**   Double arm rocker.

8-11.

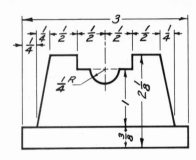

Fig. **8-54.** Bearing block.

8-12.

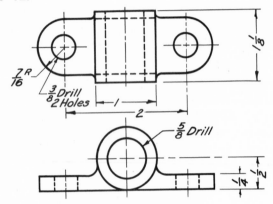

Fig. **8-55.** Light bearing.

8-13.

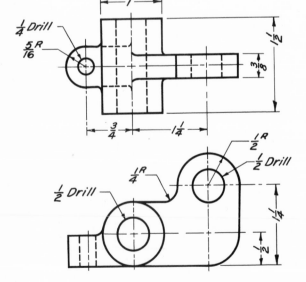

Fig. **8-56.** Bearing bracket.

8-14.

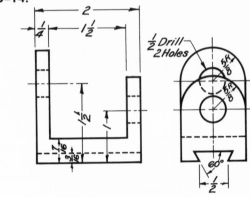

Fig. **8-57.** Slide bearing.

8-15.

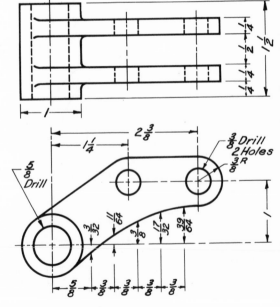

Fig. **8-58.** Twin-arm bearing bracket.

8-16.

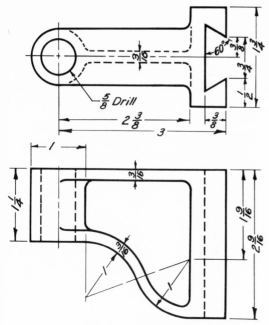

Fig. **8-59**. Slide guide.

8-18.

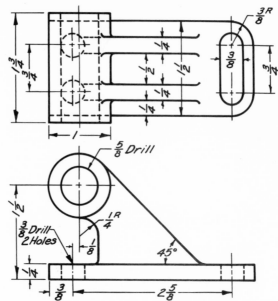

Fig. **8-61**. Bearing bracket.

8-17.

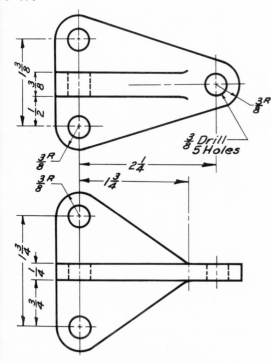

Fig. **8-60**. Anchor plate.

8-19.

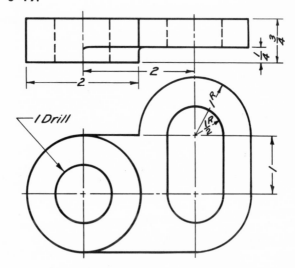

Fig. **8-62**. Floating shaft guide.

8-20.

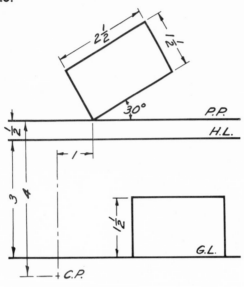

Fig. **8-63.**

8-22.

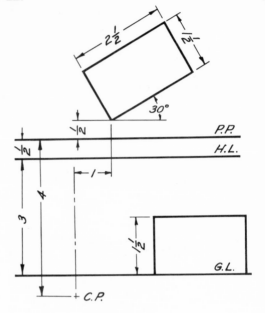

Fig. **8-65.**

8-21.

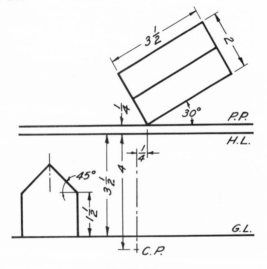

Fig. **8-64.**

8-23.

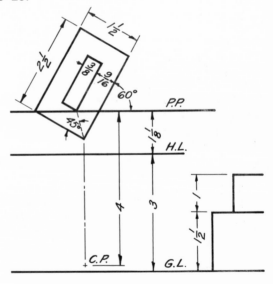

Fig. **8-66.**

8-24.

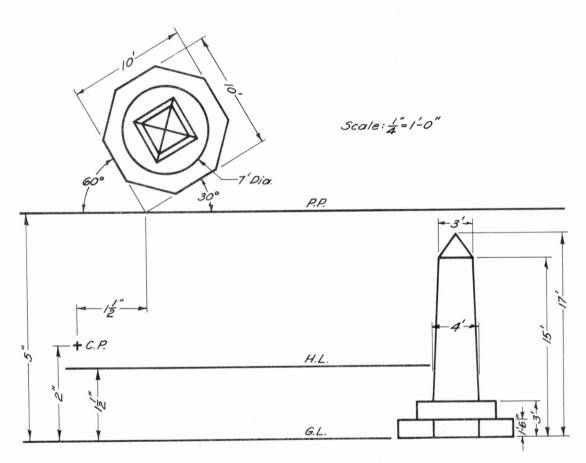

Fig. 8-67.

8-25.

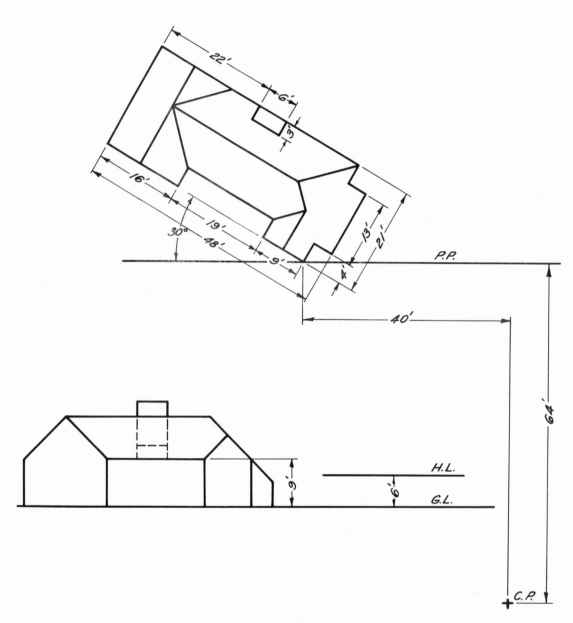

Fig. **8-68.**

III

SPATIAL ANALYSIS

9

BASIC SPATIAL
RELATIONS

9-1. INTRODUCTION

A considerable portion of the problems which confront an engineer are three-dimensional, or spatial, in nature and usually lend themselves readily to graphical solution as well as to the customary mathematical approach. A graphical solution, because of its pictorial nature, frequently permits a clearer understanding of the total problem and the interrelationships of its component parts.

Engineering problems are, more often than not, complex in nature. In the process of problem analysis and solution, such complex problems are generally broken down, or reduced, to simple basic components. The final solution is reached by the proper sequential solution of the basic components of the total problem. Graphic solutions, in this same sense, may be reduced to one or more basic spatial problems.

Some simple, practical examples of basic spatial problems are: (a) the determination of the necessary length for a cable to extend between any two points; (b) whether or not the four corners of a

bulkhead all lie in the same plane; (c) the true shape of that bulkhead; (d) the location and size of an opening to admit a control cable through a partition. Expressed in basic point-line-plane relations, these problems involve the determination of (a) the distance between two points, (b) whether a point lies in a plane, (c) the true shape of a surface, or (d) the location of the intersection point between a line and a surface. This chapter covers these and other basic relations fundamental to the solution of spatial problems by the application of the principles of orthographic projection.

It should be noted that various problems frequently lend themselves to more than one method of solution. No attempt will be made here to discuss all methods of solution. Additional methods can be developed through the application of basic principles in the analysis of the particular problem involved.

9-2. POINTS

The representation of corners of objects as points has been discussed in Art. 6–5. In the solution of spatial problems, the engineer generally isolates the points, lines, and/or surfaces that are involved from the complete structure, machine, linkage, etc. Thus a corner becomes simply a point in space and an edge becomes a line in space. Since the graphic representation of any line, plane, or other surface involves the representation of points, the first step in the solution of any spatial problem is the graphic location of these points.

In third angle projection, a point is represented (located) by establishing its distance below a horizontal plane, its distance to the rear of a frontal plane, and its distance to the left (or right) of a profile plane, as in Fig. 9–1. These planes then become the principal planes of the particular problem. Fig. 9–1(a) is a pictorial illustration of the spatial conditions and Fig. 9–1(b) shows the orthographic projections of two points in space. The nomenclature of point identification shown in Fig. 9–1 is the system used throughout this text. The actual point in space is referred to in the text and labeled in a pictorial view with a capital letter. The projections of the point are labeled with lower case letters; i.e., A is the point in space while a_H, a_F, and a_P are the horizontal (top), frontal (front), and profile (side) projections, respectively, of the point A. The words "horizontal," "frontal," and "profile" are used in the following discussions in preference to "top," "front," and "side" because they specifically recall the plane of projection used for a particular view.

The spatial relations of a system of two or more points may be represented by either of two methods. In the first method all points are located with respect to their distances from the horizontal, frontal, and profile planes, just as point A is established in Fig. 9–1. In the second method, a base, or control, point is located with respect to the horizontal, frontal, and profile planes, and all other points are located by showing their position with respect to the base point. This second method is shown in Fig. 9–1 where point B is located with respect to point A. The selection of the method to use for representing a system of points in any particular problem depends upon the conditions governing the problem. If the relations of the points to the reference planes are more important than the relations of the points to a base point, the first method is used. However, if the relations of the points to a base point are the more critical relations, the second method is used.

9–3. LINES

Lines in space can be classified in three general categories according to their position relative to the principal planes of projection, viz., normal lines, inclined lines, and oblique lines.

A *normal* line is a line that is perpendicular to one of the principal planes of projection, hence it is parallel to the other two principal planes. It is named after the two principal planes to which it is parallel. Fig. 9–2 shows the three specific normal lines. The frontal-profile line in Fig. 9–2(a) is commonly called a *vertical* line. The other two normal lines could simply be called horizontal lines, but the complete name is much more descriptive of their position in space.

An *inclined* line is a line that is parallel to only one of the principal planes of projection and inclined to the other two principal planes. Again it is named after the plane to which it is parallel. Fig. 9–3 shows the three specific inclined lines.

An *oblique* line is any line other than an inclined or normal line. It is not parallel to any principal plane. Fig. 9–4 shows an oblique line.

9–4. DIRECTION OF A LINE

A given straight line is easily located by arbitrarily selecting two points through which the line passes, as in Figs. 9–2, 9–3, and 9–4. Many times, however, only one such point may be known. In such a case, the direction and slope of the line must be known in order to locate the line. One method of giving the direction of a line is to give its azimuth (or bearing).

Azimuth, as used by map makers and by the U. S. Army, is defined as an angle measured in a horizontal plane in a clockwise manner from some established base direction which can be either north or south. In present-day usage, north is the most common base direction and will be used in this text. Since azimuth is measurable only in a horizontal plane, it will be shown and measured only in the horizontal (top) view of a line. The appearance of the frontal (front) view will not affect the azimuth in any manner. Fig. 9–5 shows

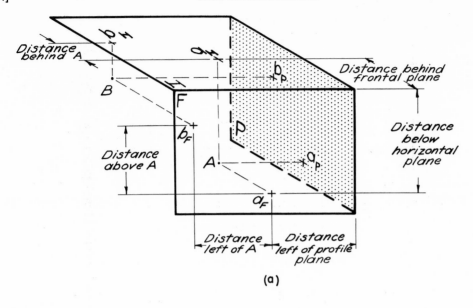

(a)

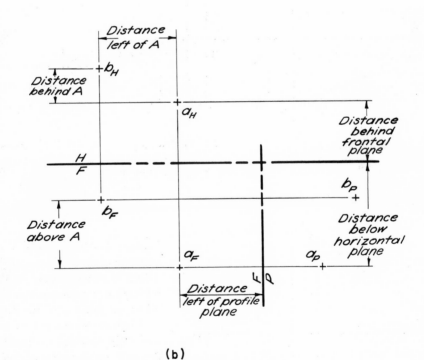

(b)

Fig. **9–1.** Representation of a point.

the azimuths of three different lines. Unless otherwise noted, north is assumed as the direction pointing to the top of the drawing. Note that both lines *DC* and *EC* have the same azimuth.

Bearing is defined as an angle measured in a horizontal plane either east or west of north-south as shown by several examples in Fig. 9–6. The magnitude of a bearing never exceeds 90°. A

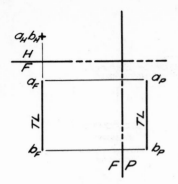

(a) Frontal-Profile(Vertical)Line

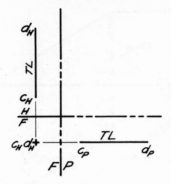

(b) Horizontal-Profile Line

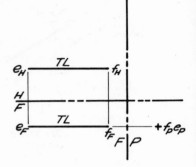

(c) Horizontal-Frontal Line

Fig. **9–2.** Normal lines.

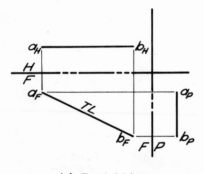

(a) Frontal Line

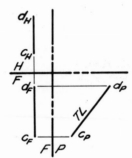

(b) Profile Line

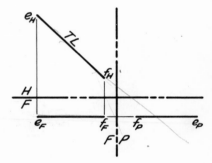

(c) Horizontal Line

Fig. **9–3.** Inclined lines.

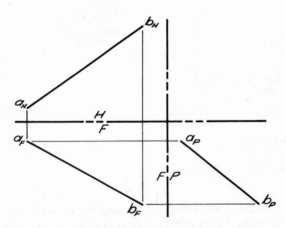

Fig. **9–4.** Oblique line.

bearing denoted as S 30° W is read as 30° west of south, and N 45° E as 45° east of north. As in azimuth, since bearing is measurable only in the horizontal view, the frontal view of the line does not affect the bearing of the line in any manner.

When given the azimuth or bearing of a line, the order in which the points of the line are given denotes the direction of the line; i.e., in Fig. 9–5 the azimuth of line *DC* is 225° while the azimuth of line *CD* is 45°. Also, the use of azimuth and bearing is interchangeable; i.e., in Fig. 9–5 the azimuth of line *DC* is 225° and its bearing is S 45° W. In Fig. 9–6 the bearing of line *GH* is N 30° W and its azimuth is 330°.

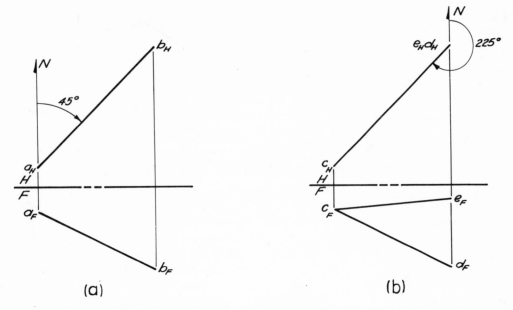

Fig. **9-5.**   Azimuth of lines.

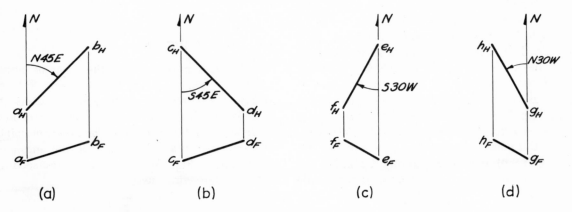

Fig. **9-6.**   Bearing of lines.

9-5. SLOPE OF A LINE

The per cent slope (usually referred to simply as slope) or *grade* of a line is usually defined as the ratio of the rise or fall (change in elevation) to the run (or horizontal distance). A rise is denoted by a positive percentage, whereas a fall is denoted by a negative percentage. A slope of 10 per cent would mean a change in elevation of 10 units for each 100 units of horizontal distance.

Fig. 9-7 shows how to lay out a line having a given bearing and slope of 10 per cent passing through point A. First, point A is plotted and the bearing laid out as in Fig. 9-7(a). Next, a horizontal distance of 100 units is laid off along the bearing as in Fig. 9-7(b), locating the horizontal view of a point B along the line. Then a change in elevation of 10 units is laid off in the frontal view along the projection line from b_H as in Fig. 9-7(c). The projections of the line are then completed as in

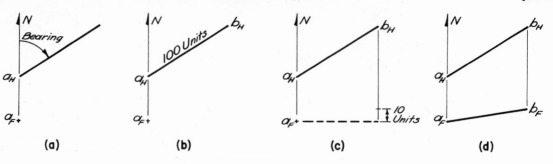

Fig. **9–7.** Construction of a line of known bearing and slope.

Fig. 9–7(d). If the slope had been given as -10 per cent, the change in elevation would have been laid off below a_F.

9–6. POINT ON A LINE

A point that is located on a line in space must appear on the line no matter from what direction the line is viewed. Or, stated in terms of orthographic projection: *If a point is on a line, it must project on that line in all views.*

Fig. 9–8 shows two examples of a point on a line. Usually the frontal and horizontal views give sufficient proof. In the case of a profile line, however, these two views do not give complete graphic proof as to whether the point is or is not on the line. Fig. 9–9 shows two cases in which a point is not on a line. The frontal view in Fig. 9–9(a) shows that point D could not be a point on line AB. In Fig. 9–9(b), point O apparently lies on the line in the frontal and horizontal views. It is not until the profile view is examined that there is complete graphic proof that the point is not on the line.

It should be noted that, if a point is on a line in space, the projections of that point will divide the corresponding projections of the line in the same ratio as the point divides the line in space. For example, in Fig. 9–10, if point X on the line AB divides the line so that the ratio of $AX/AB = 1/4$, then that same ratio will occur in all views of the line.

9–7. INTERSECTING LINES

If two lines intersect, then the point of intersection is a point common to both lines. Hence a check to determine whether or not lines intersect is as follows. If the apparent point of intersection in one view can be projected to the apparent point of intersection in an adjacent view, the lines are intersecting. Fig. 9–11 illustrates intersecting and non-intersecting lines.

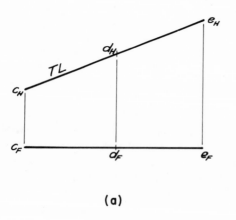

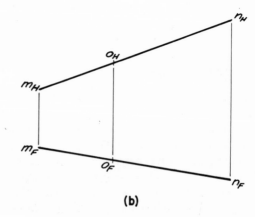

Fig. **9–8.** Point on a line.

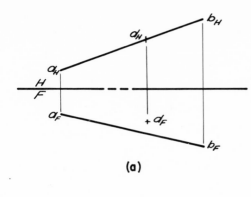

(a)

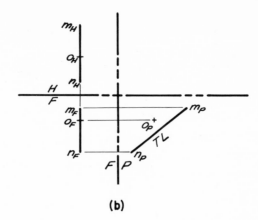

(b)

Fig. **9–9.** Point not on a line.

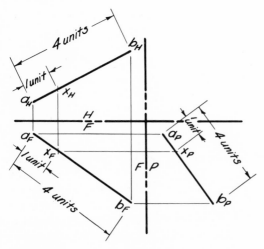

Fig. **9–10.** Point dividing a line into a ratio.

9–8. TRUE LENGTH OF A LINE

A study of the principles of orthographic projection discloses the fact that *the true length of any line will be shown when that line is projected onto a plane parallel to the line.* In Fig. 9–2, the true length of each line appears twice since the lines are parallel to two principal planes of projection. The notation "*TL*" along the projection of a line signifies that this particular projection shows the line in its true length. In Fig. 9–3, the true length of each line appears once since the lines are parallel to only one principal plane.

The true length of an oblique line as shown in Fig. 9–4 is not shown in any of the principal views. One method of determining the true length of an oblique line is shown in Fig. 9–12. A line *AB* is

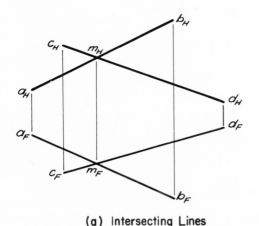

(a) Intersecting Lines

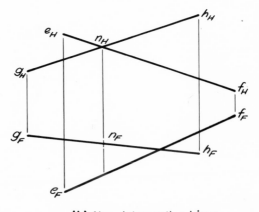

(b) Non-Intersecting Lines

Fig. **9–11.** Intersecting and non-intersecting lines.

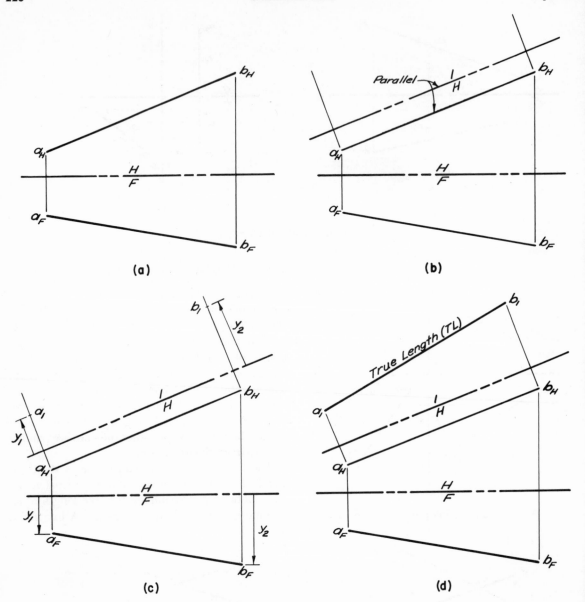

Fig. **9-12.** Determining the true length of a line.

given in Fig. 9-12(a). In Fig. 9-12(b) an auxiliary plane of projection is placed parallel to the line and perpendicular to the horizontal plane of projection. Projection lines are then drawn to the proposed auxiliary view. Next, the dimensions needed to construct the auxiliary view are determined and laid off as in Fig. 9-12(c). The auxiliary view of the line is completed and labeled as in Fig. 9-12(d). The same result could have been accomplished using an auxiliary perpendicular to the

frontal or profile planes of projection, as is done for line *CD* shown in Fig. 9-13.

An alternate method of finding the true length of a line is known as the method of revolution. In this procedure the line is revolved until it is parallel to one of the principal planes of projection, as in Fig. 9-14. The given line *AB* and the vertical axis *XY*, about which the line is to be revolved, are shown in Fig. 9-14(a). If the angle between the line and the axis is held constant, then point *B*

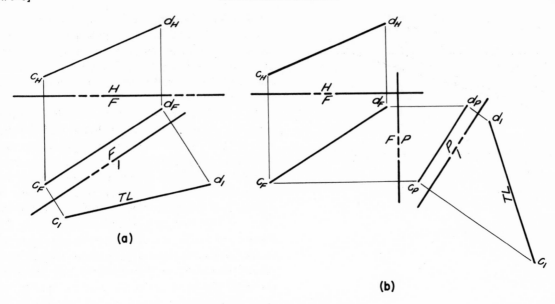

Fig. **9-13.** True length of a line.

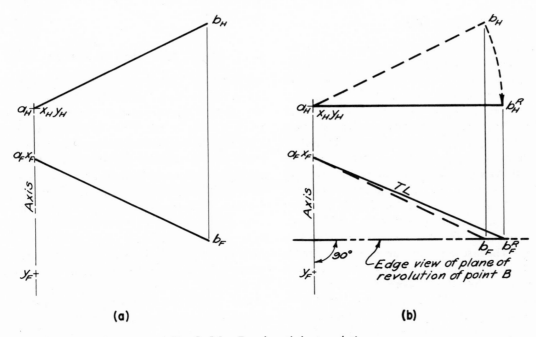

Fig. **9-14.** True length by revolution.

will describe a circle as the line AB revolves about the axis; the plane of the circle generated by point B is perpendicular to the axis. In Fig. 9-14(b), the line has been revolved $(a_H b^R_H)$ until the line is parallel to the frontal plane. Since the plane of the circle in which B moves is perpendicular to the axis of revolution, the plane would be in edge view in the frontal view. Thus the revolved position of point B can be determined and the true length of AB measured. Fig. 9-15 illustrates a line revolved so as to show its true length in the horizontal view.

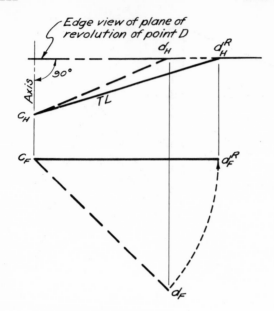

Fig. **9–15.** True length by revolution.

9-9. END VIEW OF A LINE

The end view of a line will be shown when the line is projected onto a plane perpendicular to the line. Thus, in Fig. 9–2, the end view (sometimes referred to as the point view) of each line appears in that principal view to which the line is perpendicular. Note that the projection plane showing the end view is perpendicular to the projection plane showing the true length. When the desired end view does not appear in one of the principal views, it will be necessary to project it from a view showing the line in true length. Fig. 9–16 shows the general case for determining the end view of an oblique line. The given line is shown in Fig. 9–16(a). The first step is to construct a true-length view of the line as in Fig. 9–16(b). A second auxiliary plane is then placed perpendicular to the line and to the plane of the first auxiliary view as in Fig. 9–16(c), and the projection lines to the second auxiliary are drawn. Next, the dimensions appearing in the second auxiliary are determined and laid off as in Fig. 9–16(d), giving the desired end view of the given line.

9-10. PLANES

Planes may be spatially defined by three points; a line and a point; two intersecting lines; or two parallel lines. In graphical work, planes are most frequently defined by three points and the lines joining those three points. In many cases, the plane must be thought of as being infinite in extent and not being limited to the given area defined by the three points.

As with lines, planes can be classified in three general categories: normal, inclined, and oblique. *Normal* planes are those perpendicular to two principal planes of projection and, therefore, parallel to the third principal plane. A normal plane takes its name from the principal plane to which it is parallel. For example, a horizontal plane is one that is perpendicular to both the frontal and profile planes of projection and parallel to the horizontal plane of projection. An *inclined* plane is one that is perpendicular to only one of the principal planes of projection and inclined to the other two principal planes as shown in Fig. 9–17. An *oblique* plane, as shown in Fig. 9–18, is not perpendicular to any of the principal planes of projection.

9-11. POINTS AND LINES IN PLANES

Frequently, the points and/or lines given to define a plane are not satisfactory for use in obtaining a desired graphic solution. In that case, points and lines may be added to the plane. Points are located at the intersection of two lines in the plane. Lines may be located by connecting two given points in the plane, or by drawing a line in a desired direction through one given point. In either case, the basic concept used is that any two non-parallel lines in a plane must intersect at a real point. Fig. 9–19 shows two different lines added to a plane *ABC* shown in Fig. 9–19(a). First, a frontal line is added to the plane *ABC* in Fig. 9–19(b). Since, by definition, a frontal line is a line parallel to the frontal plane, the horizontal (top) view of any frontal line must show constant depth of the line relative to the edge view of the frontal plane, as is shown in Fig. 9–3(a). Hence the horizontal view of the frontal line *CX* in plane *ABC* can be constructed as in Fig. 9–19(b). Since line *CX* is to be a line in plane *ABC*, point *X* is the intersection of lines *CX* and *AB*. Thus, the horizontal view locates the position of point *X*; the frontal view of point *X* can be found by projection; and the views of the line in the plane can be completed

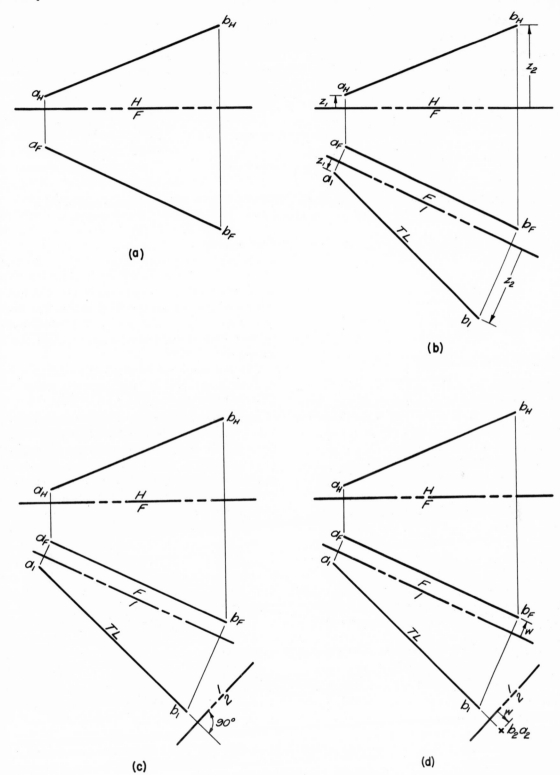

Fig. **9–16.** End view of a line.

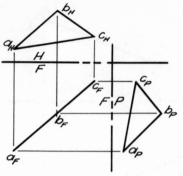 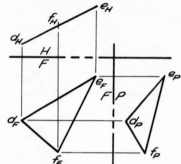 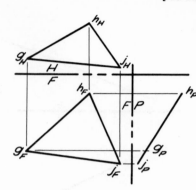

(a) Plane Perpendicular
to Frontal

(b) Plane Perpendicular
to Horizontal

(c) Plane Perpendicular
to Profile

Fig. **9–17.** Inclined planes.

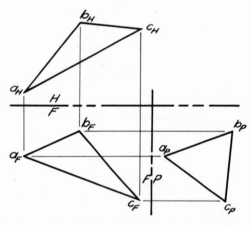

Fig. **9–18.** An oblique plane.

as shown in Fig. 9–19(b). In a like manner, a
horizontal line AY can be added to the given plane
as in Fig. 9–19(c). Any one of an infinite number
of lines may be located in a plane by the use of
similar construction.

The procedure for establishing a particular line
in a plane may also be used to locate points in a
plane. In locating such points, a point is known
to lie in a plane if it lies on some line in that plane.
Fig. 9–20 shows a point added to a plane. It is
desired to locate the horizontal view of the point
D, Fig. 9–20(a), which lies in the plane ABC
(extended). Fig. 9–20(b) shows the construction
of the frontal view of a line AD. If line AD is to
be in plane ABC, it must intersect line BC. This

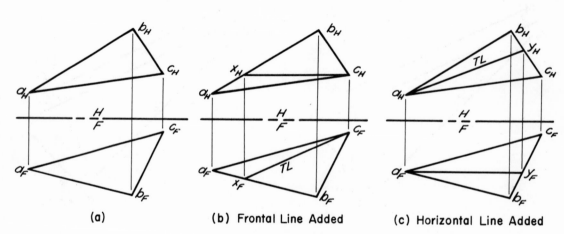

(a)   (b) Frontal Line Added   (c) Horizontal Line Added

Fig. **9–19.** Adding a line to a plane.

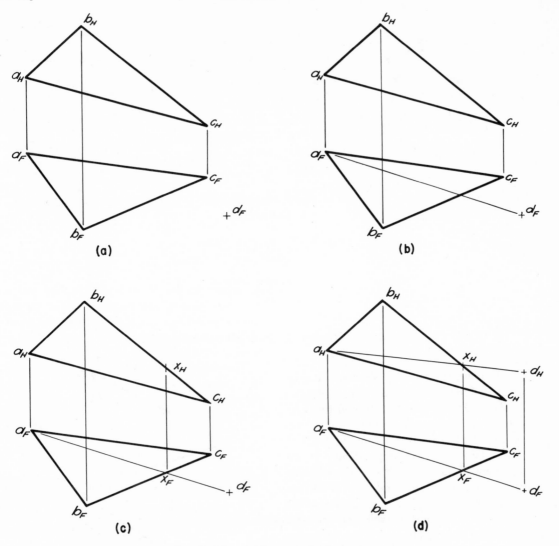

Fig. 9–20. Adding a point to a plane.

point of intersection is located in Fig. 9–20(c). Then the top view of the required point D is located in Fig. 9–20(d).

9–12. EDGE VIEW OF A PLANE

The edge view of a plane must appear on any plane of projection that is perpendicular to the given plane. This fact has already been demonstrated, in that the horizontal plane of projection appears in edge view in the frontal and profile views, and the frontal plane of projection appears in edge view in the horizontal and profile views.

An inclined plane will appear as an edge view in the principal view to which the inclined plane is perpendicular, as was shown in Fig. 9–17.

When the given plane is oblique, the plane of projection which would show the edge view of the given plane is not so obvious. The required view can be determined by an experiment. Take a stiff piece of paper and, laying a pencil on the paper, turn the paper and pencil until the end view of the pencil is seen. The edge view of the paper will also be seen. Therefore, it can be said that *the view showing the end view of a line lying in a plane will show the edge view of the plane.*

Edge View

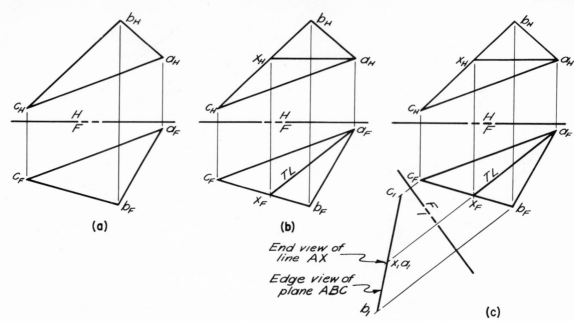

(a)

(b)

End view of
line AX

Edge view of
plane ABC

x, a_1

b_1

(c)

Fig. **9–21.** Determining the edge view of a plane.

Fig. 9–21 shows the steps in finding the edge view of an oblique plane. The given plane is shown in Fig. 9–21(a). The first step, in this solution, is the construction of a frontal line *AX*, as shown in Fig. 9–21(b). Then, as in Fig. 9–21(c), an auxiliary plane is placed perpendicular to the true-length view of the frontal line. The resulting auxiliary view shows both the end view of the line and the edge view of the plane. A horizontal line could have been added just as well, and the edge view constructed by projecting from the horizontal view. The end view of one of the given lines in the plane could also be constructed. However, this construction would require two auxiliary views; one to show the true length of the line, from which the second would be projected to show the end view of the line. Thus, the addition of an inclined line to the plane saved the construction of an additional view.

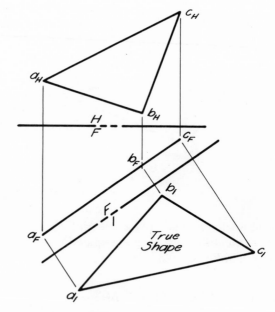

Fig. **9–22.** Determining the true shape of an inclined plane.

9–13. TRUE SHAPE OF A PLANE

The true shape of a plane will be shown when that plane is projected onto a plane of projection parallel to the given plane. A horizontal plane will project in true shape in the horizontal view and a frontal plane in true shape in the frontal

view. Fig. 9–22 shows the true shape of an inclined plane *ABC* which is perpendicular to the frontal plane of projection.

In order to show the true shape of any plane, the edge view must be located first. Fig. 9–23

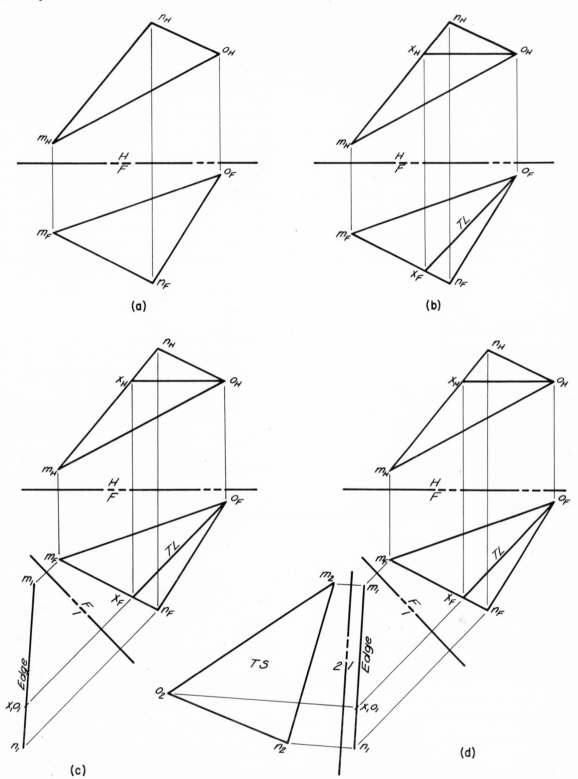

Fig. **9–23.** Determining the true shape of an oblique plane.

shows the steps in finding the true shape of an oblique plane. The given plane is shown in Fig. 9–23(a). The first step is to locate either a frontal or a horizontal line in the plane. In Fig. 9–23(b), a frontal line *OX* is located in plane *MNO*. The second step is to construct the edge view of the plane as in Fig. 9–23(c). The third and last step is to place a second auxiliary plane parallel to the edge view of plane *MNO* and project the plane onto that auxiliary. The resulting view shows the true shape of the plane, Fig. 9–23(d). Note that any view projected from the view showing the true shape of a plane must show the edge view of the plane. As can be seen from Fig. 9–23, the determination of the true shape of an oblique plane by the use of auxiliary views will always require at least two auxiliaries.

9–14. INTERSECTION OF A LINE AND PLANE

The point at which a line pierces (intersects) a plane is frequently required. This may be found directly when the plane is in edge view in one of the given views, as in Fig. 9–24. Notice that the visibility of the line is shown as though the plane were opaque. While this is theoretically not true (since mathematically a plane is a surface of no thickness), it helps the individual reading the drawing to understand the spatial conditions.

When the given plane is oblique, two methods of solution can be used. One method is to project both the line and plane onto a view that shows the edge view of the given plane. In Fig. 9–24, plane *ABC* appears as an edge view in the front view and the piercing point between plane *ABC* and line *MN* can be directly found. If the edge view of the plane does not appear in the given views, then an auxiliary showing the edge view can be constructed and the piercing point located in a similar manner.

The second method is to use an additional cutting plane. An additional cutting plane is a plane that is added to the spatial conditions and is positioned such that it is perpendicular to one of the principal planes of projection, thus cutting through that particular view. The use of an additional cutting plane is shown in Fig. 9–25. The given line and plane are shown in Fig. 9–25(a). An additional plane has been added to the problem in Fig. 9–25(b). In this example, plane Δ is placed perpendicular to the horizontal plane of projection and along the line *MN*. Thus, all points on line *MN* lie in the plane Δ. Since the horizontal view of plane Δ is in edge view, we know that line *AC* of plane *ABC* pierces plane Δ at point *X* and that line *BC* pierces at point *Y*. (Refer to horizontal view.) Therefore, since two plane surfaces will intersect in a straight line, line *XY* is the line of intersection between plane Δ and plane *ABC*. The piercing point *P* between line *MN* and plane *ABC* is located in Fig. 9–25(c). The frontal view of point *P* can be located at the point where the frontal view of *XY* crosses the frontal view of *MN* by realizing that first, all points along line *XY* are common to the plane *ABC* and plane Δ, and second, all points along line *MN* are common to line *MN* and plane Δ. Therefore, point *P* will be common to line *MN*, plane Δ, and plane *ABC*. Since point *P* is common to line *MN* and plane *ABC*, it must be the point where line *MN* pierces plane *ABC*. With the frontal view of the piercing point *P* thus located, the horizontal view of *P* is simply located by projection. The completed problem is shown in Fig. 9–25(d). In this case, the piercing point lies inside the triangle defining plane *ABC*. Since a plane may be infinite in extent, the piercing point could be outside the defining tri-

Fig. 9–24. Intersection of a line and an inclined plane.

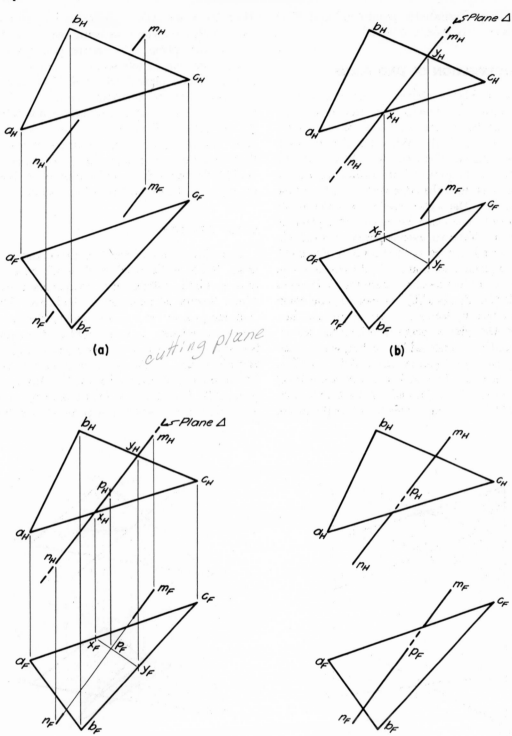

cutting plane

(a)   **(b)**

(c)   **(d)**

Fig. **9–25.** Intersection of a line and an oblique plane.

angle. [This is illustrated by point Z in Fig. 9–27(c). Refer also to Arts. 9–10 and 9–11.]

9-15. INTERSECTION OF TWO PLANES

When two planes intersect, if either or both of the given planes are in edge view, the line of intersection can be directly found as shown by the examples in Fig. 9–26. When both of the given planes are oblique, there are two methods of solution. One is to project both planes onto some view that will show the edge view of either of the given planes. The second method is to determine where lines in one plane pierce the other plane by the use of additional cutting-plane construction.

This second method is illustrated in Fig. 9–27. The given planes ABC and MNO are shown in Fig. 9–27(a). Point X is located where line AC pierces plane MNO in Fig. 9–27(b). A second point could be determined by locating where some other line in plane ABC pierces plane MNO, or the second point could be determined by locating where some line in plane MNO pierces plane ABC. In Fig. 9–27(c), the point Z where line ON in plane MNO pierces plane ABC is located. Note that Z does not lie within the triangle which defines the plane.

Here the plane ABC is considered as an infinite plane with the given lines being only some of the lines in that plane. Connecting points X and Z locates the line of intersection between the two planes. Since planes ABC and MNO could be considered infinite in extent, the line XZ is only a portion of the infinite line of intersection between the two planes. However, it is customary to indicate only that portion of the intersection which lies within the lines defining the given planes. Fig. 9–27(d) illustrates the completed problem showing the segment XY of the line of intersection.

9-16. VISIBILITY

The illustrations of the two preceding articles (Figs. 9–24, 9–25, 9–26, and 9–27) have been drawn with the visibility of an opaque plane instead of the theoretical plane of no thickness. This is common practice as it makes reading the drawing easier and quicker. In some problems the visibility is easily determined by inspection, as in Fig. 9–24 and Fig. 9–26. In Fig. 9–24, an inspection of the frontal projection reveals that the line MN is above plane ABC from point M to the piercing point P and below plane ABC from point P to point N.

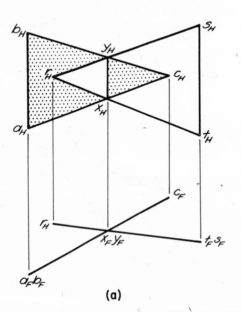

(a)

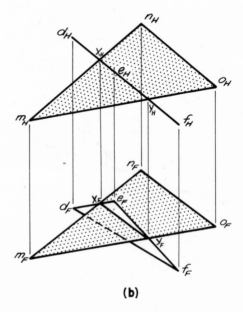

(b)

Fig. **9-26.**   Line of intersection between planes.

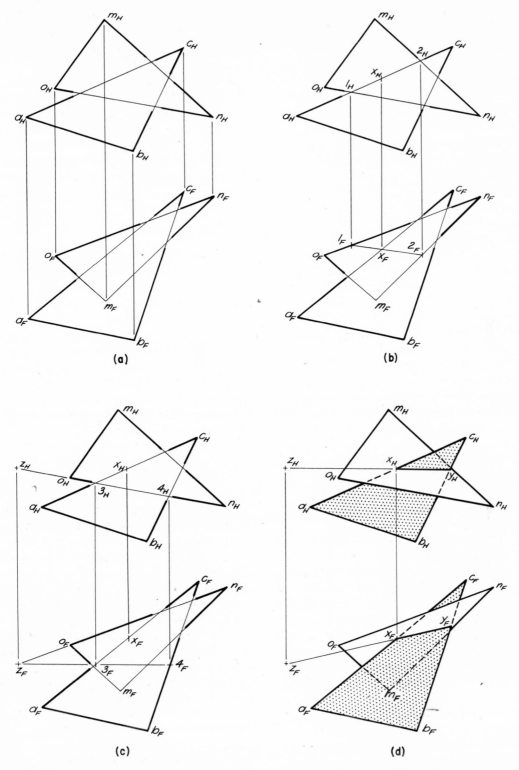

Fig. 9–27. Determination of the line of intersection between oblique planes.

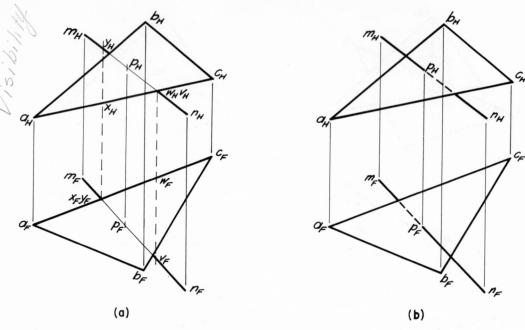

Fig. **9-28.** Visibility of a line piercing a plane.

Thus, the horizontal projection can be drawn with correct visibility. In Fig. 9-26(b), an inspection of the horizontal projection reveals that plane *MNO* is in front of plane *DEF* to the left of the line of intersection.

Thus, in the frontal projection, that portion of line *DF* that passes behind plane *MNO* would be drawn as a hidden line.

In other problems the visibility may not be so readily determined by inspection. When this occurs, the visibility can be determined by a simple construction. In Fig. 9-28(a), the line *MN* and its piercing point *P* with plane *ABC* are given. The construction used to determine visibility involves the investigation of the places where the line *MN* crosses lines of the plane *ABC*. In the frontal projection, where $m_F n_F$ crosses $a_F c_F$, assume a point *X* on line *AC* and a point *Y* on line *MN*. Project these assumed points to the horizontal projection. This proves that point *X* on line *AC* is in front of point *Y* on line *MN*. Therefore, in the frontal view, the line *MN* would be hidden as it passes behind plane *ABC*. The line would be hidden until it pierces the plane. To the right of

the piercing point, the line would be visible as it is then in front of the plane.

The same construction and analysis are used to determine the visibility in the horizontal projection. At the place where $m_H n_H$ crosses $a_H c_H$, assume a point *W* on line *AC* and a point *V* on line *MN*. The point that is the highest (the point that is above the other point) will be the visible point. Fig. 9-28(b) shows the views completed with correct visibility. It should be pointed out that the place where line *MN* crosses line *AB* in the horizontal projection and the place where line *MN* crosses line *BC* in the frontal projection could have been used in the same manner.

Fig. 9-29 shows the construction to determine the visibility of the views of two intersecting planes. Note that once the visibility at one place in a view is determined, logic dictates the visibility at all other places in the same view.

Fig. 9-30 shows the construction applied to determine the visibility of a tetrahedron. In this case, only the visibility of the interior edges of each view is of concern since the outside edges of a view must be visible.

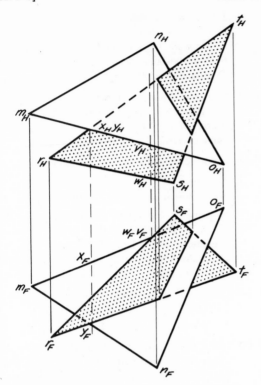

Fig. **9-29.** Visibility of intersecting planes.

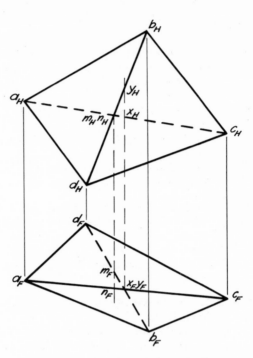

Fig. **9-30.** Visibility of a tetrahedron.

Problems

When plotting points such as $A(2\frac{1}{2}, 1, 3)$ refer to Appendix, Plotting Problems. All problems are designed to be worked on $8\frac{1}{2}'' \times 11''$ sheets, and when a problem has several parts, all parts are to be worked on the same sheet.

9-1. Measure and record the azimuths and bearings of the following lines.

a. $A(1, 7, 8)$ $B(2\frac{1}{2}, 5\frac{1}{2}, 6\frac{1}{2})$
b. $C(4, 6, 8)$ $D(6\frac{1}{2}, 6, 7)$
c. $E(2\frac{1}{2}, 1\frac{1}{2}, 3)$ $F(\frac{1}{2}, 2\frac{1}{2}, 3)$
d. $G(7, 1, 4)$ $H(4, 2, 2\frac{1}{2})$

9-2. Measure and record the grades of the lines given in Problem 9-1.

9-3. a. Locate point M so that it lies on line $A(2\frac{1}{4}, 5, 7)$ $B(5, 7, 9)$ and is $1''$ below point B.
   b. Locate the horizontal line $R(2\frac{1}{2}, y, 3\frac{3}{4})$ $S(5\frac{1}{2}, y, 2\frac{3}{4})$ which intersects line $C(1\frac{3}{4}, \frac{3}{4}, 2\frac{1}{2})$ $D(4\frac{1}{2}, 2\frac{1}{4}, 4\frac{1}{2})$.

9-4. a. Locate the line OP which intersects line $A(1\frac{1}{2}, 6\frac{3}{4}, 7\frac{1}{4})$ $B(5, 5\frac{1}{2}, 8\frac{1}{2})$. Point O is $1''$ east of, $1''$ to the north of, and $1\frac{1}{2}''$ below point A. Line OP has a bearing of S $60°$ E. Point P is $\frac{1}{2}''$ east of point B.
   b. Locate the line $E(1, y, 2\frac{1}{2})$ $F(5, \frac{1}{2}, 4)$ which intersects line $C(1\frac{1}{2}, \frac{1}{2}, 3\frac{1}{2})$ $D(6, 2, 2\frac{1}{4})$.

9-5. Locate the line $M(4, 1\frac{1}{2}, 7)N$ which has a bearing of S $45°$ W, intersects line $A(2, 1, 8)$ $B(3\frac{1}{4}, 3, 4\frac{1}{2})$, and is $3''$ long.

9-6. a. Find the true length of line $A(2, 5, 7)$ $B(5, 6, 9)$.
   b. Locate the frontal line $C(2, 3, 4)D$ whose length is $4''$ with point D $2''$ lower than point C.

9-7. In this problem the same line is to be drawn at three different locations on the sheet. Determine its true length as directed and compare the true lengths.
   a. Find the true length of $A(1, 7, 8\frac{1}{4})$ $B(3, 8, 9)$ by projecting from the top view.
   b. Find the true length of $A(5, 4, 5\frac{1}{4})$ $B(7, 5, 6)$ by projecting from the front view.
   c. Find the true length of $A(1, \frac{3}{4}, 2)$ $B(3, 1\frac{3}{4}, 2\frac{3}{4})$ by projecting from the right side view.

9-8. a. Find the true length of line $A(2, 5, 8\frac{1}{2})$ $B(5, 6\frac{1}{2}, 7)$ by revolving about a vertical (frontal-profile) axis.
   b. Find the true length of line $C(2, 1\frac{1}{2}, 2)$ $D(5, \frac{1}{2}, 4)$ by revolving about a horizontal profile axis.

9-9. a. Locate the line $A(2, 6\frac{1}{2}, z)$ $B(5, 5\frac{1}{2}, 7)$ whose length is $4''$.
   b. Locate the horizontal and frontal views of the sphere whose diameter is $C(4\frac{1}{2}, \frac{1}{2}, 3\frac{1}{2})$ $D(5\frac{1}{2}, 1\frac{1}{2}, 2\frac{1}{2})$.

9-10. Line $A(\frac{1}{2}, 3\frac{1}{2}, 7)$ $B(1\frac{1}{2}, 3\frac{1}{2}, 7)$ $C(3\frac{1}{2}, 1\frac{1}{2}, 5)$ $D(3\frac{1}{2}, \frac{1}{2}, 3)$ is the center line of a $\frac{1}{2}''$ diameter rod which has been bent to the shape indicated. Disregarding bend allowance, what is the length of rod required?

9-11. A bar $2''$ long is suspended from the ceiling by strings $4''$ long. The strings are $3''$ apart at the ceiling. Determine the position of the bar if it is turned $90°$ about a vertical axis through the center of the bar.

9-12. Locate the end view of line $A(2, 2, 5)$ $B(4\frac{1}{2}, 5, 7)$.

9-13. Locate points $P(1, 3, z)$ and $N(3, y, 5\frac{1}{2})$ in plane $A(2, 3, 6)$ $B(4, 1, 8)$ $C(6, 4, 5)$.

9-14. Point $A(2, 4, 6)$ is the control point in a series of borings to establish the position of the bedrock under the site of a proposed building. Survey data locate three other points with respect to A. Point B lies at a horizontal distance of 84 feet on a bearing of N 38° E and is 20 feet above A. Point C lies at a horizontal distance of 166 feet on a bearing of S 81° E and is 27 feet below A. Point D lies at a horizontal distance of 200 feet on a bearing of N 75° E and is 20 feet below A.

Borings are made at A, B, and C, striking bedrock at depths of 103 feet, 149 feet, and 33 feet respectively. Assuming the plane of the bedrock to be unbroken, at what depth will the boring at D strike bedrock? Select a suitable scale.

9-15. Construct a horizontal line $C(4, 3, 8)D$, a profile line $B(2, 1, 8)F$, and a line $A(1, 4, 6)E$ having a bearing of N 45° E. All the lines are to lie in the plane of ABC.

9-16. Construct the edge view of the following planes.
   a. $A(2, 7, 8)$ $B(3, 7, 9)$ $C(1, 5, 9)$
   b. $M(3, 1, 2)$ $N(4, 2, 4)$ $O(5, \frac{1}{2}, 2\frac{1}{2})$

9-17. A plane is located by $A(1, 1, 8)$ $B(3\frac{1}{2}, 1, 6\frac{1}{2})$ $C(1, 3, 6)$ $D(3\frac{1}{2}, 3, 4\frac{1}{2})$. The center of a $\frac{1}{2}''$ diameter sphere is located at point $H(2\frac{1}{2}, 2, 5\frac{1}{2})$. Determine the clearance between plane $ABCD$ and the sphere.

9-18. Construct the true shape of the following planes.
   a. $M(3, 5\frac{1}{2}, 7)$ $N(4, 5, 8)$ $O(5, 6, 9)$
   b. $R(3, 2, 2\frac{1}{2})$ $S(4, 1, 4)$ $T(5, 2\frac{1}{2}, 3)$

9-19. $A(1, 1, 4\frac{1}{2})$ $B(2, 1, 5\frac{1}{2})$ $C(3\frac{1}{2}, 2, 5\frac{1}{2})$ $D(5, \frac{1}{2}, 4)$ are points on the center line of a cable. Pulleys of $1\frac{1}{2}''$ diameter are to be used for the change of direction at B and C. If the diameter of the cable is $\frac{1}{4}''$, locate the centers of the two pulleys.

9-20. Points $A(1, 3, 8)$ and $B(4, 2, 6)$ are on the center lines of two horizontal frontal pipes. Points A and B are to be joined by a symmetrical ogee pipe. Determine the radius of curvature and the degrees of arc required.

9-21. Points $A(\frac{1}{2}, 2, 7)$, $B(2\frac{1}{2}, 1, 6\frac{1}{2})$, and $C(2, 3\frac{1}{2}, 5)$ are on the circumference of a circle inscribed in a regular hexagon. Two sides of the hexagon are horizontal. Construct the frontal and horizontal projections of the hexagon.

9-22. Construct the frontal and horizontal views of the smallest sphere that would still touch the lines $A(1, 2, 4\frac{1}{2})$, $B(2, 1, 6)$, $AC(3\frac{1}{2}, 3, 5)$, and BC.

9-23. Construct the line that bisects angle $A(1, 4, 6\frac{1}{4})$ $B(1\frac{1}{4}, 1\frac{1}{4}, 5\frac{1}{4})$ $C(3, 3, 7\frac{1}{4})$.

9-24. A $\frac{1}{4}''$ diameter cable runs from $A(1, 4, 6)$ to $B(3\frac{1}{2}, 2\frac{1}{2}, 6)$ passing over a $1\frac{1}{2}''$ diameter pulley whose center is located at point $C(2\frac{1}{4}, 1\frac{1}{4}, 4\frac{3}{4})$. Show the frontal and horizontal views of the cable.

9-25. Locate the point P where line $A(2\frac{1}{2}, 2, 8)$ $B(4\frac{1}{2}, 4\frac{1}{2}, 6\frac{1}{2})$ pierces plane $C(2, 3, 6)$ $D(3\frac{1}{2}, 5, 7)$ $E(5, 2, 8)$. Show correct visibility.

9–26. Locate the point P where line $M(1\frac{1}{2}, 1, 8)$ $N(4, 4, 5)$ pierces plane $A(2, 3, 5)$ $B(5, 3\frac{1}{2}, 7)$ $C(6\frac{1}{2}, \frac{1}{2}, 4)$. Show correct visibility.

9–27. Locate the line of intersection between plane $A(1\frac{1}{4}, \frac{1}{2}, 8)$ $B(3\frac{1}{2}, 4, 4\frac{1}{2})$ $C(6, 2, 6)$ and plane $M(1, 1, 4\frac{1}{2})$ $N(2\frac{3}{4}, 3\frac{3}{4}, 8)$ $O(5\frac{1}{2}, 2, 6)$. Show correct visibility.

9–28. Points $A(1, 1, 5)$, $B(3\frac{1}{2}, 2, 6)$, and $C(3, 3, 4)$ are three points on the side of a hill. These points are to be anchor points for cables guying a television transmitter antenna. The base of the antenna is to lie in the plane of points A, B, and C, and is to be equidistant from each point. The antenna is vertical and is 75 feet tall. Using a scale of 1 inch = 50 feet, determine the length of the guy cables, running from the top of the antenna to points A, B, and C.

10

ANGULAR SPATIAL RELATIONS

10-1. INTRODUCTION

The preceding chapter discussed the basic spatial relations of points, lines, and planes. Any spatial problem may be solved through the proper use of these basic relations involving true lengths, end views, edge views, and true shapes, provided this solution is preceded by a careful analysis as to the proper choice and arrangement of those projections necessary to solve the problem. Engineers, through long experience in working with spatial problems, have developed methods of solving certain types of problems. This chapter discusses those methods which have been developed in order to determine the angular relations existing between lines and/or planes. The determination of the size of the angle between a plane surface and an angular line; of whether a line is perpendicular to some plane; and of the angle between two planes, are examples of the types of problems that fall into this category.

10-2. ANGLE BETWEEN TWO LINES

The angle between two lines is measurable only in a view that shows both lines in true length. This

view will also show the true shape of the plane formed by the intersecting lines. This is illustrated in Fig. 10-1, where the angle between lines *AB* and *CD* is required. Construction proves that the two lines intersect at a point *E* (refer to Art. 9-7). The two lines are therefore coplanar, and a true-shape view of the plane *DEB* will show the required angle. The true-shape view is found by the method discussed in Art. 9-13. Note that the situation could occur in which the lines would not intersect within the confines of the drawing area. In such a case, an additional line could be drawn parallel to and intersecting one of the given lines by the method discussed in the next article. The true size of the angle between these lines would be the same as between the original lines.

Two lines are considered to have an angular relation whether they are intersecting or non-intersecting. Thus, in determining the angle between two non-intersecting lines, this relationship will likewise be shown in the view showing both lines in true length. Fig. 10-2 shows two non-intersecting lines, *MN* and *RS*. Since the two lines do not lie in the same plane, a different method must be used to determine the required view. An end view of either one of the lines is the first step in the solution.

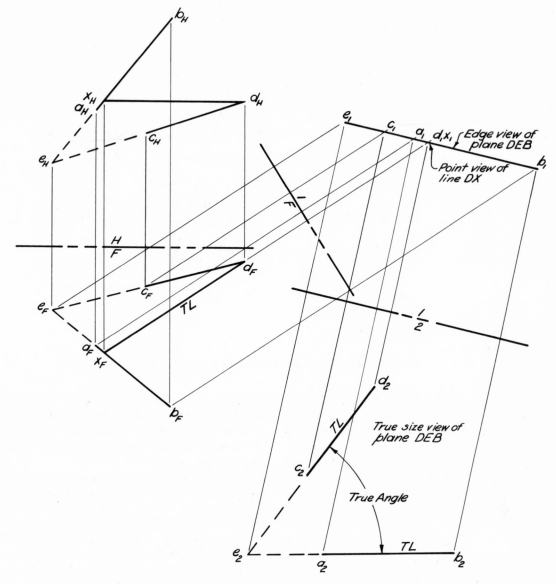

Fig. **10–1.** Angle between intersecting lines.

In the illustration, the end view of line *RS* is obtained (second auxiliary). The other line (*MN*) is also projected through to this view. A third auxiliary is then constructed showing the true length of line *MN*. Line *RS* also shows in true length in this auxiliary because *RS*, showing as an end view in the second auxiliary, must be parallel to the plane of the third auxiliary. Thus, the third auxiliary shows the true length of both lines and the desired angle between them. A shorter method requiring only two auxiliaries is discussed in Art. 10–7.

10–3. PARALLEL LINES

When the angle between two lines is 0° or 180°, the lines are defined as being parallel. Since two parallel lines are coplanar (lie in the same plane), the view showing both lines in true length could also be the view showing the true shape of the plane of the two lines if the following construction is used. In Fig. 10–3, the edge view of the plane containing two parallel lines *AB* and *CD* is obtained in a first auxiliary view. Note that the horizontal line *XY*

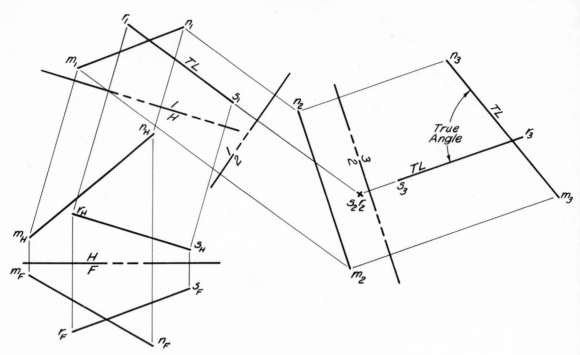

Fig. **10-2.** Angle between non-intersecting lines.

was added to the plane of lines *AB* and *CD* in order to determine the direction of projection for the first auxiliary. The fact that the two lines in this first auxiliary lie in a single edge view proves that they are coplanar. The second auxiliary in Fig. 10–3 shows the true shape of the plane defined by the parallel lines *AB* and *CD*. Note that the second

auxiliary shows the true distance (clearance) between the two parallel lines. A study of the views in Fig. 10–3 also yields the following rule: *When two lines are parallel, their projections in any view are parallel.*

Normally, two adjacent views offer sufficient proof of parallelism. The one exception is exempli-

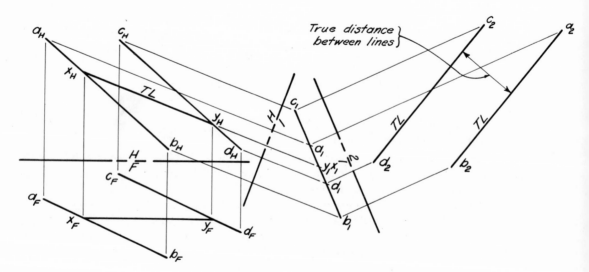

Fig. **10-3.** Parallel lines.

fied by two profile lines. Fig. 10–4 shows two profile lines which in the frontal and horizontal views (adjacent views) appear to be parallel lines; however, the frontal and profile views (again adjacent views) prove the lines are not parallel. Therefore, it can be stated: Two adjacent views offer sufficient proof of parallelism for two oblique lines. In the case of normal or inclined lines, two adjacent views offer sufficient proof of parallelism provided that either one or both of the views show the true length of both lines.

10–4. PERPENDICULAR LINES

When the angle between two lines is 90°, the lines are defined as being perpendicular. Perpendicular lines may be intersecting or non-intersecting. In Fig. 10–5, the lines MN and ST have been given as being perpendicular. The third auxiliary view, showing both lines in true length, proves this to be true. A further study of Fig. 10–5 reveals that the 90° relationship between the two lines is also shown in both the first and second auxiliaries.

In the first auxiliary, the lines project perpendicular to each other even though only line MN shows in true length and ST appears foreshortened. In the second auxiliary, line ST shows in true length and

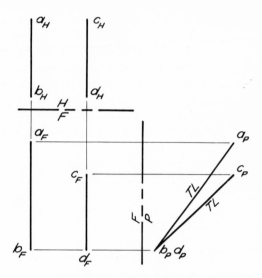

Fig. **10–4.** Non-parallel lines.

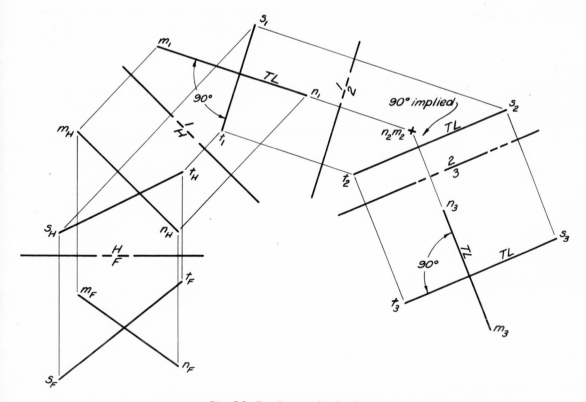

Fig. **10–5.** Perpendicular lines.

line *MN* shows in end view, which also proves that the two lines are perpendicular. These observations yield the following rule: *If two lines are perpendicular, the view that shows the true length of either or both of the lines must also show the 90° angle between the lines.* This rule has the following corollary: If a view shows the true length of either or both of two lines but does not show a 90° angle, or if a view shows a 90° angle and neither line is true length, the lines are not perpendicular.

A frequently encountered problem involving perpendicular relations of lines is one in which it is desired to establish one line perpendicular to a second line at a particular point on the second line. Fig. 10–6 shows the steps for constructing a line of a given azimuth which is also to be the perpendicular bisector of the given line *AB*. In Fig. 10–6(a), the given line *AB* is shown; its midpoint *M* is known from the ratio rule (Art. 9–6). The horizontal projection of a line having the required azimuth can be drawn through the midpoint in the horizontal view and point *N* arbitrarily chosen along the line. In Fig. 10–6(b), an auxiliary showing the true length of line *AB* is constructed, and in Fig. 10–6(c) the problem is completed by construct-

ing the desired perpendicular. *MN* must appear at 90° to the true-length view of line *AB* if it is the perpendicular bisector of *AB*. Thus, the direction of *MN* in the auxiliary view is established and point *N* can be located by projection from the horizontal view. The line *MN* may then be projected back to the frontal view. It might be noted here as a general rule that when an auxiliary view is required, it should be projected from the principal view that gives the most information. In this particular illustration, projection was made from the horizontal view since it contained views of the two lines involved.

Fig. 10–7 shows how, using only two views, two different lines can be drawn through a point *D* so that each line is perpendicular to a given line *RS*. The line to be established, *DE*, is drawn as a horizontal line in Fig. 10–7(b). It is therefore seen in true length in the horizontal view. Because of the rule of perpendicular relations, stated above, the horizontal view of line *DE* is drawn at 90° to line *RS*. In so doing, the line *DE* is now established as being perpendicular in space to the line *RS*. In a like manner, the frontal line *DG* in Fig. 10–7(c) is also established as being perpendicular to line *RS*.

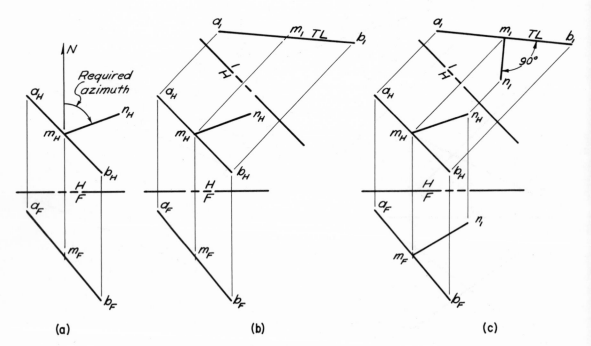

Fig. **10-6.** Determination of a line perpendicular to and intersecting another line.

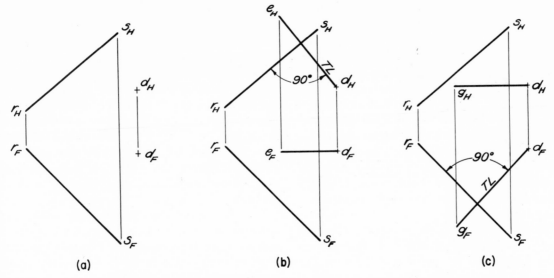

Fig. **10–7.** Determination of perpendicular non-intersecting lines.

The construction of lines *DE* and *DG* forms the basis of the establishment of a plane perpendicular to a line. This is discussed in Art. 10–8.

It should also be noted here that an infinite number of lines can be drawn through a point so that the lines are perpendicular to another line, but only one line can be drawn through a point so that the line is perpendicular to and at the same time intersecting another line.

10–5. ANGLE BETWEEN A LINE AND A PLANE

The angle between a line and a plane is measurable only in a view that shows the true length of the line and the edge view of the plane. Fig. 10–8 shows one method of constructing this view. First, the views necessary to show the true-shape view of the given plane *ABC* are constructed. These consist of: (a) determining the edge view of plane *ABC* through the use of the frontal line *AX*, and (b) determining the true shape of plane *ABC* by projecting onto a second auxiliary plane placed parallel to the edge view. The line *MN* is projected into each view. A third auxiliary view is now constructed which shows the true length of the given line *MN*. The plane must appear as an edge view in this third auxiliary view because the plane, showing in true shape in the second auxiliary, must be

perpendicular to the plane of the third auxiliary. Thus, the angle between the line and the plane is measurable. A second method requiring the construction of only two auxiliary views is discussed in Art. 10–11.

10–6. SLOPE OF A LINE

In Art. 9–5, the slope of a line has been expressed as a grade, or per cent slope. The slope angle of a line is also measurable as the angle between the line and a horizontal plane, and may be expressed in degrees. To show the slope angle of a line, the auxiliary showing the true-length view of the line is projected from the horizontal view as in Fig. 10–9.

10–7. LINE PARALLEL TO A PLANE

When the angle between a line and a plane is 0° or 180°, the line and plane are defined as being parallel. Fig. 10–10 shows a line *AB* which is parallel to plane *MNO*. This parallelism is proved by obtaining a view showing the edge view of the plane and the true length of the line as discussed in Art. 10–5. A study of Fig. 10–10 reveals two relations. First, if a line and plane are parallel, the view showing the edge view of the plane also shows the view of the line parallel to the edge view. Secondly, if a line and plane are parallel, the view

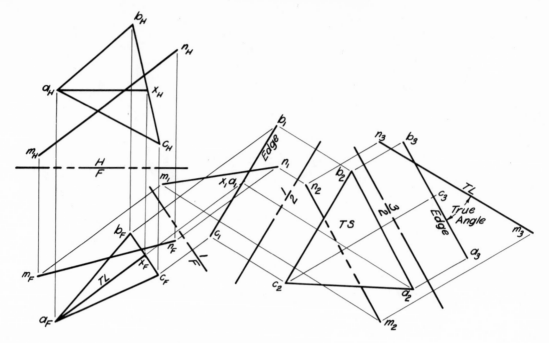

Fig. **10–8.**   Angle between a line and a plane.

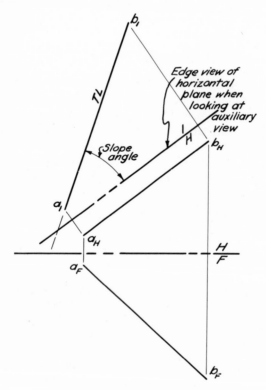

Fig. **10–9.**   Slope angle of a line.

showing the true shape of the plane also shows the true length of the line. The third auxiliary view is not essential in this figure, but has been added to show that any view projected from a true-size view will show the parallelism of the line and plane. Note that the line *AB* would vary in length all the way from a point view to a true-length view, depending on the direction of projection.

Further analysis of the spatial conditions yields the following rule: *If a given line is parallel to a plane, there must be a line (or family of lines) in that plane parallel to the given line.* This rule is the most common proof, or basis of construction, of a line parallel to a plane. Fig. 10–11 shows the steps in proving a line parallel to a plane using such construction. The given line and plane are shown in Fig. 10–11(a). In Fig. 10–11(b), the horizontal projection of line *TX* in plane *RST* has been constructed parallel to the horizontal projection of line *MN*. This is the only direction a line (or family of lines) in plane *RST* can assume if the line in the plane is to be parallel to line *MN*. In Fig. 10–11(c), the frontal view of line *TX* has been located. If the frontal view of a line *TX* is parallel to the frontal view of line *MN*, then line *MN* is parallel to

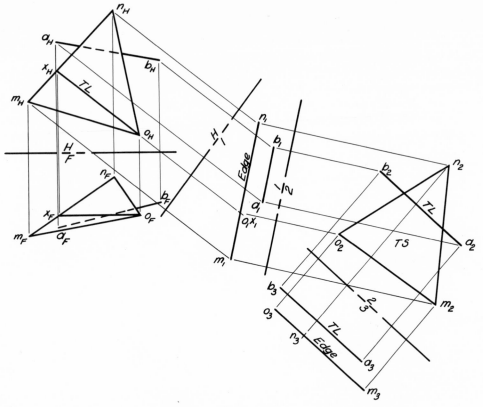

Fig. **10–10.** Line parallel to a plane.

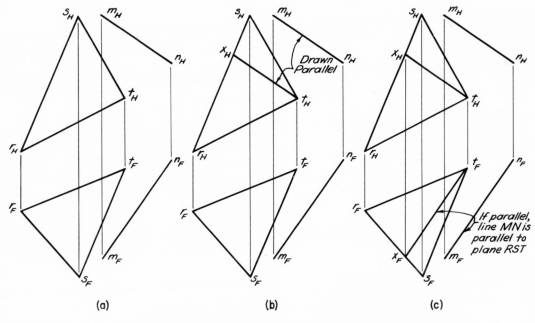

Fig. **10–11.** Proving a line parallel to a plane.

plane *RST* since the plane contains a line parallel to the given line. If the frontal view of line *TX* were not parallel to the frontal view of *MN*, then line *MN* could not be parallel to plane *RST* since there would not be a line in *RST* parallel to *MN*.

Fig. 10–12 shows the steps in constructing a line parallel to a plane. In this example it was desired to establish a line *EG* of indefinite length and having a certain azimuth in addition to being paral-

lel to the plane *ABC*. Fig. 10–12(a) shows the plane and the given point *E*. The horizontal view of line *EG* has been established at the desired azimuth. Fig. 10–12(b), (c), and (d) show the successive steps in completing the location of line *EG* parallel to plane *ABC*.

The ability to construct a line parallel to a plane or, conversely, to construct a plane parallel to a line, provides a second method of determining the

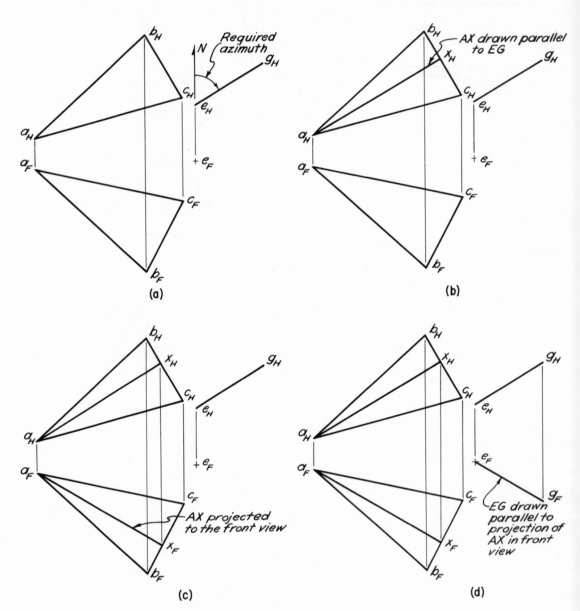

Fig. **10–12.** Constructing a line parallel to a plane.

angle between two non-intersecting lines. Fig. 10–13 illustrates this method, which is shorter than the method presented in Art. 10–2. The given lines are MN and RS. A plane through line MN parallel to line RS is constructed by drawing line NX parallel to line RS. Then successive views showing first the edge view and then the true shape of plane MNX are constructed. Note in the view showing the edge view of MNX that lines MN and RS appear as apparently parallel. The angle between lines MN and RS is measurable in the true-shape view of MNX since both lines appear in true length.

10–8. LINE PERPENDICULAR TO A PLANE

When the angle between a line and a plane is 90°, the line is defined as being perpendicular to the plane. Fig. 10–14 shows a line AB perpendicular to a plane RST. This perpendicularity is proved by utilizing the construction discussed in Art. 10–5 wherein the edge view of the plane and the true length of the line are found in a single view. A study of the views of Fig. 10–14 reveals two relations. First, the view that shows the edge view of a plane will show the true length of a line perpendicular to the plane. Secondly, the view that shows the true shape of a plane will show the end view of a line perpendicular to the plane.

Further analysis of the spatial conditions involving the perpendicular relations of a line and a plane will yield the following rule: If a line is perpendicular to a plane, then the line must be perpendicular to all lines in that plane. Since two is the minimum number of lines that can represent a plane, this rule could be reworded as: *If a line is perpendicular to a plane, then the line must be perpendicular to any two intersecting lines in that plane.* The word "intersecting" is necessary since a line could be perpendicular to two parallel lines and still not be perpendicular to the plane of those lines.

Fig. 10–15 shows the application of the above rule in proving whether or not a line is perpendicular to a plane. The given line and plane are shown in Fig. 10–15(a). In Fig. 10–15(b), the frontal line AY and the horizontal line CX have been added to the plane. The perpendicularity of the given line MN with lines AY and CX may now be determined using the rule developed in Art. 10–4 to the effect

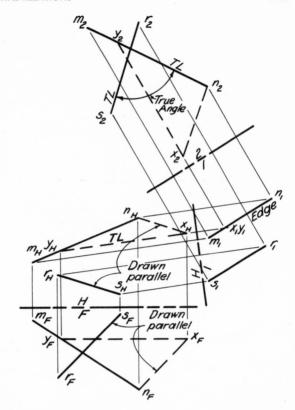

Fig. 10–13. Angle between non-intersecting lines (parallel line and plane method).

that if two lines are perpendicular, the view showing the true length of either also shows the 90° angle. If MN is perpendicular to both AY and CX, then the line MN is perpendicular to a plane ABC. If line MN is perpendicular to only one or neither of the two lines, line MN is not perpendicular to the plane ABC.

Fig. 10–16 shows the construction of a line through a point so that the line is perpendicular to a plane. Fig. 10–16(a) shows the given conditions. In Fig. 10–16(b), frontal and horizontal lines have been added to the plane. If the line through point R is to be perpendicular to plane MNO, then the horizontal projection of the line must be perpendicular to the true-length view of the horizontal line OX, as in Fig. 10–16(c). Point S is arbitrarily chosen along the line through R. The frontal view of line RS also must be perpendicular to the true length view of the frontal line MY as in Fig. 10–16(d). Thus the direction of a line perpendicu-

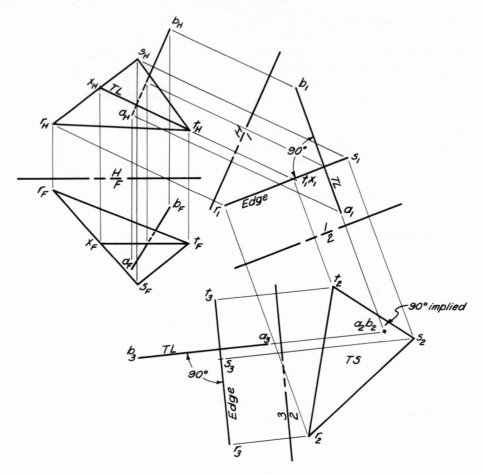

Fig. **10-14.** Line perpendicular to a plane.

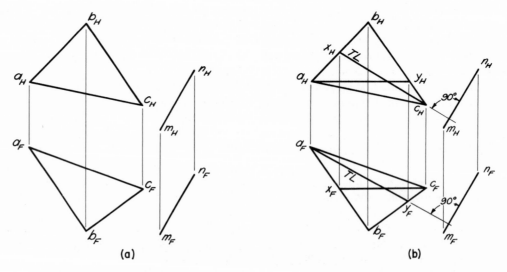

(a)   (b)

Fig. **10-15.** Proving a line perpendicular to a plane.

ar to a plane and passing through a point is established.

The construction shown in Fig. 10–7 and discussed in Art. 10–4 can be used in constructing a plane perpendicular to a line. This is illustrated in Fig. 10–17; the given conditions are shown in Fig. 10–17(a). The first step in constructing plane MNO perpendicular to line AB is to construct a horizontal line OX perpendicular to line AB as in

Fig. 10–17(b). The second step is to construct a frontal line MY perpendicular to line AB as in Fig. 10–17(c). This is accomplished by drawing the horizontal view of MY so as to locate point Y as the intersection of lines OX and MY. Then the frontal view of line MY can be drawn locating point M. Now the plane MNO contains two intersecting lines, OX and MY, both of which are perpendicular to line AB. Therefore plane MNO is perpendicular

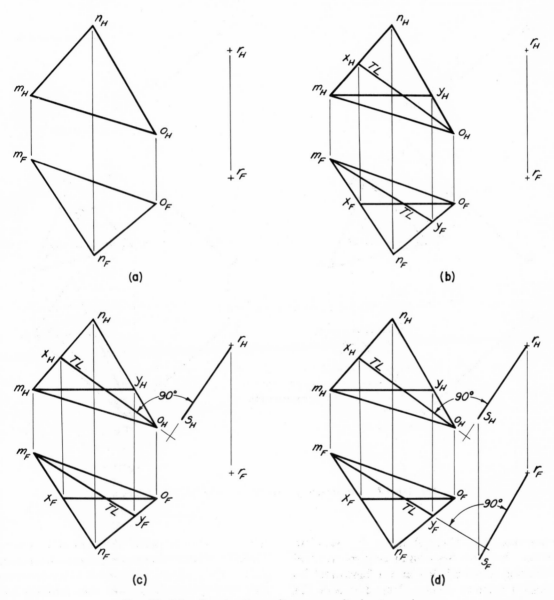

(a)   (b)   (c)   (d)

Fig. **10–16.** Constructing a line perpendicular to a plane.

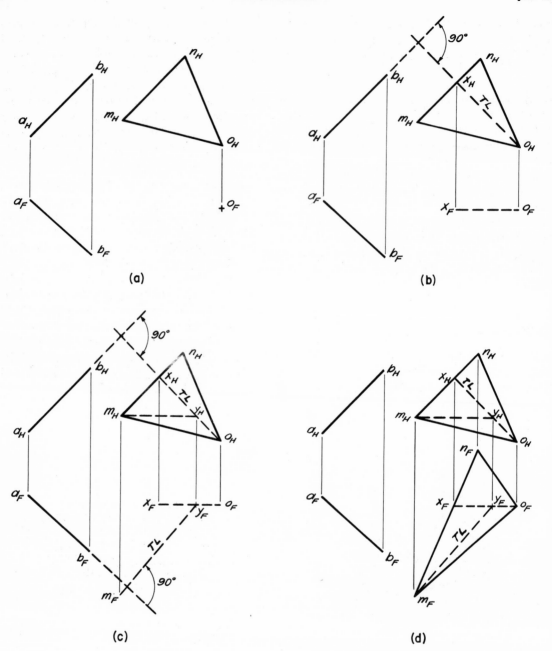

Fig. **10-17.** Constructing a plane perpendicular to a line.

to line *AB*. Fig. 10–17(d) shows the completed solution. Note that this solution consists essentially of drawing a frontal line and a horizontal line through a common point. These two lines then define the required plane. The rest of the solution is merely locating other given points in the required plane. The positions of *M* and *N* in the horizontal view were given in this case. Any arbitrary location of M and N could have been selected. In doing so, however, it is well to keep the points as widely separated as is convenient.

10-9. ANGLE BETWEEN TWO PLANES

The angle between two planes, sometimes referred to as a dihedral angle, is measurable only in a view that shows the edge view of both planes. Since the line of intersection of two planes is a line common to both planes, the view showing the end view of this line of intersection will also show the edge view of both planes and, therefore, the angle between the planes. Fig. 10-18 illustrates this construction. If the line of intersection is not given, it can be located by the methods discussed in Art. 9-15.

10-10. PARALLEL PLANES

When the angle between two planes is 0° or 180°, the planes are defined as being parallel. Fig. 10-19 shows two parallel planes the true shapes of which are determined by finding the true shape projection of one of them. A study of the views of Fig. 10-19 reveals the following two relations. First, if two planes are parallel, the view that shows the edge view of one will also show the edge view of the other parallel to the first. This view also shows the true distance, or clearance, between the two planes. Secondly, if two planes are parallel, the view that shows the true shape of one will also show the true shape of the other.

Further analysis of the spatial conditions involving parallel planes will yield the following rule: If two planes are parallel, for any line in one plane there must be a parallel line (or family of lines) in the other plane. Since two is the minimum number of lines that can represent a plane, this rule can be worded as: *If two planes are parallel, then two intersecting lines in one plane must be parallel to two intersecting lines in the other.* The word "intersecting" is necessary because, if lines are parallel to the line of intersection of the two planes, there could be an infinite number of lines in one plane parallel to lines in the other plane and the planes would not be parallel.

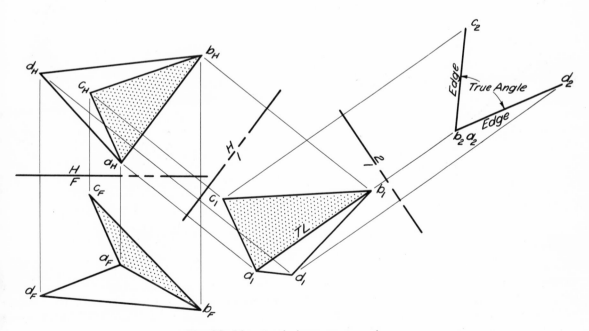

Fig. **10-18.** Angle between two planes.

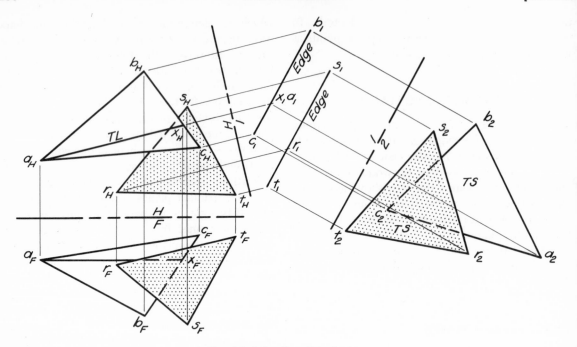

Fig. **10-19.** Parallel planes.

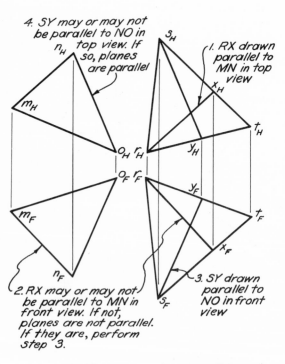

Fig. **10-20.** Proving planes parallel.

Fig. 10-20 illustrates the use of the above rule in proving whether or not two planes are parallel. In the first step, the horizontal projection of line *RX* in plane *RST* is constructed parallel to the horizontal projection of line *MN* in plane *MNO*. Then, in the second step, the frontal view of line *RX* in plane *RST* is located and the frontal views of lines *RX* and *MN* are checked to determine if they are parallel. If they are not parallel, the planes cannot be parallel. However, even though the frontal view of lines *RX* and *MN* are parallel, as in Fig. 10-20, the planes still are not necessarily parallel since lines *RX* and *MN* might be parallel to the line of intersection of the planes. To complete the proof, the construction is repeated (in steps 3 and 4), this time assuming that *SY* is parallel to *NO*. If line *SY* is parallel to line *NO* in the horizontal view, as it is in Fig. 10-19, then planes *RST* and *MNO* are parallel. If lines *SY* and *NO* were not parallel, the planes would not be parallel. It should be noted that this construction need not originate using the horizontal view. Both constructed lines could originate in the frontal view, or in the horizontal view.

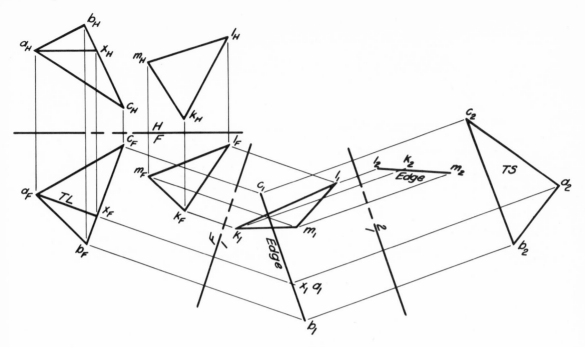

Fig. **10-21.** Perpendicular planes.

10-11. PERPENDICULAR PLANES

When the angle between two planes is 90°, the two planes are defined as being perpendicular. Fig. 10–21 shows two perpendicular planes projected so as to find the true shape of one of the planes. A study of the views of Fig. 10–21 reveals this relation: If two planes are perpendicular, the view showing the true shape of one must show the edge view of the other. Note that the converse of this relationship is not necessarily true, viz.: If two planes are perpendicular, the view showing the edge view of one does not necessarily show the true shape of the other.

Analysis of the spatial conditions involving the common perpendicularity of planes will yield the following rule: *If two planes are perpendicular, there must be a line (or family of lines) in one plane that is perpendicular to the second plane.*

Fig. 10–22 illustrates the proof of whether or not two planes are perpendicular by applying the above rule. The given planes are shown in Fig. 10–22(a). The first step is to construct a frontal and a horizontal line in either of the given planes as in plane

ABC in Fig. 10–22(b). A line perpendicular to the first plane is then constructed through some point O in the second plane, as line OZ in Fig. 10–22(c) and (d). If this line lies in the second plane (i.e., if point Z is in projection in both views), the planes are perpendicular, as is the case in Fig. 10–22. If the line does not lie in the second plane, the planes are not perpendicular.

The ability to prove planes perpendicular and, conversely, to construct perpendicular planes provides a shorter method for finding the angle between a line and a plane than was presented in Art. 10–5. This method is illustrated in Fig. 10–23. Line MN and plane ABC are given. A plane MNO is constructed perpendicular to plane ABC by constructing line NO perpendicular to plane ABC. Then the true-shape view of plane MNO is found. This view must also show the edge view of plane ABC since the two planes are perpendicular. Hence this view shows both the true length of line MN and the edge view of plane ABC and the angle between them is measurable by the use of only two auxiliary views. Note that the line NO which was constructed perpendicular to plane ABC must be at 90° to the edge view of plane ABC.

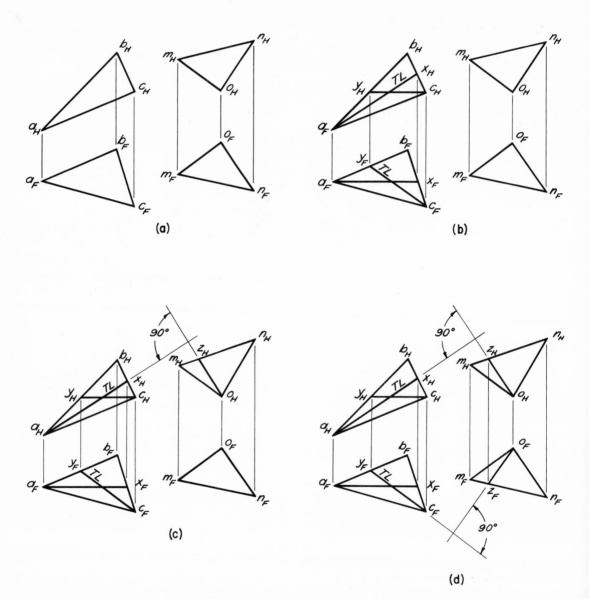

Fig. **10–22.** Proving planes perpendicular.

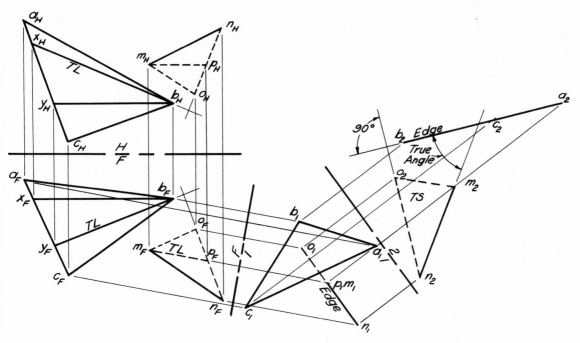

Fig. **10–23.** Angle between a line and a plane (perpendicular plane method).

Problems

Refer to the Appendix when plotting points. All problems are designed to be worked on $8\frac{1}{2}'' \times 11''$ sheets. When a problem has several parts, all parts are to be worked on the same sheet.

10-1. Determine the angle between line $A(2, 3, 7)$ $B(3\frac{1}{2}, 3, 8\frac{1}{2})$ and line $C(2, 4, 6)$ $D(3, 5, 6)$.

10-2. Determine the angle between line $R(1, 4\frac{1}{2}, 6)$ $S(3, 3, 8)$ and $M(1, 3, 7)$ $N(3, 4\frac{1}{2}, 5\frac{1}{2})$.

10-3. Line $M(1, 2, 6)$ $N(4, y, z)$ has a bearing of N 75° E and is parallel to line $R(3, 2, 5)$ $S(6, 4, Z)$. Construct the frontal and horizontal views of the lines.

10-4. $A(1, 1\frac{1}{2}, 7)$ $B(2, 1, 8)$ $CD(3, 3, 5)$ is a parallelogram base of a truncated prism. $DG(5, 3\frac{1}{2}, 4)$ is one of the equal lateral edges. Construct the frontal and horizontal views of the prism. Show correct visibility.

10-5. a. Locate line $M(5, 7, 7\frac{1}{4})N$ which is perpendicular to and intersects line $A(4, 6, 8)$ $B(5, 7, 9)$. Point N is on line AB.

      b. Locate line $R(2, 3, 4)$ $S(4\frac{1}{2}, y, 4)$ so that it is perpendicular to line $C(3, \frac{1}{2}, 2\frac{1}{2})$ $D(5, 2\frac{1}{2}, 4\frac{1}{2})$.

10-6. Line $A(2, 3, 5)$ $B(5, 4\frac{1}{2}, 7\frac{1}{2})$ represents the center line of a water pipe. This pipe is to be connected to point $C(5\frac{1}{2}, y, 5)$ by another pipe running from a 90° joint midway between points A and B. Locate the frontal view of point C.

10-7. Line $A(1, 2, 5)$ $B(3, 3, 4)$ is one edge of a square. Another corner of the square is on the line $AM(3\frac{1}{4}, y, 6)$. Construct the frontal and horizontal views of the square.

10-8. Determine the angle between line $A(4\frac{1}{2}, 1, 7\frac{1}{2})$ $B(6, 3, 7)$ and plane $M(5, 2\frac{1}{2}, 8)$ $N(6, 4, 7)$ $O(7, 1\frac{1}{2}, 6)$.

10-9. Determine the angle between line $R(1\frac{1}{4}, 2\frac{1}{2}, 5)$ $S(3\frac{1}{2}, 5, 6\frac{1}{2})$ and plane $A(1, 4, 5\frac{1}{2})$ $B(2, 3, 7)$ $C(3, 4\frac{1}{2}, 6)$.

10-10. a. Construct the line $A(6, 5\frac{1}{4}, 8\frac{1}{2})$ $B(4\frac{1}{2}, y, z)$ which has a bearing of S 45° W and is parallel to plane $M(1, 5\frac{1}{2}, 8)$ $N(2, 6, 7)$ $O(3\frac{1}{2}, 5, 9)$.

      b. Determine whether or not line $R(5, 2, 3)$ $S(6\frac{1}{2}, 1, 4)$ is parallel to plane $A(1, 1\frac{1}{2}, 3)$ $B(3, \frac{1}{2}, 4\frac{1}{2})$ $C(4, 3, 3\frac{1}{2})$.

10-11. a. Construct line $D(3\frac{1}{4}, y, 8)$ $E(4\frac{3}{4}, y, 6\frac{1}{2})$ parallel to plane $A(3, 5, 7)$ $B(4\frac{1}{4}, 4\frac{3}{4}, 6\frac{1}{2})$ $C(5\frac{1}{2}, 6, 8)$.

      b. Construct a plane that contains line $M(5, 1\frac{1}{2}, 2)$ $N(7, 1, 3)$ and is parallel to line $R(1, 1, 4)$ $S(3, 2, 2\frac{1}{2})$.

10-12. Construct line $M(3\frac{1}{4}, 3\frac{3}{4}, 7)N$ perpendicular to plane $A(3, 2, 6)$ $B(4\frac{1}{2}, 4\frac{1}{2}, 5\frac{1}{4})$ $C(5\frac{1}{2}, 3\frac{1}{4}, 7\frac{1}{4})$. Point N is in plane ABC.

10-13. Construct a plane $M(6, 4, 8)NO$ perpendicular to line $A(1, 5, 7)$ $B(3\frac{1}{2}, 3, 5\frac{1}{2})$.

10-14. Construct plane $M(1, y, 7\frac{1}{2})$ $N(2, 1, 9)$ $O(4, 4, 6\frac{1}{2})$ perpendicular to line $R(4\frac{1}{2}, 1\frac{3}{4}, z)$ $S(6\frac{1}{2}, 4, 9)$.

10-15. Determine the orthographic projection of plane $A(1, 2, 5\frac{1}{2})$ $B(2\frac{1}{2}, 2, 5\frac{1}{2})$ $C(2\frac{1}{2}, 3\frac{1}{2}, 5\frac{1}{2})$ onto plane $M(3, 3\frac{1}{4}, 8\frac{1}{2})$ $N(4, 2, 6\frac{1}{2})$ $O(6, 4\frac{1}{2}, 7\frac{1}{2})$.

10-16. Line $M(1\frac{1}{4}, y, z)$ $N(3, y, z)$ intersects both lines $A(1\frac{1}{2}, 1, 7)$ $B(4\frac{1}{2}, 4, 9)$ and $R(1\frac{1}{2}, 4, 6\frac{1}{2})$ $S(6\frac{1}{2}, 2, 7\frac{1}{2})$. Line MN is also perpendicular to plane ABC $(6, 2\frac{1}{2}, 6)$. Construct the frontal and horizontal views of line MN.

10-17. Determine the angle between planes $M(1\frac{3}{4}, 2\frac{1}{4}, 5\frac{1}{4})$ $N(3, 1, 6\frac{1}{2})$ $O(2\frac{1}{2}, 4\frac{1}{2}, 6\frac{1}{2})$ and $MNP(1, 1, 7)$.

10-18. A right circular cylinder whose diameter is 1″ and whose length is 1″ is placed so that its cylindrical face touches both planes $A(1\frac{1}{4}, 1\frac{1}{2}, 6)$ $B(1, 2\frac{3}{4}, 4\frac{3}{4})$ $C(2\frac{1}{2}, 1\frac{3}{4}, 7)$ and $BCD(2\frac{3}{4}, 1, 5)$. The cylinder is located midway between points B and C. Determine the lines of tangency between the cylinder and the planes.

10-19. a. Determine whether the planes $A(2, 6\frac{1}{2}, 8)$ $B(3, 6, 7\frac{1}{4})$ $C(4, 6\frac{1}{4}, 7\frac{1}{2})$ and $M(5, 6, 7\frac{1}{2})$ $N(6, 7\frac{1}{4}, 8\frac{1}{2})$ $O(7, 6\frac{1}{2}, 8)$ are parallel.

      b. Construct the plane $R(4\frac{1}{2}, y, 2\frac{3}{4})$ $S(5\frac{3}{4}, 1, 4)$ $T(7, 1\frac{1}{2}, z)$ parallel to plane $D(1\frac{1}{2}, 1\frac{1}{4}, 3\frac{1}{4})$ $E(2\frac{3}{4}, \frac{1}{2}, 4)$ $F(3\frac{3}{4}, 2, 2\frac{1}{4})$.

10-20. Point $R(4, 2\frac{3}{4}, z)$ is the upper left corner of a $1\frac{1}{2}″$ square $RSTU$. The plane of $RSTU$ is parallel to and 1″ away from plane $A(1, 3, 6)$ $B(2\frac{1}{4}, 3\frac{3}{4}, 7\frac{1}{2})$ $C(3\frac{1}{4}, 2\frac{1}{2}, 6\frac{3}{4})$. Plane $RSTU$ is in front of plane ABC and two edges of the square are horizontal. Construct the frontal and horizontal views of the square.

10-21. a. Construct a plane $R(4, 7, 9)$ $S(3\frac{1}{2}, y, z)$ $T(4\frac{1}{2}, y, z)$ so that it is perpendicular to both planes $A(1\frac{1}{4}, 7, 8\frac{1}{2})$ $B(1\frac{1}{2}, 6, 9\frac{1}{4})$ $C(2\frac{3}{4}, 6\frac{1}{2}, 8)$ and $M(5\frac{1}{2}, 6\frac{1}{2}, 7\frac{1}{2})$ $N(6\frac{1}{4}, 5\frac{1}{2}, 9\frac{1}{4})$ $O(7, 7\frac{1}{2}, 8\frac{1}{2})$.

      b. Construct a plane RST so that it is parallel to and equidistant from both lines $A(1, \frac{1}{4}, 4)$ $B(3, 2, 2\frac{3}{4})$ and $C(5, 2, 3)$ $D(7, \frac{1}{2}, 4\frac{1}{4})$. Locate points R, S, and T as desired.

10-22. Locate plane $R(4, 3, 6\frac{1}{2})$ $S(5, 4\frac{1}{2}, 8\frac{1}{2})$ $T(7, y, 8)$ so that it is perpendicular to plane $M(1, 3, 6)$ $N(2, 2, 8\frac{1}{2})$ $O(3\frac{1}{4}, 4, 7\frac{1}{2})$.

10-23. Line $A(3\frac{1}{2}, y, 8)$ $B(5, y, 7\frac{3}{4})$ lies in plane $M(3, 2, 8\frac{1}{2})$ $N(6, 4, 7\frac{1}{2})$ $O(4, 3, 6\frac{1}{2})$ and is one edge of a square $ABCD$ whose plane is perpendicular to plane MNO. Construct the frontal and horizontal views of $ABCD$.

11

SPECIAL PROBLEMS INVOLVING SPATIAL RELATIONS

11-1. INTRODUCTION

Beyond the more basic problems involving the spatial relations of points, lines, and planes and the interangular relations which may occur between them, there are certain problems that merit special consideration. These problems frequently occur in the design process in many fields of engineering. Some occur so frequently in their field that special terminology has evolved, and special concepts of the spatial relations involved in their solution have been developed. Primarily they involve the establishment of lines and planes in particular positions with reference to other lines and planes, or the determination of the location and length of certain lines (i.e., "shortest distances"). This chapter discusses the spatial relations of such problems and defines terminology where applicable.

11-2. STRIKE AND DIP OF A PLANE

In discussing the position of a plane in space, it is convenient to use the terms "strike" and "dip."

These are terms common in mining and petroleum, and civil engineering, or wherever the direction and slope of a plane are considered. The *strike* of a plane is defined as the direction of a horizontal line lying in the plane. This direction is usually stated as a bearing (see Art. 9-4). The *dip* of a plane is defined as the angle that the plane makes with a horizontal plane. Dip is the acute angle and is always measured below the horizontal.

Since the angle between two planes is measurable in the view which shows both planes in edge view (see Art. 10-9), the auxiliary view showing the dip of a plane will be projected from the horizontal view as in Fig. 11-1. Here the plane ABC has a strike of N 60° E and a dip of 45°. To rigidly define a plane by strike and dip, the direction that the plane dips from the strike must also be given. This is the direction that is perpendicular to the strike and points down the slope of the plane. It is generally indicated by a short, heavy arrow in the horizontal view. In Fig. 11-1, the direction of dip is southeasterly.

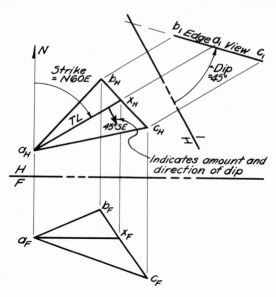

Fig. 11–1.   Strike and dip of a plane.

11–3. PRINCIPAL ANGLES OF LINES AND PLANES, COMPOUND ANGLES

These are the angles which a line or plane make with the principal planes of projection. The angl that a plane makes with the horizontal plane ha been discussed in the preceding article; the angl that a line makes with the horizontal plane ha been discussed in Art. 10–6. By similar method the other principal angles of lines and planes ca be determined. The principal angles of a line AB are shown in Fig. 11–2 and the principal angle of a plane ABC are shown in Fig. 11–3.

In machining processes, statements are fre quently made that an oblique axis (line) or surface (plane) makes a compound angle with the principa axes or planes of a machine or machine part. Thi refers to the fact that the location of such obliqu lines and planes is established by giving any two of the principal angles that they make with the principal axes or planes of the machine or machine part.

11–4. SHORTEST DISTANCE (CLEARANCE) FROM A POINT TO A LINE OR PLANE

An engineer is frequently concerned with clear-ances or "shortest distances." Typical examples of clearance are the distance between moving parts or the distance between electric circuits to prevent arcing. The shortest distance from a point to a line or plane is the perpendicular distance from the point to the line or plane. The construction of a line perpendicular to another line has been dis-cussed in Art. 10–4. Fig. 11–4 illustrates how this construction is applied to the shortest distance from a point D to a line AB. First the true-length view (first auxiliary) and then the end view of line AB (second auxiliary) are obtained. Since the shortest distance (line DE) from point D to the line AB is a line through point D perpendicular to line AB, line DE will be seen in true length in the second auxiliary. The location of line DE (if desired) in the first auxiliary is therefore parallel to the second auxiliary plane of projection. With two views of the shortest distance DE located, the frontal and hori-zontal views of DE can be located by projection.

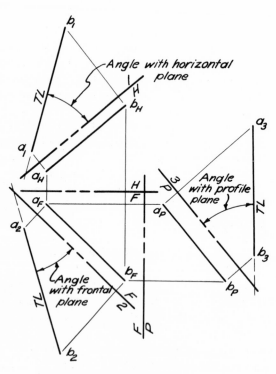

Fig. 11–2.   Principal angles of a line.

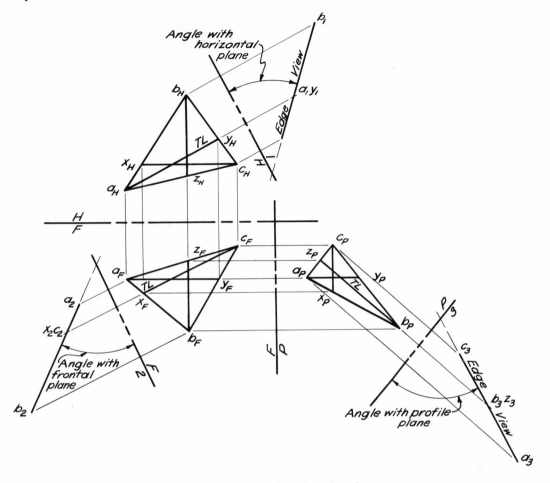

Fig. **11–3.** Principal angles of a plane.

The construction of a line through a point and perpendicular to a plane has been discussed in Art. 10–8. In the method described, the point where the perpendicular line pierces the given plane would need to be located and the distance from the given point to the piercing point determined. A second method of determining the shortest distance (establishing a perpendicular) from a point to a plane is shown in Fig. 11–5. An auxiliary is constructed showing the point R and the edge view of the plane MNO. In this view the shortest distance from the point to the plane will appear in true length and will be perpendicular to the edge view. Since the plane shows as an edge view, the piercing point S of the line and plane

can be directly located, and the clearance can be projected back to the frontal and horizontal views if necessary.

11–5. SHORTEST DISTANCE (CLEARANCE) BETWEEN TWO NON-INTERSECTING LINES

The shortest distance between two non-intersecting lines is the distance measured along a line perpendicular to both the given lines. Fig. 11–6 shows the necessary construction for determining the shortest distance between the given lines AB and CD. A view showing the true length of both AB and CD simultaneously is found by the method

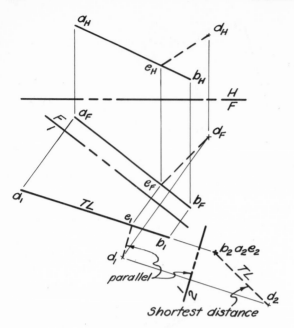

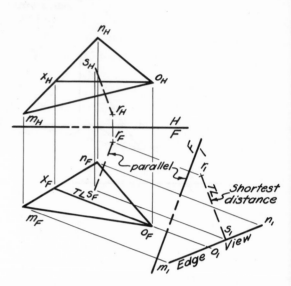

Fig. **11–4.** Shortest distance between a point and a line.

Fig. **11–5.** Shortest distance between a point and a plane.

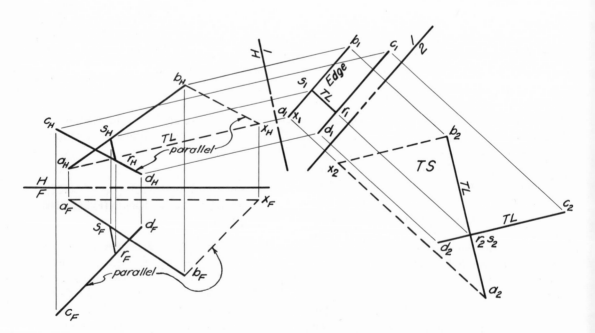

Fig. **11–6.** Shortest distance between non-intersecting lines.

discussed in Art. 10–7. This consists of establishing a plane through one line (*AB*) such that the plane is parallel to the second line, and obtaining first the edge view and then the true-shape view of this plane (*ABX*). The latter view also shows both lines *AB* and *CD* in true length. In this view the line perpendicular to both non-intersecting lines would show as an end view at the point where *AB* and *CD* appear to intersect. This common perpendicular is called line *RS*. Since line *RS* appears as an end view in the second auxiliary, the first auxiliary must show its true length. With two views of line *RS* located, the line can be projected back to the frontal and horizontal views, if desired.

In projecting the line *RS* back to the horizontal view, $r_H s_H$ projects parallel to the first auxiliary plane since line *RS* is true length in the first auxiliary. This fact also means that $r_H s_H$ must project at 90° to $a_H x_H$, which is the true length view of the horizontal line *AX* lying in plane *ABX*. Thus it is proved that the shortest distance (*RS*) between two non-intersecting lines (*AB* and *CD*) is perpendicular to a horizontal line (*AX*) lying in a plane (*ABX*) parallel to the two given lines.

11–6. SHORTEST SLOPE DISTANCE BETWEEN TWO NON-INTERSECTING LINES

Any shortest distance between two non-intersecting lines will always appear in true length in that auxiliary view showing the non-intersecting lines as apparently parallel. The slope of a line is always measured in a view showing the true length of the line projected from the horizontal view (Art. 10–6). Therefore the relationship just proved in Art. 11–5 can be altered to read: The shortest distance of any specified slope connecting two non-intersecting lines will be a line perpendicular to a horizontal line lying in a plane which is parallel to the two given lines. Because of these relationships, two conditions will always be found: first, the slope angle of any shortest distance is always measurable in the required first auxiliary since the line appears in true length and the edge view of the horizontal plane is shown; and second, all shortest distances will have the same bearing in the horizontal view since they are all true length in the required first auxiliary. Fig. 11–7 shows

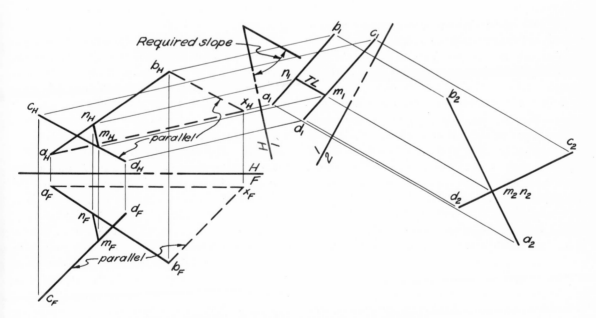

Fig. **11–7.** Shortest slope distance between non-intersecting lines.

the construction to locate the shortest line of a specified slope connecting the non-intersecting lines AB and CD. The direction of projection for the second auxiliary is established by constructing a line of the required slope in the first auxiliary as shown in Fig. 11-7, and projecting parallel to this slope line.

If the required slope angle is 0° (or 180°), the construction would determine the shortest horizontal connector of the two non-intersecting lines. If the required slope is 90° the shortest connector is a vertical line and would appear as an end view in both the horizontal and the second auxiliary views.

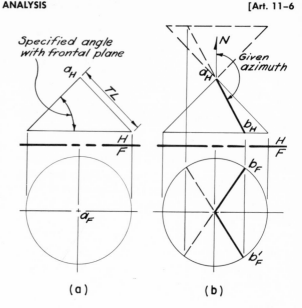

(a)   (b)

Fig. 11-8. Line at a specified angle to a plane.

11-7. LINE AT A SPECIFIED ANGLE WITH A PLANE OR ANOTHER LINE

When a line must be constructed at a specified angle with a plane or another line, the construction can be accomplished by establishing auxiliaries to obtain views showing the plane of the angle in true size. This has been discussed in Chapter 10. Many times the construction can be simplified with the aid of a right circular cone whose lateral surface is the locus of all lines drawn at the required angle to the plane or line.

While the initial requirements of a problem must be analyzed to determine the position of the conical locus of such lines, a view showing the true length of the cone's axis (the cone appears as an isosceles triangle) and a circular view of the base of the cone must always be constructed. Fig. 11-8 shows the construction of a line having a given azimuth and a given angle with the frontal plane. The line is to be drawn through point A. The locus of all lines that make a specified angle with the frontal plane is a right circular cone whose base angle is the required angle and whose base is parallel to the frontal plane. The horizontal view of the cone will appear as an isosceles triangle with the vertex at a_H, and the frontal view of the cone will be a circle as in Fig. 11-8(a). The vertex of the cone is at point A and the slant height of the cone is the true length of all elements of the cone. Then a line of the given azimuth is drawn through point A and the point where the line intersects the base of the

cone (B) is located as in Fig. 11-8(b). There are two possible solutions, AB and AB', since both are elements of the cone. The upper nappe of the cone could be shown as indicated by the dashed line construction in the horizontal view of Fig. 11-8(b). The solutions so obtained would merely be extensions of lines AB or AB'. If the required azimuth did not fall within the isosceles view of the cone, there would be no solution for the given conditions.

In Fig. 11-9 it is required to draw a frontal line AC at some specified angle with line AB. The locus of all lines that make the required angle with line AB is a right circular cone whose vertex angle is twice the required angle and whose axis is the line AB. The cone will appear as an isosceles triangle in the view showing the true length of the line AB and as a circle in the view showing the end view of the line. In this example the true length view is projected from the frontal view because of the requirement that line AC also be a frontal line. A frontal line must project parallel to the edge view of the frontal plane. Note that there are again two possible answers, AC and AC', as shown in Fig. 11-9. Dependent upon the initial conditions, there may be zero, one, or two possible real solutions in problems involving a single cone.

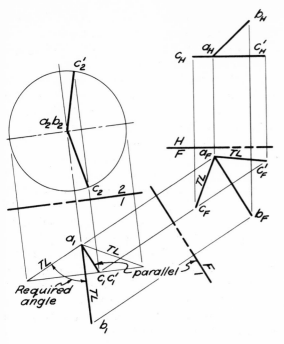

Fig. **11–9.** Line at a specified angle to another line.

11–8. LINE AT SPECIFIED ANGLES WITH TWO PLANES OR LINES

If a line is to be constructed at specified angles with two planes, the use of conical loci is the only practical solution. Again an analysis of the statement of the problem is essential in order to determine the positions of the cones for the proper solution of the problem.

Consider the case of a line at some specified angle with the horizontal plane and another specified angle with the frontal plane. In Fig. 11–10 such a line is to be constructed through point A. First, assume some convenient length for the line if the length is not specified. Consider the locus of all lines of that length passing through point A. The locus would be a sphere with its center at point A and a radius equal to the true length of the line as in Fig. 11–10(a). Next, consider the locus of all lines of the assumed length that make the required angle with the frontal plane. This locus would be a right circular cone with vertex at point A, a slant height equal to the true length of the

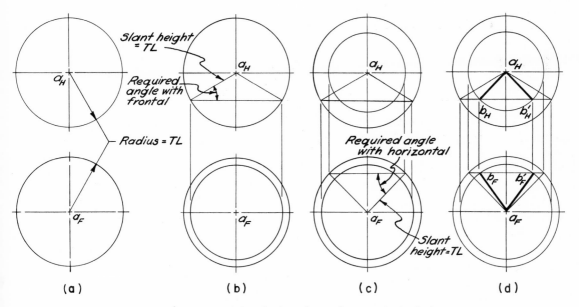

Fig. **11–10.** Line at specified angles with two principal planes.

line, and a base parallel to the frontal plane as in Fig. 11–10(b). The horizontal view would appear as an isosceles triangle and the frontal view would appear as a circle. The base of the cone would intersect the sphere, the edge of the base of the cone being the line of intersection of the cone and sphere. Finally, consider the locus of all lines of the assumed length that make the required angle with the horizontal plane. This locus would be a right circular cone whose base is parallel to the horizontal plane, as in Fig. 11–10(c). The edge of the base of this cone would also be a line on the surface of the sphere. Since the edges of both bases are lines on the surface of the same sphere, the points where the edges of the bases cross each other must be real points of intersection. The term "real points" is used because, if the edges of the bases of the two cones were not intersections on the surface of a sphere, the two bases could cross each other without the rims of the bases actually intersecting. Thus point B in Fig. 11–10(d) is a point common to the two cones and the line AB is an element of both cones and there-fore the required line. In this example, the edges of the bases intersect at two points resulting in two possible solutions, lines AB and AB'. If the edges were tangent, there would be only one solution and, if there were no intersection of bases, there would be no solution. By considering the other nappe of each cone, the number of solutions in each case is doubled. Specification of general direction and either positive or negative slope would limit the number of solutions to one.

It is important to note here that, in problems involving the use of two conical loci as in the example above, the slant height of both cones must be the same since both slant heights must be radii of the same sphere. A view (or views) showing the true length of the axes of both cones will also show the true lengths of the slant heights and the edge views of the bases. Only one view of the actual intersection of the edges at the point where they cross is necessary to locate the point. This fact is used in Fig. 11–11 where a line is constructed at a given angle to the frontal plane and a given angle to plane ABC. In the auxiliary view of Fig. 11–11,

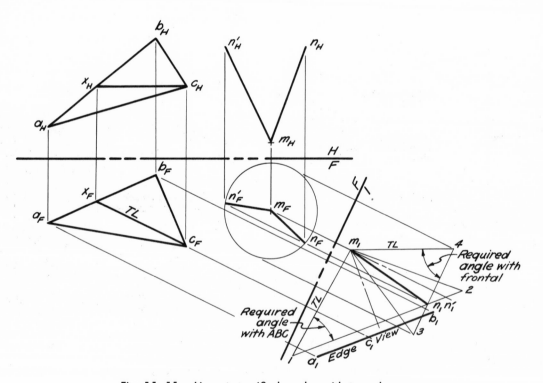

Fig. 11–11. Line at specified angles with two planes.

triangle *M12* represents the isosceles view of the cone that is the locus of lines making the required angle with plane *ABC*. Triangle *M34* represents the isosceles view of the cone that makes the required angle with the frontal plane. The axes of both cones are likewise in true length in this first auxiliary and the bases are seen as edges. Since both cones were constructed with equal slant heights, the edges of the bases intersect at points *N* and *N'*. These points may be projected to the frontal view, locating them on the circle which is the frontal view of the cone *M34*. Lines *MN* and *MN'* are two of the possible solutions. Dependent upon the angle between the two given planes and the two specified angles, there are 0, 1, 2, 3, or 4 solutions if both nappes are used.

Fig. 11–12 shows the two-cone method applied in the construction of a line intersecting two non-intersecting lines at specified angles to each. First the view showing the true lengths of both the non-intersecting lines *AB* and *CD* was found by the

method discussed in Art. 10–2, in which the lines are successively projected so as to: (a) show the true length of one; (b) show the end view of that line; and (c) show the true length of both lines. Since this third view would become crowded with construction, a removed view was constructed with center lines parallel respectively to the true length of *AB* and to the true length of *CD*. These center lines then represent true lengths on which are constructed the two locus cones. Triangle *X12* represents the isosceles view of the cone with elements making the specified angle with line *AB* (the center line of the cone is parallel to *AB*). Triangle *X34* represents the isosceles view of the cone with elements making the specified angle with line *CD*. In each case the vertex angle is twice the specified angle. Since the slant heights of the cones are made the same, the bases intersect at point 5. The construction of the circular view of cone *X34* locates another view of point 5. Line *X5* is a line parallel to the desired line making the

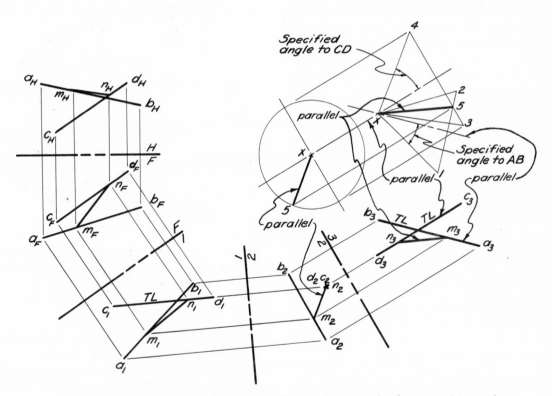

Fig. **11–12.** Shortest connector at specified angles to each of two non-intersecting lines.

specified angles with both lines *AB* and *CD*. The desired line may now be located. First, from the end view of line *CD*, a line *MN* is drawn parallel to the corresponding view of *X5*. This locates point *M* on line *AB*. Then, point *M* is projected to the view showing the true length of lines *AB* and *CD*, and again line *MN* is drawn parallel to the corresponding view of *X5*. The location of line *MN* is now definitely established and it can be projected to the frontal and horizontal views. By construction, line *MN* intersects both lines *AB* and *CD* and is at the specified angle to each.

11–9. PLANE AT A SPECIFIED ANGLE WITH A PRINCIPAL PLANE

If a plane is to be constructed at some specified angle with a second plane, it must be tangent to a right circular cone which has a base angle of the specified value and whose base is parallel to the second plane.

A plane that is tangent to a cone will contain a line that is an element of the cone and a line that is tangent to a circular section of the cone. If a line is tangent to a circle, the line must lie in the plane of that circle.

Fig. 11–13 shows a plane passed through line *MN* and making a specified angle with the frontal plane. Plane *MNO* is the required plane since it contains the given line *MN*; contains an element of the cone, line *MO*; and also contains a line that is tangent to a circular section of the cone, line *NX*.

11–10. PLANE AT SPECIFIED ANGLES WITH TWO PRINCIPAL PLANES

If a plane makes specified angles with two of the principal planes, then a line perpendicular to that plane will make complementary specified angles with the same principal planes. This is proven in Fig. 11–14. In this illustration, an auxiliary view is first constructed showing the angle plane *ABC* makes with the horizontal plane. Since plane *ABC* is shown in edge view, any line perpendicular to plane *ABC* will appear in true length and at right angles to the edge view. Since the perpendicular line is true length, its angle with the horizontal is measurable. Plane geometry proves that the angle

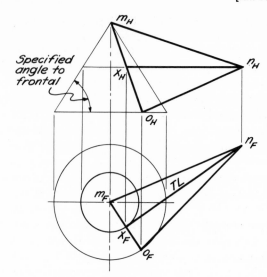

Fig. **11–13.** Plane through a line at a specified angle to another plane.

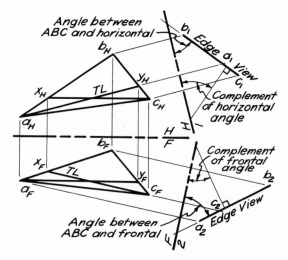

Fig. **11–14.** Proof that the principal angles of a line perpendicular to a plane are the complements of the principal angles of the plane.

of the perpendicular line with the horizontal is the complement of the angle between plane *ABC* and the horizontal plane. Next, an auxiliary is constructed showing the angle plane *ABC* makes with the frontal plane. The same argument as above proves that the angle between the frontal plane and a line perpendicular to plane ABC is the complement of the angle between plane ABC and the frontal plane.

Therefore, to construct a plane at specified angles with two principal planes, first construct a line which would be perpendicular to the required plane (i.e., making complementary angles with the principal planes). Then construct the required plane perpendicular to this line. This is illustrated in Fig. 11–15. A plane is to be constructed so that it makes angles of 60° with the horizontal plane and 45° with the frontal plane. In Fig. 11–15(a), a line AB is constructed at the complementary angles: 30° with the horizontal and 45° with the frontal using the method of conical loci (Art. 11–8). Remember that in both cones the slant height must have the same length. In Fig. 11–15(b), the line AB is shown without the conical construction necessary to locate it. Plane MNO is constructed perpendicular to line AB and becomes the required plane. Plane MNO is constructed by the methods of Art. 10–8 as illustrated in Fig. 10–17.

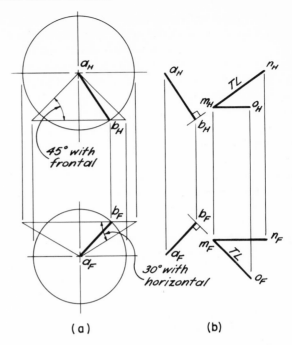

(a)   (b)

Fig. 11–15. Construction of a plane at specified angles to two principal planes.

Problems

Refer to Appendix, Plotting Problems, when plotting points such as $A(2\frac{1}{2}, 1, 3)$. All problems are designed to be worked on $8\frac{1}{2}'' \times 11''$ sheets. When a problem has several parts, all parts are to be worked on the same sheet.

11–1. The head of a transit is located at point $A(6\frac{1}{2}, 1\frac{1}{2}, 3\frac{1}{2})$. It is desired to sight on a rod held vertically at point $B(1, 2, 7)$. The top edge of a barn roof runs from point $C(3, 1\frac{3}{4}, 4)$ to point $D(5, 1\frac{3}{4}, 5\frac{1}{2})$. Determine the minimum vertical angle at which the rod can be seen.

11–2. Construct a line $A(1, 4, 7)B$ which is $5''$ long, has a bearing of S 60° E, and a slope of $-40°$.

11–3. Construct a line $C(6, 3, 6)D$ which is $4''$ long, has a bearing of 65° W, and a slope of $-30°$.

11–4. Determine the strike and dip of plane $A(4, 2\frac{1}{4}, 6\frac{1}{2})$ $B(6, 3, 8\frac{1}{2})$ $C(7, 1, 7)$.

11–5. Locate plane $A(1, 2, 5)$ $B(2\frac{1}{2}, 1\frac{1}{4}, z)$ $C(4\frac{1}{4}, y, 5\frac{3}{4})$ which has a strike of N 60° E and a dip of 45° in a NW direction.

11–6. Plane $A(1, y, 4)$ $B(2, 1, 6)$ $C(3\frac{1}{2}, y, 5)$ has a strike of N 35° E and a dip of 60° in a NW direction. Locate point D lying in plane of and equidistant from points A, B, and C.

11–7. Points $A(5, 2\frac{1}{2}, 6)$ and $D(6\frac{1}{2}, 3\frac{1}{2}, 5)$ are diagonally opposite corners of a square which lies in a plane having a strike of S 70° W and a dip of 30° in a NW direction. Construct the square.

11-8. Line $R(1, 2, 7)$ $S(3, 2, 5)$ is in plane RST which has a dip of 30° in a SW direction. Plane $ABC(3\frac{1}{2}, y, 7\frac{3}{4})$ is perpendicular to plane RST and has the same strike as does plane RST. ABC is a triangle whose base lies in plane RST. The altitude of ABC is 1″, side AC is $1\frac{1}{2}$″, and side BC is 2″. Construct the frontal and horizontal views of ABC.

11-9. a. Determine the angle that line $A(\frac{1}{2}, 5, 6\frac{1}{2})$ $B(2\frac{1}{2}, 4, 6\frac{1}{2})$ makes with the horizontal plane.
b. Determine the angle that line $C(5, 3, 4\frac{1}{2})$ $D(7, 1\frac{1}{4}, 3\frac{1}{2})$ makes with the frontal plane.

11-10. Determine the angles that line $A(1, 3, 7)$ $B(3, 4, 5)$ makes with the three principal planes.

11-11. Determine the angles that plane $A(1, 3, 4)$ $B(2, 2, 7)$ $C(3, 4, 5\frac{1}{2})$ makes with the three principal planes.

11-12. a. Determine the clearance between point $M(5, 6, 7\frac{1}{2})$ and line $A(2, 5, 7)$ $B(6, 7, 9\frac{1}{2})$.
b. Point $R(3\frac{1}{2}, \frac{1}{2}, z)$ must clear line $C(2, 2, 2\frac{1}{2})$ $D(5, 1, 4)$ by exactly 1″. Locate point R.

11-13. Locate points $R(3, y, 6\frac{1}{2})$ and $S(4\frac{1}{2}, 3, z)$ that are 1″ away from plane $A(1, 3, 5)$ $B(3\frac{1}{2}, 2, 8)$ $C(5, 5, 7)$.

11-14. Construct a view showing the true length of both lines $A(\frac{1}{2}, 2, 5\frac{1}{4})$ $B(2\frac{1}{2}, 1, 6\frac{3}{4})$ and $C(1, 2, 6\frac{1}{2})$ $D(2\frac{3}{4}, 1, 5)$.

11-15. Locate the common perpendicular to lines $A(\frac{1}{2}, 4\frac{1}{2}, 7)$ $B(2\frac{1}{2}, 3\frac{1}{4}, 8)$ and $D(2\frac{1}{2}, 3\frac{1}{2}, 6)$ $E(3\frac{1}{2}, 5\frac{1}{2}, 8)$.

11-16. Lines $A(4, 1, 7)$ $B(7, 3, 5)$ and $C(4\frac{1}{4}, 2\frac{3}{4}, 5\frac{1}{2})$ $D(6\frac{1}{4}, 2, 7)$ represent two control cables in the tail section of an aircraft. Determine the clearance between the cables.

11-17. Locate the shortest vertical and the shortest horizontal connectors of lines $A(\frac{3}{4}, 4, 5)$ $B(3\frac{3}{4}, 2, 6)$ and $C(1, 3, 6\frac{3}{4})$ $D(3\frac{1}{4}, 4\frac{1}{2}, 5\frac{1}{2})$.

11-18. Locate the shortest line (MN) that slopes downward at 20° from line $C(1, 3\frac{1}{4}, 6\frac{1}{4})$ $D(3, 4\frac{1}{2}, 5\frac{1}{2})$ to line $A(\frac{1}{2}, 3\frac{3}{4}, 4\frac{1}{4})$ $B(3, 2\frac{1}{2}, 6\frac{1}{2})$.

11-19. Locate line $A(3\frac{1}{2}, 3\frac{1}{2}, 6)B$ which has an azimuth of 315°, is 3″ long, and makes an angle of 30° with the frontal plane. Point B is above point A.

11-20. Locate and determine the length of line $A(3\frac{1}{2}, 4, 7)$ $B(2\frac{1}{2}, 2\frac{3}{4}, z)$ which makes an angle of 45° with the horizontal. Point B is to the rear of point A.

11-21. Construct line $C(4, 3, 6)D$ that is perpendicular to line $A(1, 3\frac{1}{2}, 7\frac{1}{2})$ $B(3\frac{1}{2}, 2, 5)$ and also makes an angle of 30° with the horizontal. Point D is below and to the left of point C.

11-22. Construct line $A(3\frac{1}{2}, 3, 6\frac{1}{2})B$ which is 2″ long, and makes an angle of 30° with the frontal and 45° with the horizontal. Point B is to the left of, above, and to the rear of point A.

11-23. Construct line $A(3\frac{1}{2}, 3\frac{3}{4}, 6\frac{1}{4})B$ that makes an angle of 30° with the frontal and 45° with plane $M(1, 1, 7)$ $N(2, 2\frac{1}{4}, 8\frac{1}{4})$ $O(3\frac{1}{2}, 1\frac{1}{2}, 6)$. Point B is to the left of and below point A.

11-24. Construct the shortest line MN that intersects both lines $A(\frac{1}{2}, 3\frac{1}{2}, 6)$ $B(2\frac{1}{4}, 2\frac{1}{4}, 4\frac{1}{4})$ and $C(1, 2\frac{1}{4}, 6\frac{3}{4})$ $D(3\frac{1}{4}, 3\frac{1}{2}, 4\frac{1}{4})$, making an angle of 30° with line AB and 45° with line CD.

11-25. Construct plane $A(2\frac{1}{2}, 4\frac{1}{4}, 6\frac{3}{4})$ $B(5\frac{1}{2}, 2, 8\frac{1}{2})C$ which makes an angle of 45° with the frontal.

11-26. Construct plane $R(1, 3, 6\frac{1}{2})$ $S(2\frac{1}{2}, 4, 5\frac{1}{3})T$ which makes an angle of 60° with plane $A(\frac{1}{2}, 2\frac{1}{2}, 4\frac{1}{4})$ $B(3\frac{1}{4}, 4, 5\frac{1}{4})$ $C(2\frac{1}{4}, 1, 6\frac{1}{2})$.

11-27. Construct a plane which makes an angle of 60° with the frontal and 45° with the horizontal.

11-28. Construct a plane that passes through point $M(2\frac{3}{4}, 2, 4\frac{3}{4})$ and makes an angle of 30° with the horizontal and an angle of 60° with plane $A(1, 2\frac{1}{2}, 5)$ $B(1\frac{3}{4}, 3\frac{3}{4}, 4\frac{1}{4})$ $C(3, 3, 6)$.

12

VECTOR GEOMETRY

12-1. INTRODUCTION

Numerical quantities used by the engineer in his daily work may be classified as either scalar or vector quantities. *Scalar quantities* are completely described by (a) a number representing magnitude, and (b) a unit of measure. For example, typical scalar quantities are: speed = 25 miles per hour, time = 25 seconds, or temperature = 100° Centigrade. *Vector quantities* are those having the direction of application specified, in addition to a number representing magnitude and a unit of measure; thus, velocity, force, and displacement are vector quantities. As previously noted, a speed of 25 miles per hour is a scalar quantity stating the speed only, but when the direction of motion is prescribed, the quantity becomes a vector quantity: velocity. A velocity of 25 miles per hour due east is a vector quantity describing the speed and the direction of a given object. The exact position of this object can be forecast for any time of travel.

Because vector quantities require both a unit of measure and a direction, problems involving vectors lend themselves quite naturally to a graphical

method of solution. This chapter defines the terminology used in vector geometry and explains the theories involved in the graphical solution of vectorial problems.

12-2. VECTOR REPRESENTATION

A vector may be represented by a directed line segment as in Fig. 12–1. Here the position of the line segment shows the line of action, and the scaled length indicates the magnitude (10 units in this case). Note that the line of action does not of itself show whether the vector is acting up to the right or down to the left. The arrowhead must be added to show the *sense*, or specific direction, of the vector. The end of the vector with the arrowhead is called the tip and the other end is called the tail. The vector shown in Fig. 12–1 could represent a force, an acceleration, a displacement, or any vector quantity of 10 units applied in the direction indicated. A vector may be applied anywhere along its line of action without changing the external effect of the vector.

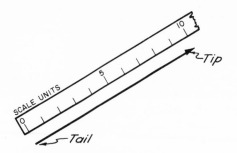

Fig. 12–1. Graphical representation of a vector.

12–3. VECTOR SYSTEMS

Two or more vectors whose lines of action are related form a vector system. The *components* of a vector system are the individual vectors of the system. The *resultant* of a vector system is the single vector whose effect is the same as that of the system and could replace the vector system.

Vector components may lie in a common plane, in which case they are said to be *coplanar*. If they do not all lie in the same plane, the system is termed a *non-coplanar* system. If two or more vector components have a common line of action, they are *collinear*. When the lines of action (extended, if necessary) of the vector components intersect at a common point, they are *concurrent*. If the lines of action do not intersect at a common point, they are *non-concurrent*.

Since collinear vectors may be considered as coplanar, vector systems may be grouped under four general headings: (a) coplanar, concurrent; (b) coplanar, non-concurrent; (c) non-coplanar, concurrent; and (d) non-coplanar, non-concurrent. The following portions of this chapter discuss in detail the first three general headings, but non-coplanar, non-concurrent systems become so complex that they are considered to be beyond the scope of this text.

Coplanar, Concurrent Vector Systems

12–4. VECTOR COMPOSITION

Vector composition is the process of geometrically adding the components of a vector system to determine the resultant. The resultant of a coplanar, concurrent vector system is easy to determine when the vectors are collinear. In this case, the resultant is simply the algebraic sum[1] of the vector quantities. When the vectors of the system are not collinear, the resultant is the geometric sum of the vector quantities. Fig. 12–2(a) shows a vector system of two vectors, V_x and V_y. Point O is the point of concurrency, or intersection, of the vectors. Fig. 12–2(b) shows the resultant V_r as determined by the parallelogram method. In this method the resultant is the diagonal of the parallelogram formed by lines drawn parallel to V_x and V_y. Fig. 12–2(c) shows the polygon method of determining the resultant. In the polygon method, the vectors of a system are arranged tip to tail with each vector drawn parallel to its actual line of action. Thus, V_x is added to V_y by placing the tail of V_x so that it touches the tip of V_y. The resultant

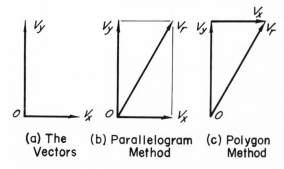

(a) The Vectors   (b) Parallelogram Method   (c) Polygon Method

Fig. 12–2. Resultant of a two-vector coplanar, concurrent system.

is drawn from the tail of the first vector to the tip of the last vector. In the case of a two-vector system, the polygon is a triangle. Figs. 12–3 and 12–4 show two other coplanar, concurrent vector systems and their resultants. Note that the resultant must pass through the point of concurrency.

The parallelogram method of determining the resultant of a three-vector system is shown in Fig. 12–5. The subresultant V_m of vectors V_a and V_b is first determined as in Fig. 12–5(b). V_m then is

[1] The reader is referred to Chapter 15 for a detailed treatment of graphical algebra.

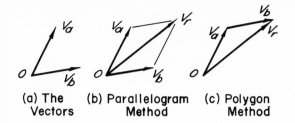

(a) The   (b) Parallelogram   (c) Polygon
   Vectors   Method   Method

Fig. **12-3.** Resultant of a two-vector coplanar, concurrent system.

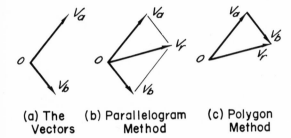

(a) The   (b) Parallelogram   (c) Polygon
   Vectors   Method   Method

Fig. **12-4.** Resultant of a two-vector coplanar, concurrent system.

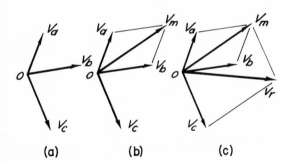

(a)   (b)   (c)

Fig. **12-5.** Resultant of a three-vector coplanar, concurrent system—parallelogram method.

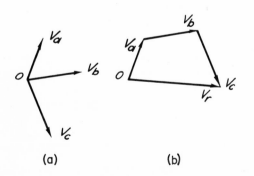

(a)   (b)

Fig. **12-6.** Resultant of a three-vector coplanar, concurrent system—polygon method.

considered as replacing both V_a and V_b, and the total resultant of the system, V_r, is determined from vectors V_m and V_c as in Fig. 12-5(c). When using the parallelogram method in any vector system of three or more vectors, two vectors are combined to form a subresultant; that subresultant is then combined with another vector of the system to form a new subresultant, etc., until the total resultant is determined.

The vector polygon method of determining the resultant of a three-vector system is shown in Fig. 12-6. The vector system shown in Fig. 12-6(a) is the same system as in Fig. 12-5(a). In the polygon method, as was stated before, the vectors are joined tip to tail and the resultant is drawn from the tail of the first vector to the tip of the last vector. This is shown in Fig. 12-6(b). By comparing Figs. 12-5 and 12-6 the comparative simplicity of the polygon method can be appreciated.

Either the polygon or parallelogram method can be used to determine the resultant of a coplanar, concurrent vector system where the vectors are not applied at the apparent point of concurrency. (Refer to Fig. 12-7.) Since vectors can be shifted anywhere along their line of action without changing their external effect, the lines of action are simply extended to locate the point of intersection or concurrency. The resultant is then determined as though the vectors were applied at the point of concurrency.

A system of vectors acting on a bar is shown in Fig. 12-7(a). The point of concurrency O is found in Fig. 12-7(b). The vector polygon is then drawn and the resultant determined in Fig. 12-7(c). The vector system and the resultant are shown in Fig. 12-7(d). Note that the point on the beam through which the resultant V_r acts has been determined by extending V_r from the point of concurrency to the beam.

12-5. EQUILIBRANT OF A VECTOR SYSTEM

The equilibrant of a vector system is the one vector that will cancel or balance the effect of a vector system. As previously mentioned, the resultant of a vector system is a single vector that has the same effect as the vector system. The equilibrant, therefore, must have the same magnitude as the resultant and act along the same line of

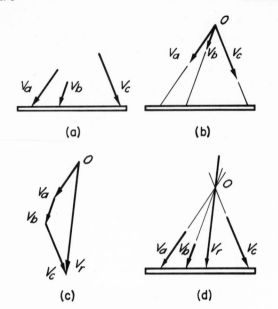

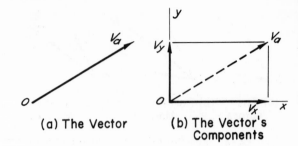

Fig. **12-9.** Resolution of a vector into a co-planar, concurrent system.

Fig. **12-7.** Resultant of a coplanar, concurrent vector system acting on a beam.

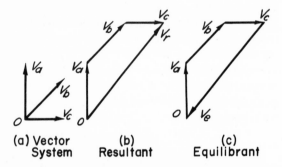

Fig. **12-8.** Resultant and equilibrant of a co-planar, concurrent vector system.

action but in the opposite sense. Fig. 12-8 shows the determination of the resultant and the equilibrant of a vector system. Fig. 12-8(c), which shows the equilibrant, also illustrates an important fact. If a vector polygon of a concurrent system is a closed figure (all vectors are joined tip to tail), the vector system is in equilibrium.

12-6. VECTOR RESOLUTION

Vector resolution is the process of changing a single vector into any desired number of components whose combined effect is the same as that of the single vector. Normally, only two components are desired. These are the two components acting at right angles to each other along the x- and y- axes. Where there are only two components, the parallelogram method is usually used. Fig. 12-9 shows the resolution of a vector V_a into two components, V_x and V_y, which are parallel respectively to (here coincident with) the x- and y-axes.

Coplanar, Non-Concurrent Vectors

12-7. PARALLEL VECTORS

The magnitude of the resultant of two parallel vectors acting with the same sense is equal to their numerical sum; e.g., the weight of a man standing at attention is (or should be) equally divided on each of his legs. Fig. 12-10 shows two parallel vectors, V_a and V_b. The resultant V_r will lie between the two vectors, and be closer to the larger of them. It will have the same sense as both.

The ratio of the distances m and n from each of the vectors to the resultant is the inverse of the ratio of the magnitude of the vectors, or $m:n = V_b:V_a$. The geometric construction to locate the line of action of the resultant is shown. Each vector is projected perpendicularly onto the line of action of the other vector. Diagonals from these projected lengths are then drawn from the tip of one projected vector to the tail of the other. Triangle *12P* is similar to triangle *43P*. Since m and n are the altitudes of their respective triangles, then $m:n = V_b:V_a$.

The magnitude of the resultant of two parallel vectors acting with opposite senses will be their numerical difference. Refer to Fig. 12–11. The sense of the resultant will logically be the sense of the larger of the two vectors. The line of action of the resultant will lie outside of the two vectors, on the side of the larger vector. The geometric construction to locate the resultant is the same as when the vectors are in the same direction, and is shown in Fig. 12–11. Again $m:n = V_b:V_a$.

Opposing, unequal, parallel vectors acting on a body can also be thought of as the combination of two vectors of equal magnitude but opposite sense (a couple) plus a single vector whose magnitude is the difference between the opposing vectors and whose sense and line of action are the same as the larger of the two given vectors. This concept of couples is explained in the next article.

12-8. COUPLES

A *vector couple* consists of two parallel vectors of equal magnitude but opposite sense. A simple example of a couple would be the forces applied by the thumb and forefinger when turning the station selector knob on a radio or TV set. Adding the two vectors, we find that the magnitude of the resultant of the vector couple is zero. However, the effect of a vector couple is to introduce a moment. A *moment* is an effect that causes rotation. The moment of a vector couple is the product of the perpendicular distance between the vectors and the magnitude of one of the vectors. Since the resultant of a vector couple is zero, no single vector can counteract the effect of a vector couple. The only equilibrant for a vector couple is another vector couple of equal but opposite moment. Fig. 12–12 shows a vector couple whose moment is V_ad with a clockwise rotational effect.

In Fig. 12–11, as previously indicated, the opposing vectors cause a rotational effect. These vectors could be replaced by a couple with a moment of $V_a(m - n)$ plus a vector acting along the line of action of V_b with the sense of V_b and a magnitude equal to $V_b - V_a$. As solved in the figure, the rotational effect of V_r is the same as that for V_b, since $V_b (m - n) = V_r m$.

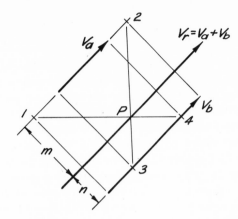

Fig. **12-10.** Resultant of two parallel vectors acting with the same sense.

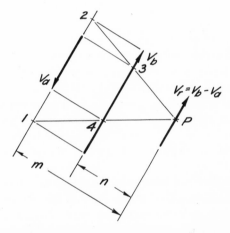

Fig. **12-11.** Resultant of two parallel vectors acting with opposite senses.

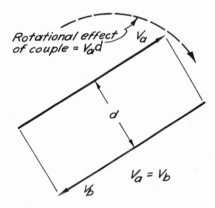

Fig. **12-12.** A vector couple.

12–9. SPACE DIAGRAMS—VECTOR DIAGRAMS

A space diagram is a drawing to a linear scale showing the spatial relationships (locations) of the vectors in a system. The lines representing the vectors are not necessarily drawn to any vector scale, but are usually represented by a number and unit of measure along the lines of action. Fig. 12–7(a) shows an example of a space diagram. Figs. 12–2(a) and 12–3(a) are also space diagrams where the object is considered to be a point. A vector diagram is a drawing showing the vectors drawn to some vector scale. Figs. 12–2(c), 12–3(c), and 12–7(c) are examples of vector diagrams. Any vector polygon is also a vector diagram. In some cases, the vector diagram may be superimposed on the space diagram, as in Figs. 12–2(b) and 12–3(b).

12–10. BOW'S NOTATION

With the coplanar, concurrent vector systems thus far considered, identification of vectors has presented no problem. With a more complicated vector system, however, some method is required so that the individual components in the vector system can be easily identified. Such a system was introduced by Robert H. Bow.[2] Bow's notation proved very convenient in handling vector diagrams and has been used by engineers since its introduction. The system of notation consists of assigning an individual letter or number to each space in or around the space diagram. [See Fig. 12–13(a).] Any vector is named by the two letters of the spaces it separates (i.e., the vector representing V_1 would be AB). Lower case letters are generally used in the space diagram and capital letters in the vector diagram. Bow's notation may be applied in the space diagram in either a clockwise or counter-clockwise manner. The only restriction is that, within any one problem, the method of application be consistent. The vector polygon must be constructed in the same order that the notation was applied on the space diagram. [See Fig. 12–13(a).] The use of clockwise or counter-clockwise notation will change the shape of the vector polygon, but will not change the results

[2] Bow, Robert Henry (CE, FRSE), *Economics of Construction in Relation to Framed Structures. Part II—Diagrams of Forces* (London: E. & F. N. Spon, 1873).

of the problem. It is customary to use a clockwise notation and that direction is used in this text.

12–11. COMPOSITION OF A COPLANAR, NON-CONCURRENT VECTOR SYSTEM

Fig. 12–13(a) shows the space and vector diagrams of a coplanar, non-concurrent vector system. The space diagram of Fig. 12–13(a) shows a vector system where the exact location and sense of the resultant are unknown. An assumed location for the resultant was arbitrarily chosen to lie between V_1 and V_3. In the application of Bow's notation to the space diagram, the space between the resultant and V_1 was arbitrarily called a; the space between V_1 and V_2, b; the space between V_2 and V_3, c; and the space between V_3 and the resultant, d. The unknown position of the resultant

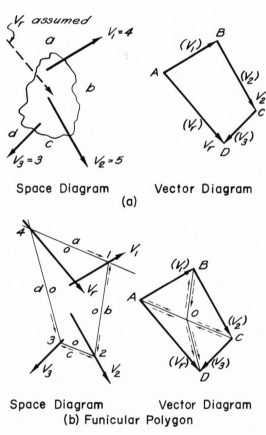

Space Diagram   Vector Diagram

(a)

Space Diagram   Vector Diagram

(b) Funicular Polygon

Fig. 12–13. Location of the resultant of a coplanar, non-concurrent vector system.

ould have been assumed as lying between any two nown vectors. The effect would merely be a earrangement of the notation used. The vector liagram is next drawn as shown in Fig. 12–13(a). Iere the vector diagram consists only of the vector polygon drawn to some scale. Bow's notation alls for vector V_1 to be named AB in the vector liagram since it separates spaces a and b in the pace diagram. Vectors V_2 and V_3 are similarly named in the vector diagram. The resultant AD is lrawn in the vector diagram and the direction of he line of action, sense, and magnitude of the esultant determined, but the position of the result-int in the space diagram is, as yet, unknown.

The position of the resultant in the space diagram can be located by the use of a funicular (or string) polygon. In order to construct a *funicular polygon*, he vectors of a given system are each first resolved nto two components in such a manner that adja-cent vectors share a mutual line of action with components of equal magnitude but opposite senses. This resolution is accomplished in the vector diagram. For example, OB in the vector diagram of Fig. 12–13(b) may be considered as a component of both AB and BC. As a component of AB it is acting upward, but as a component of BC it is acting downward. Thus OB actually represents two components of adjacent vectors having equal magnitude but opposite senses, acting along a mutual line of action.

These components are then drawn in the space diagram in such a manner that components coinci-dent in the vector diagram are coincident in the space diagram. In this position the coincident components, since they are equal and opposite, cancel each other. Therefore, the line of action of these pairs is meaningless vectorially. (It is for this reason that the lines are called strings and the con-struction in the space diagram is sometimes called a string polygon rather than a funicular polygon.) Each pair of coincident components cancels each other except the two that comprise the resultant, and the lines of action of these two intersect on the line of action of the resultant. Thus the funicular polygon locates a point on the line of action of the desired resultant. Since the direction of the line of action, magnitude, and sense of the resultant has been previously determined, the resultant is now completely located.

The initial step in the construction of the funicular polygon is the resolution of the vectors. A pole point (point of concurrence for all compo-nents) in the vector diagram is first selected at a convenient location determined by the layout of the vector polygon, the space available for problem solution, and an experience factor gained from the solution of similar problems. The pole point may be inside or outside the vector polygon. In Fig. 12–13(b), the pole point O in the vector dia-gram [same vector diagram as Fig. 12–13(a)] is selected as shown and the lines OA, OB, OC, and OD are drawn. These can be considered as com-ponents of the vectors in the vector polygon. For example, OA can be considered as a component of both vector AB and vector AD. Also, vector AB can be considered as the resultant of components AO and OB. Therefore, the given vector $V_1(AB)$ can be replaced by its components AO and OB; $V_2(BC)$ can be replaced by BO and OC; and $V_3(CD)$ replaced by CO and OD.

The construction of the funicular polygon on the space diagram is shown in Fig. 12–13(b). From some arbitrary point on the line of action of V_1, such as point 1, the vector V_1 is replaced by its two components by drawing components ao and ob parallel respectively to AO and OB in the vector diagram. Line ob is extended until it intersects the adjacent line of action, locating point 2 on vector V_2, while line ao is extended an indefinite distance in both directions since the location of the resultant is unknown. Vector V_2 is then replaced by its com-ponents bo and oc acting through point 2. Since ob has already been constructed, only oc need be drawn. Line oc is drawn from point 2 parallel to OC in the vector diagram. Note that since ob represents two equal but opposite components, they nullify each other. Therefore, components ao and oc have replaced vectors V_1 and V_2. When oc is extended to locate point 3, and vector V_3 is replaced by co and od, it can be similarly shown that ao and od have replaced vectors V_1, V_2, and V_3. Since ao and od are the components of AD, the resultant vector, AD, can replace both ao and od, acting through point 4. The exact position of the resultant in the space diagram can now be located by transferring the direction of the line of action and the sense of the resultant from the vector dia-gram to the space diagram, drawing the line of action through point *4*. Thus, the resultant of the system has now been completely determined. If the equilibrant of the system were desired, the construction would be the same; however, the sense of *ad* would be reversed in both diagrams.

The closing of the vector polygon of a non-concurrent system does not necessarily mean that the system is in equilibrium, since the vector polygon gives only a summation of vectors and does not give a summation of moments. The funicular polygon gives the effect of a summation of moments since each vector is replaced by pairs of equal and opposite components whose lines of action are coincident. For a non-concurrent system to be in equilibrium, both the vector and funicular polygons must be closed figures. Fig. 12–14 illustrates a case

where a system is not in equilibrium due to moments. The construction of the vector polygon of Fig. 12–14 yields a closed figure and apparently the system is in equilibrium. A pole point *O* is then selected and the components *OA*, *OB*, *OC*, and *OD* are drawn as shown. The funicular polygon on the space diagram is drawn by arbitrarily selecting point *1* on the line of action of vector *ab* and drawing component *ob* to locate point *2* on the line of action of vector *bc*. Similarly, points *3* and *4* are located by drawing components *oc* and *od*. If the funicular polygon were a closed figure, then component *oa* would pass between points *1* and *4*. Instead, component *oa* acts through point *4* with a sense as shown in Fig. 12–14 and also acts through point *1* with the sense shown. (Component *oa* is common to both vectors *ab* and *ad*.) The result of this effect is a vector couple whose moment can be determined by scaling the value of *OA* in the vector diagram and the distance *L* in the space diagram. The moment arm *L* is the perpendicular distance between the two lines of action of component *oa*. In Fig. 12–14 the result is a counter-clockwise moment whose magnitude is $L(OA)$. The choice of the pole point *O* has no effect on the resulting moment since, when *OA* is increased, *L* is proportionately decreased and vice versa. The only way that this system can be placed in equilibrium is to introduce another moment of equal magnitude but opposite turning effect.

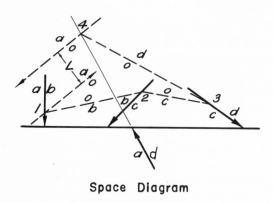

Space Diagram

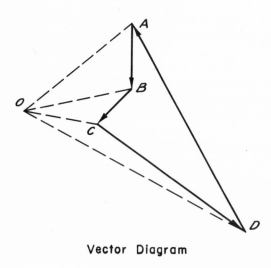

Vector Diagram

Fig. 12–14. Coplanar, non-concurrent vector system with a resultant moment.

12–12. DETERMINATION OF THE REACTIONS ON A BEAM OR TRUSS

In structural design problems, it is necessary to determine the reactions which hold the loads or forces on a beam or truss in equilibrium. Since forces on a beam or truss are usually considered coplanar, but are non-concurrent, the methods of Art. 12–11 can be used to determine the reactions. Fig. 12–15 shows a beam loaded as indicated in the space diagram. Since all the loads have vertical lines of action, the reactions also have vertical lines of action. It should be noted that a slight change in the application of Bow's notation has been made in the space diagram. Here, instead of using the letter identifying a given space only once, the letter is used twice; once at each boundary (line of action) of the space. For example, in the space diagram he letter *b* appears at each boundary of the space *b*. This variation is often used when there are many vectors involved in the problem. In the vector diagram of Fig. 12–15, the vector polygon *ABCD* is drawn to a vector scale. If the beam is in equilibrium, the vector polygon is closed by vectors *DE* and *EA* acting upward (the reactions). However, the magnitude of each is unknown. The pole point *O* is then selected and components *OA*, *OB*, *OC*, and *OD* are drawn. Since the lines of action of the loads and the reactions are known, the funicular polygon can be constructed on the space diagram. The funicular polygon is started from an arbitrary point on the left reaction (point *1*). Points *2, 3, 4,* and *5* are located in succession. If the beam is to be in equilibrium, the funicular polygon must close and component *oe* must be the closure. The component *OE* in the vector diagram is drawn parallel to *oe* in the funicular polygon, locating point *E* in the vector polygon. Then *DE* represents the magnitude of the right reaction and *EA* the magnitude of the left reaction.

Fig. 12–16 shows a truss loaded as indicated in the space diagram. A truss is a framework whose members are arranged to form a system of triangles. All joints are considered to be pin-connected. There is no change in the method of determining the reactions from that used in connection with a beam, since the truss can be considered as merely a beam of greater height. In Fig. 12–16, the load *cd* is shown at a known angle to the vertical. Therefore, to be in equilibrium, one of the reactions must be at some angle to the vertical. This angle is initially unknown. The left end of the truss has been chosen to be pin-anchored. A pin connection will resist any loading, including angular loading, since the pin cannot move. The symbol for the left reaction in the space diagram of Fig. 12–16 is the symbol used when the exact line of action is unknown. The right end of the truss has been chosen to be roller-supported. A roller support will resist vertical loading only, since the truss (or beam) is free to move laterally.

The vector polygon *ABCD* has been drawn to scale in the vector diagram in Fig. 12–16. The reaction *DE* is known to be vertical, so a vertical line is drawn from *D*. However, the magnitude is unknown so that point *E* cannot now be located. The pole point *O* is then selected and components

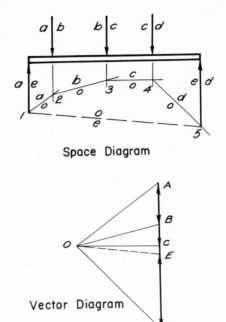

Space Diagram

Vector Diagram

Fig. 12–15. Determination of the reactions on a beam.

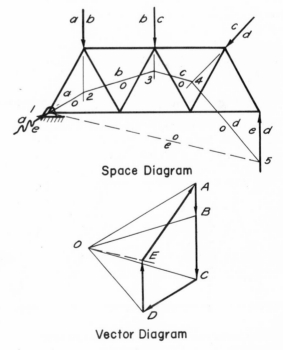

Space Diagram

Vector Diagram

Fig. 12–16. Determination of the reactions on a truss.

OA, OB, OC, and *OD* are drawn. The lines of action are known for all vectors except the reaction *EA.* But its line of action must pass through the pin, and thus one point on its line of action is known. Selecting this as point *1,* the funicular polygon in the space diagram is drawn. Points *2, 3, 4,* and *5* are located on the lines of action of their respective vectors. If the truss is to be in equilibrium, the funicular polygon must close and component *oe* must be the closure. *OE* in the vector diagram is drawn parallel to *oe* in the funicular polygon, locating point *E* on the vertical line through point *D.* Thus, *DE* represents the magnitude of the vertical reaction. Vector *EA* is drawn and represents the magnitude, line of action, and sense of the inclined reaction which passes through the pin anchor point.

In this problem, note that Bow's notation must be applied in such an order that the two unknown reactions are adjacent to each other. If such an order is not used, the vector diagram becomes impossible to construct. Fig. 12–17 shows two possible orders for Bow's notation applied to the same truss, with Fig. 12–17(a) showing the incorrect order and Fig. 12–17(b) showing the correct order. If the vector diagram for Fig. 12–17(a) is attempted, vectors *AB* and *BC* can be laid off to scale, but the next vector is the unknown reaction *CD.* Since the location of *D* is unknown, it is impossible to complete the diagram by then laying off *DE* and *EA.* However, if the notation of Fig. 12–17(b) is used, the vector diagram can be constructed by laying off the known loads *AB, BC,* and *CD.* Then the reactions *DE* and *EA* can be deter-

mined as previously discussed. This order of notation utilizes the fact that a vector (*bc* in this case) may be applied anywhere along its line of action without altering the external effect.

12–13. ANALYSIS OF LOADS IN A TRUSS BY METHOD OF ISOLATED JOINTS

When the loads and reactions on a truss are known, the loads in each member of the truss can be individually determined because each joint must be in equilibrium. The procedure is to consider each joint in the truss as an isolated joint, or body (point). The problem then becomes one of coplanar, concurrent vectors. Fig. 12–18(a) shows a truss with its loads and reactions. Note the application of Bow's notation to include areas within the space diagram.

Each joint must be analyzed in the same order as the application of Bow's notation on the space diagram. In Fig. 12–18, the notation is applied in a clockwise order, hence each joint must be analyzed by examining the loads in a clockwise order starting from the known load.

Fig. 12–18(b) shows an analysis of joint Ⓐ. The reaction *EA* at joint Ⓐ is known and the vectors *AV* and *VE* are determined by the vector diagram. Fig. 12–18(c) and (d) show the analysis of joints Ⓑ and Ⓒ. In each joint there are only two unknown vectors. The known vectors are either the given loads or members whose loads have been previously determined. The order in which the various joints are solved for their unknown vectors has been chosen so that no joint will have more than two unknown vectors. No more than two unknown vectors can be determined for any joint and the line of action of both of the unknown vectors must be known.

Fig. 12–18(e) shows the analysis of joint Ⓓ. In this case, all vectors acting on the joint are known either by direct solution or indirectly through the symmetry of loading and structure. The construction of the vector diagram of joint Ⓓ is, however, a positive check on the previous solutions. If the vector polygon closes, the solutions are verified.

The question as to whether a member of the truss is in tension or compression can be determined by observing the sense of each vector. If the member is pushing against the joints, the member is in com-

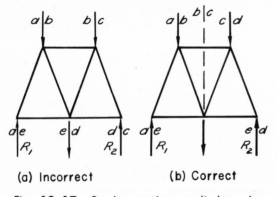

(a) Incorrect   (b) Correct

Fig. **12–17.** Bow's notation applied to determine the reactions of a truss.

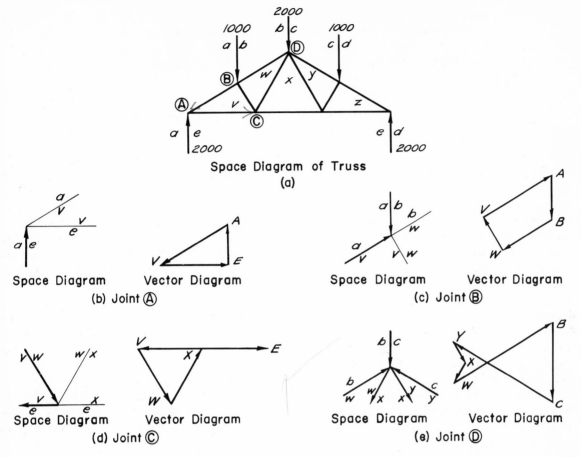

Fig. 12–18. Joint-by-joint analysis of a truss.

pression. If the member is pulling on the joints, the member is in tension. (The vector diagram gives the sense, which is then transferred to the space diagram to determine how the member is acting on the joint.) For example, a study of the senses of the vectors acting on joint Ⓑ shows that all members involved are in compression, while a study of the senses of the vectors acting on joint Ⓒ shows that all members except the member VW are in tension. Member VW is in compression, which verifies the study made of joint Ⓑ.

12–14. ANALYSIS OF LOADS IN A TRUSS BY MAXWELL DIAGRAM

The analysis of the loads in a truss by the isolated joint method involves more drawing than necessary and requires considerable space. The isolated joint

method also has no accuracy check until late in the solution, and it is possible to omit an accuracy check. A method which saves both time and space and incorporates an accuracy check was developed by James Clerk Maxwell.[3] The method is actually a uniting of all the separate vector polygons into one vector diagram.

Fig. 12–19 shows the Maxwell diagram. The space diagram is the same as in Fig. 12–18. The vector polygon *ABCDEA* is first constructed. The vector polygon for joint Ⓐ is then added to the load polygon by drawing ray *AV* parallel to member *av* and ray *EV* parallel to member *ev*. The intersection of the rays closes the joint polygon and locates point *V*. Similarly, the vector polygon for

[3] MAXWELL, J. Clerk, "Reciprocal Figures, Frames, and Diagrams of Forces," *Transactions, Royal Society of Edinburgh,* 1869–70.

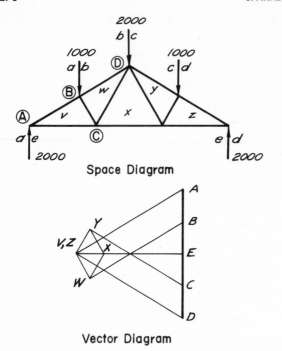

Space Diagram

Vector Diagram

Fig. 12-19. The Maxwell vector diagram, symmetrical loading.

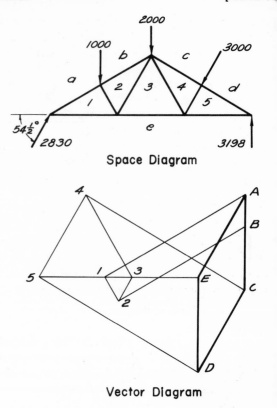

Space Diagram

Vector Diagram

Fig. 12-20. The Maxwell vector diagram, unsymmetrical loading.

joint Ⓑ is added by drawing rays *VW* and *BW* locating point *W*. In a like manner, the vector polygons of the other points are added to the load polygon. Rays *DZ* and *EZ* locate point *Z*. Rays *ZY* and *CY* locate point *Y*. Rays *YX*, *WX*, and *EX* locate point *X*. Point *X* is a check on the accuracy of solution as the three rays must intersect at a single point. An examination of the vector diagrams of Fig. 12-18 shows that all are included within the Maxwell diagram. Therefore, all vectors may be scaled off the Maxwell diagram using the scale that was used initially to lay out the vector polygon *ABCDEA*. The determination of compression or tension is made by mentally isolating (or by drawing a sketch of) that portion of the Maxwell diagram which pertains to a particular joint and noting the senses of the vectors involved. In isolating a particular joint, it must be remembered to study the vectors in the clockwise order that was established by the notation in the space diagram. Note that no senses are indicated in the Maxwell diagram, because the sense of a vector ray would depend upon the particular joint being considered. The Maxwell diagram of Fig. 12-19 is the typical

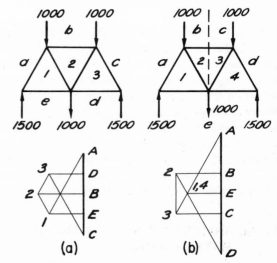

(a)   (b)

Fig. 12-21. Methods of applying Bow's notation to a Maxwell diagram. The method shown at the left is preferred.

symmetrical diagram resulting from symmetrical loading. Fig. 12–20 shows a Maxwell diagram for an unsymmetrically loaded truss. Note in Fig. 12–20 that numbers instead of letters are used to identify areas within the truss. This is another common variation of Bow's notation.

The order in which Bow's notation is used greatly affects the shape of the Maxwell diagram. Fig. 12–21 shows two orders for Bow's notation applied to the same truss and the resulting Maxwell diagrams. Fig. 12–21(a) shows the preferred order where every line in the corresponding Maxwell diagram represents a load in a member of the truss. Fig. 12–21(b) shows an order that is not recommended. Note that this latter order is the one required when determining the reactions by the method discussed in Art. 12–12 and Fig. 12–17(b). However, if this order is used in conjunction with the construction of a Maxwell diagram, it must be realized that the line of action of the vector bc also divides the middle interior area into two triangles as shown in Fig. 12–21(b). This creates a misleading Maxwell diagram because all lines of the diagram do not represent loads in members of the truss. For example, there is no member 23 or A3 in this case. It is recommended that, when the problem includes both the determination of the reactions and the construction of a Maxwell diagram, the notation best suited for each phase be used even if it means changing the notation for each phase of the problem. If an attempt is made to combine the methods, such as by combining the notation of the applied loads as in Fig. 12–21(b) with the notation of the interior areas as in Fig. 12–21(a), it is impossible to construct the Maxwell diagram.

Non-coplanar, Concurrent Vector Systems

12–15. COMPOSITION OF A NON-COPLANAR, CONCURRENT VECTOR SYSTEM

Non-coplanar, concurrent vectors are handled similarly to coplanar, concurrent vectors; the only difference is that the non-coplanar, concurrent vectors involve three dimensions instead of two. For this reason, a minimum of two related orthographic views is required to describe completely a non-coplanar vector system. Through the combination of the principles of spatial relations and the principles of the vector geometry for coplanar, concurrent vector systems, the handling of a non-coplanar, concurrent vector system becomes a relatively easy task.

Fig. 12–22 shows a pictorial view of a non-coplanar, concurrent vector system consisting of the vectors V_a, V_b, and V_c which are concurrent at point O. Fig. 12–23 shows the resultant as determined by the parallelogram method. A study of the orthographic views of the vector system [Fig. 12–23(a)] shows that the front view of a parallelogram formed by lines parallel to V_a and V_b would have poor intersections (i.e., they would intersect at a very shallow angle). Therefore, the subresultant V_m of vectors V_a and V_c is first determined, as in Fig. 12–23(b). Vector V_b is shown dotted as it is not used in this phase. Then V_m and V_b are combined to give the total resultant, V_r, as in Fig. 12–23(c). V_a and V_c are shown dotted as they have been previously combined to give V_m. Note that the construction is performed simultaneously in the two related views. Also note that accuracy checks are immediately available since the tips of the sub-

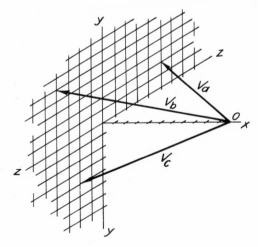

Fig. **12–22.** Pictorial of a non-coplanar, concurrent vector system.

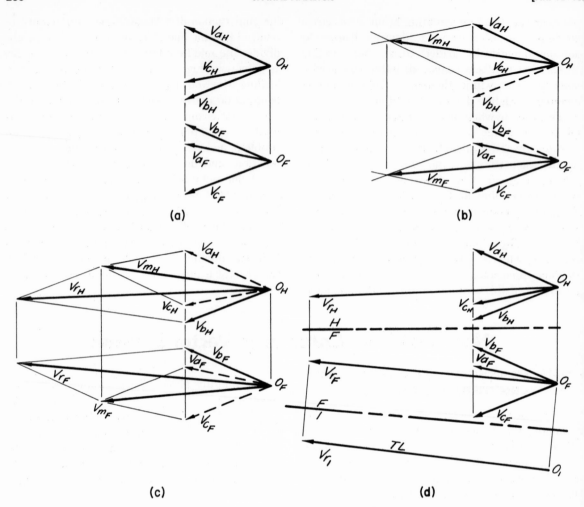

Fig. **12-23.** Resultant of a non-coplanar, concurrent vector system—parallelogram method.

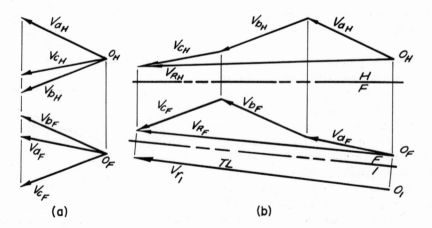

Fig. **12-24.** Resultant of a non-coplanar, concurrent vector system—polygon method.

resultant (V_m) and the resultant (V_r) must be in projection between views. It must be realized that in this example the orthographic views do not show the true value of the resultant since its line of action is not parallel to either principal plane of projection. The true value of the resultant must be found by revolution or by an auxiliary view, as in Fig. 12–23(d).

Fig. 12–24 shows the resultant of the vector system of Fig. 12–22 as determined by the vector polygon method. Again the true value of the resultant must be found by revolution or by an auxiliary view. If the equilibrant were desired, the sense of the resultant would have to be reversed.

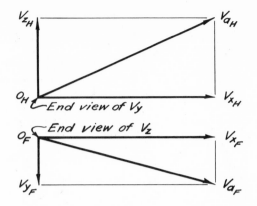

Fig. **12–25.** Resolution of a non-coplanar vector.

12–16. RESOLUTION FOR NON-COPLANAR COMPONENTS

When a single vector is divided into non-coplanar components, any three components could be selected as long as the lines of action of these components were known. However, three mutually perpendicular components are usually selected. These components are generally selected as those acting along the x-axis, the y-axis, and the z-axis. Fig. 12–25 shows a vector divided into these components. The frontal view shows the given vector, V_a, and the x- and y-components, V_x and V_y. Since the z-component, V_z, shows only as an end view, it has no effect on the frontal view and the lengths of V_x and V_y can be readily established.

If V_z had not appeared as an end view in the frontal view but had some finite length instead, there would be no way of establishing the relative lengths of V_x and V_y. This is because there would then be a quadrilateral composed of four sides, each of whose directions was known, but which would have only one known length (the given vector). In order to close a polygon where the directions of all sides are known, there must be a maximum of two sides of unknown length. Hence, elimination in the quadrilateral of one of the three components of unknown length is necessary in order to effect a solution. This may be accomplished in one of two ways: (a) by obtaining a view of the components showing the end view of one of the unknown components, as is the case in Fig. 12–25; or (b) by obtaining a view of the components showing the plane of two of the unknown components as an edge. In essence, the second method establishes the direction of the resultant of the two components which are being seen in edge view. The value of V_z is established in the horizontal view of Fig. 12–25 where V_y shows as an end view.

12–17. ANALYSIS OF SPACE TRUSSES

A vector can be readily resolved into three components under the conditions just discussed. Since, in structures, the applied load is resisted by the members of the structure, the structures considered in the following discussions are those made up of three members (space trusses). Fig. 12–26 shows a tripod with a load applied vertically down-

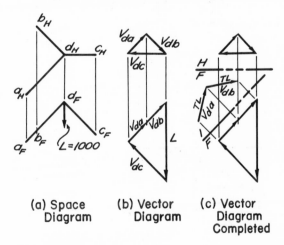

(a) Space Diagram

(b) Vector Diagram

(c) Vector Diagram Completed

Fig. **12–26.** Determination of loads on members of a space truss.

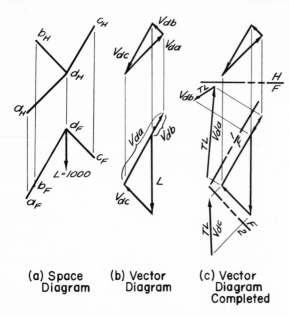

(a) Space Diagram (b) Vector Diagram (c) Vector Diagram Completed

Fig. **12–27.** Determination of loads on members of a space truss.

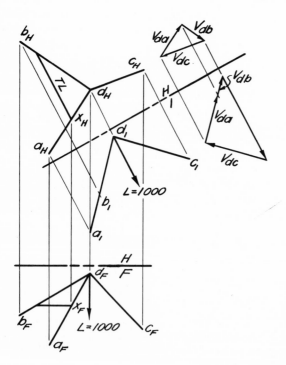

Fig. **12–28.** Determination of loads on members of a space truss.

ward. Fig. 12–26(a) is the space diagram. Note that the frontal view shows the edge view of the plane of two of the legs. This is necessary, as previously noted, so that there will be only two unknown directions in the frontal view of the vector diagram. The vector diagram (vector polygon) is constructed as shown in Fig. 12–26(b). First the applied vector, L, is drawn to scale. Since the applied vector is vertical, it appears in true value (length) in the frontal view. The frontal view of the vector diagram is completed by drawing the component acting along DC parallel to the frontal view of member DC in the space diagram and a line representing the two components parallel to the plane ABD which appears as an edge in the frontal view of the space diagram. These two components represent the components acting along members DA and DB, but the values of these components are unknown as yet. In the horizontal view of the vector diagram, the direction of the component acting along DC is known and the length of the horizontal view of DC is established by projection from the frontal view. The horizontal view of the vector diagram is completed by components drawn parallel to the horizontal views of DA and DB in the space diagram. By projecting the intersection of these two components in the horizontal view back to the frontal view, this view of the vector diagram is completed. Both views of the vector diagram show a closed polygon with the vector components joined tip to tail, and, therefore, the system is in equilibrium. The vector component acting along CD appears in its true value in the frontal view. However, the vector components acting along DA and DB do not appear in true length in either view. The true value of the components DA and DB must be determined by an auxiliary view as in Fig. 12–26(c) or by revolution.

Fig. 12–27 shows another tripod, but no leg appears in true length. The vector diagram, Fig. 12–27(b), is constructed as in the previous discussion. Note that the frontal views of the components acting along DA and DB overlap in the vector diagram. Since no component appears in its true value in the frontal and horizontal views, the true values of each must be obtained by auxiliary views as in Fig. 12–27(c), or by revolution.

Fig. 12–28 shows another tripod, but no two legs appear in edge view. The vector diagram cannot e drawn working with these given views. This is because both the frontal and horizontal views of the vector diagram would contain three unknown directions. However, an auxiliary view of the space diagram can be constructed showing two legs in edge view. The vector diagram can be drawn working with the horizontal and auxiliary views. Note that the true values of the components do not appear in the vector diagram. The construction to obtain true values has been omitted from Fig. 12–28 for the sake of clarity of view and space. These values could be obtained through the use of auxiliary views or by revolution.

Fig. 12–29 shows a tripod (or space truss) on the side of a vertical wall. The method of solution for this problem remains unchanged from those previously discussed.

The space trusses shown are all of the simplest form, a tripod. It is possible to have more complex space trusses, but all can be subdivided into the tripod form. The solution of a complex space truss would then consist of working from tripod form to tripod form.

In all of the foregoing discussions of loads in space trusses, no mention has been made of

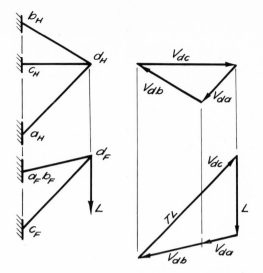

Fig. 12–29. Determination of loads on members of a space truss.

whether a member is in compression or tension. This can be determined by a study of how a member acts on the joint, as is discussed earlier, in Art. 12–13.

Problems

All problems are designed to be worked on $8\frac{1}{2}'' \times 11''$ sheets.

COPLANAR, CONCURRENT VECTOR SYSTEMS

12–1. a. In the upper half of the working area, determine the magnitude, line of action, and sense of the resultant of the vector system shown in Fig. 12–30(a). Use the parallelogram method and a vector scale of $1'' = 10$.

  b. In the lower half of the working area, determine the magnitude, line of action, and sense of the resultant of the vector system shown in Fig. 12–30(b). Use the polygon method and a vector scale of $1'' = 10$.

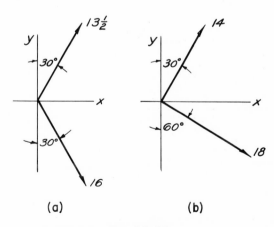

(a)   (b)

Fig. **12–30.**

12-2. Determine the magnitude, line of action, and sense of the resultant of the vector system shown in Fig. 12–31. Use the parallelogram method and a vector scale of $1'' = 20$.

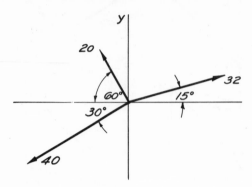

Fig. **12–31.**

12-3. Determine the magnitude, line of action, and sense of the resultant of the vector system shown in Fig. 12–32. Use the polygon method and a vector scale of $1'' = 20$.

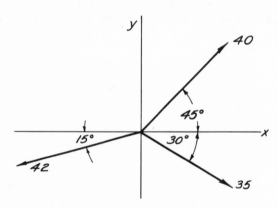

Fig. **12–32.**

12-4. a. In the upper half of the working area, determine the X- and Y-components of a vector whose magnitude is 50, acting up and to the right from the origin, at an angle of 30° with the x-axis. Use a vector scale of $1'' = 20$.

    b. In the lower half of the working area, determine the X- and Y-components of a vector whose magnitude is 77, acting down and to the right from the origin, at an angle of 37° with the x-axis. Use a vector scale of $1'' = 20$.

12-5. Determine the magnitude, line of action, and sense of the equilibrant of the vector system shown in Fig. 12–33. Use a vector scale of $1'' = 10$.

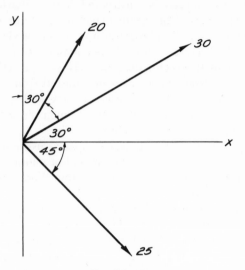

Fig. **12–33.**

12-6. Determine the magnitude, line of action, and sense of the equilibrant of the vector system shown in Fig. 12–34. Use a vector scale of $1'' = 10$ pounds.

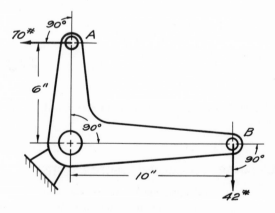

Fig. **12–34.**

12-7. The two cables AB and AC shown in Fig. 12–35 support a 750-pound weight. The force acting in cable AB is 700 pounds. Determine the force acting in cable AC and its required length. Select your own scales.

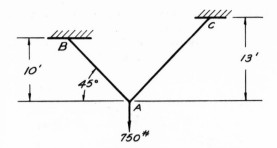

Fig. **12-35.**

12-8. At the beginning of a four-hour watch, a ship's position is latitude N 30°30'30" and longitude W 70°20'20" and its course is N 30° E. At two bells, the heading is altered to N 60° E to investigate a reported floating object believed to be a lifeboat. At four bells, the heading is again changed to due north and held until the ship crosses the original course line at which time the N 30° E heading is resumed. During the watch, a constant average speed of 20 knots has been maintained. What is the latitude and longitude of the ship at the end of the four-hour watch?

Notes: 1. A nautical mile is equal to one minute of arc.
2. One knot is equal to one nautical mile per hour.
3. "Bells" are sounded every 30 minutes of time with eight bells ending a four-hour watch. One bell is sounded a half-hour after the change of watch, etc.
4. Considering the short distances involved in this problem, the convergence of lines of longitude can be ignored and considered parallel as on a Mercator chart.

12-9. The skipper of a sailboat leaves his dock at point A at 1600 hours, sailing a course of N 45° E at a speed relative to the water of 45 knots. (A knot is one nautical mile per hour.) The tide is ebbing due north at three knots. At 1900 hours, the skipper estimates his position to be due south of a lighthouse at point Y. When he takes a bearing on the lighthouse, however, he gets a bearing of N 15° W. He sights back at point A and reads a bearing of S 59° W. Plot the assumed and actual positions and determine the direction and amount of drift and the rate of drift. In plotting, assume a point A and then plot point Y 3" to the right and 7" above point A. Then use a vector scale of 1" = 5 knots.

COPLANAR, NON-CONCURRENT VECTOR SYSTEMS

12-10. a. In the upper half of the work area, determine the magnitude and sense, and locate the line of action of the resultant of the vector system shown in Fig. 12-36(a).
b. In the lower half of the work area, determine the magnitude and sense, and locate the line of action of the equilibrant of the vector system shown in Fig. 12-36(b).

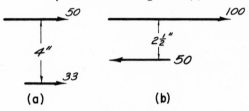

(a)   (b)

Fig. **12-36.**

12-11. Determine the magnitude, line of action, and sense of the resultant of the vector system shown in Fig. 12-37. Also determine the point where the line of action of the resultant crosses the reference line.

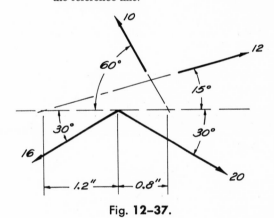

Fig. **12-37.**

12-12. Determine the magnitude, line of action, sense, and point of application of the resultant of the vector system shown in Fig. 12-38.

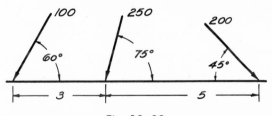

Fig. **12-38.**

12-13. Determine the magnitude, line of action, sense, and point of application of the equilibrant of the vector system shown in Fig. 12-39.

Fig. **12-39.**

12-14. Determine the reactions on the beam shown in Fig. 12-40. (*Note:* One kip = 1,000 pounds.)

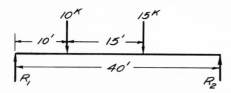

Fig. **12-40.**

12-15. Determine the reactions on the beam shown in Fig. 12-41.

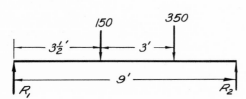

Fig. **12-41.**

12-16. Determine the reactions on the beam shown in Fig. 12-42. (*Note:* One kip = 1,000 pounds.)

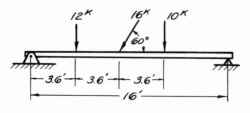

Fig. **12-42.**

12-17. Design a wedge with the minimum slope that will prevent the roller at the right end of the beam shown in Fig. 12-43 from being pushed out. Then determine the reactions on the beam.

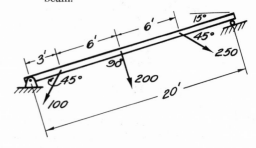

Fig. **12-43.**

12-18. Determine the loads in each member of the truss shown in Fig. 12-44. Use a joint-by-joint analysis and perform a graphic check of your results.

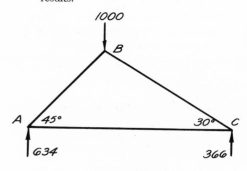

Fig. **12-44.**

12-19. Determine the loads in each member of the truss shown in Fig. 12-45. Use a Maxwell diagram.

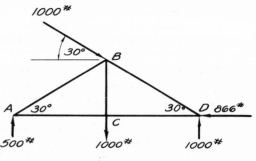

Fig. **12-45.**

12–20. A body is held in equilibrium by four cords as shown in Fig. 12–46. Construct a Maxwell diagram and determine the load in each cord.

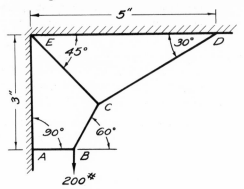

Fig. **12–46.**

12–21. Construct a Maxwell diagram and determine the load in each member of the truss shown in Fig. 12–47.

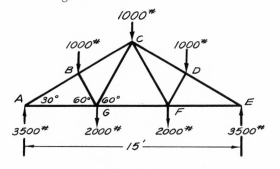

Fig. **12–47.**

12–22. Determine the reactions on the truss shown in Fig. 12–48 and then construct a Maxwell diagram and determine the loads in each member of the truss.

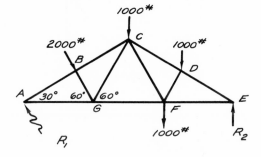

Fig. **12–48.**

12–23. Determine the reactions and the loads in each member of the coplanar structure shown in Fig. 12–49.

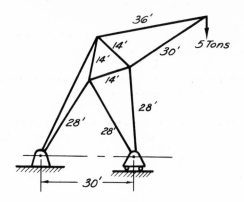

Fig. **12–49.**

NON-COPLANAR, CONCURRENT VECTOR SYSTEMS

12–24. Determine the magnitude, bearing, slope, and sense of the resultant of the vector system shown pictorially in Fig. 12–50.

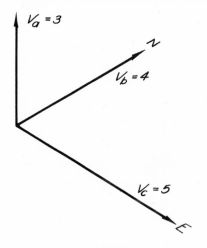

Fig. **12–50.**

12-25. Lay out the vector system shown in Fig. 12-51. Then determine the magnitude, bearing, slope, and sense of the equilibrant. Use a vector scale of $1'' = 10$.

12-26. Determine the loads in each member of the frame shown in Fig. 12-52.

12-27. Determine the loads in each member of the frame shown in Fig. 12-53.

12-28. Determine the loads in each member of the hanging frame shown in Fig. 12-54. Point P is equidistant from points A, B, and C.

12-29. Determine the magnitude, sense, and line of action of the force acting through point P that would produce a tension of 1,000 pounds in members AP and CP and 1,500 pounds in member BP of the hanging frame shown in Fig. 12-55.

12-30. Lay out the frame shown in Fig. 12-56. Determine the loads in each member if the frame supports a 3,000-pound load applied vertically downward through point D.

12-31. Determine the load in each cable and the reaction at point A of the system shown in Fig. 12-57.

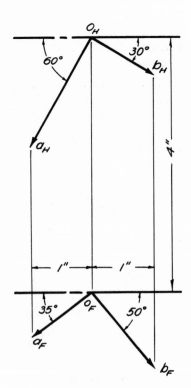

Fig. **12-51.**

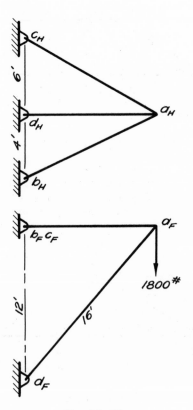

Fig. **12-52.**

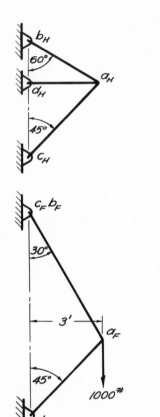

Fig. **12–53.**

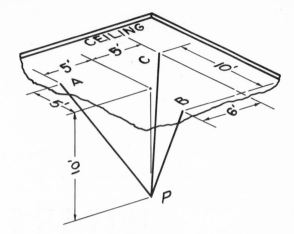

Fig. **12–55.**

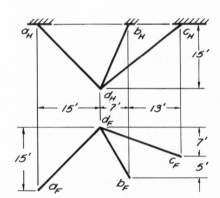

Fig. **12–56.**

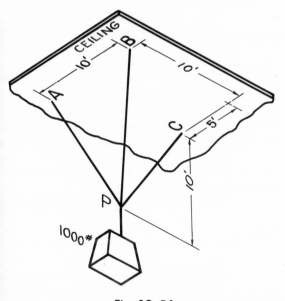

Fig. **12–54.**

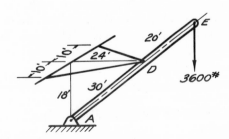

Fig. **12–57.**

13

INTERSECTIONS AND DEVELOPMENTS

13-1. INTRODUCTION

The design engineer encounters structures which have intersecting surfaces. He must, therefore, be able to determine the line of intersection between such surfaces. Often he must also develop the surfaces so that they can be fabricated.

The degree of accuracy needed in determining the line of intersection between two surfaces varies with the problem conditions. In some problems, such as in the design of ducts, the tolerance required is sufficiently large that scaled drawings of the structure can be used in determining the line of intersection and in developing the surfaces. Other problems, such as the design of plates for the hull of a ship, require that the intersections be determined and the developments made on full-size drawings which are sometimes laid out on the floor of a large area known as a loft room. In the

aircraft industry, developments often must be accurate to 0.005 of an inch because of the need to avoid turbulent airflow over intersecting surfaces.

Intersections need not be the intersection of tangible surfaces; instead, the designer may be interested in shaping moving parts so that they do not interfere with each other. Here the designer would be working with the intangible surfaces generated by the moving parts. Or, he might want to design a stationary surface so as to allow the passage of a moving part; in this case, the designer would be working with both tangible and intangible surfaces.

The subject of intersections and developments can be a complex and lengthy topic when dealt with completely. This text is concerned only with a basic coverage of the subject. However, the methods presented form the basis for more complete treatments.

Intersections

13-2. TYPES OF INTERSECTIONS

All of the intersections mentioned in the introductory remarks require the accurate location of

a line of intersection. In some intersections, such as those encountered when illustrating fillets or rounds as discussed in Art. 7–18, the intersection of the surfaces requires only an approximate accuracy so that the reader of the drawing can obtain a good idea of what the intersection actually looks like. However, whether accurately plotting an intersection or merely approximating an intersection, the engineer must know how to determine the actual intersection, because he could not approximate an intersection if he could not visualize the intersection from past experience.

13–3. TYPES OF SURFACES

Geometrical surfaces may be classified under two broad categories: (a) ruled surfaces and (b) double-curved surfaces. *Ruled surfaces* are those generated by a straight line moving according to certain rules. These can be further subdivided into plane, single-curved, and warped surfaces. *Double-curved surfaces* are those generated by a curved line moving according to certain rules. All geometric figures are made up of either one or more of these surfaces. Fig. 13–1 shows pictorially some of the basic geometric figures made by these surfaces, while Fig. 13–2 shows the orthographic views of the same figures.

Plane-surfaced figures need no explanation and single-curved surfaces, such as the cone and cylinder, are familiar shapes. Considering the other single-curved surfaces illustrated, it is difficult to distinguish any essential difference between pictorial views of the circular and elliptical cylinders (Fig. 13–1) other than that one is a right cylinder and the other is an oblique cylinder. Note that in the orthographic views (Fig. 13–2) the bases of both cylinders show as circles in the horizontal view. The true difference between the cylinders is in the shape of a right section (or cross section). In the case of the circular cylinder, the horizontal view is the cross section; in the case of the elliptical cylinder, an auxiliary view must be constructed to show the true shape of the cross section. Since a cylinder is generated by a straight line moving so that successive positions are parallel and touching a curved line, it is possible to have parabolic, hyperbolic, and many other forms of cylinders. The other single-curved surface shown is the helical convolute which is generated by a straight line moving so that it is always tangent to a helix.

In the family of warped surfaces shown, the conoid is generated by a straight line moving so that one point on the line is in contact with a straight line and another point is in contact with a curved line. Successive positions of the generating line always lie in parallel planes. The warped cone is generated by a straight line moving so that it is in contact with two differently curved bases and also intersecting the straight line which passes through the center of each base. The hyperboloid of revolution is generated by a straight line moving about another straight line to which it is not parallel and does not intersect. The remaining warped surface illustrated is the right helicoid which is generated by a straight line moving so that it makes a constant angle (90°) with the axis of a helix and is in contact with the helix. The conoid is used in the blending of a curved surface to a plane surface, while the warped cone is used in the blending of two different curved surfaces. The hyperboloid has a use in some gear problems, while the helicoid is used in some ramp and conveyor problems.

In the family of double-curved surfaces shown, the sphere, generated by a circle revolving about one of its diameters, is so common that it needs no further explanation. The torus is generated by a circle moving about some axis not coincident with an axis of the circle. The spheroid is generated by an ellipse revolving about one of its axes (in this case the minor axis), and the paraboloid is generated by a parabola revolving about its axis.

13–4. METHODS OF PLOTTING INTERSECTIONS

The location of a line of intersection is accomplished by determining a number of points along the intersection and connecting those points with straight lines or smooth curves, depending on the surfaces involved. The number of such points that must be determined bears a direct relation to the accuracy required. An important fact to remember is that the line of intersection between two figures, such as a prism and a cylinder, or two cylinders, is a continuous, closed line that never intersects itself.

There are two methods generally used in the determination of points along a line of intersection. These methods are: (a) the edge view method, and

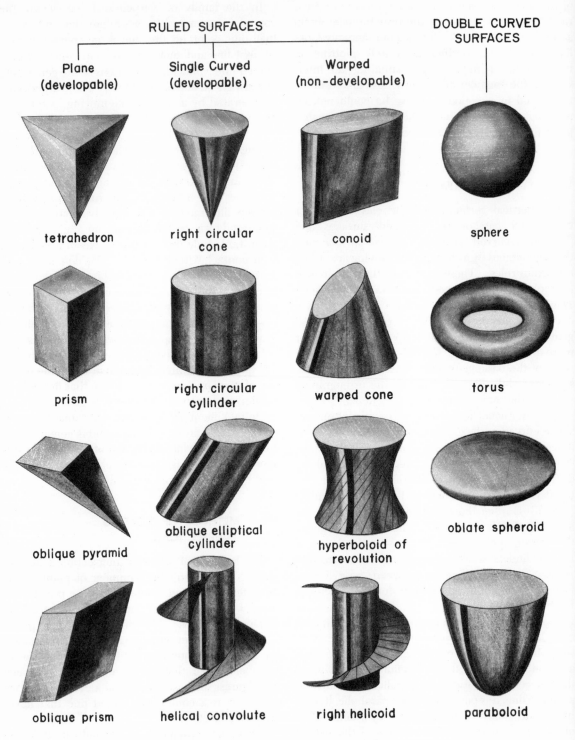

Fig. 13-1. Pictorials of geometric figures.

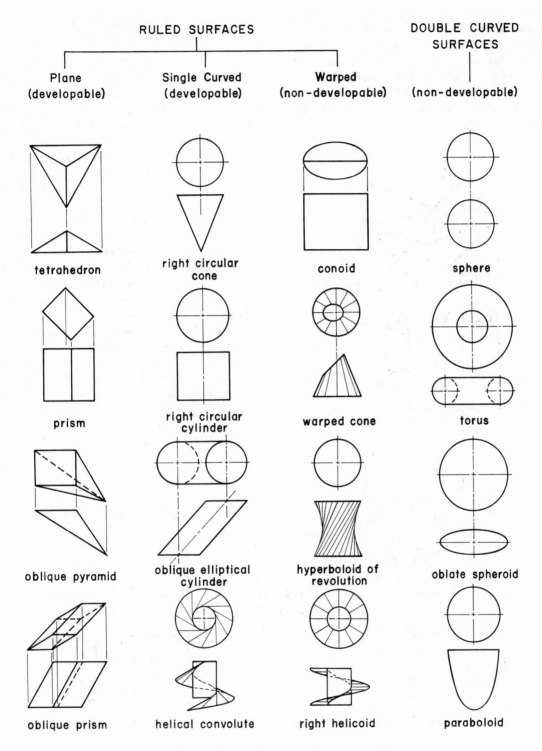

RULED SURFACES   DOUBLE CURVED
                                                      SURFACES

Plane   Single Curved   Warped
(developable)   (developable)   (non-developable)   (non-developable)

tetrahedron   right circular   conoid   sphere
                   cone

prism   right circular   warped cone   torus
                   cylinder

oblique pyramid   oblique elliptical   hyperboloid of   oblate spheroid
                   cylinder   revolution

oblique prism   helical convolute   right helicoid   paraboloid

Fig. **13-2.** Orthographic views of geometric figures.

(b) the cutting plane method. The basis of both methods has been presented in Chapter 9. Both methods consist essentially of locating the point where a line element of one surface pierces the other surface. The next four articles discuss the application of these two methods in determining the intersections between a few of the basic geometric figures.

13-5. INTERSECTIONS OBTAINED BY THE EDGE VIEW METHOD

The edge view method, based on determining points of intersection by utilizing the edge view of one of the intersecting surfaces, is applicable when either or both of the surfaces are plane, as in Fig. 13-3 where the intersection between a pyramid and a prism has been determined. From an examination of the given pyramid $MNOP$ and prism $ABCDEFGH$, as shown in Fig. 13-3(a), the points where edges MN and MO of the pyramid intersect the surface $BCGF$ of the prism can be located since $BCGF$ appears in edge view in the horizontal view. The position of these two points can be located in the horizontal view, and their exact location determined by projecting to the frontal view. Similarly, the point where edge MP intersects surface $CDHG$ can be located. These points are shown as points 1, 2, and 4 in Fig. 13-3(a).

The points where the edge CG of the prism intersects surfaces MNP and MOP of the pyramid are not as simple to locate. These two points, 3 and 5, may be located by constructing an auxiliary showing the edge views of MNP and MOP as in Fig. 13-3(b). Note that a view showing the end view of line MP, the line of intersection between the two surfaces, results in the edge view of both

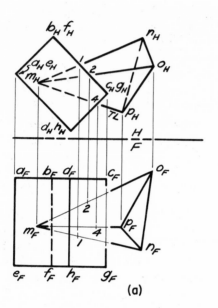

(a)

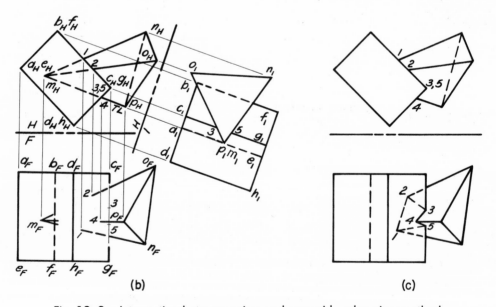

(b)   (c)

Fig. **13-3**. Intersection between prism and pyramid—edge view method.

surfaces. Now all points where the edges of one figure intersect the surfaces of the other figure are located, and the views can be completed as in Fig. 13–3(c). In determining the visibility of the various portions of the line of intersection in each view, the rule of visibility is that if either of the intersecting surfaces which cause the line is invisible, the line of intersection is invisible in that view.

Fig. 13–4 shows the procedure in determining the intersection between a prism and a cone. The positions of the given prism and cone are established in Fig. 13–4(a). The intersection is located by constructing a number of elements of the cone (lines running from the base to the vertex), such as AV, and determining where such elements pierce the surfaces of the prism. The point 1 where element AV pierces the front surface of the prism is located in Fig. 13–4(b). Using other elements, more points can be located on the line of intersection. Note in Fig. 13–4(b) that there is an alternate element, $A'V$ (shown dotted), that can be located in the front view from the position of AV in the horizontal view. This frequently is the case in symmetrical figures. The completed intersection is shown in Fig. 13–4(c). Since the surface of the cone passes through the surfaces of the prism, there are two lines of intersection shown.

13–6. USE OF CUTTING PLANES

The use of the cutting plane method in determining the line of intersection between two figures is based on the method as discussed in Art. 9–14 wherein a cutting plane is used to determine the piercing point of a line and a plane surface. When using the cutting plane method, much time can be saved if a cutting plane is used that cuts simple shapes from both of the intersecting figures. Hence a knowledge of the intersections of cutting planes with the more common geometric figures is valuable.

Since the line of intersection of two planes is a straight line, the line of intersection between a cutting plane and any plane-surfaced figure is a series of straight lines. In Fig. 13–5(a) the cutting plane A-A intersects the prism along the straight lines 12431; cutting plane B-B gives the intersection 56875. When cutting plane-surfaced figures, the cutting planes may be passed, as needed, perpendicular to either view. In Fig. 13–5(b) the cutting plane A-A gives the intersection 1231; cutting plane B-B gives the intersection 45674. A cutting plane perpendicular to the frontal view is not used in Fig. 13–5(a) because the intersection cut by such a plane would merely coincide with the lines already shown in the hori-

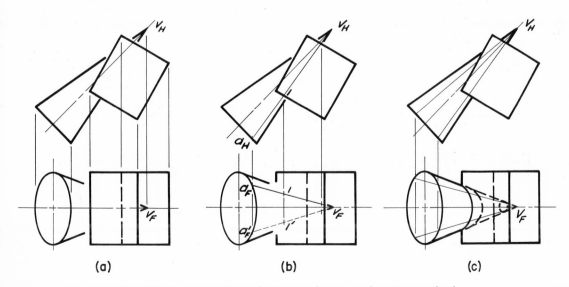

(a)   (b)   (c)

Fig. **13–4.** Intersection of prism and cone—edge view method.

zontal view and hence would add no new information.

Fig. 13–6 shows the intersections between various cutting planes and a cylinder. When the cutting plane is parallel to the axis of the cylinder, as A-A in Fig. 13–6(a) and B-B in Fig. 13–6(b), the intersection is a rectangle. However, when

the cutting plane is not parallel to the cylinder's axis, as C-C in Fig. 13–6(c), the intersection is a curved line. A plane passed perpendicular to the axis of a circular cylinder will cut circles from the cylinder; planes passed at other angles will cut ellipses. If the cylinder is other than circular, various curves will result when the cutting plane is other than parallel to the axis. Since curves other than circles are difficult to construct, cutting planes parallel to the axis of the cylinder, or, in the case of circular cylinders, perpendicular to the axis, are used wherever possible.

Fig. 13–7 shows the intersections between various cutting planes and cones. When the cutting plane passes through the vertex of the cone, as A-A in Fig. 13–7(a), the intersection is a triangle no matter what the cross section of the cone. If the cone is a circular cone, a cutting plane perpendicular to the axis of the cone, as B-B in Fig. 13–7(b), cuts a circle from the cone; a cutting plane that intersects opposing elements of the cone, as C-C in Fig. 13–7(c), cuts an ellipse; a cutting plane parallel to an element of the cone, as D-D in Fig. 13–7(d), cuts a parabola; and a cutting plane parallel to the axis of the cone, as E-E in Fig. 13–7(e), cuts an hyperbola from the cone. Planes B-B, C-C, D-D, and E-E cut what are known as conical sec-

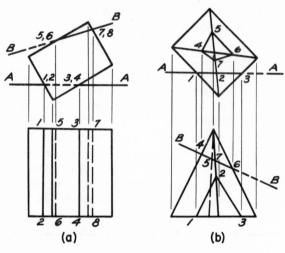

Fig. **13–5.** Intersections between cutting planes and plane-surfaced figures.

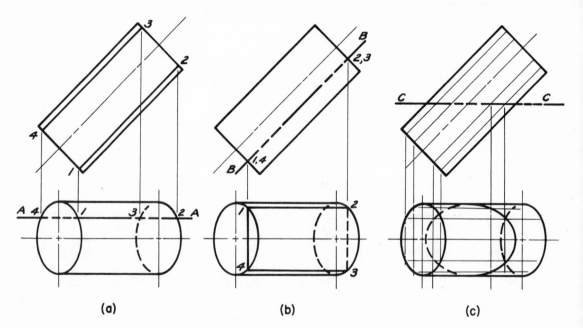

Fig. **13–6.** Intersections between cutting planes and cylinders.

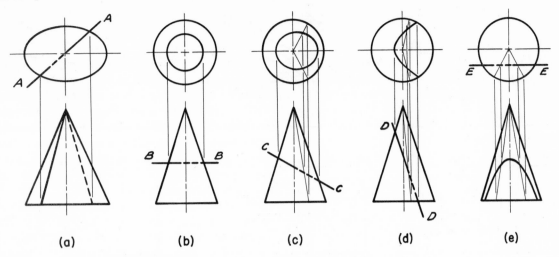

(a)   (b)   (c)   (d)   (e)

Fig. **13–7.** Intersections between cutting planes and cones.

tions from a cone. Since the ellipse, parabola, and hyperbola are difficult to construct, cutting planes passing through the vertex of a cone or, when the cone is circular, cutting planes perpendicular to the axis of the cone are used wherever possible.

The intersection between any cutting plane and a sphere is a circle, as shown by *A-A* and *B-B* in Fig. 13–8. If the cutting plane is an inclined plane, as plane *B-B*, the true shape of the circle will be seen in an auxiliary view. Thus no special consideration need be given to locating cutting planes through a sphere.

13–7. INTERSECTIONS OBTAINED BY THE CUTTING PLANE METHOD

The intersection of a prism and a pyramid has been presented in Art. 13–5 and shown in Fig. 13–3, where two points on the line of intersection have been located through the use of an auxiliary view. These two points can also be located by using a cutting plane. Fig. 13–9 shows the same prism and pyramid as in Fig. 13–3. Points *1*, *2*, and *4* on the line of intersection can be directly located as discussed in Art. 13–5, and shown in Fig. 13–9(a). Points *3* and *5*, where the edge *CG* pierces the surfaces of the pyramid, must now be located. A cutting plane is placed so that it contains line *CG* and intersects the pyramid [plane *A-A*, Fig. 13–9(b)]. Cutting plane *A-A* intersects

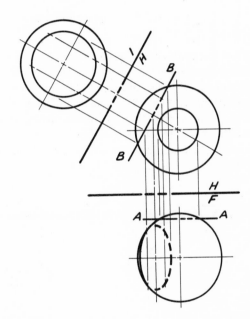

Fig. **13–8.** Intersections between cutting planes and spheres.

the edges of the pyramid at points *X*, *Y*, and *Z* which can be located in the horizontal view and projected to the frontal view. Since lines *XY*, *YZ*, *ZX*, and *CG* are all lines in plane *A-A*, the points *3* and *5* where line *CG* intersects lines *ZX* and *XY* can be located in the frontal view. Moreover, line *ZX* is a line in plane *MOP* and *XY* a line in plane

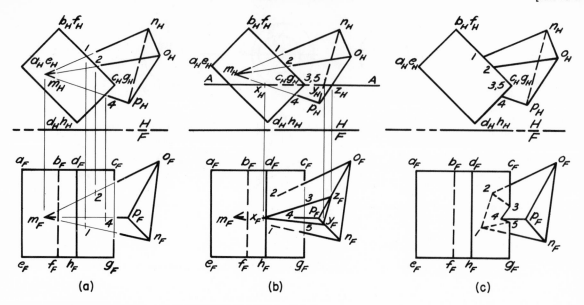

Fig. 13-9. Intersection between prism and pyramid—cutting plane method.

MNP of the pyramid. Therefore, points *3* and *5* are the points where the edge *CG* pierces planes *MOP* and *MNP*. The intersection is shown completed in Fig. 13-9(c). A comparison of Figs. 13-3 and 13-9 shows that the use of a cutting plane saves the necessity of constructing an auxiliary, thus saving time and increasing the possible accuracy of construction.

In general, when locating the line of intersection of two objects, try to use a cutting plane that will cut circles or straight lines from both objects. Fig. 13-10 shows the intersection between a cylinder and a prism. A cutting plane such as *A-A*, placed parallel to the axis of the cylinder, cuts straight lines from both the prism and the cylinder (*ABCDA* on the prism, lines *1* and *2* on the cylinder). The

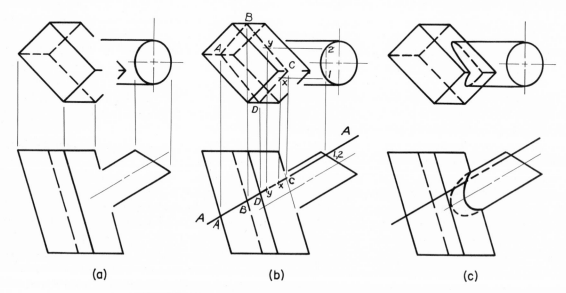

Fig. 13-10. Intersection between prism and cylinder.

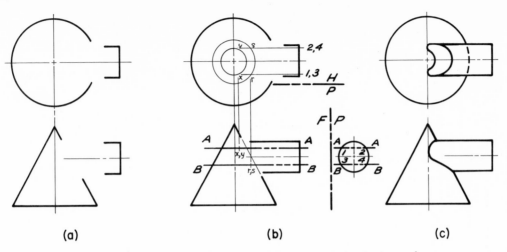

(a)   (b)   (c)

Fig. 13–11. Intersection between cone and cylinder.

location of the two points X and Y on the line of intersection is shown in Fig. 13–10(b) and the completed intersection is shown in Fig. 13–10(c). Fig. 13–11 shows the intersection between a cylinder and a cone. In this case, cutting planes parallel to the axis of the cylinder and perpendicular to the axis of the cone, as planes A-A and B-B, cut straight lines $1, 2$ and $3, 4$ from the cylinder and circles from the cone. The two cutting planes give points X, Y and R, S on the line of intersection. In order to locate the lines of intersection between the cutting plane and the cylinder in the horizontal view, an end view of the cylinder is required. The use of several more cutting planes results in the completed intersection shown in Fig. 13–11(c).

13–8. CRITICAL POINTS

It is not feasible to show examples of all possible combinations of intersecting surfaces. If the general rules of procedure are known and thought is exercised when locating the cutting planes, intersections reduce to a virtually mechanical routine. The ease with which an intersection is determined is influenced to a considerable extent by the determination of the *critical* or *key* points of the intersection. A procedural error that is frequently made is to cover the problem with a quantity of closely spaced cutting planes located uniformly across the intersection area. Then when one

attempts to locate the lines and points in the adjacent view, he frequently becomes bewildered in a maze of lines, or, if he does struggle through toward a solution, he often discovers that he lacks several necessary points. If carefully chosen cutting planes are used encompassing necessary critical (or key) points, it will usually be found that, for the average intersection, anywhere from four to seven cutting planes will be sufficient to give a reasonably accurate location of the intersection. The ability to locate cutting planes which will yield desirable critical points is acquired through experience and familiarity with the various types of surfaces.

In general, *critical points* are those points at which the direction changes on the path of intersection. In the case of plane-surfaced objects, the critical points are the piercing points of the edges of either object with the planes of the other. When either or both of the surfaces are curved surfaces, the critical points are either the points that limit the position of the line of intersection, or are those points where the line of intersection is tangent to a surface element of either object.

Fig. 13–12 shows the intersection between two cylinders and the location of the critical points of this intersection. Fig. 13–12(a) shows the given views of the cylinders and the location of four key cutting planes. The effect of cutting plane A-A is to locate point 1 where the rearmost element of the inclined cylinder pierces the vertical cylinder,

TABLE 13–1
Table of Typical Intersections
(Procedures Used in Solving for the More Common Intersections of Various Surfaces)

Type of Intersection	Cutting Planes Passed Perpendicular to—	Position of Cutting Planes in View in Which Passed	Direction of Projection for Related View	Types of Elements Obtained in Related View*
Two plane surfaced objects (polyhedra)	Any view	Any direction	Any direction	Straight lines from each object
Plane surfaced object (polyhedron) and cylinder	(1) Any view (2) True-length view of axis of cylinder	(1) Parallel to axis of cylinder (2) At 90° to axis of cylinder	(1) Any direction (2) To show axis of cylinder as a point	(1) Straight lines from each object (2) Straight lines from polyhedron; circles from cylinder
Polyhedron and cone	(1) Any view (2) True-length view of axis of cone	(1) Through apex of cone (2) At 90° to axis of cone	(1) Any direction (2) To show axis of cone as a point	(1) Straight lines (2) Straight lines from polyhedron; circles from cone
Polyhedron and warped (ruled) surface	View which shows various positions of generatrix of ruled surface as straight lines	Parallel to directrix—i.e., containing any position of generatrix	Any direction	Straight lines from each object
Polyhedron and sphere	Any view	Any direction	90° to cutting planes	Circles from sphere; straight lines from polyhedron
Two cylinders (1) Bases in the same or parallel planes (2) Bases in different planes (not parallel); this method may also be used to solve Type (1)	(1) View showing edge view of bases (2) View showing axes of both cylinders parallel	(1) Parallel to bases (2) Parallel to the axes of both cylinders	(1) 90° to cutting planes (2) Any direction	(1) Intersecting circles or ellipses (2) Straight lines
Cylinder and cone	Point view of axis of cylinder	(1) Through apex of cone parallel to axis of cylinder (2) Parallel to base of cone	(1) Any direction (2) 90° to cutting planes	(1) Straight lines (2) Straight lines from cylinder; circles from cone
Cylinder and sphere	(1) Any view (2) View showing true length of cylinder	(1) Parallel to axis of cylinder (2) 90° to axis of cylinder	(1) 90° to cutting plane (2) To show axis of cylinder as a point	(1) Straight lines from cylinder; circles from sphere (2) Circles
Two cones (1) Bases in the same or parallel planes (2) Bases in different planes (not parallel); this method may also be used to solve Type (1)	(1) View showing edge view of bases (2) View showing the point view of the line connecting the two apexes.	(1) Parallel to bases (2) Through the point view of line containing the two apexes and cutting *both* cones	(1) 90° to cutting planes (2) Any direction	(1) Intersecting circles or ellipses (2) Straight lines
Two spheres	Any view	Any direction	90° to cutting planes	Circles

*Intersection of these elements give points as line of intersection of bodies.

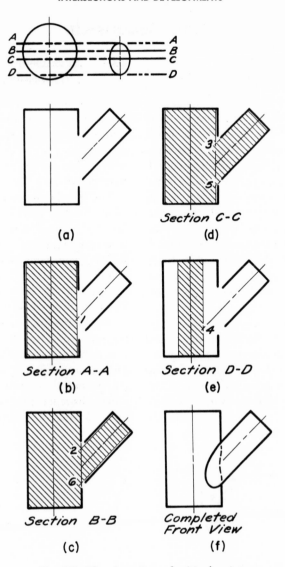

Fig. **13-12.** Location of critical points.

as shown in Fig. 13–12(b). (The shaded area in this case and in the other views of this figure represents the portions of the cylinders cut by the individual cutting planes.) Other critical points are successively located in Fig. 13–12(c), (d), and (e). Fig. 13–12(f) shows the frontal view of the completed intersection. The six critical points are sufficient to construct the line of intersection since the intersection is a smooth curve and points 1, 2, 4, and 6 are points where the curve is tangent to the vertical elements of the large cylinder while points 3 and 5 are points where the curve is tangent

to the inclined elements of the small cylinder. If more points are desired in order to locate the intersection more accurately, they may be added between the key cutting planes.

13-9. TABLE OF INTERSECTIONS

As a further aid in the solution of intersection problems, a few typical intersection combinations are listed in Table 13–1 together with suggested methods of solution.

Developments

13–10. DEVELOPABLE AND NON-DEVELOPABLE SURFACES

After the intersections between the surfaces of two objects are determined, the next step is often the task of developing the surfaces of the object or objects involved in the intersection. A *develop-ment* is a pattern made on a plane surface such that when the pattern is folded or rolled it will assume the shape of the desired object. A pattern or development can be accurately made for plane and single-curved surfaces (see Figs. 13–1 and 13–2); hence, these are known as *developable surfaces*. However, the pattern that can be made for a warped or double-curved surface will only approximate that surface and hence these are known as *non-developable surfaces*.

There are many examples of the use of developed surfaces, ranging from the design of ducts and other sheet metal parts to the design of paper party hats and horns. Another example occurs when an accurate model must be constructed to aid in the fabrication of a machine part or other piece of equipment.

13–11. DEVELOPMENT OF THE CYLINDER-PRISM

The development of any surface is a pattern of the surface, such that all lines of the surface (pattern) are true length. Therefore, before a development can be laid out, the true length of all lines to be shown in the development must be determined.

The development of a cylindrical surface is shown in Fig. 13–13. A cylindrical surface, like the label on a can or jar, can, in a sense, be unrolled to form its pattern. The first step is to construct in the given views, a number of elements of the cylindrical surface. In Fig. 13–13 all elements such as 1, 2, etc., are true length in the frontal view. The true distance between the elements is shown in the horizontal view. The development, or pattern, will show all elements in true length and true distance from each other. This can be accomplished by projecting the true lengths of the elements from the frontal view and placing them the correct distance apart with the aid of a stretch-out line. A *stretch-out line* is a line whose length is

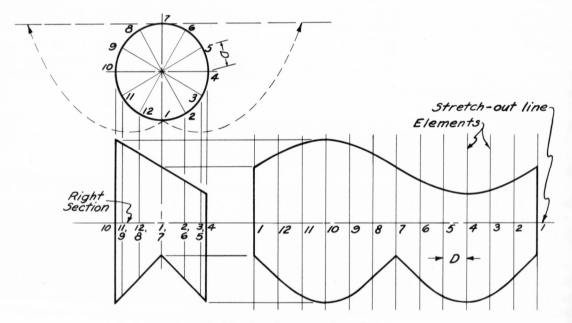

Fig. **13–13.** Development of a cylinder.

qual to the perimeter of a right section of the
bject, in this case the circumference of the cyl-
nder. If the number of elements chosen is such
hat the chordal distance between elements in the
orizontal view is nearly equal to the arc distance
etween the elements, then the length of the
tretch-out line can be determined by laying off
he chordal distances. If the elements are sym-
netrically arranged as they are in Fig. 13–13, only
ne divider setting is necessary to lay out the
tretch-out line. However, if considerable accu-
acy is necessary, the length of the stretch-out line
an be calculated. Since the development would
ave to be rolled into its desired shape, the ele-
nents are drawn as long, dashed lines instead of
olid, corner lines, to indicate a rolled surface. The
levelopment is completed by drawing smooth
urves through the end points of the elements.

Note that the development begins and ends on
he shortest seam line. This is done so that when
he pattern is rolled into its actual shape, the
oining of the ends (seam line) of the pattern
equires the least amount of soldering, welding,
iveting, or of any other method of joining the two
nds. In actual practice some allowance would
ave to be made for bending radius and type of
eam, but that is a technical procedure of fabrica-
ion and beyond the scope of this chapter.

A second point of importance is that the development is laid out with the inside surface up. This is
ustomary in problems such as the design of ducts
where the inside dimensions may be the critical
limensions. Another reason is that, particularly
n sheet metal work, the lines of the pattern are
ometimes scribed, or scratched, on the surface
of the metal. Laying out the development with
the inside surface up would hide all scribe lines on
the finished product. In the orthographic views of
Fig. 13–13, imagine that the surface is slit along
element 1 and then peeled back as indicated. Then
the frontal view would show the inside surface and
the elements would be numbered as is shown in the
development.

The development of the lateral surface of a prism
is shown in Fig. 13–14. The concepts for development are practically identical with those for a
cylinder. The first step, after determining true
lengths, is again to lay out the stretch-out line. In
this case, its length is the perimeter of a right sec-

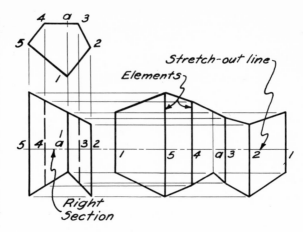

Fig. **13–14.** Development of a prism.

tion of the prism. Next, each edge (element) is
drawn and the true length of each edge is projected
from the front view to the development. In this
example an additional element (a) is necessary to
locate the high point of the bottom cut in the back
face of the prism. As per convention, the development is laid out with the inside surface up and cut
on the shortest seam line. The edges of the prism
are shown in the development by solid lines as the
pattern must be bent along these lines in order to
assume its proper shape.

In either of the above examples, if a top or
bottom surface is required, auxiliary views may be
constructed to show the true shape of the required
surface and then that surface added to the development.

13–12. DEVELOPMENT OF THE CONE-PYRAMID

A cylinder can be considered as a cone whose
vertex is at infinity. In this light, the development
of a cone is essentially the same as the development
of a cylinder in that the length of the stretch-out
line is the circumference of a right section and the
true length of all elements will be shown spaced
along the stretch-out line in the development.
However, since the elements of a cone intersect at
a real point, the vertex, they also intersect at a real
point in the development. Fig. 13–15 shows the
development of a portion of a right circular cone.

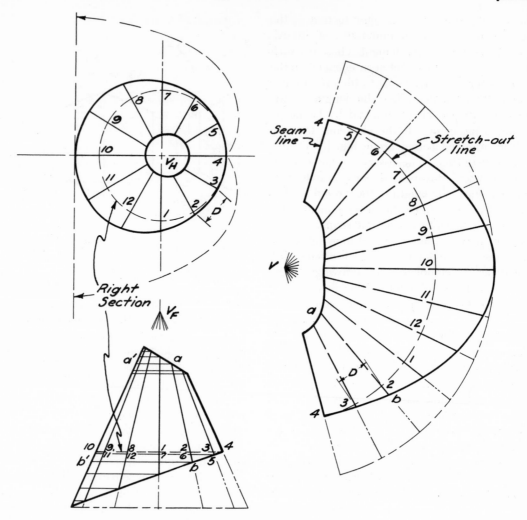

Fig. 13-15. Development of a cone.

Note that even though only a portion of a cone is to be developed, the imaginary vertex, V, is located and all elements of the cone are shown from vertex to base. The elements are equally spaced for simplicity and greater accuracy. Since the horizon (or limiting) elements of a cone are true length, the true length of all elements may be determined as shown in the frontal view (e.g., AB projects in true length A'B' on the left horizon element of the cone). In laying out the development, a location for the vertex, V, is chosen, and the stretch-out line is laid off as a circle arc whose radius is the true length of an element from the vertex to the right section (as is element V4). The length of the stretch-out line can be calculated, or laid off by chordal dis-

tances as determined from the horizontal view (e.g., distance D). Then the true length of each element of the actual surface can be laid off as lengths on each side of the stretch-out line (e.g., A2 = A'10 and 2B = 10B') and the end points connected by smooth curves as in Fig. 13-15. By convention, the development is cut on the shortest seam line, laid out inside up, and the elements are shown as long dashes to indicate a rolled surface.

The development of a pyramid is similar to that of a cone. When constructing the principal views, a pyramid can only be oriented so that the frontal or horizontal view shows the true lengths of a maximum of two of the edges from the vertex to the base. The true lengths of the other edges must then be determined. One method for doing this is shown in Fig. 13–16 where a true length diagram has been constructed. In this diagram, D_1 is the distance in the horizontal view from V_H to 1; D_2 is the distance from V_H to 3; and D_3, from V_H to 4. V_F and points 1, 3, and 4 on the right section are projected from the frontal view. ($V5$ and $V2$ are true length in the frontal view.) Hence triangles have been constructed which show the true lengths of all sides. In fact, this construction process is actually revolution. Since edge BH lies on the line $v_F 4_F$, points B and H can be projected to line $v_F' 4_F'$ in the true-length diagram and the true length of line BH is determined. Similarly, the true lengths of edges FL and CJ can be determined. Since the true lengths of the edges from the vertex to the right section all vary, the stretch-out line is not an arc, but must be laid out by *triangulation*. To accomplish this, the position of the seam line ($V2$) of the development is chosen and its true length laid out. Then, knowing the true lengths of edge $V1$ (from the true-length diagram) and line 12 of the right section (from the horizontal view) the position of point 1 is located by using these distances as radii from points V and 2. The other points along the stretch-out line are located by similar construction. The development is completed, as in Fig. 13–16, by laying off the true lengths of all edges and connecting the end points with straight lines.

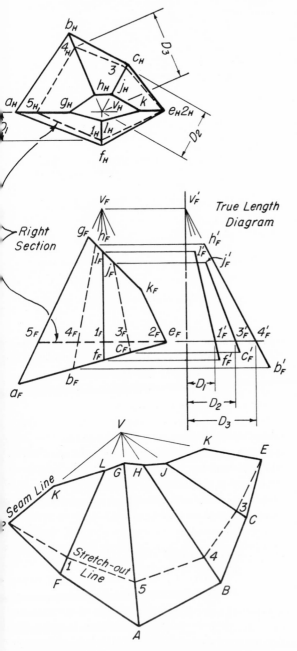

Fig. 13–16. Development of a pyramid.

13–13. DEVELOPMENT OF COMPOSITE SURFACES

Most actual surfaces encountered are not simple cylinders, prisms, cones, or pyramids, but frequently are combinations of any or all of the developable surfaces. In such a problem, the solution is to analyze the object and determine the basic surfaces involved. Fig. 13–17 shows a transition surface connecting a circular opening to a rectangular opening. In essence, this is a warped surface, but it can be subdivided with sufficient conformity into a series of oblique cones and planes which are developable. The horizontal view shows the true shape of the openings and the frontal view shows the true length of the selected seam line $P4$. Since no other lines are shown in true length, a true-length diagram is constructed as shown. Due to the symmetry of the object, the true-length diagram is less involved than it would be for a non-symmetrical object. Using triangulation, the development can be laid out by successively constructing the planes and the portions of oblique cones. $P4$ would first be established at some

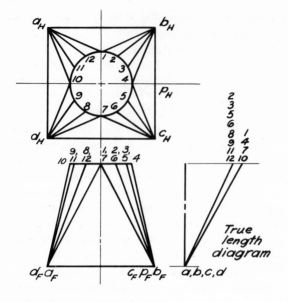

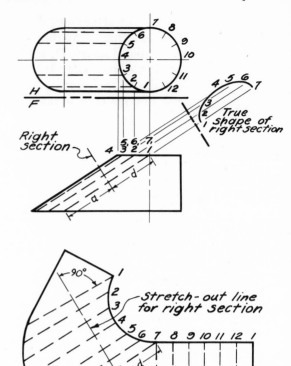

Fig. **13-18.** Development of a transition piece.

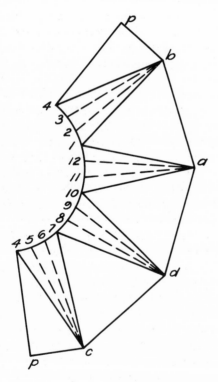

Fig. **13-17.** Development of a composite surface.

desired location. With the true lengths of *4B* and *PB* as radii, point *B* would be located. Next, with the true lengths of *3B* and the chord *34*, point *3* would be established. This procedure would be continued for the entire pattern.

In Fig. 13–18 another transition piece is shown where the subdivisions of the surface are two planes, a right circular cylinder and an oblique elliptical cylinder. In this case an auxiliary view showing the true shape of a right section of the cylindrical portion is necessary to determine the stretch-out line for the oblique cylinder.

13-14. DEVELOPMENT OF WARPED SURFACES

When the surfaces in a problem are theoretically non-developable, the only solution is to approximate the surface. In Fig. 13–19, a warped cone is used for the transition between two circular open-

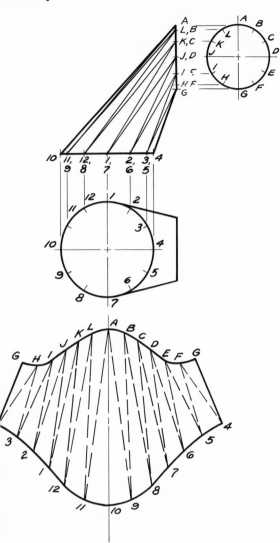

Fig. 13–19. Development of a warped cone.

development of any warped surface can only be approximated, usually using the triangulation method as in this discussion.

13–15. DEVELOPMENT OF DOUBLE-CURVED SURFACES

As with warped surfaces, the development of double-curved surfaces can be only approximate. The double-curved surface that is a frequent problem is the sphere. Scientists have for centuries attempted to find better methods to more closely approximate, on a flat sheet of paper, the surface of a sphere. The reason for all this activity is the desire to create a map showing the earth's surface as nearly true size and true shape as possible. Although map projections are computed mathematically, the concept is fundamentally graphic. The usual attack is to project the sphere onto a developable surface such as a plane, cylinder, or cone. A number of methods have been employed, but none has been completely satisfactory.

One method is frequently used when it is required to make a pattern for a spherical surface. The method, known as the gore method, is based on the intersection of an elliptical cylinder and the sphere as in Fig. 13–20(a). The major diameter of the cylinder is the diameter of the sphere. As the minor diameter approaches the diameter of the sphere, the angle θ becomes smaller and smaller. Obviously the smaller θ becomes, the more nearly the portion of the cylinder that cuts through the sphere approximates that portion of the sphere. The outside surface of the piece cut from the sphere is called a gore. The gore is now cut by a series of parallel planes as in Fig. 13–20(b). From the horizontal and frontal views it can be seen that chord *13* approximates arc *123*; chord *46* approximates arc *456*; and chord *79* approximates arc *789*. The error of this approximation becomes smaller as θ becomes smaller. Since arcs *N147*, *N258*, and *N369* are great circle arcs, they are equal arcs. Chords *58*, *25*, and *N2* approximate arcs *58*, *25*, and *N2*. The error of this approximation becomes smaller as the interval between planes becomes smaller. With the above knowledge, the development can be laid out as in Fig. 13–20(c), where one-half of one section, or gore, is developed. Due to symmetry, the other half would be identical. If

ings in different planes. Each circular end is uniformly subdivided and lines are drawn between each respective pair of subdivisions as in Fig. 13–19 (e.g., A-10, L-11, etc.). Then adjacent elements are joined by diagonals, as illustrated, thus forming triangles which are assumed to be plane surfaces. The smaller these triangles, the truer will be the assumption. With this assumption, the development can be laid out by triangulation. A true-length diagram for all elements and diagonals would be required. This has been omitted from Fig. 13–19 for the sake of simplification. The

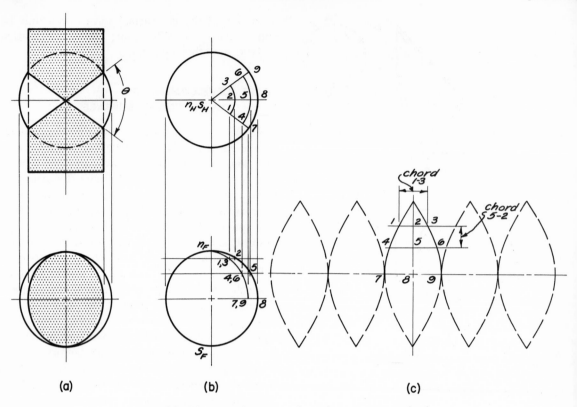

Fig. **13–20.** Development of a sphere—gore method.

the angle θ is chosen so that it divides into 360° (the circumference of the sphere) a whole number of times, the approximation of the spherical surface can be completed by laying out that number of gores.

There are other methods for approximately developing the surface of a sphere, but it is not considered within the scope of this text to discuss all methods. They can be found in texts dealing exclusively with descriptive geometry or map projections. The important fact to remember is that, no matter what method is used, the result is only an approximation. This is true for any non-developable surface.

Problems

13–1. Find the lines of intersection and develop one of the surfaces of Fig. 13–21(a).

13–2. Find the lines of intersection and develop one of the surfaces of Fig. 13–21(b).

13–3. Find the lines of intersection and develop one of the surfaces of Fig. 13–21(c).

13–4. Find the line of intersection and develop the surface of the vertical cylinder of Fig. 13–22(a).

13–5. Find the line of intersection and develop the inclined cylinder of Fig. 13–22(b).

13–6. Find the line of intersection and develop the vertical cone of Fig. 13–22(c).

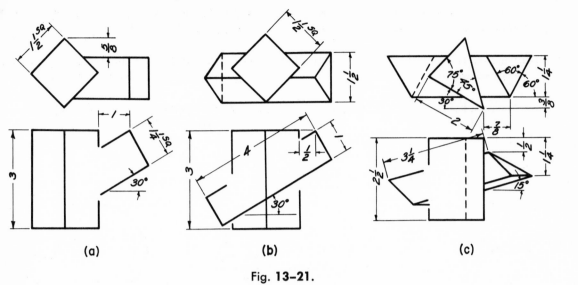

(a) (b) (c)

Fig. **13–21.**

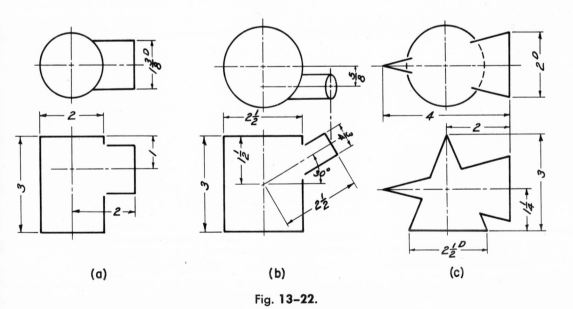

(a) (b) (c)

Fig. **13–22.**

13-7. Find the line of intersection and develop the vertical cone of Fig. 13–23(a).

13-8. Find the line of intersection and develop the inclined cylinder of Fig. 13–23(b).

13-9. Find the line of intersection and develop the cone of Fig. 13–23(c).

13-10. Find the lines of intersection and develop t prism of Fig. 13–24(a).

13-11. Find the lines of intersection and develop t prism of Fig. 13–24(b).

13-12. Find the lines of intersection and develop t cylinder of Fig. 13–24(c).

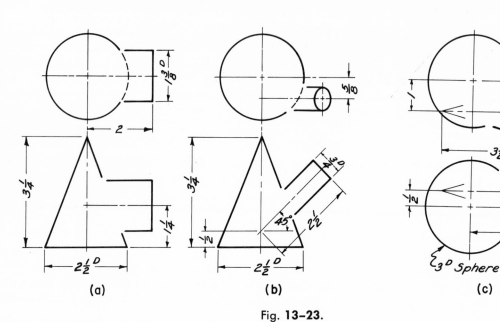

Fig. **13–23.**

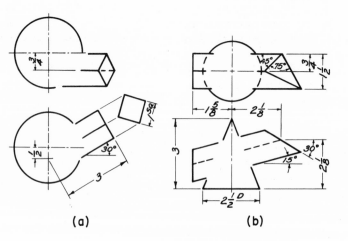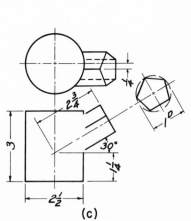

Fig. **13–24.**

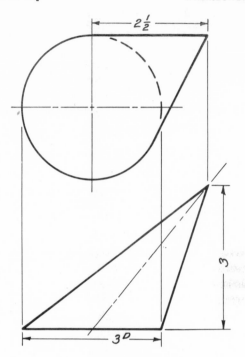

Fig. **13-25.**

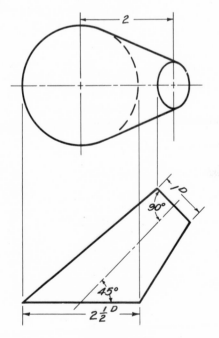

Fig. **13-26.**

13-13. Develop the surface of the oblique cone of Fig. 13–25.

13-14. Develop the surface of the transition section of Fig. 13–26.

13-15. Develop the surface of the transition section of Fig. 13–27.

13-16. Using 12 gores, develop the surface of a sphere whose diameter is 3″. Show only three gores.

13-17. Using 24 gores, develop the surface of a sphere whose diameter is 3″. Show only four gores.

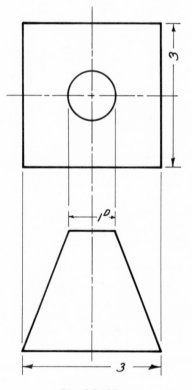

Fig. **13-27.**

IV
GRAPHICAL
MATHEMATICS

14

GRAPHS AND DIAGRAMS

14-1. INTRODUCTION

Previous chapters have discussed applications of the fundamental principles of graphics, and how they can be utilized not only as a means of communication, but also as a means of solving spatial problems. These applications of graphics have been based on the principles of orthographic projection. This chapter, as well as succeeding ones, introduces additional methods and techniques for presenting and analyzing data and solving problems. Again, the basic approach is graphical, but the fundamentals are based upon geometry rather than projection theory.

In analyzing a series of correlated quantitative or qualitative facts, it is frequently useful to present such data in a form appropriate for visual interpretation and analysis. Word descriptions or tabular formats may be used, but graphs and diagrams provide a more rapid, versatile, and powerful technique. To illustrate, compare the tabular presentation of data, Fig. 14–1(a), with that of the line graph in Fig. 14–1(b) and the bar diagram in Fig. 14–1(c). The two graphical presentations

[Fig. 14–1(b) and (c)] provide a superior means for visual comparison of the data. When technically trained personnel use graphs as a means of communication among themselves, a form similar to Fig. 14–1(b) is most common. However, when diagrams serve as a means of presenting data to lay personnel, a form similar to that of Fig. 14–1(c) is frequently used.

14-2. DEFINITIONS

Before studying the techniques of construction of various forms of charts, graphs, and diagrams, it is important to establish a clear understanding of these three terms. The term "chart" has two meanings, the first of which is associated with mapping, while the second describes any of the forms of graphical presentation described in this chapter. Thus. the term "chart" includes all graphs and diagrams. A *graph* is that special form of chart in which the data to be presented are plotted with reference to some type of grid. A *diagram* is that form of chart used to present data without the use of a grid. These differences should become more

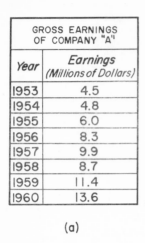

GROSS EARNINGS OF COMPANY "A"	
Year	Earnings (Millions of Dollars)
1953	4.5
1954	4.8
1955	6.0
1956	8.3
1957	9.9
1958	8.7
1959	11.4
1960	13.6

(a)

(b)

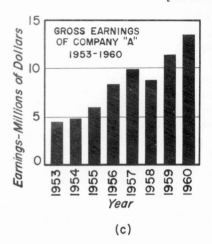

(c)

Fig. **14-1.** Presentation of correlated data.

evident as the various forms are discussed. Throughout this text the specific terms "graph" and "diagram" are used rather than the general, all-inclusive term "chart."

14-3. CLASSIFICATION

Graphs and diagrams may be classified, according to use, into two broad categories depending on whether their application is for technical purposes or for popular appeal. While the primary concern of the technically trained person is the former, he must also be versed in the latter application. Graphs and diagrams are most frequently used by scientific personnel to: (a) present results of experimental investigations, (b) represent phenomena which follow natural laws, (c) represent equations for further computational purposes, and (d) derive empirical equations to represent empirical test data. However, in addition to these applications, information and ideas must often be presented in a way understandable to the layman in order to have the information or idea accepted. For this popular appeal, graphs and diagrams are invaluable, for through graphics it is possible to present information in a very clear and striking manner.

This chapter presents the more common forms of graphs and diagrams required by the technically oriented in their professional work. As a background for this study, it is assumed that the reader is versed in the use of the rectangular coordinates, and has a rudimentary understanding of fundamental terminology such as grid, axes, origin, abscissa, ordinate, and variables.

Graphs

14-4. RECTILINEAR GRAPHS

The most frequently occurring form of graph involves data plotted on a rectilinear grid. Such graphs, called *rectilinear graphs*, are used for either the actual or final presentation of data, or as an initial plot for determining more appropriate subsequent forms of presentation.

Rectilinear graphs are, for convenience, grouped into three basic categories: mathematical, time-series, and engineering. The *mathematical graph* is the result of plotting a series of pure numbers, either positive or negative, showing the relationship of an equation. Fig. 14-2(a), representative of a typical mathematical graph, portrays the relationship between various values of x and y for the parabola $x^2 - 2x + 2y - 8 = 0$. The *time-series graph* is any plot in which one of the related variables is measured as a unit of time. Such a graph is the Population Growth of Continental United States, Fig. 14-2(b), on which the horizontal values are expressed in ten-year intervals. The time-series graph is among the more common forms utilized in scientific investigations because time is a frequent variable in experimentation. The *engineering graph* is a plot of two related variables exclusive of time, as in Fig. 14–2(c), where the efficiency and total head for a centrifugal pump have been plotted against capacity.

Rectilinear graphs, as a means of presenting data, have several advantages as well as limitations. The advantages include a means for (a) observing the direction (trend) of a given set of data, (b) comparing relative changes or trends among several curves, (c) comparing a large quantity of data in a limited space, and (d) ready interpolation of values between the given data. Normally, rectilinear graphs are not appropriate when it is desired to stress variations in absolute amounts or to present just a few plotted points.

14–5. CONSTRUCTION OF RECTILINEAR GRAPHS

In drawing a graph, the construction may be divided into a series of fundamental steps. While the procedure described in this article and those immediately following concerns graphs plotted on rectilinear grids, they are also applicable to graphs drawn on any type of grid.

The actual construction of a graph consists of the following eight steps:

1. Select the form of graph paper and grid spacing most suitable for representing the data.
2. Establish the location of the horizontal and vertical axes.
3. Determine, for the axes, scale units which will appropriately display the data.
4. Identify scales, including basic scale units and suitable captions.
5. Plot the points representing the data.
6. Draw the curve or curves.
7. Provide curve identification, if more than one curve has been plotted, and appropriate titles.
8. Ink graph, if necessary, for reproduction.

In subsequent articles, each of these steps is analyzed in detail.

14–6. SELECTION OF SUITABLE GRIDS

Rectilinear grid rulings are usually selected from the wide variety of graph paper available com-

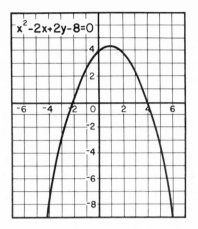

(a) Mathematical

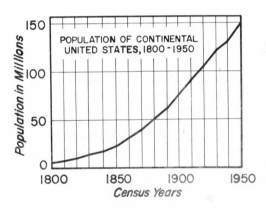

(b) Time–Series

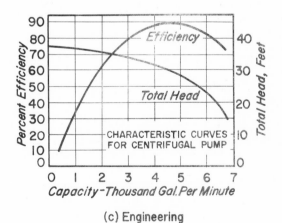

(c) Engineering

Fig. **14–2.** Types of rectilinear graphs.

mercially, but may be individually ruled to satisfy the special needs of a particular problem. The more common commercial rulings include 4, 5, 6, 8, 10, 12, 16, and 20 divisions per inch as well as 5 and 10 divisions to the centimeter. These grids are available in several colors, including green, orange, and blue, printed on either opaque or translucent stock. When graphs are prepared for use in publications or for briefing of lay personnel, the primary objective is to show the relationship between variables. The grids of such graphs should be as coarse as possible (the space between the grid lines should be large), with the rulings of the grid lines limited to those necessary to guide the eye and to achieve the desired accuracy when reading values. Many technical graphs, however, are used for computation and analysis, and, therefore, require close interpolation. Such graphs are normally plotted on a finely ruled grid to assure the proper accuracy when reading values.

14-7. ESTABLISHMENT OF THE AXES

Once the appropriate graph paper has been selected, the location of the axes must be established. The axes consist of a horizontal line named the x-axis, or *abscissa*, and a vertical line named the y-axis, or *ordinate*. The intersection of the two axes is the *origin*. When the data involve only positive values the origin is placed in the lower left portion of the graph. If, when using commercial graph paper, there is sufficient border area to permit placement of scale values and captions, the edges of the printed grid may be used as the axes.

However, with many of the commercial graph papers this would result in crowding. In such cases, the axes are placed sufficiently within the grid so that all labeling of axes and scale captions are also within the grid area. Data containing negative values necessitate a shift in the origin to accommodate such a range of values. An example of this is the plot of the parabola in Fig. 14-2(a).

Normally, in graphing the results of tests or experiments, the *independent* variable is plotted along the abscissa and the *dependent* variable along the ordinate. The independent variable is defined as the one over which an individual exerts control in any test, such as the pump capacity in Fig. 14-2(c). The dependent variable is the one over which an individual has no control during a test. An example of this is the pump efficiency in the same figure.

In the graphing of most data, it is essential that the zero values, or origin, be included on the graph. When a visual comparison of either magnitudes or amount of change is required, as in interpreting the centrifugal pump characteristics [Fig. 14-2(c)], the origin must be included as part of the graph. One variation exists when values along one axis are all considerably above or below the zero value. Under these conditions the portion of unused grid may be broken out to save space (Fig. 14-3). In graphs where only the absolute magnitude of values is of interest, the origin is often omitted and the axis scale starts at a value other than zero. The efficiency vs. load curve in Fig. 14-4 is a typical example of this.

Occasionally, it is necessary to represent several related, dependent variables, requiring different ordinate scales, in terms of the same independent

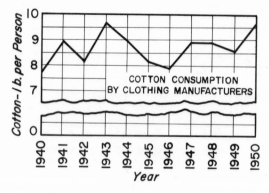

Fig. **14-3.** Breaking the ordinate scale.

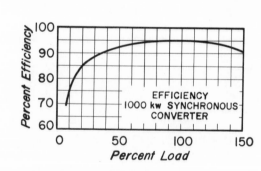

Fig. **14-4.** Scale ordinate omission.

variable. When only two ordinate axes are required, they are frequently placed on both sides of the graph [Fig. 14–2(c)]. If more than two scales are required, the additional ones are placed parallel to the others, generally on the left side of the graph.

14–8. DETERMINATION OF SCALE UNITS

In determining suitable units for any axis scale, units must be selected which will both fit the grid subdivisions and utilize to best advantage the available grid area. These units must be compatible with the grid subdivisions, such as the values shown in Fig. 14–5(a). Here, the grid subdivisions are easily read since each subdivision represents five units. Scales similar to that in Fig. 14–5(b) should be avoided, since each grid subdivision now represents 6.25 units. This necessitates awkward interpolations. Scales for the axes should be selected to obtain maximum utilization of the available grid area, but at the same time they must not give a distorted picture of the data. To anyone reading a graph, a relatively steep sloping curve indicates a significant change, while a flat curve indicates insignificant change. Thus, units should be selected which provide the reader with the proper significance of the information. The slope

of a curve may be made steeper by increasing the unit distance on the ordinate axis and decreasing the abscissa, or may be made flatter by decreasing the unit distance on the ordinate axis and increasing the abscissa. However, in graphing certain types of data, established formats must be followed. An example of this is the stress-strain graph, Fig. 14–6, depicting the strength of steel rods. In Fig. 14–6(a) the data are shown in conventional form, while Fig. 14–6(b) illustrates how the graph can be distorted from the accepted format by increasing the abscissa scale and reducing the ordinate scale, thus flattening the curve. Altering the curve in this manner is

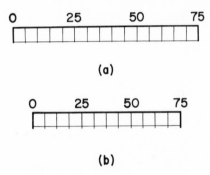

Fig. **14–5.** Scale unit selection.

STRESS - STRAIN GRAPHS OF 0.44 CARBON STEEL ROD

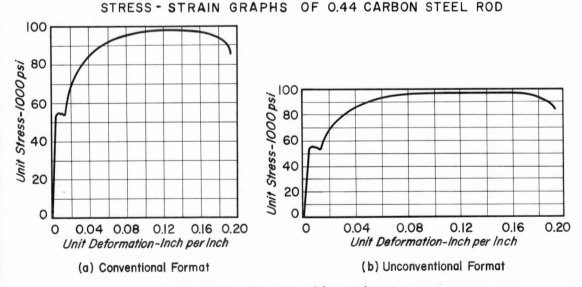

Fig. **14–6.** Conventional format distortion.

often done by the unscrupulous graph designer when he desires to overemphasize some aspect of the curve.

The stress-strain graph (Fig. 14–6) is also an example of an exception to one of the principles established in Art. 14–7—that the independent variable be plotted on the abscissa. In obtaining data for such a plot, the independent variable is the loading (or stress) applied to the test sample; but accepted procedure dictates that the dependent variable elongation (or strain) be plotted on the abscissa.

14–9. IDENTIFICATION OF SCALES

A completed scale includes both the identification of values at uniform intervals along the grid and an appropriate descriptive caption. Scales along the abscissa usually have values and captions placed directly below the axis and read from the bottom of the graph. Ordinate scale values also read from the bottom and are placed to the left of the axis. While captions for ordinate scales sometimes read from the bottom, accepted practice usually has them reading from the right. A typical ordinate scale is illustrated in Fig. 14–7(a).

When locating the identifying scale units along grids having certain lines accented, only these accented, more heavily printed divisions are

assigned values [Fig. 14–7(b)]. Identifying values are stated completely when they contain no more than three digits. However, when scale identification units contain more than three digits, labeling as in Fig. 14–7(c) should be avoided in favor of dropping the zeros, with the omission becoming part of the scale caption [Fig. 14–7(d)]. The same form may be used in technical graphs. However, if more convenient, such shortening of units may be noted through the use of powers of 10 [Fig. 14–7(e)]. Such shortening of values is not indicated by including the powers of 10 in the caption [Fig. 14–7(f)], since it is not clear whether scale units have been, or should be, multiplied by the power of 10.

The techniques of scale identification discussed above, while illustrated through the use of ordinate scales, apply equally to abscissa scales. In addition there are certain specialized scale units often used on abscissa scales. These units depict time measurements such as days, weeks, months, and years, as well as location descriptions. When space permits, years are indicated as in Fig. 14–2(b), but limited space may necessitate vertical labeling as shown in Fig. 14–1(b), or an abbreviation as shown in Fig. 14–8(a). Days and months are usually indicated as in Fig. 14–8(b) and Fig. 14–8(c), but limited space may again necessitate vertical labeling. Location descriptions may be applied in the same way as the special time descrip-

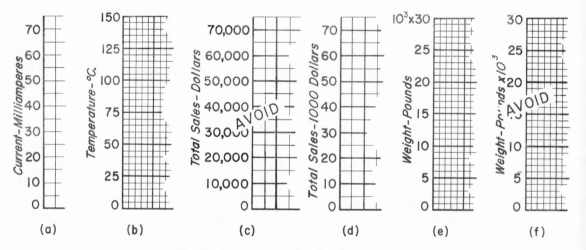

Fig. 14–7. Numerical scale identification.

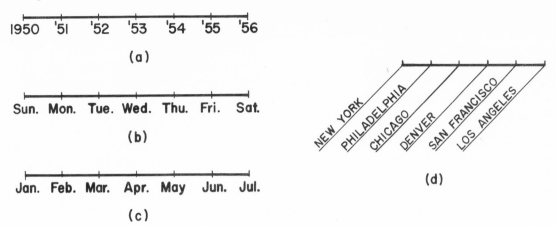

Fig. **14-8.** Non-numerical scale identification.

tions, but frequently they are placed on a slant as in Fig. 14-8(d) for ease of reading.

Scale captions, as previously stated, usually read from the bottom of the graph for abscissas and from the right side of the graph for ordinates. All scale captions should include, in this order: (a) specification of the variable, (b) symbol, if any, for the variable, and (c) unit of measure.

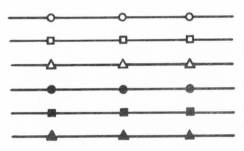

Fig. **14-9.** Point symbols.

14-10. PLOTTING OF DATA

Points used in plotting data should be indicated on technical graphs, but such identification is omitted on mathematical and popular-appeal graphs. On technical graphs, especially those based on experimental findings, symbols are used to indicate the points representing data to be utilized in plotting the curve. These symbols are given in Fig. 14-9 in their preferred order of usage. Open symbols, especially the circle, are preferred, but solid symbols are used if more than three curves require identification on the same graph. The use of dots, plus signs, and x's as symbols should be avoided. The primary objective of mathematical graphs, theoretical graphs (graphs not based on experimental findings), and popular-appeal graphs is emphasis on the significance of the curve. Therefore points used in plotting these curves are not indicated since such markings detract from the purpose of the graph.

14-11. DRAWING THE CURVE

The form of a curve on a graph reflects the type of data represented. If the data are discontinuous —not supported by theory or natural law—the plotted points are connected by straight lines. An example of this is the correction curve for a pressure gage, Fig. 14-10(a). When the data are continuous (empirical, but based on natural laws), a smooth curve is drawn through the plotted points. In these curves the variable accuracy of the data used in plotting the points may make it impracticable for the curve to pass through every plotted point. In such instances an average curve is drawn which is representative of the author's opinion. This drawing of such an average curve is frequently referred to as "fairing" a curve through the given data. Illustrative of this is the performance curve for a turbine, Fig. 14-10(b). Theoretical curves, which

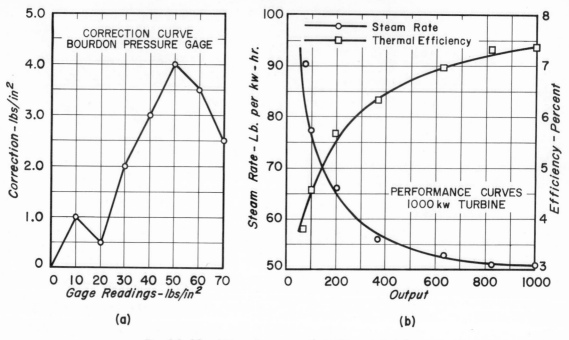

(a)   (b)

Fig. **14-10.**   Discontinuous and continuous graphs.

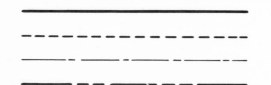

Fig. **14-11.**   Line types for curve representation.

are plotted using data calculated from mathematical equations, are also drawn as continuous smooth lines and pass through every point.

Care should be taken in drawing the curve. A study of Fig. 14-10 shows that the curve is never drawn through the symbols used to designate points. A fine line is used in technical graphs which are to be used as sources for obtaining future data. A heavier line is used when the graph is prepared for publication or popular-appeal use. When graphs are drawn for subsequent reproduction, using commercial grids printed on tracing paper, the curves are often drawn on the back side of the paper. This permits erasures without damage to the printed grid, and does not affect the quality of the reproduction.

14-12. TITLES AND CURVE IDENTIFICATION

The title for a graph should be clearly stated, but concise, and should contain sufficient information to describe completely the data being presented, including source references. If the graph represents the results of experimental tests, the title should also include the date of the experiment and the observer's name. Titles may be located within or outside the grid as space permits. A title located within a printed grid may be emphasized by enclosing it within a ruled border. When ruling one's own grid, grid lines should be omitted in the area of the title. If possible, the title should be placed in such a position that it will not interfere with the reading of the graph.

Several curves drawn on the same grid require individual identification. This is accomplished by labeling the curves as in Fig. 14-2(c), or through the use of a legend as in Fig. 14-10(b). If several theoretical curves are presented on the same graph, they may be identified through the use of different types of lines with an accompanying legend. Examples of lines commonly used are shown in Fig. 14-11. The uniformly spaced dashed line is also frequently used to denote the extension of a curve beyond the given data. This extension is called extrapolation.

14–13. GRAPHS FOR REPRODUCTION

Graphs prepared for either publication or projection (slides) require special consideration. Such graphs are seldom used for accurate reading of values since the objective generally is to emphasize the trends or direction of the data. Therefore, only essential facts need to be presented. More satisfactory results can be obtained if the grid rulings are drawn on blank paper rather than commercially prepared grids, with rulings kept as coarse as possible to facilitate ease of reading. Graphs for reproduction must also be inked to obtain satisfactory copy.

14–14. SEMILOGARITHMIC GRAPHS

Certain types of information are best represented by plotting the data on a semilogarithmic grid. This grid consists of uniformly spaced rulings along the abscissa, and logarithmically spaced rulings along the ordinate. When data are presented on such a grid, the resulting graph is known as a semi-

logarithmic graph, a ratio graph, or a rate of change graph.

On semilogarithmic graphs, the slope of the plotted curve at any point is a direct measure of the respective rate of increase or decrease of the data. This makes such a graph useful in statistical analysis both to show the rates at which a variable changes and to predict future trends from current information. If any portion of a curve on a semilogarithmic graph plots as a straight line, the rate of change of the data over that portion of the curve is constant. In comparing semilogarithmic graphs with rectilinear graphs, it is important to note that the former are used to show percentage changes in data while the latter show quantitative changes. The semilogarithmic graph, as with rectilinear graphs, is not appropriate for emphasizing absolute changes in values.

A typical semilogarithmic graph is shown in Fig. 14–12(a). The solid line, based on United States Census data, represents the actual population growth of Los Angeles, California. The dashed line has been faired through the data to represent the trend of the growth from which the future population increases may be predicted.

A semilogarithmic grid also has the unique property of presenting exponential equations as

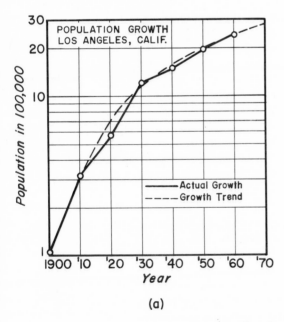

(a)

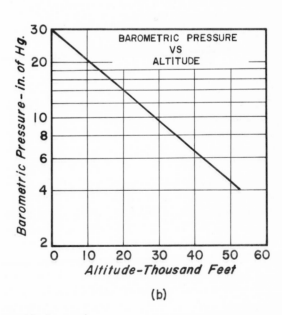

(b)

Fig. 14–12. Semilogarithmic graphs.

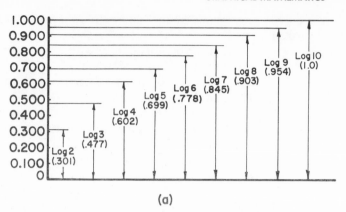

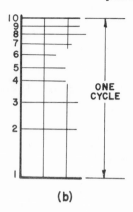

Fig. **14–13.** Logarithmic scale design.

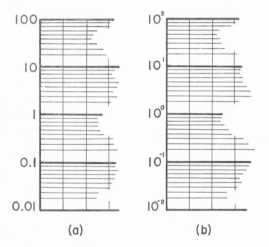

Fig. **14–14.** Cycle identification.

straight lines. This property, important in the derivation of empirical equations from empirical data, is discussed in detail in Art. 18–8. An example of this is the plot of barometric pressure vs. altitude in Fig. 14–12(b).

A thorough understanding of the theory of the logarithmic grid ruling is essential not only to be able to lay out such a grid, but to better appreciate its significance. This theory is developed by starting with a uniformly divided ordinate axis scale, Fig. 14–13(a). Assume that the divisions represent logarithms to the base 10 of numbers 1 through 10. At the appropriate locations on the scale, the logarithms are replaced with their corresponding whole numbers. The result is a set of rulings as in Fig.

14–13(b). This is a non-uniform scale with the numbers spaced at distances proportional to the logarithms of the numbers. In working with logarithmic grids, the scale of Fig. 14–13(b) is referred to as one cycle. Commercially available graph paper with logarithmic grid rulings often contains two or more of these cycles.

In assigning scale units to a logarithmic grid ruling, a full cycle begins with a power of 10 and ends with the next higher power of 10. Note that the cycles in Fig. 14–14(a) range from 0.01 to 0.1, 0.1 to 1.0, 1.0 to 10, and 10 to 100. In terms of powers of 10 these are expressed as 10^{-2} to 10^{-1}, 10^{-1} to 10^{0}, 10^{0} to 10^{1}, and 10^{1} to 10^{2}. A logarithmic scale approaches but cannot reach zero, since the $\log_{10} 0$ is at negative infinity. Logarithmic scale designations may be labeled in many ways. Frequently, only cycle end points are labeled, using either of the techniques of Fig. 14–14. If the logarithmic scale is large enough, intermediate points within a cycle may be labeled. The two ordinate scales of Fig. 14–12 are typical of this latter technique.

14–15. LOGARITHMIC GRAPHS

The logarithmic grid ruling developed in the previous article also serves as the basis for logarithmic graphs. In logarithmic graphs, both axes are graduated using logarithmic cycles, as compared to the semilogarithmic graph in which one axis uses a uniform spacing. Logarithmic graphs are used to advantage in plotting a wide range of values in a limited space. This is possible because, in a given limited space, the use of logarithmic cycles allows a much greater range of values to be plotted than does a rectilinear ruling. Another advantage of the logarithmic graph is the ease of comparison of relative directions or trends of two or more curves. However, logarithmic graphs, as with rectilinear and semilogarithmic, are not the most appropriate grid form when it is desirable to emphasize changes in absolute values.

The logarithmic graph is used more frequently in the solution of problems than as a means of presenting data. Power curves plotted on this grid become straight lines. This property forms the basis for the derivation of empirical equations from empirical data and is discussed in detail in Art. 18–7.

A typical logarithmic graph, Fig. 14–15, presents a comparison of pressure vs. specific volume for saturated water vapor.

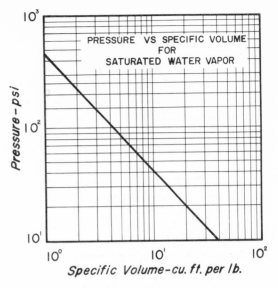

Fig. **14–15.** Logarithmic graph.

14–16. TRILINEAR GRAPHS

A trilinear graph utilizes a grid which is especially useful in the analysis of chemical compounds, mixtures, and alloys containing three variables. The basis of the grid is an equilateral triangle. Use of the graph is predicated on the fact that the sum of the perpendiculars to the three sides of an equilateral triangle from an interior point is equal to the altitude of the triangle. Although the three altitudes of the triangle are not drawn, each serves as an axis for plotting one of the variables, with its scale ranging from 0 per cent at the base to 100 per cent at the vertex. A sample trilinear coordinate grid is shown in Fig. 14–16(a). In plotting variables, the perpendicular distance from any point to each of the three sides represents the percentage of the three variables contained in the total mixture.

A representative application of the trilinear graph used in the field of metallurgy is shown in Fig. 14–16(b). The graph shows the phases (crystal structure) present in an alloy composed of elements A, B, and C at a certain temperature t. At point x, the alloy is composed of 18 per cent of element A (distance xR), 49 per cent of element B (distance

xT), and 33 per cent of element C (distance xS), and would, when viewed under a microscope, indicate the presence of β and γ phases, but no α phase. Such information is valuable to the metallurgist in predicting the behavior of the alloy when in service.

14–17. POLAR GRAPHS

The polar graph is used in representing two variables, one linear and the other angular. In appearance, the grid consists of a number of concentric circles which measure the magnitude of the linear variable, and uniformly spaced radial lines which measure the angular variable. One familiar application of polar graphs is the representation of mathematical curves plotted in polar coordinates [Fig. 14–17(a)]. In engineering, the polar coordinate grid finds application in plotting information such as illumination intensity, heat intensity, sound distribution, etc. Fig. 14–17(b) shows an illumination intensity graph where the distribution of illumination, measured in foot-candles, is shown for a given light source. Candle power for any specified direction is found by reading the distance from the origin to the curve. Polar graphs are also the basis for many of the automatic recording instruments in use today.

CRYSTAL STRUCTURE FOR ALLOY
AT TEMPERATURE "t"

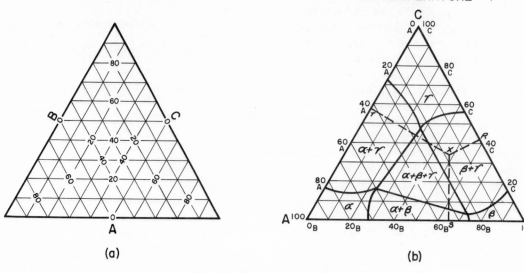

Fig. **14-16.** Trilinear graph.

Trifolium (three-leaved rose)
$\rho = 4 \sin 3\theta$

(a) Mathematical Graph

Lamp In Enameled Reflector

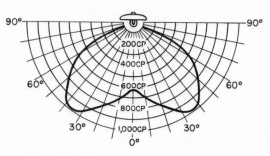

(b) Illumination Intensity Graph

Fig. **14-17.** Polar graphs.

14-18. SPECIAL GRIDS

Preceding articles have described the more common grids used in presenting technical data.

Many other specialized grids have been designed to present specific types of data required by industry and research. Study of such specialized grids is beyond the intended scope of this book.

Diagrams

14–19. BAR DIAGRAMS

The bar diagram is one of the more common types of popular-appeal diagrams because of the ease with which it is understood by non-technical users. The readiness with which these diagrams portray and summarize statistical data has resulted in their wide acceptance in popular literature such as newspapers and periodicals.

Bar diagrams are appropriate when it is desirable to make simple comparisons of quantities. While the length of the individual bars is proportional to the value of the variable represented, the bars are all made the same width. The bars may be drawn either vertically or horizontally, but vertical bars have proven to be more readable. Fig. 14–18 is typical of a bar diagram, in this case portraying the volume of mail handled by a city post office during an average business day.

Bar diagrams can assume other forms as indicated in Fig. 14–19 where the same data of Fig. 14–18 are represented in several different ways. Fig. 14–19(a) presents a layout in which the bars are placed horizontally. Fig. 14–19(b) shows a *mirror diagram,* so named because of its symmetry about an imaginary vertical axis. Studies have shown that this mirror diagram is the form non-

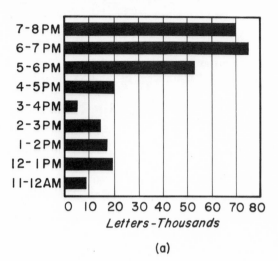

(a)

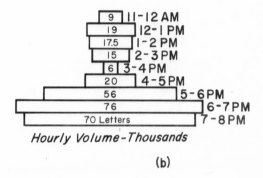

Hourly Volume-Thousands

(b)

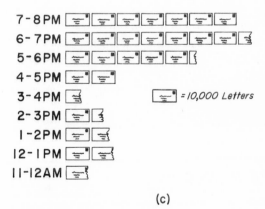

(c)

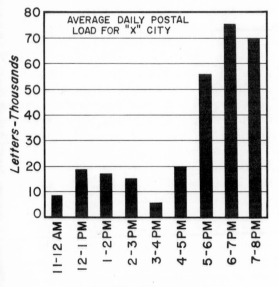

Fig. **14–18.** Bar diagram.

Fig. **14–19.** Bar diagram variations.

technical readers remember best. The bars in a bar diagram are frequently subdivided into easily countable units. These subdivisions may be simply rectangles, or they may be pictures symbolic of the data being presented. In Fig. 14–19(c) the unit subdivisions are in the form of letters, each letter symbolizing 10,000 pieces of mail handled by the post office.

To achieve a well-designed and effective bar diagram the following principles should be applied:

1. Spacing between the bars is normally made equal to the width of the bars. However, wider spaces are often used when the diagram contains few bars, and closer spacing is used when the diagram has several bars.
2. While printed coordinate paper may be used, a clearer presentation is obtained if the diagram is drawn using blank paper.
3. Since the principal purpose of the diagram is to compare values, the heights (or lengths) of bars must always be proportional to their magnitudes, and the zero reference axis should normally be included.
4. The grid portraying magnitudes may be omitted if the magnitude of each bar is given. If at all possible, the magnitude should be labeled along the bar, rather than at the end. Labeling at the end tends to make the bar look longer, thus distorting its appearance.
5. Bars may be filled in or shaded for clarity of presentation.

The *percentage bar diagram* is formed by subdividing the total length of a bar into several segments. The total length of the bar represents 100 per cent, or the total quantity, while the length of each segment represents the percentage of a subdivision of the total quantity. The diagram of Fig. 14–20 shows the percentage distribution of exports by the United States to the various continents. This diagram has been subdivided by making the length of each percentage subdivision equal to the corresponding percentage of the total length. Assuming the total length of the diagram

of Fig. 14–20 to be three inches, the segment representing 34.8 per cent exports to Europe has a length of 0.348 × 3″ or 1.04″. The various segments may be shaded for emphasis and lettering may be placed either on the diagram or adjacent to it, as space permits.

Percentage bar diagrams are often combined with the bar diagram. This is done when it is desirable to give a breakdown of the composition of individual bars in a bar diagram.

14–20. AREA DIAGRAMS

Area diagrams are especially useful in presenting a comparison of related variables which are expressed as percentages. They are primarily used to illustrate the subdivision and distribution of a total quantity. The emphasis is on amount and not on the relative change or trend of the data. While the most frequent popular application is the distribution of money, area diagrams are also used to show the composition of a variety of different things. One type of area diagram is the pie or sector diagram. Although the pie diagram is the poorest form for presenting data, its continued popular acceptance has made it the most frequently used.

A *pie diagram* is formed by subdividing the area of a circle into several wedge-shaped segments. The total area of the circle represents 100 per cent or the total quantity, while each area segment represents the percentage of a subdivision of the total quantity. The pie diagram of Fig. 14–21(a) shows the percentage distribution of a family income. To construct the diagram, the circle must be subdivided into appropriate segments. The simplest way to do this is to determine the number of degrees within each segment. Since 360° represents the whole circle or 100 per cent, one per cent is represented by 3.6°. Thus, the 25 per cent food allocation sector in Fig. 14–21(a) requires an angle of 25 × 3.6° or 90°. The angles for the other sectors are determined in a similar manner.

The various sectors of a pie diagram are usually shaded for emphasis as in Fig. 14–21(a). Lettering identifying a sector is placed directly on the sector. If the area is too small to permit this, the lettering may be placed outside the circle with a leader pointing to the sector.

FOREIGN DISTRIBUTION OF UNITED STATES EXPORTS

Fig. 14–20. Percentage bar diagram.

DISTRIBUTION OF A FAMILY INCOME

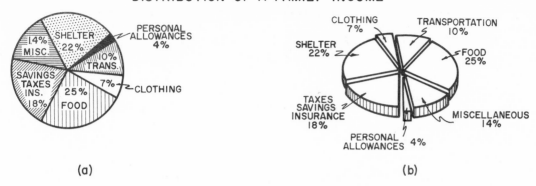

(a)   (b)

Fig. **14-21.** Sector (or pie) diagrams.

Pie diagrams are often more effective if presented in pictorial form. Fig. 14–21(b) portrays the same family income distribution redrawn in pictorial form. The construction of the pictorial diagram is based on the principles of pictorial drawing discussed in Chapter 8. The most frequently used form of pictorial is isometric, but any type is appropriate. Here, as with other forms of graphs and diagrams, the unscrupulous designer may purposefully distort the presentation. Due to the condensation or enlargement of areas, depending on their position in the pictorial, emphasis on certain desired areas may be altered. In the pie diagram, a sector placed front and center will appear enlarged. The same sector, if placed horizontally to the left or right in the diagram, appears smaller.

14-21. VOLUME DIAGRAMS

Volume diagrams are composed of pictorially presented geometric solids, the volumes of which are proportional to the variables being compared. The most frequently used solids are spheres and prisms. The primary advantage of these diagrams is that they have smaller space requirements than the area diagrams and therefore are very useful in comparing quantities with widely divergent variables. However, this form of diagram is most deceptive to read. For example, in Fig. 14–22(a), the larger sphere has a volume 8 times that of the smaller sphere, yet it does not appear this large. This visual deception can be reduced by using countable units, as in Fig. 14–22(b), instead of the one geometric solid.

14-22. FLOW AND ORGANIZATION DIAGRAMS

Both flow and organization diagrams have one common feature: each schematically portrays the various divisions of an entity as well as the interrelationships between the various divisions. *Flow diagrams* are used to present the flow of a process,

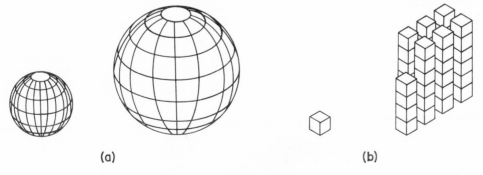

(a)   (b)

Fig. **14-22.** Volume diagrams.

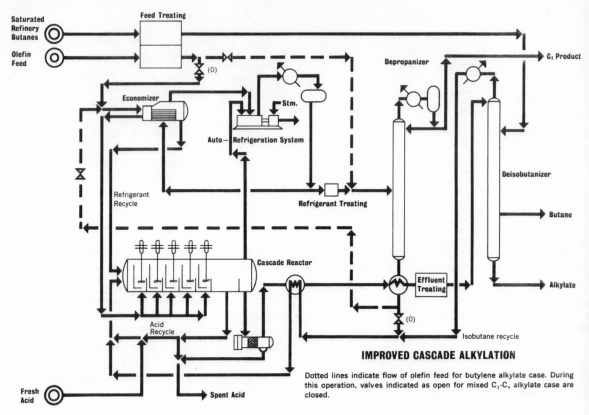

Fig. **14-23**.   Flow diagram.   (Courtesy of The M. W. Kellogg Co.)

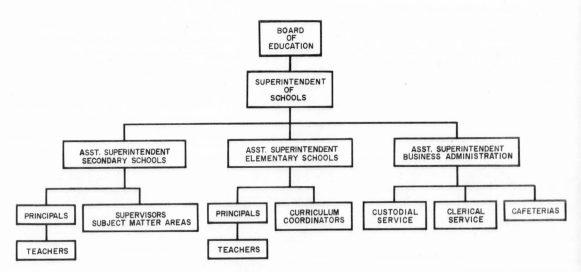

Fig. **14-24**.   Organization diagram.

whereas *organization diagrams* represent the physical or personnel structure of an organization or company.

A flow diagram for a chemical process is shown in Fig. 14–23. Note that schematic symbols have been used to make the steps more self-explanatory and appealing. However, rectangles or other geometric shapes may be used to simplify the drafting.

An example of an organization diagram is shown in Fig. 14–24. Portrayed here is the organization of a typical school district. The various divisions have been enclosed in rectangles, but circles or other geometric shapes may be used. While the rectangular shape is the simplest to draft and letter, the circle or ellipse seems to have a greater appeal to the layman.

14–23. PICTORIAL DIAGRAMS

All of the various types of diagrams previously discussed either are or may be presented in pictorial form. The volume diagram of Fig. 14–22 is in pictorial form. The sector diagram and the flow diagram may be drawn in the pictorial form illustrated in Fig. 14–21(b) and Fig. 14–23. Bar diagrams often use symbols [Fig. 14–19(c)]. Bar diagrams may also be drawn in a three-dimensional pictorial form. The bars would take a form similar to those in Fig. 14–22(b), but would be stretched out in a single row, each column representing a quantity to be compared. The bars might be composed of object units. Typical of this is the use of stacks of coins of varying heights to represent sums of money which are being compared.

Problems

The tabular data in each of the following problems are to be presented graphically. No indication has been made as to the most appropriate form of graph or diagram. The selection of the best-suited form may be made and assigned by the instructor, or the decision may be left to the discretion of the student. In some instances the problems may require more than one curve or more than one sequence of bars.

14–1. The compressive strength of concrete for varying time of mixing and age. Data indicate the results as obtained by experimental tests after one week, one month, three months, and one year.

Time of Mixing (minutes)	Compressive Strength (lb./sq. in.)			
	1 week	1 month	3 months	1 year
1	660	1,670	2,740	3,650
2	900	1,950	3,000	3,900
3	1,150	2,160	3,250	4,050
4	1,275	2,330	3,400	4,150
5	1,400	2,470	3,500	4,280
6	1,500	2,560	3,620	4,375
7	1,600	2,650	3,700	4,450
8	1,645	2,720	3,750	4,520
9	1,660	2,780	3,780	4,575
10	1,690	2,800	3,820	4,600

14–2. Effect on the compressive strength of concrete at 28 days according to the number of gallons of water used per sack of cement when mixing.

Compressive Strength (lb./sq. in.)	Water per Sack of Cement (U. S. gallons)
5,700	4
4,600	5
3,700	6
2,950	7
2,400	8

14–3. The volt–ampere characteristics of a tungsten lamp. The terminal voltage is e, and the current is i.

e, volts	i, amperes
2	.022
4	.033
8	.050
16	.076
32	.115
64	.173

14–4. The electrical conductivity of Material "A" at various temperatures in degrees Fahrenheit.

Conductivity (Mho meters)	°F	Conductivity (Mho meters)	°F
.002	0	.035	180
.004	44	.058	212
.008	86	.090	240
.017	134		

14-5. The estimated population of the ten largest states in the United States as of July 1, 1961.

State	Population
New York	17,033,000
California	16,397,000
Pennsylvania	11,468,000
Illinois	10,258,000
Ohio	9,876,000
Texas	9,788,000
Michigan	7,954,000
New Jersey	6,244,000
Massachusetts	5,234,000
Florida	5,222,000

14-6. The growth of an industrial plant in terms of number of employees.

Year	Employees
1957	4,830
1958	5,200
1959	5,932
1960	6,693
1961	6,843
1962	7,086

14-7. The approximate composition of a nickel-silver alloy by percentage.

20.0%	Zn
12.5%	Ni
10.5%	Pb
2.0%	Sn
55.0%	Cu

14-8. Crude steel production (monthly average) in metric tons.

Country	Metric Tons
United States	8,710
United Kingdom	1,750
U. S. S. R.	4,050
Japan	926
West Germany	1,930
East Germany	228
France	1,117
Canada	401

14-9. Average yield strength of various metals when annealed, cold drawn, and cold rolled.

Material	Yield Strength—1,000 psi (2% Offset)		
	Annealed	Cold Drawn	Cold Rolled
Red brass	15	55	60
Yellow brass	18	55	60
Silicone bronze	22	75	90
Copper	10	40	48
Cupro-nickel (55–45)	30	50	65

14-10. Passenger car registration in the United States.

Year	Cars	Year	Cars
1900	8,000	1935	22,567,827
1905	77,400	1940	27,465,826
1910	458,377	1945	25,793,493
1915	2,332,426	1950	40,333,591
1920	8,131,522	1955	52,173,234
1925	17,481,001	1960	59,566,721
1930	23,034,753	1961	61,683,865

14-11. Range of investments made by a large organization.

Government bonds	51.5%
Municipal bonds	8.4%
Public utility bonds	13.8%
Other corporation bonds	3.1%
Mortgages and sale agreements	12.7%
Miscellaneous	10.5%

15

GRAPHICAL
ARITHMETIC
AND ALGEBRA

15–1. INTRODUCTION

Development of a logical approach to problem solution is a basic part of the education of engineers and scientists. The tools available to accomplish this are mathematics and graphics. In formal education the major emphasis is generally placed on the mathematical solution. However, many mathematical principles can be presented graphically, and often these graphical presentations are more meaningful and require less time. In comparing the graphical solution of any problem with the mathematical, neither is *always* the better method. Circumstances in a particular problem should dictate whether one or the other, or a combination of both approaches, will provide the most appropriate solution.

15–2. ACCURACY OF SOLUTIONS

A mathematical solution to a problem usually results in an absolute answer, whereas a graphical solution results in an approximate answer. The foundations for graphical methods are based on

the principles of geometry, an exact science resulting in absolute solutions; however, it is impossible to obtain a true geometric line of infinitesimal thickness in an actual drawing. A drawn line will be several thousandths of an inch thick. This fact, coupled with the accuracy of original data, accuracy of drawing equipment, scale used, geometrical construction selected, drawing medium, and care taken by the draftsman result in approximate answers of varying accuracy. Since an approximate solution is sufficient for many engineering problems, the graphical approach is frequently appropriate. Before attempting this application of graphics, however, it is necessary to understand the reason for the factors affecting its accuracy, and the means of controlling this accuracy.

The accuracy of the solution to any problem is directly dependent upon the accuracy of the initial data. In engineering most data are in the form of measurements obtained either directly through the use of scales or indirectly by instruments which depend on scales for the display of data. The precision of such measurements depends on the scales selected and the care used in the construction of the instrument. This immediately sets a limit to the accuracy attainable in the final solution, whether mathematical or graphical. In order for graphical solutions to provide answers of maximum accuracy, drawing scales must be selected which are readable with the same precision as that of the original data.

The equipment used in graphical solutions is generally the same as that used for other graphics work. As indicated in Chapter 2, this equipment must be kept in excellent working order and should be checked periodically. It is particularly important where accuracy of solutions is concerned to see that T-squares are tested for straightness, and triangles for both straightness of edges and correctness of angles. To assure the maximum precision from a scale, always use the more accurate engine-divided scale rather than a printed one. Since fine, precise lines are required to attain the necessary accuracy, a hard pencil (at least 4H to 6H) which will hold a point should be used. Pencils in the range of 6H to 9H may be used where extreme precision is involved.

Since geometric constructions form the basis for graphical solutions, care should be taken to select those constructions producing the greatest accuracy. Frequently, points must be located by the intersection of two lines. Whenever possible, select constructions which will result in lines intersecting near 90° rather than at acute angles, since the point of intersection is more clearly defined. When the direction of a line is to be established through the use of two points, greater precision will result if the two points are reasonably far apart. Finally, one should always select constructions which minimize cumulative errors. In general, the simplest construction will be the most satisfactory.

The care exercised by the draftsman is most important if an accurate solution is to be obtained. As previously stated, always use a well-pointed, hard pencil to obtain sharp, fine lines. Careful selection must be made of an appropriate scale for the drawing, remembering that the scale should be readable to the same precision as the initial data. For most graphical solutions, use of a scale reading 50 units to the inch is recommended. With this scale, values to one-hundredth of an inch can be readily estimated. For extreme precision, points should be laid out by using a fine needle point,

keeping the impression very small. Standard protractors, which have a precision of $\frac{1}{4}°$, are often not precise enough for graphical solutions. In such instances, the desired accuracy can be achieved by constructing the angle either with the aid of a table of tangents or a table of chords.

Care should be observed in the selection of the drawing medium. Best results are obtained through the use of a hard-surfaced paper. Changes in humidity may cause considerable expansion or shrinkage of the drawing medium. While this is usually not serious with problems requiring a relatively short time to execute, it can affect the results of problems solved over a relatively long period of time. If possible, one should work under conditions where the humidity is controlled. Humidity effects can also be lessened by using the more stable drawing media. Among the newer stable materials are glass cloths and plastic drawing surfaces.

15–3. NETWORK GRAPHS

The fundamental operations of addition, subtraction, multiplication, and division may be performed graphically utilizing network graphs. A network graph is the graphical presentation of a family of curves, which is usually plotted on an appropriate grid so as to appear as straight lines. Fig. 15–1(a) is a typical network graph. This graph is used to obtain the sum of two numbers x and y. The theory of construction and application for network graphs is developed in detail in subsequent articles, but a brief statement is appropriate here to demonstrate the basic operation of all such graphs. To determine the sum of x and y by the graph of Fig. 15–1(a), locate the coordinate point (x, y) for the two numbers to be summed. The particular member of the family of curves on which this point lies represents the sum. For example, if $x = 4$ and $y = 6$, their sum is represented by the coordinate point which is on the curve labeled 10. If the coordinate point lies between two curves, interpolation is necessary.

15–4. ADDITION AND SUBTRACTION BY NETWORK GRAPHS

The basic form for a straight line plotted on a rectilinear grid is $y = mx + b$, where m is the

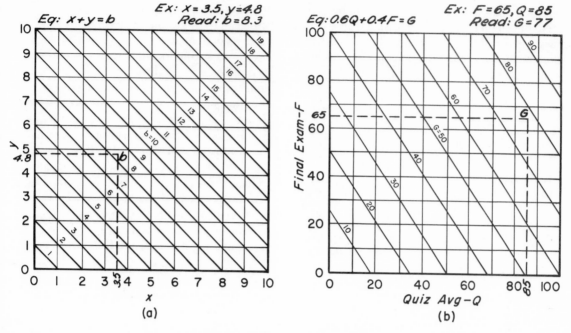

Fig. **15-1.** Network graph—addition.

slope and b is the y intercept. If the slope is made equal to -1, the equation becomes $y = -x + b$. Rewriting this equation, it becomes $x + y = b$. If various values of b are assumed and the curves plotted, a family of parallel, straight lines results as shown in Fig. 15-1(a). This family of curves, or network, may now be used to find the sum of two numbers x and y. The sample solution (shown by dashed lines) illustrates that if $x = 3.5$ and $y = 4.8$, their sum, b, is 8.3. While interpolation is necessary in this example, it is readily performed since the curves appear as straight lines.

A practical example of a network graph for addition is shown in Fig. 15-1(b). This graph determines the final grade (G) for a course in which the average of the one-hour exams (Q) constitutes 60 per cent of the grade and the final exam (F) constitutes 40 per cent, assuming Q and F are scores ranging from 0 to 100. The design of the network graph is based on the general equation $x + y = b$, where $x = 0.6Q$, and $y = 0.4F$, and $b = G$. Thus the general equation is rewritten $0.6Q + 0.4F = G$. The final grade G is assigned values ranging from 0 to 100, and the family of curves is determined and then plotted as shown in the figure.

A typical solution, shown on the graph by dashed lines, indicates a student's final grade to be 77 for a corresponding exam average of 85 and a final exam score of 65.

Subtraction can be performed using the network graph of Fig. 15-1(a). However, a more convenient form of network graph can be designed. Starting with the basic form for the straight line, $y = mx + b$, let slope m equal one. The equation becomes $y = x + b$, or, transposing x, $y - x = b$. The family of curves representing this equation for various values of b is plotted in Fig. 15-2. The curves plot as parallel, straight lines as did those for the addition network graph, except that these curves have a positive slope rather than a negative one. This graph is in a form for readily finding the difference between two numbers, x and y. The sample solution, in dashed lines, shows that if $y = 7.5$ and $x = 3.5$, their difference, $y - x$ (or b), equals 4.

Addition and subtraction of three numbers may be accomplished by combining two network graphs. A network graph constructed to add $a + b + c = d$ is best accomplished by splitting the equation into the two parts $a + b = y$ and

$y + c = d$. Each of these equations can be represented by a network graph which is constructed so as to share the common y-scale. To achieve this common scale, the equations are rewritten as $y - a = b$ and $d - y = c$. The network graph

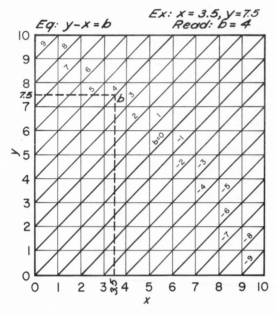

Fig. 15–2. Network graph—subtraction.

for each of these equations is designed in the usual manner. They are then placed side by side, joining the common y-scale as shown in Fig. 15–3 The network graph for $d - y = c$ is laid out with the positive abscissa direction to the left to permit joining of the common y-scales. The y-scale is not calibrated since specific values are not required for solution. The typical solution, represented on Fig. 15–3 by dashed lines, shows that when $a = 4.5$, $b = 3$, and $c = 1$, their sum $d = 8.5$.

A network graph may be designed to determine the final grade (G) in a course. If a grade is made up of 20 per cent of the homework average (W), 50 per cent of the hour exam average (Q), and 30 per cent of the final exam grade (F), the equation for computing this final grade is $0.5Q + 0.3F + 0.2W = G$. The values Q, F, and W are scores ranging from 0 to 100. As with the previous example, this equation must be split into two parts: $0.5Q + 0.3F = y$, and $y + 0.2W = G$. To obtain the common y-scale for joining the two network graphs, the equations are rewritten as $y - 0.5Q = 0.3F$, and $G - y = 0.2W$. Fig. 15–4 shows the network graph based on these equations. The typical solution in dashed lines shows a final grade G of 71.5, based on values of $Q = 75$, $F = 60$, and $W = 80$.

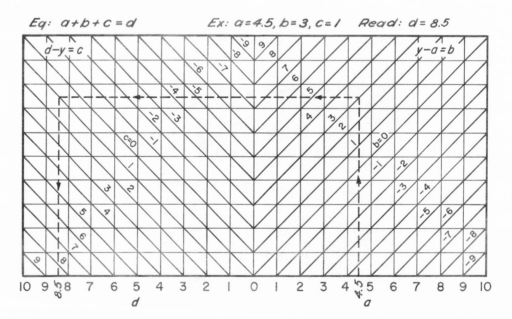

Fig. 15–3. Network graph—addition of three numbers.

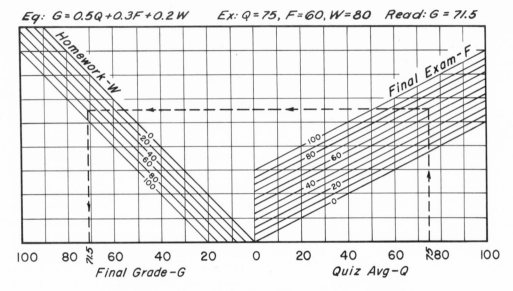

Fig. **15–4.** Network graph—addition of three variables.

The application of network graphs to addition and subtraction has somewhat limited use since the analytic approach is often faster and simpler. However, for repetitive computations, network graphs provide a rapid means for checking the analytical solution. Similar graphs for multiplication and division as presented in the next article use these techniques as a basis for construction.

15–5. MULTIPLICATION AND DIVISION BY NETWORK GRAPHS

A network graph for multiplication can be obtained by plotting the family of curves represented by $xy = b$ on a rectilinear grid. Fig. 15–5 presents such a graph. The curves, however, plot as hyperbolas and thus are more time-consuming to con-

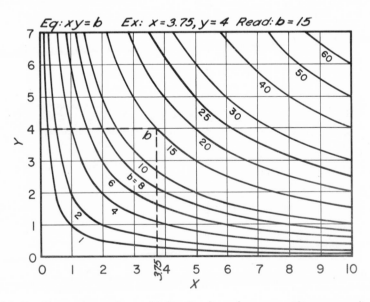

Fig. **15–5.** Network graph—multiplication based upon rectilinear coordinates.

struct as well as more difficult to interpolate. If logarithms of the equation $xy = b$ are taken, the equation becomes $\log x + \log y = \log b$ which is in the form of a straight line. Thus, if a logarith-

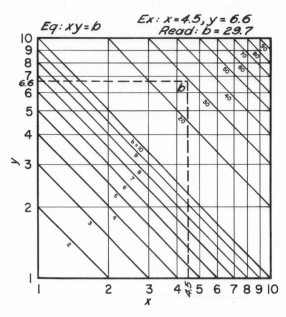

Fig. 15–6. Network graph—multiplication based upon logarithmic coordinates.

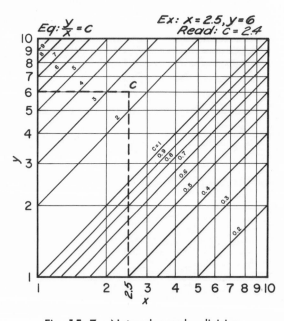

Fig. 15–7. Network graph—division.

mic grid is used, the equation will plot as a straight line (see Art. 14–15) making the network graph simpler to draw and easier to interpolate. Fig 15–6 presents such a network graph for $xy = b$. The solution, indicated by dashed lines on the figure, shows that when $x = 4.5$ and $y = 6.6$ $b = 29.7$.

A network graph for division is constructed utilizing the same principles. The basic equation is $y/x = c$, which also plots as a straight line on a logarithmic grid. The graph for this family of curves is presented in Fig. 15–7. The solution is shown for $x = 2.5$ and $y = 6$, resulting in $c = 2.4$.

Combinations of multiplication and division may be performed by joining two or more network graphs. If a network graph representing the equation $x = ab/c$ is required, the equation is first split into the two parts $a/c = y$, and $x = by$. To make the y-scales coincide, these may be rewritten as $a = cy$ and $x/y = b$. The two network graphs for these equations are then constructed with y-values on the vertical axis in each graph, and are laid out adjacent to each other as in Fig. 15–8. The network graph on the left does not have the reversed abscissa direction as did the combination graph for addition, Fig. 15–3. This is because the normal use of commercial logarithmic grids precludes such reversals of direction. When the designer constructs his own grid, such a reversal is possible.

15-6. GRAPHICAL ARITHMETIC

The principles of plane geometry also provide a graphical basis for performing addition, subtraction, multiplication, and division; as well as for determining squares, square roots, and mean proportionals. With the exception of addition and subtraction, solutions to the above depend upon one of the following two geometrical principles: first, if two triangles are similar, the corresponding sides of the triangles are proportional; and second, the square of the hypotenuse of a right triangle is equal to the sum of the squares of the other two sides.

The following articles present graphical solutions for arithmetical procedures utilizing these principles of plane geometry. Some of these are not frequently used per se in solving a problem, since

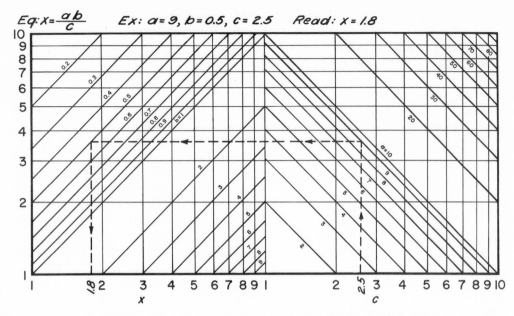

$$Eq: x = \frac{ab}{c} \qquad Ex: a=9, b=0.5, c=2.5 \qquad Read: x=1.8$$

Fig. **15-8.** Network graph—combined multiplication and division.

he mathematical solution is more convenient.
uch graphical solutions are presented as the
nitial steps in the logical development of graphical
nathematics. The principles developed are also
he basis for the more advanced solutions which
ollow.

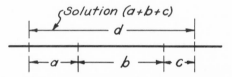

Fig. **15-9.** Graphical addition by line segments.

5-7. ADDITION AND SUBTRACTION

The concept that lines of varying lengths may
epresent magnitudes of quantities, as presented
n Chapter 12, may also be utilized in graphical
rithmetic. The sum of three quantities, a, b, and
, is to be determined graphically. The solution
or $a + b + c = d$ is shown in Fig. 15-9. As the
irst step in the solution, a fine line is drawn which
erves as a base line. Selecting a suitable scale,
ine segments representing quantities a, b, and c
re laid off consecutively along the base line. Their
um is represented by the overall distance d which
s scaled to determine its magnitude.

Subtraction is merely the addition of a negative
quantity, and is accomplished by laying off the
distance representing the negative quantity in the
pposite direction. If the previous problem were
tated $a + b - c = e$, the first step in the solution

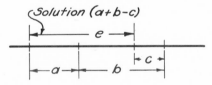

Fig. **15-10.** Graphical addition including negative number.

would be the drawing of the base line as in Fig.
15-10. Then, selecting a suitable scale, the line
segments representing quantities a and b are laid
off as before (Fig. 15-9). Quantity c, however, is
laid off in the negative direction, thus subtracting
it from the sum of $a + b$. The answer is distance
e, which is scaled to determine its magnitude.

15-8. MULTIPLICATION

Graphical multiplication is based on the geometry of similar triangles. The basis for this procedure is shown in Fig. 15-11, where any two intersecting lines AO and DO have been drawn with two parallel lines AD and CB between them. This configuration establishes the two similar triangles OCB and OAD, in which

$$\frac{OC}{OB} = \frac{OA}{OD},$$

or

$$(OD)(OC) = (OB)(OA).$$

If, in Fig. 15-11, the distance OC is assumed to be one unit in length, then

$$(OD)(1) = (OB)(OA).$$

This equation forms the basis for the graphical multiplication, $a \times b = c$. If, when constructing

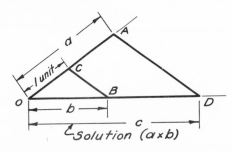

Fig. 15-11. Graphical multiplication based upon similar triangles.

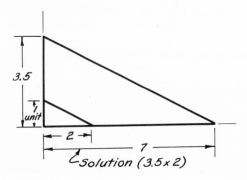

Fig. 15-12. Graphical multiplication of 3.5 by 2.

the figure, OA represents the quantity a and OB represents the quantity b, the relationship

$$(OD)(1) = (OB)(OA)$$

becomes $OD = a \times b$, or $OD = c$. This assumes OC equals one unit in terms of the scale selected for the construction. Thus OD may be scaled to determine the magnitude of c, the product of $a \times b$.

This solution for graphical multiplication is simplified if the angle AOD formed by the intersecting lines in Fig. 15-11 is made a right angle since much of the construction can then be drawn using the T-square and a 90° triangle. As an example, determine the product of 3.5×2. Referring to Fig. 15-12, horizontal and vertical lines are drawn which serve as the two legs of the right angle. A suitable scale is next selected, and 3.5 is laid off on the vertical leg while 2 is measured along the horizontal leg. The unit distance is measured along the vertical. Following the procedure established in Fig. 15-11, the product 7 is scaled along the horizontal leg.

Graphical multiplication can be extended to determine the product of more than two numbers, for example,

$$a \times b \times c = d.$$

The first step of the solution consists of breaking down the multiplication into the following steps:

$$a \times b = M$$
$$M \times c = d.$$

The graphical solution for $a \times b = M$ is constructed as in Fig. 15-13(a). Using the value of M just determined, $M \times c = d$ is then solved [Fig. 15-13(b)] and the answer is scaled. To save space and time the two solutions are usually combined into one, as in Fig. 15-13(c).

15-9. DIVISION

Graphical division, like multiplication, is based on the geometry of similar triangles. The basis for the procedure is shown in Fig. 15-14, where two intersecting lines AO and BO have been drawn with any two parallel lines AB and CD between

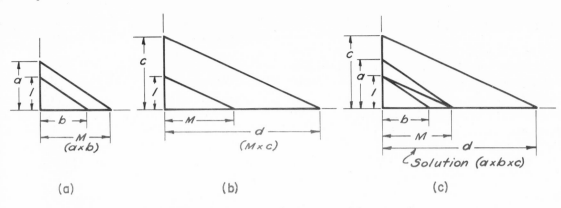

(a)　　　　　　　　　　　(b)　　　　　　　　　　　(c)

Fig. 15-13. Graphical multiplication of three numbers.

them. This configuration establishes two similar triangles OBA and OCD, in which

$$\frac{OA}{OB} = \frac{OD}{OC}.$$

If the distance OC is assumed to be one unit in length, then the previous ratio becomes

$$\frac{OA}{OB} = \frac{OD}{1}$$

or

$$\frac{OA}{OB} = OD.$$

This equation forms the basis for the graphical division $a/b = c$. If, when constructing Fig. 15-14, OA represents the quantity a and OB represents the quantity b, the relationship

$$\frac{OA}{OB} = OD$$

becomes $OD = a/b$, or $OD = c$. This assumes OC equals one unit in terms of the scale selected for the construction. Thus OD can be scaled to determine the magnitude of c, the quotient of a/b.

As with graphical multiplication, the solution for division is simplified if the angle AOB, Fig. 15-14, is a right angle. For example, determine the quotient of 4/2.5, for which the solution is shown in Fig. 15-15. After drawing horizontal and vertical lines a suitable scale is selected, and 2.5 is laid off on the vertical line while 4 is laid off

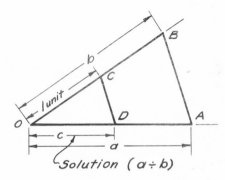

Fig. 15-14. Graphical division based upon similar triangles.

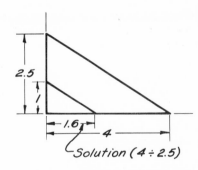

Fig. 15-15. Graphical division of 4 by 2.5.

on the horizontal. The unit distance is measured along the vertical line. Following the method of Fig. 15-14, the quotient, 1.6, is scaled on the horizontal line.

15–10. COMBINED MULTIPLICATION AND DIVISION

The solution to a combined multiplication and division problem can also be obtained graphically by utilizing the principles of similar triangles. For example, the value of R must be determined in the relationship

$$R = \frac{a \times b}{c}.$$

This can be rewritten

$$\frac{a}{c} = \frac{R}{b}.$$

As in the previous problems, the two legs of an angle are drawn, Fig. 15–16, again making them vertical and horizontal for convenience. Selecting a suitable scale, $OA = a$ is laid off on the vertical leg, and $OB = b$ and $OC = c$ on the horizontal leg. Line AC is drawn, and parallel to this is the line from B to D. This construction forms the two

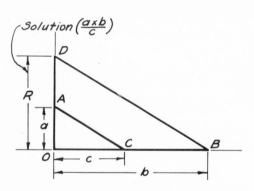

Fig. 15–16. Graphical multiplication and division.

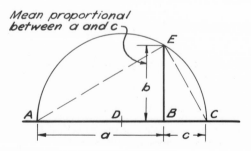

Fig. 15–17. Mean proportional between two numbers.

similar triangles AOC and DOB, in which the following relationship exists:

$$\frac{OA}{OC} = \frac{OD}{OB}$$

or

$$OD = \frac{OA \times OB}{OC} = \frac{a \times b}{c}.$$

Thus, the scaled length of line OD represents R, the solution to the problem.

15–11. DETERMINATION OF MEAN PROPORTIONAL

The mean proportional between two quantities may be obtained by geometric principles. A corollary from plane geometry states that if a perpendicular is drawn to the diameter from a point on a semicircle, this perpendicular is the mean proportional between the segments of the diameter. To determine graphically the mean proportional b between two quantities a and c, line segments $AB = a$ and $BC = c$ are drawn end-to-end along a straight line (Fig. 15–17). The midpoint of AC is located at D, and with D as a center and DA or DC as a radius, the semicircle is drawn. Then the perpendicular BE is drawn. Line BE is scaled and is the mean proportional b between a and c.

This relationship is also evident from an analysis of similar triangles. If the lines AE and EC, represented by dashed lines in Fig. 15–17, are drawn, the similar triangles AEB and ECB are formed. In these similar triangles

$$\frac{AB}{BE} = \frac{BE}{BC}$$

or

$$\frac{a}{b} = \frac{b}{c}.$$

Thus b is the mean proportional between a and c.

15–12. DETERMINATION OF SQUARE ROOTS

Square roots may be determined graphically utilizing the construction of Fig. 15–17. To do this the quantity c is made equal to unity. Then the mean proportional relationship

$$\frac{a}{b} = \frac{b}{c}$$

becomes

$$\frac{a}{b} = \frac{b}{1}$$

or

$$b^2 = a.$$

Hence, b equals the square root of a.

15–13. DIVISION OF TRIANGULAR AND TRAPEZOIDAL AREAS

A triangular area may be proportionately divided by using graphics. To demonstrate this technique as well as to establish proof for the graphical procedures, assume that the triangular area ABC of Fig. 15–18 is to be divided into three equal areas. To divide the area, a semicircle is drawn, with any side of the triangle as a base. Side BC might be selected and then divided proportionately according to the areas desired—in this example, into three equal segments, BW, WX, and XC. Perpendiculars to BC are drawn from points W and X to points Y and Z on the semicircle. Using BY and BZ as radii and B as a center, arcs are drawn to establish C' and C''. Lines $A'C'$ and $A''C''$, parallel to AC, establish the three equal areas $A'BC'$, $A''A'C'C''$, and $AA''C''C$.

Proof that the three areas determined in Fig. 15–18 are equal is established in the following steps:

1. Area $ABC = \frac{1}{2}(AC)(OB)$.

2. By construction, $BW = \frac{BC}{3}$, and $WC = \frac{2BC}{3}$.

3. Since, from plane geometry, WY is the mean proportional between BW and WC,

$$WY = \sqrt{(BW)(WC)}$$
$$= \sqrt{\left(\frac{BC}{3}\right)\left(\frac{2BC}{3}\right)} = \sqrt{2}\left(\frac{BC}{3}\right).$$

4. $BY = \sqrt{(BW)^2 + (WY)^2}$
$$= \sqrt{\left(\frac{BC}{3}\right)^2 + \left[\sqrt{2}\left(\frac{BC}{3}\right)\right]^2}$$
$$= \frac{BC}{3}\sqrt{1+2} = \frac{BC}{3}\sqrt{3} = \frac{BC}{\sqrt{3}}.$$

5. By construction, $BC' = BY = \frac{BC}{\sqrt{3}}$.

6. Triangle $A'BC'$ is similar to triangle ABC.

7. Hence, $\frac{A'C'}{AC} = \frac{BC'}{BC} = \frac{BC}{\sqrt{3}(BC)} = \frac{1}{\sqrt{3}}$

or, $A'C' = \frac{AC}{\sqrt{3}}$.

8. In similar manner, $BO' = \frac{BO}{\sqrt{3}}$.

9. Therefore, area $A'BC'$
$$= \frac{1}{2}(A'C')(BO') = \frac{1}{2}\left(\frac{AC}{\sqrt{3}}\right)\left(\frac{BO}{\sqrt{3}}\right)$$
$$= \frac{1}{3}\left[\frac{1}{2}(AC)(BO)\right] = \frac{1}{3}\text{ area }ABC.$$

By a similar proof, the area of triangle $A''BC''$ may be shown equal to two-thirds the area of triangle ABC, thus proving that the geometric construction has divided the area into three equal parts. The area could have been divided into any proportionate areas by initially dividing side BC into corresponding proportional segments.

Utilizing the same basic construction, a trapezoidal area may be proportionately divided. Fig. 15–19 demonstrates the division of a trapezoid into four equal areas. Construction is as follows. Proof of the construction parallels that for the triangle, and is left as an exercise for the reader.

The first step in dividing the trapezoid $BCDE$ (Fig. 15–19) into four equal areas is to extend side BC and side DE to intersect at O, forming triangle BOE. A semicircle is drawn using OE as a base. Using O as a center and OD as a radius, swing an arc to establish point 1, and drop a perpendicular from point 1 to OE at 2. Line $2E$ is divided into the four equal parts 2-3, 3-4, 4-5, and $5E$. Perpen-

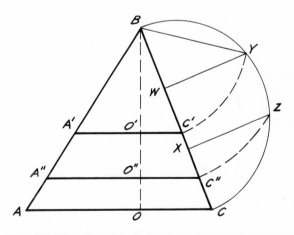

Fig. **15–18.** Graphical division of triangular area.

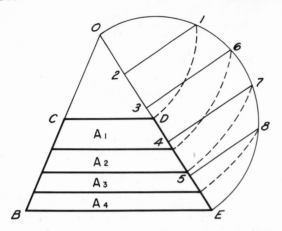

Fig. **15-19.** Graphical division of trapezoidal area.

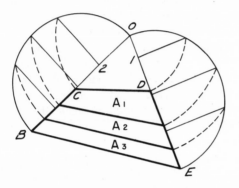

Fig. **15-20.** Graphical division of quadrilateral area.

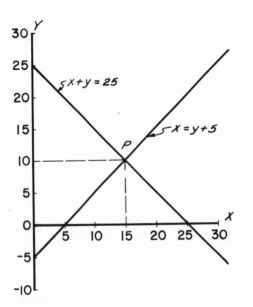

Fig. **15-21.** Graphical solution of linear system.

diculars from points 3, 4, and 5 establish points 6, 7, and 8 respectively on the semicircle. Using $O6$, $O7$, and $O8$ as radii, swing arcs to line OE. These arcs establish points on OE, and lines through these points, drawn parallel to BE, divide the trapezoid into four equal areas A_1, A_2, A_3, and A_4.

The same basic construction may be extended to the division of quadrilateral areas in general. A typical example is the division of the quadrilateral $BCDE$, Fig. 15-20, into three equal areas. Either of the two opposite sides of the quadrilateral is extended to intersect at a point, O. If BC and DE are extended, semicircles are drawn using OE and OB respectively as bases. Following the construction described for the trapezoid, OD and OC are used as radii to swing arcs to the respective semicircles, with perpendiculars then being drawn to sides OE and OB establishing points 1 and 2. Lines $1E$ and $2B$ are each divided into three equal segments and, proceeding as with the trapezoidal construction, points are finally established on OE and OB. By connecting corresponding points as shown, the quadrilateral is divided into the three equal areas A_1, A_2, and A_3.

15-14. SOLUTION OF SYSTEMS OF EQUATIONS

Graphics may be used to advantage as a means of solving simultaneous equations involving two unknowns. To accomplish this, both equations are represented graphically on the same rectilinear grid. The point or points of intersection of the two curves have x- and y-coordinates which satisfy both equations, and thus represent the solution of the system.

As an illustration, consider the simultaneous equations $x + y = 25$ and $x = y + 5$. To obtain a solution to this system of equations, both are plotted on a rectilinear grid, Fig. 15-21. In this case both are linear equations and therefore plot as straight lines. The point P is common to both curves, and its coordinates $x = 15$, $y = 10$ represent the solution to the equations.

A pair of equations such as $y = 6 + x$ and $y = 3 + x$ are sometimes encountered. If a graphical solution is attempted, the lines are found to be parallel rather than intersecting. Such equations have no common solution and therefore cannot form a system. Such pairs of equations are called inconsistent equations.

The graphical solution for a system of quadratic equations is shown in Fig. 15–22. The equations are $4y^2 - 9x^2 = 36$ and $x^2 + y^2 = 36$ which form a hyperbola and a circle respectively. In the solution, the curves intersect at four points indicating the four sets of values which are solutions. If the equation of the circle were $x^2 + y^2 = 9$, as shown by the dashed circle, there would be only two solutions. In this example, if the radius of the circle becomes less than 3, there is no intersection and the roots are imaginary.

15–15. DETERMINATION OF ROOTS OF QUADRATIC EQUATIONS

There are several methods for graphically determining the roots of the quadratic equation of the form $Ax^2 + Bx + C = 0$. One method consists of rewriting the equation in the form $Ax^2 + Bx + C = y$. Various values of x then are substituted in the equation and the corresponding values of y are determined. Using these values of x and y, the curve is plotted on a rectilinear grid. At those locations where the curve crosses the x-axis, the coordinate values of y equal zero and the corresponding x-coordinate values represent roots of the original quadratic. For example, if the roots are to be determined for the equation $x^2 - 4x + 3 = 0$, the first step is to write it in the form $x^2 - 4x + 3 = y$. For various values of x the corresponding values of y are calculated, and these values are plotted to obtain the curve in Fig. 15–23. From this curve it is readily apparent that when $y = 0$, $x = 1$ and 3, which values of x are the roots of the original equation.

A second, and more general, method for determining the roots of a quadratic equation is based on the fundamental procedure for solving systems of equations as described in Art. 15–14. The quadratic, $x^2 - 4x + 3 = 0$, may be rewritten in the form $x^2 = 4x - 3$. In this form, the portion on each side of the equality may, in turn, be made equal to a new variable, y, and then written as

$$y = x^2$$

and

$$y = 4x - 3.$$

The graphical solution is obtained for these simultaneous equations by plotting each as shown in Fig. 15–24. The parabola, $y = x^2$, and the line,

$y = 4x - 3$, intersect at points A and B whose coordinates are solutions of the simultaneous equations. The x-coordinates of points A and B must also be the roots of the equation $x^2 - 4x + 3 = 0$. In this example the roots are 1 and 3. If the parabola and the line were tangent, there would be two

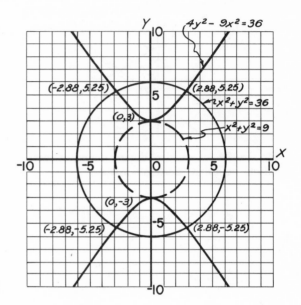

Fig. **15–22.** Graphical solution of quadratic system.

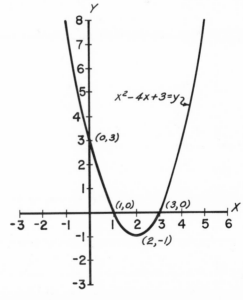

Fig. **15–23.** Graphical determination of roots of quadratic equation—curve plotting method.

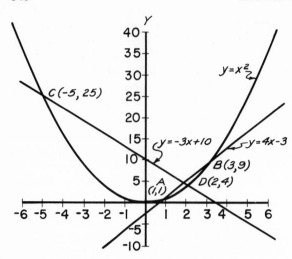

Fig. 15–24. Graphical determination of roots of quadratic equation—parabola method.

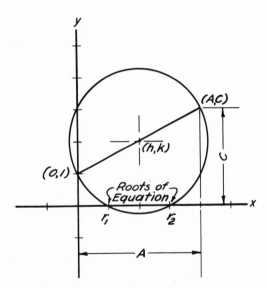

Fig. 15–25. Graphical determination of roots of quadratic equation—offset circle theory.

real and equal roots, and if they did not intersect, the roots would be imaginary.

This form of solution is especially convenient if a number of different equations of the form $Ax^2 + Bx + C = 0$ are to be solved. The parabola $y = x^2$ need only be drawn once. The various solutions are obtained by plotting the straight-line portion of the simultaneous equations.

For example, a solution is desired for the equation

$$x^2 + 3x - 10 = 0.$$

This is rewritten as

$$y = x^2$$

and

$$y = -3x + 10.$$

Using the previous solution (Fig. 15–24), the equation $y = -3x + 10$ is plotted as shown. This line intersects the parabola at points C and D, which have x-coordinate values of -5 and 2 respectively. These values are the roots of the equation $x^2 + 3x - 10 = 0$.

While the preceding method is useful when many quadratic equations are to be solved, another technique, the offset-circle method, provides a rapid graphical solution when only one quadratic equation is involved. This method of solution is based on a circle which passes through a fixed point with coordinates $(0, 1)$, and a variable point, with coordinates (A, C), whose center is not at the origin. These two points are also to be extremities of a diameter of the circle. Fig. 15–25 shows such a typical circle. The general equation for such a circle is

$$(x - h)^2 + (y - k)^2 = r^2$$

where h and k respectively are the x- and y-coordinates of the center of the circle and r is the radius of the circle. Referring to Fig. 15–25, the following relationships are evident:

$$h = \frac{A}{2}$$

$$k = 1 + \frac{(C - 1)}{2} = \frac{C + 1}{2}$$

$$r = \frac{1}{2}\sqrt{A^2 + (C - 1)^2}.$$

Substituting these values for h, k, and r into the general equation of the circle,

$$\left(x - \frac{A}{2}\right)^2 + \left(y - \frac{C+1}{2}\right)^2 = \left[\frac{1}{2}\sqrt{A^2 + (C - 1)^2}\right]^2.$$

This reduces to

$$x^2 - Ax + y^2 - Cy - y + C = 0.$$

When $y = 0$, this equation becomes

$$x^2 - Ax + C = 0.$$

The points r_1 and r_2 on Fig. 15–25 are the roots of this equation, and thus are the roots of any quadratic written in the general form

$$x^2 - Ax + C = 0.$$

As an illustration of this technique, the roots of the quadratic $x^2 + 3x + 2 = 0$ are desired. First, rewrite the equation in the general form $x^2 - (-3)x + 2 = 0$, where $A = -3$ and $C = 2$. On a rectilinear coordinate grid (Fig. 15–26), plot the point with coordinates $(-3, 2)$ and the point with coordinates $(0, 1)$. The line connecting these points is the diameter of the circle, and the midpoint of the line is the center of the circle. Draw the circle, and points $x = -1$, and $x = -2$, where the circle crosses the x-axis, are the required roots.

15–16. SOLUTION OF ALGEBRAIC WORD PROBLEMS

Many algebraic "word problems" can be solved using graphical approaches. Frequently such solutions provide better analysis and understanding of the problem than numerical methods. The following four examples are representative of typical solutions.

Example I. Involving work, rate, and time. A performs a specified job in 6 days. B does the same job in 8 days. When will A complete the job after both A and B have worked together for 3 days?

To solve the problem a graph is plotted showing units of work completed vs. time (Fig. 15–27). One unit of work represents the completion of the job by each individual working alone. A completes the job when point C is reached, and the line OC

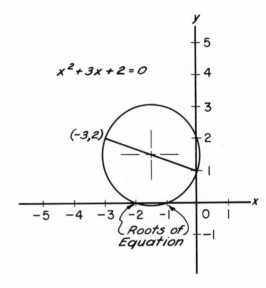

Fig. **15–26.** Graphical determination of roots of quadratic equation—offset circle method.

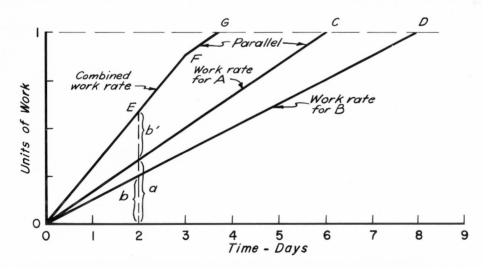

Fig. **15–27.** Graphical solution of problem involving work, rate, and time.

shows A's rate of work. From line OC can be determined the amount of work completed by A in any given time. In a similar manner line OD represents B's rate of work. To obtain the combined rate for A and B working together, the individual rate curves are added graphically. To do this, assume any time, for example, 2 days. Distances a and b represent the work completed respectively by A and B. The distance b', equal to b, is added to a. Ordinate E now represents the

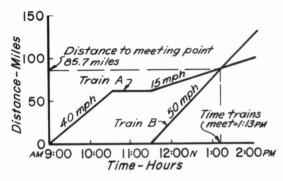

Fig. 15–28. Graphical solution of problem involving distance, rate, and time.

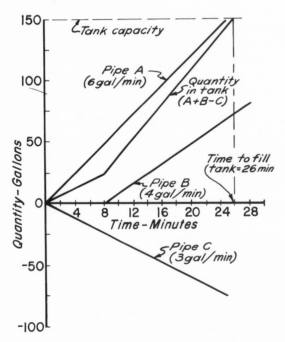

Fig. 15–29. Graphical solution of problem involving mixtures, rate, and time.

total combined work accomplished by both men in 2 days. A line through 0 and E indicates the combined rate of work for both individuals. Since both work together for 3 days, line $0E$ is extended to point F. After the third day, A works alone; so line FG is drawn parallel to the rate line, $0C$, for A. At point G the job is completed; the required time is $3\frac{3}{4}$ days.

In this example, the graphic solution greatly aids the visualization of the problem. This solution assumes that work is done at a constant, uniform rate. Actually, work rates would be variable, but the solution would remain basically the same. Lines "A" and "B" would be curved to represent variable rates, but could be added using the same techniques.

Example II. Involving distance, rate, and time. Train A left station X at 9:00 A.M., traveling 40 mph. At 10:30 A.M. an accident delayed the train for one hour, and it then proceeded at a reduced rate of 15 mph. A second train B left X at 11:30 A.M., traveling 50 mph. At what time did the second train overtake the first? How far from X is the meeting point?

To solve this problem, a graph is constructed consisting of two curves (Fig. 15–28). Each curve shows the distance traveled by each train at any time. The intersection of the curves represents the meeting point. The graph is laid out with time on the x-axis and distance traveled on the y-axis. The curve for train A is drawn starting at 9:00 A.M. at a slope representing 40 mph for the first $1\frac{1}{2}$ hours. For the next hour the curve is horizontal representing no motion. The remainder of the curve is drawn at a slope representing 15 mph. The curve for B is drawn starting at 11:30 A.M., at a slope representing 50 mph. The coordinates at the intersection are 1:13 P.M. and 85.7 miles, which are the desired answers.

Example III. Involving mixtures, rate, and time. A 150-gallon tank is filled by two pipes, A and B. Pipe A has a flow rate of 6 gallons per minute while pipe B has a rate of 4 gallons per minute. A third pipe, C, drains the tank at a rate of 3 gallons per minute. Initially, the tank is empty and the drain open. Pipe A starts discharging into the tank. After eight minutes pipe B also starts filling the tank. How long does it require to fill the tank?

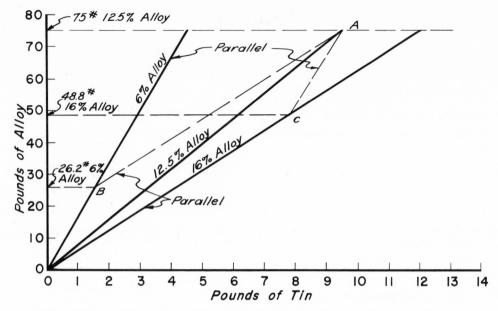

Fig. 15-30. Graphical solution of problem involving mixtures and percentages.

Plot a graph showing the quantity in the tank at any instant.

This problem may be solved by constructing a graph showing the rate at which each individual pipe fills or empties the tank. By graphical addition and subtraction the curves are combined to show the composite effect. The necessary graph plots time on the abscissa and quantity on the ordinate (Fig. 15-29). Curve A starts at zero time and shows the filling rate for pipe A. Curve B starts at eight minutes and shows the filling rate for pipe B. Curve C starts at zero time and shows the rate at which the tank is drained. These three curves are added graphically, using the same method as in Example I, to determine the net filling rate. This curve represents the quantity in the tank at any time. The tank holds 150 gallons. Twenty-six minutes corresponds to an ordinate value of 150 gallons and is the time required to fill the tank.

Example IV. Involving mixtures and percentages. Two tin-copper alloys contain respectively 16 per cent tin and 6 per cent tin. How many pounds of each are required to make 75 pounds of alloy containing $12\frac{1}{2}$ per cent tin?

To solve this problem, a graph is constructed showing pounds of tin on the abscissa and pounds of alloy on the ordinate (Fig. 15-30). On this graph, lines can be plotted representing alloys containing 6 per cent, $12\frac{1}{2}$ per cent, and 16 per cent tin. Point A on the $12\frac{1}{2}$ per cent curve, the coordinates of which are 75 pounds of alloy and 9.38 pounds of tin, represents the desired alloy mixture. The solution to the problem may be obtained by locating a point B on the 6 per cent curve whose ordinate value is the amount of 6 per cent alloy needed. Point B is located through the use of plane geometry by drawing a line through A parallel to the 16 per cent line until it intersects the 6 per cent curve. The ordinate value of B represents 26.25 pounds of 6 per cent alloy. The difference between this value and 75 pounds is 48.75 pounds, the quantity of 16 per cent alloy required.

The solution can also be obtained by locating a point C on the 16 per cent curve whose ordinate value is the amount of 16 per cent alloy required. This is accomplished in a manner similar to the locating of B, by drawing a line through A parallel to the 6 per cent curve until it intersects the 16 per cent curve at C. The ordinate value of C represents 48.75 pounds of 16 per cent alloy. By locating the two quantities independently in this manner and then checking them, the possibility of construction errors is reduced.

Problems

Solve each of the following problems graphically.

15-1. Design a network graph for determining the final grade in a course. The homework average is considered $\frac{1}{8}$ of the final grade, examination average $\frac{1}{2}$, and final examination $\frac{3}{8}$. Assume all grading is expressed in scores ranging from 0 to 100.

15-2. Design a network graph for the equation

$$W = EI.$$

This equation gives the power W in watts, when E is the electrical potential in volts and I is the current in amperes.
Range: $E = 1$ to 100 volts
$I = 0.1$ to 10 amperes

15-3. Design a network graph for the equation

$$I = \frac{E}{R}.$$

This equation gives the current I in amperes, when E is the electrical potential in volts and R is the resistance in ohms.
Range: $E = 0.1$ to 100 volts
$R = 1$ to 100 ohms

15-4. Design a network graph for the equation

$$M = \frac{wL^2}{12}.$$

This equation gives the maximum bending moment for a uniformly loaded beam, fixed at both ends. M is the moment in pound-feet, w is the load in pounds per foot, and L is the length of the beam in feet.
Range: $L = 10$ to 100 feet
$w = 10$ to 500 pounds per foot

15-5. Design a network graph for the equation

$$T = \frac{Lfd}{2}.$$

This equation gives the torque which must be applied to a screw to overcome collar-bearing friction. T is the torque in inch-pounds. L is the axial load in pounds, f is the coefficient of friction, and d is the mean collar diameter in inches.
Range: $L = 100$ to 10,000 pounds
$f = 0.10$ to 0.60
$d = 0.5$ to 5 inches

15-6. Multiply:

a. 5×3 c. 6.25×1.25
b. 2.5×3.75 d. -4×2.8

15-7. Divide:

a. $25/5$ c. $8.75/3.5$
b. $12.6/3$ d. $-12/5$

15-8. Determine the product of $1.8 \times 2.5 \times 4.5$.

15-9. Multiply 7.5 by 3.5 and divide the product by 3.

15-10. Divide 6.75 by 9 and multiply the quotient by 4.

15-11. Determine the mean proportional between:

a. 4 and 9   c. 3 and 10
b. 4 and 16   d. 2 and 9

15-12. Determine the square of:

a. 3.5   c. 4.9
b. 1.7   d. 2.5

15-13. Determine the square root of:

a. 28   c. 7
b. 14   d. 32

15-14. The coordinates of the three corners of triangle ABC, expressed in inches, are:

	A	B	C
x	0	2	3
y	0	3	0

Divide the area of this triangle into four equal parts.

15-15. Divide the triangle ABC of Problem 15-14 into three parts so that the resulting areas are in the ratio $1:2:3$.

15-16. The coordinates of the four corners of the trapezoid $ABCD$, expressed in inches, are:

	A	B	C	D
x	0	1	3	3.5
y	0	2	2	0

Divide the area of this trapezoid into three equal parts.

15–17. Divide the trapezoid *ABCD* of Problem 15–16 into three parts so that the resulting areas are in the ratio 1:2:4.

15–18. The coordinates of the four corners of the quadrilateral *ABCD*, expressed in inches, are:

	A	B	C	D
x	0	1	2.5	3.5
y	0	3	2.5	1

Divide the area of this quadrilateral into four equal parts.

15–19. Solve each of the following systems.

a. $2y = x - 3$
  $2x + y = 11$

b. $x + 3y = 0$
  $2x - y = 7$

c. $x^2 + y^2 = 16$
  $2x - y = 4$

d. $y = x^2 - 4x - 5$
  $2y + x = 3$

e. $y = x^2 - 2x + 1$
  $x^2 + y^2 = 25$

f. $x^2 + y^2 = 25$
  $xy = -6$

15–20. Determine the roots of the following quadratic equations.

a. $x^2 - x + 1 = 0$

b. $x^2 - 4x + 3 = 0$

c. $x^2 + 18 = 11x$

d. $3x^2 - 5x - 2 = 0$

e. $2x^2 - 7x + 3 = 0$

f. $4x^2 + 4x + 1 = 0$

g. $2x^2 + 4x - 5 = 0$

h. $x^2 - 5x + 15 = 0$

15–21. John can paint a structure in 10 hours. After working for 3 hours, he is joined by Charles, who can do the work in 14 hours. If they work together until the completion of the painting, how long does Charles work?

15–22. Mr. Smith can perform a task in 12 hours. Mr. Smith and Mr. Jones, working together, can do the work in 8 hours. How long would it take Mr. Jones, working alone, to complete the task?

15–23. In a crew race, crew *A* rows at a uniform rate of 350 yards per minute. Crew *B* covers 80 yards in the first minute and over the next five minutes increases its rate 85 yards each minute. For the remainder of the race, crew *B* maintains its rate as of the end of the sixth minute. If both crews started at the same time, in how many minutes will crew *B* overtake crew *A*?

15–24. A train normally travels between cities *A* and *B* at an average speed of 50 mph. On a certain day it leaves city *A* one and one-half hours late but travels at an average speed of 65 mph,

arriving at city *B* on schedule. What is the distance between cities *A* and *B*?

15–25. At 8:00 A.M. a freighter leaves Boston harbor for London traveling at the rate of 16 knots. At 1:00 P.M. the same day a passenger ship leaves Boston, sailing the same course at 22 knots. Three hours after departure the freighter is delayed one hour due to a temporary engine failure. How long will it take for the passenger ship to overtake the freighter?

15–26. Bob decided to walk from *A* to *B*, a distance of 14 miles. For $1\frac{1}{4}$ hours he walked at the rate of 3 miles per hour. Then, after resting for $\frac{1}{2}$ hour, he resumed the trip walking at the rate of $2\frac{1}{2}$ miles per hour. Two hours after Bob started, Jerry starts from *A* on a bicycle at a rate of 7 miles per hour riding toward *B*. How far from *A* does Jerry overtake Bob? How long does it take each to make the trip?

15–27. The cost of preparing plates for printing a book is $15,000. Cost of printing a single book is $1.00. If the book is sold for $5.00, how many copies must be sold before any profit is realized?

15–28. The distance, *s*, which a body falls in time, *t*, starting from rest, is expressed by the equation $s = 16t^2$. Find the depth of a cavern if the sound of a stone striking the bottom is heard five seconds after dropping the stone. (Velocity of sound is 1,050 feet per second.)

15–29. One hundred cubic centimeters of a 10 per cent solution of a certain medicine are available. If this is to be reduced to a 6 per cent solution, how much distilled water must be added?

15–30. How much pure alcohol must be added to 10 quarts of a mixture containing 25 per cent alcohol to obtain a mixture containing 35 per cent alcohol?

15–31. The acetic acid strength in a barrel of vinegar is 6 per cent. How many quarts of pure acetic acid must be added to increase the strength to 10 per cent? (One barrel contains 31.5 gallons.)

15–32. A certain mixture contains 18 per cent alcohol, and a second mixture contains 28 per cent alcohol. How many gallons of each must be used to obtain 100 gallons of a mixture containing 21.3 per cent alcohol?

15–33. A 150-gallon tank is filled through two pipes, *A* and *B*, and emptied through a third pipe *C*.

Pipe *A* delivers water at 6 gallons per minute, pipe *B* delivers water at 2 gallons per minute, and pipe *C* discharges water at 3 gallons per minute. A valve in pipe *A* is opened and eight minutes later a valve in pipe *B* is also opened. Pipe *C* is open and discharging at all times. Construct a graph showing the quantity of water in the tank at any time. How much time is required to fill the tank?

15–34. A square piece of sheet metal measures 12″ on a side. An open box is to be made from this by removing equal squares from the four corners and bending up the sides. If x represents the length of a side of the squares cut from the corners, what value of x will result in a box of maximum volume?

15–35. A rectangular box is to have a length 3″ more than its width, and a width of 2″ more than its depth. What must be the depth of the box to make its volume 200 cu. in.?

15–36. What are the dimensions of the largest rectangle which can be inscribed in a 14″ circle?

15–37. At what time between 3 and 4 o'clock are the hands of a clock together?

15–38. At what time between 8 and 9 o'clock are the hands of a clock opposite each other?

15–39. At what time between 6 and 7 o'clock are the hands of a clock 15 minutes apart?

16

GRAPHICAL
CALCULUS

16-1. INTRODUCTION

The engineer and the scientist very frequently deal with problems involving rates of change or total changes of functions over certain intervals. Such problems may be solved through the application of differential and integral calculus. Differentiation is concerned with the determination of the rate of change of a variable, while integration determines the total change. The processes of differentiation and integration are the inverse of one another in the same sense that multiplication and division are the inverse of one another.

If the equation representing data involving rate of change or total change is known, a solution may be obtained through the application of the conventional calculus. However, the solution of many problems is often complicated because the data are either observed or obtained from experimental testing. Under these conditions, before applying conventional mathematical operations to determine rate of change or total change, the basic equation representing the data must be determined. The complexity of such an equation often makes it

desirable to employ methods of solution which do not require the determination of such basic equations. These solutions may be accomplished through graphical, semigraphical, or mechanical means.

This chapter presents both graphical and semigraphical methods for determining the rate of change and the total change of a function directly from a graphical plot of the data. While the fundamental concepts of graphical and conventional calculus are identical; it should be emphasized that knowledge of the formal (or conventional) calculus is not required to understand and solve problems by graphical calculus. Frequently, knowledge of graphical calculus contributes to better understanding of the fundamental principles involved in the formal calculus.

16-2. FUNDAMENTAL CONCEPTS

Before investigating the principles of graphical differentiation and integration, certain fundamental concepts must be defined. A thorough understanding of these concepts is essential to the successful application of the principles of the calculus to graphical analysis.

Function. If, for every change in one quantity, there is a corresponding change in a second quantity, the second quantity is said to be a *function* of

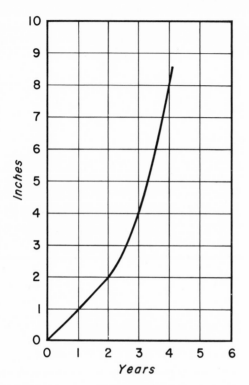

Fig. **16-1.** Rate of change—growth of a tree.

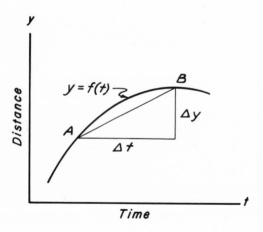

Fig. **16-2.** Non-uniform rate of change.

the first. This is because its variation depends on, or functions according to, the first quantity. For example: a long pole is heavier than a short pole of the same diameter and material; the weight in this case is a function of the length of the pole. As another example, a tree grows taller as it grows older. Here the height (distance) is a function of time.

Functions are usually expressed in terms of their related quantities. For the first example above, the relationship might be expressed as pounds per foot; in the second example as inches per year. Plotted graphically, the curve for the second example might appear as in Fig. 16-1.

These relationships may be expressed in formal mathematics by the expression $y = f(x)$; i.e., y is a function of x. In the first example above, y would represent the weight and x the length; in the second example, y would represent the height and x the age (time). Such relationships can also be expressed or illustrated graphically. Fig. 16-2 shows a general curve $y = f(t)$ plotted with reference to rectangular coordinates, in which distance has been plotted as a function of time for a moving object.

Rates of Change. As previously stated, a change in one quantity can cause a change in a second quantity which is a function of the first. The amount of change can vary. For example, a tree might grow an inch each year for the first two years in which case we would assume that it is growing at a uniform *rate* expressed as inches per year. Then conditions might change and the tree, receiving plenty of water and food, would begin to grow faster and faster for several years, i.e., two inches the third year, four inches the fourth year, etc. The change in growth for the third year would be two inches per year; for the fourth year, four inches per year. It could then be said that the *rate of change* of growth was increasing, since the amount of the *change* itself increased each year. This condition is represented by Fig. 16-1.

Rate of change may be either uniform or variable. If uniform, then the particular relationship of two quantities is plotted as a straight line on rectangular coordinate paper. In Fig. 16-3, the straight line represents a uniform rate of change for distance plotted as a function of time for a moving object. The rate is represented by the slope of the line. The general equation for this line is $y = mt + b$. The value represented by b, the point where the line crosses the y-axis, indicates whether or not the object has moved some initial distance at the start of the investigation. The letter m is a constant representing the slope ratio, or rate of slope. Δt stands for a small increment of time. Δy stands for a correspondingly small increment of distance. In this case, for any fixed interval of time, Δt, the corresponding change in distance, Δy, is a fixed amount and $\Delta y/\Delta t$ is the rate of change of distance with respect to time.

If, in this illustration, there had been no change of distance with respect to time, the rate would be zero and the data would plot as a horizontal line. Fig. 16–4 is representative of this condition. The equation representing these data is $y = b$, and for any fixed interval of time, Δt, the corresponding change in distance, Δy, is zero. Thus $\Delta y/\Delta t = 0$, signifying no rate of change.

Frequently data are encountered where the rate of change is non-uniform. In these instances, when distance is plotted as a function of time, the resulting graph is a curved line as presented in Fig. 16–2. For such data an average rate over a specified interval, such as from A to B in Fig. 16–2, may be readily obtained. To do this a chord is drawn connecting the end points A and B of the desired interval. The slope, $\Delta y/\Delta t$, of this chord represents the average rate of change over the selected interval.

With functions having a non-uniform rate, it is frequently necessary to determine the instantaneous rate of change at some specific instance. In calculus such an instantaneous rate of change for a function is known as the derivative, and is defined as

$$\frac{dy}{dx} = \frac{df(x)}{dx} = \lim_{\Delta x \to 0} \frac{f(x + dx) - f(x)}{\Delta x} = \lim_{\Delta x \to 0} \frac{\Delta y}{\Delta x}.$$

A theorem of calculus states that the value of the derivative for any point on a curve is equal to the slope of the tangent line to the curve at that point. In Fig. 16–5 the same curve, $y = f(t)$, depicted in Fig. 16–2 has been redrawn to illustrate this theorem and the definition of a derivative. Assume that the instantaneous rate (or the derivative) is required for point A. This rate is equal to the slope, dy/dt, of the tangent line to the curve at A. It is

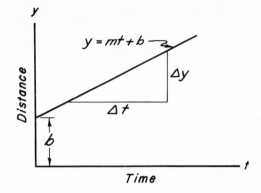

Fig. 16–3. Uniform rate of change.

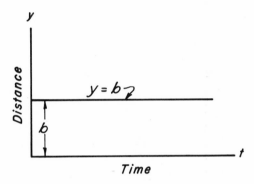

Fig. 16–4. Zero rate of change.

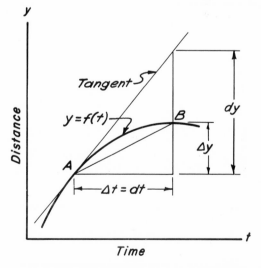

Fig. 16–5. Instantaneous rate of change.

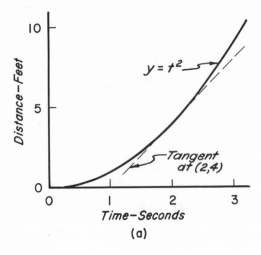

(a)

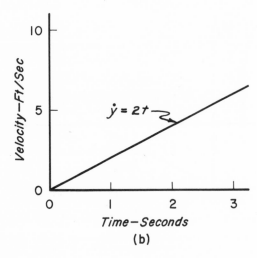

(b)

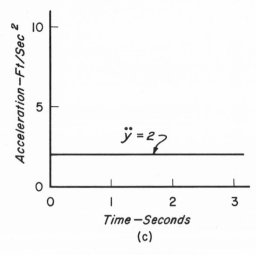

(c)

Fig. **16-6.** Related curves.

also apparent that as point B is moved closer to A (Δt is shortened) the average rate for the interval, represented by the slope of the chord AB, approaches the instantaneous rate dy/dt for point A. A commonly accepted shorthand symbol for representing dy/dt is $\dot{y}$, and the representation of d^2y/dt^2 (the second derivative of y with respect to t) is $\ddot{y}$. The symbols y' and y'' are used to represent dy/dx and d^2y/dx^2. Graphical methods for obtaining such tangents are discussed in Art. 16-3.

Related Curves. When performing graphical calculus, complete curves are constructed as a result of the differentiation or integration. These curves, in combination with the original plot, form sets of related curves. Demonstrating this relationship are the graphs in Fig. 16-6 which represent the motion of an object with constant acceleration. The original curve, Fig. 16-6(a), portrays graphically the displacement of the object as a function of time. Mathematically this is expressed by the equation $y = t^2$, where y represents distance and t represents time. Graphical differentiation of this curve would result in the curve of Fig. 16-6(b), which expressed mathematically is $\dot{y} = 2t$. This curve represents the rate of change of distance the object moves with respect to time. For motion of an object the rate of change, $\dot{y}$, is the velocity, which in this example is changing at a constant rate since the graph is a straight line of constant slope. Fig. 16-6(c) presents the result of the graphical differentiation of the velocity vs. time curve. Mathematically the equation of this curve is written $\ddot{y} = 2$ and represents the rate of change of velocity with respect to time. Here, $\ddot{y}$ represents acceleration and, since the graph is a horizontal line, the rate of change of acceleration with respect to time is zero. Thus, the acceleration is a constant. This acceleration vs. time graph is frequently referred to as the first derivative of the velocity or the second derivative of displacement with respect to time.

If, in Fig. 16-6, the original curve had been the acceleration-time relationship, $\ddot{y} = 2$, then the curve $\dot{y} = 2t$ would represent the result of the graphical integration of the acceleration curve. It would also portray graphically the summation of the area under the acceleration curve. In similar manner, the graph $y = t^2$ would represent the integral curve based on the velocity-time curve, $\dot{y} = 2t$, and present graphically the summation of area under the velocity curve.

Frequently, related curves are designated as higher or lower order curves of a given curve, rather than as the type of operation performed, i.e., differentiation or integration. Thus, differentiation results in the rate of change of a function of the next higher order, while integration results in a summation for functions of the next lower order.

Slope Relationship. A fundamental theorem of calculus states that the slope of a curve for any point on the curve is equal to the value of the ordinate of the next lower order derived curve for the corresponding abscissa value. This theorem can be illustrated by a study of the related curves of Fig. 16–6. If a tangent is drawn to the curve in Fig. 16–6(a) at the point (2, 4), its slope is 4 which corresponds to the ordinate value for $t = 2$ on the next lower order curve, $\dot{y} = 2t$. In a similar manner the slope of $\dot{y} = 2t$ is equal to a constant 2 for any value of t which corresponds to the ordinate value for all points on the lower order curve, $\ddot{y} = 2$. If the units (distance, velocity, etc.) are considered, they also are correct. The units associated with the slope of the curve $y = t^2$ are distance/time or velocity, which is the ordinate unit for the next lower order curve. In a similar manner the units associated with the slope for any point on the curve $\dot{y} = 2t$ are velocity/time or acceleration, the ordinate units for $\ddot{y} = 2$.

Area Relationship. Another fundamental theorem of calculus states that the area under a curve bounded by any two ordinate lines is equal to the difference in the value of the two corresponding ordinates of the next higher order related curve. The curves of Fig. 16–6, which have been used to demonstrate the slope relationship, are repeated in Fig. 16–7 to illustrate this area relationship. To simplify the analysis the units (distance, velocity, etc.) are temporarily disregarded, using only abstract numbers. If the area A_1, which is bounded by the curve $\ddot{y} = 2$ and the ordinates corresponding to $t = 1$ and $t = 2$, is determined, it is found to be 2. The values of the corresponding ordinates for the curve $\dot{y} = 2t$ are 2 and 4. Thus the difference, D_1, between these two ordinates is 2 and equals the area A_1 under the next lower order

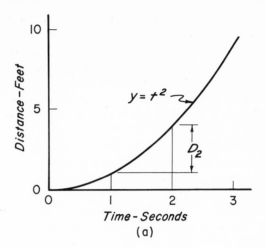

(a)

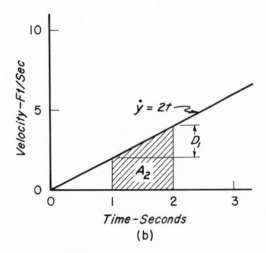

(b)

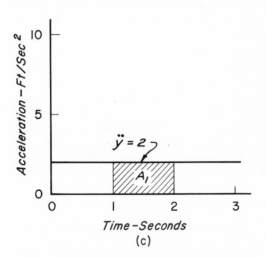

(c)

Fig. **16–7.** Area relationship.

curve. Another illustration of the area relationship is the trapezoidal area, A_2, bounded by the curve $\dot{y} = 2t$ and the two ordinates corresponding to $t = 1$ and $t = 2$. The area of this trapezoid is $\frac{1}{2}(4 + 2)(1) = 3$. The values of the corresponding ordinates for the next higher order curve, $y = t^2$, are 1 and 4, and their difference, D_2, is 3 which is equal to the previously determined area A_2.

If the units (distance, velocity, etc.) are considered for these curves, they also are correct. For the curve $\ddot{y} = 2$, the units of the area are acceleration multiplied by time which equals velocity, the unit in which the ordinates of the next higher order curve are measured. In a similar manner the units of area for the curve $\dot{y} = 2t$ are velocity multiplied by time which equals displacement, the unit of measure for the ordinates of the curve $y = t^2$.

In these examples, the magnitudes of the areas have been accurately determined since the area

shapes were rectangular or trapezoidal. When the areas are defined by such simple geometric forms, they may be easily calculated. However, such geometric simplicity is infrequently encountered. Therefore, in many cases approximations of the area are necessary. The next section discusses such approximations.

16–3. FUNDAMENTAL CONSTRUCTIONS FOR GRAPHICAL CALCULUS

The previous discussion of related curves has brought out two fundamental relationships necessary to the study of graphical calculus: slope and area. Before graphical differentiation and integration can be successfully performed, procedures must be developed for constructing tangents to curves and making close approximations of areas under curves.

Tangents to Curves. Unless a curve is a segment of a circle, it is difficult to obtain a true tangent to any point on the curve. However, constructions are available which approximate tangents with sufficient accuracy for application to graphical calculus.

One such construction is illustrated in Fig. 16–8. Here a chord is selected and drawn so that it subtends a segment of the curve closely approximating an arc of a circle. The perpendicular bisector of the chord is constructed. Point P, where this bisector crosses the curve, locates the point of tangency on the curve, and the tangent is drawn parallel to the chord. Even though the curve is not a perfect circle, if the selected chord is kept reasonably short, the curve segment so closely approximates a circular arc that the error introduced is within acceptable limits. When the curve is relatively flat, longer chords may be selected. A rapidly changing curvature necessitates shorter chords.

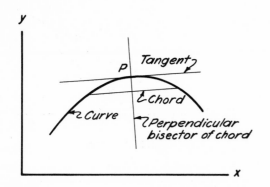

Fig. **16–8.** Tangent line construction—chordal method.

A modification of the above construction permits a more precise location of the point of tangency of a line to a non-circular arc. For small segments, the curve may be assumed to be parabolic without introducing any appreciable error. In Fig. 16–9, two parallel chords are drawn to the curve at any desirable slope. These chords are each bisected and a line is drawn through the midpoints. The

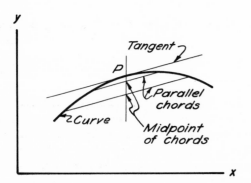

Fig. **16–9.** Tangent line construction—parallel chord method.

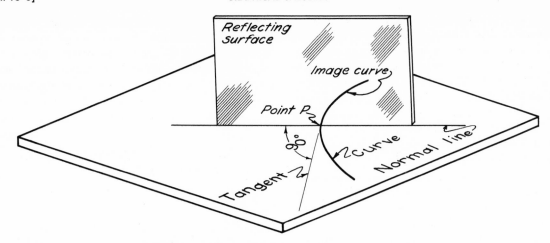

Fig. 16-10. Tangent line construction—mirror method.

point where this line intersects the curve locates an approximate tangency point P to the curve, and the tangent has the same slope as the two parallel chords.

A third method for approximating a tangent to a curve involves the use of a reflecting surface. In Fig. 16-10, a reflecting surface is placed with the plane of the surface perpendicular to the plane of the paper at the point P on the curve where a tangent is desired. The reflecting surface is gradually pivoted until the curve and its image form a continuous, smooth, unbroken curve. A line is drawn along the base of the reflecting surface. This line is a normal to the curve at P. The tangent will then be perpendicular to this normal at P. If a glass mirror is used as a reflecting surface, the thickness of the glass must be considered since the normal is at the back reflecting surface and not along the front surface of the glass. Use of a polished metallic surface as a mirror will eliminate this problem.

Area Approximation. The application of graphical calculus frequently requires that the area under a curve for a specific interval be transformed into an equivalent area of rectangular shape, with the base of the rectangle extending over the same interval. For example, in Fig. 16-11 the area under the curve $y = x^2$ for the interval from $x = 2$ to $x = 5$ can be calculated and is found to be equal to 39 square units. The rectangle $abcd$ with an altitude of 13 and a base of 3 has the same identical

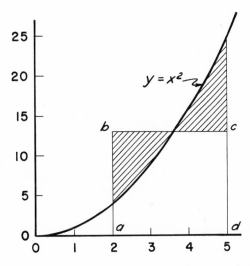

Fig. 16-11. Equivalent area under curve segment.

area. In practice, rather than attempting to locate the line bc precisely by the use of mathematics (frequently this is impossible when the equation of the curve is unknown), it is located approximately by eye.

Locating the line bc by inspection utilizes the fact that the line creates two shaded portions of exactly equal area as shown in Fig. 16-11. Thus the line bc is positioned and drawn by inspection so that the two shaded portions appear by eye to be of equal area. For small areas, the eye is quite sensitive to slight differences, and a close approximation can be achieved.

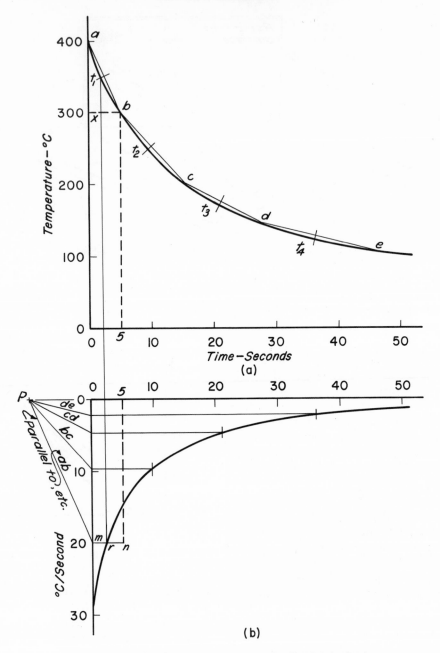

Fig. **16-12.**   Graphical differentiation—chordal method.

16-4. GRAPHICAL DIFFERENTIATION—CHORDAL METHOD

In Art. 16–2 it has been stated that a derivative is the instantaneous rate of change of a function, and that a derivative curve can be constructed if the slopes of tangents to a curve corresponding to various abscissa values are known. By plotting the magnitudes of these slopes as ordinates against the original abscissa values the derivative curve is graphed. The major difficulties in such a construction are first, the determination of accurate tangents, and second, the necessity of calculating the slope of these tangents. The chordal method is one graphical technique for solving these difficulties.

To illustrate the chordal method of differentiation, assume experimental data have been obtained, based on observations of a cooling body. From these data the curve of temperature vs. time has been drawn as shown in Fig. 16–12(a). In analyzing these data it is desired to construct a derivative curve showing the rate of cooling at any instant. This derivative curve and the steps involved in its construction are illustrated in Fig. 16–12.

Preliminary examination of the given curve indicates its slope to be decreasingly negative. Therefore, the shape of the derivative curve will be convex upward with the maximum negative y-value occurring at time zero. Thus y-values of the derivative curve will lie entirely in the negative range.

A set of axes is drawn for the derived curve using, for convenience, the same length scale division as on the original curve. To facilitate the transfer of dimensions vertically, the x-axis for the derivative curve is drawn directly below the original. The new x-axis has identical scale divisions both in size and value. The new y-axis has scale divisions equal to the original y-axis in length only. (Values are assigned to this scale later in the article.)

Ordinate values of a derivative curve are a measure of the slope of the corresponding points on the given curve. To measure such a slope, tangents must be constructed to the given curve at selected points. The method of establishing these tangencies is that illustrated in Fig. 16–8. A series of chords, ab, bc, cd, etc., are drawn which cut the given curve so that the various curve segments are closely symmetrical about their respective chords. Perpendicular bisectors to the chords then locate the actual tangency points, t_1, t_2, t_3, etc., for tangents to the curve parallel to the respective chords.

Before proceeding further, values must be assigned to the y-axis scale divisions of the derivative curve. To help establish the scale range, the largest ordinate value should be estimated. This can be done by determining the average slope over the initial curve interval ab. This slope, as read from

the graph, is $(300 - 400)/5$ or -20. Obviously, the slope at a is somewhat greater than this average value, and a logical estimate would appear to be about -25. Values are now arbitrarily assigned to the scale divisions on the y-axis as shown.

In order to locate graphically the ordinates on the derivative curve, a pole point P is located to the left of the origin of the axes a distance equal to a whole number of units of the x-axis scale. The exact location of P will be discussed shortly. Through P and parallel to chord ab, a line is drawn until it intersects the y-axis at m. Line mn is now drawn parallel to the x-axis and extending over the interval covered by chord ab. Ordinate $0m$ represents the average value of the slope for the original curve from a to b, provided P has been properly positioned. Line $0m$ also represents at point r the slope corresponding to point t_1 on the original curve. Point r is located by projecting downward from t_1 onto mn. From data of the original curve, the slope of the tangent through t parallel to ab is determined as 100 degrees/5 seconds or 20 degrees per second. To meet the requirement that ordinates on the derived curve represent the slope of the original curve at the corresponding points, point P must be positioned so that the ordinate $0m$ equals 20 degrees per second.

To facilitate illustration of the technique for locating point P, Fig. 16–13 repeats a portion of Fig. 16–12 with the horizontal scale enlarged. By construction, triangles abx and $P0m$ are similar. Since corresponding sides of similar triangles are proportional, then

$$\frac{ax}{0m} = \frac{xb}{P0}$$

or

$$0m = \frac{(ax)(P0)}{(xb)}.$$

The slope relationship says that the slope of a curve at any point on the curve is equal to the ordinate of the next lower order curve for the corresponding abscissa value. Since $0m$ is equal to the ordinate of the derived curve at point r, it must then be numerically equal to the slope of the given curve at point t_1. This slope is ax/xb. Hence, to make the above equation obey the slope relationship, the value of $P0$ must be one. However, this would mean that the ordinate scales of both curves must

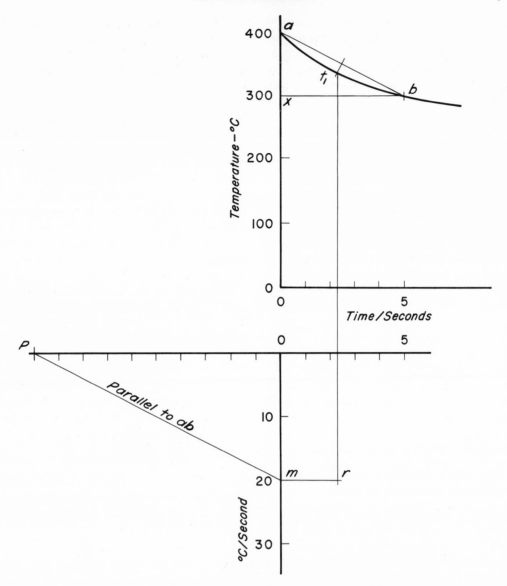

Fig. **16-13.** Theory of graphical differentiation—chordal method.

be identical in length and value. This is not true in this example, and is not desirable in most problems.

In order to make the above equation conform to the slope relationship, the equation can be rewritten as:

$$0m = \frac{(ax)}{(xb)} \frac{(P0)}{SM}$$

where *SM* equals the value of a single division (or group) of the higher order curve divided by the

value of a single division (or similar group) of the lower order curve, and is called the "scale multiplier." This equation now obeys the slope relationship if $P0 = SM$. Since in Fig. 16-13 $SM = 100/10 = 10$, then *P0* must also equal 10 units. The units of *P0* are measured in terms of the abscissa units.

A simple method for the location of point *P* should now be apparent. After selecting the ordinate scale division values for the derivative curve, the value for a single division or group is divided into the corresponding value for a single division or similar group on the original curve. This quotient is the distance point P must be located from the origin of the derivative curve. In this example the distance is $100/10 = 10$ units.

The construction described above ultimately results in a point r, which is one point on the derived curve. Repeating this construction in Fig. 16–12 for chords bc, cd, etc., gives a series of points determining the complete derivative curve. This basic approach to differentiation may be applied with modifications. Such modifications are in the location of the tangencies to the original curve. Either the mirror method of Fig. 16–10 or the parallel chord method of Fig. 16–9 may be used. Except for this substitution, the construction is identical.

In reviewing this method, note that the intervals selected along the x-axis are not necessarily equal. Their width is dependent on selecting chords so that subtended curve segments are as symmetrical as possible. Usually the smaller the interval used the greater will be the accuracy. Other factors affecting accuracy are the accuracy of the given data and the drafting accuracy.

16–5. GRAPHICAL DIFFERENTIATION BY DISTANCE TRANSFER METHOD

In Art. 16–3 it has been stated that the area under a curve for a given interval is equal to the difference in ordinates on the next higher curve for the same interval. This relationship forms the basis of a second method of graphical differentiation, known as the distance transfer method, which will be applied to the same example used in Art. 16–4. Fig. 16–14 reproduces the original plotted curve from which the derivative curve is to be derived.

The first step in the construction of the derivative curve is the establishment of the axes. The axes are laid and the scale value assigned in the same manner as described for the chordal method of Art. 16–4. Then the original curve is divided into intervals of equal width. In this example a width equivalent to five seconds has been selected. Examination of the original curve for the interval

$x = 0$ to $x = 5$ indicates a corresponding difference in ordinates of 100. To meet the requirements of the area relationship between derived curves, the area under the derivative curve for the same interval must also be 100.

To obtain this area, an approximating rectangle is constructed for the derivative curve over the interval 0 to 5. Since the abscissa scales are identical on both related curves, for an interval width of 5 the height (or ordinate) of this rectangle is $100/5$ or 20.

While this method of determining the height of the approximating rectangle could be continued over the remaining intervals, a simpler method is desirable which would eliminate the tedious arithmetic and reduce sources of error in calculations. As an aid in determining this simpler method, Fig. 16–15 reproduces the initial portion of the original curve of Fig. 16–14 with the abscissa scale enlarged. Referring to Fig. 16–15, in order to satisfy the area relationship the equation $D = (a)(x)$ must hold true. However, in the example of Fig. 16–15 the length of the vertical scale of the derivative curve is ten times the length of the vertical scale of the original curve. To compensate for this difference in scale lengths the previous equation must be modified into the form

$$(SM)(D) = (a)(x).$$

The term (SM), as defined in Art. 16–4, is the scale multiplier, which in the given example must equal 10. Since the altitude, a, is the desired quantity, the equation is rewritten

$$a = \frac{(D)(SM)}{x}.$$

If the numerical values, $x = 5$ and $SM = 10$, from the given example are substituted, the equation reduces to $a = 2D$. Thus, by using the value $2D$ as the height of the approximating rectangle the area relationship is satisfied. This distance may be easily transferred using dividers.

Fig. 16–14 shows the approximating rectangles, A_1, A_2, A_3, A_4, etc., constructed by this method for the entire curve. Completion of the differential curve requires that a smooth curve be drawn so that the "triangles" (shown shaded on rectangle A_1) will be of equal area for any one approximating rectangle. Frequently, simply drawing the curve

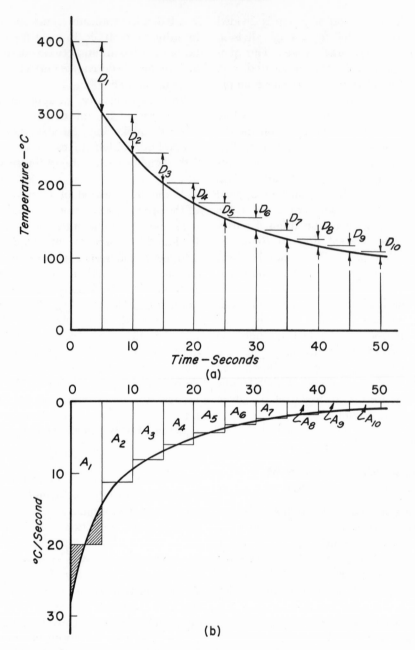

Fig. 16–14. Graphical differentiation—distance transfer method.

through the midpoints of the bases of the rectangles will be of sufficient accuracy.

Obviously, care must be used in selecting the interval width along the x-axis. If an interval of four rather than five had been selected, the height of the approximating rectangle would become

$a = \dfrac{5D}{2}$. The inconvenience of transferring this ratio by dividers is apparent. If there are segments of a curve where a specified interval does not give the desired accuracy, the width of the interval may be reduced. If this is done, however, the equation

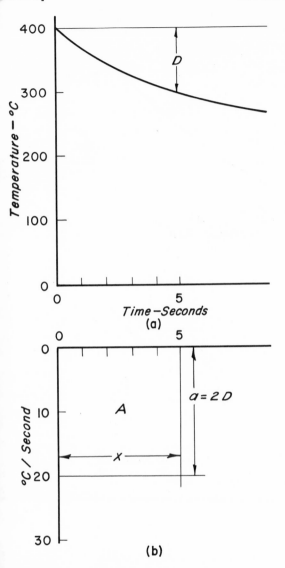

Fig. 16-15. Theory of graphical differentiation—distance transfer method.

for the height must also be changed. If, for a portion of the given example, an interval $x = 2$ had been used, the height would have become $a = 5D$. Thus, for this portion only, the altitude of the approximating rectangles would be transferred as five times the difference between the ordinates.

In reviewing this distance transfer method, note that the interval selected must be uniform with the exception of the technique described above for

obtaining increased accuracy. Usually the smaller the interval used, the greater will be the accuracy. Other factors affecting accuracy include the accuracy of the basic data and the graphical accuracy in transferring distances.

16-6. GRAPHICAL INTEGRATION BY CHORDAL METHOD

As previously stated, in calculus the process of integration is the inverse of differentiation. When a curve representing the rate of change of a function is given, the integral (or higher order) curve to be constructed shows the total change of the function over selected intervals. Fig. 16-16(a) shows the graph of an object moved by a force of varying magnitude. It is desired to construct a curve showing both the total work performed in moving the object and the amount of work done on the object in moving over any specified distance.

The chordal method of constructing the integral curve is based on the previously stated theorem that the area under a curve for any stated interval is equal to the difference in ordinates on the next higher curve for the same interval. The first step in constructing the integral curve is to draw a set of axes as in Fig. 16-16(b). The x-axis scale divisions are identical to the original curve both in size and value while the y-axis has scale divisions equal in length only. Since inspection shows the area under the given curve is increasing as the x-values increase, all values on the y-axis of the integral curve will be positive with the starting point at zero. The curve starts at zero since there can be no work prior to some displacement.

Values must be assigned to y-axis scale divisions on the integral graph. By inspection the area under the original curve is estimated to be approximately fifty. Therefore, the values assigned to the y-axis of the integral curve are selected to range from zero to sixty in increments of twenty as shown.

The approximating rectangle $0abc$ is drawn on the original graph over the x-axis interval from 0 to 0.5 using the method illustrated in Fig. 16-11. A pole point, P, is located a whole number of x-axis units to the left of the origin of the original graph. The exact location of P will be discussed in detail shortly. The ray Pa is drawn, and from the origin

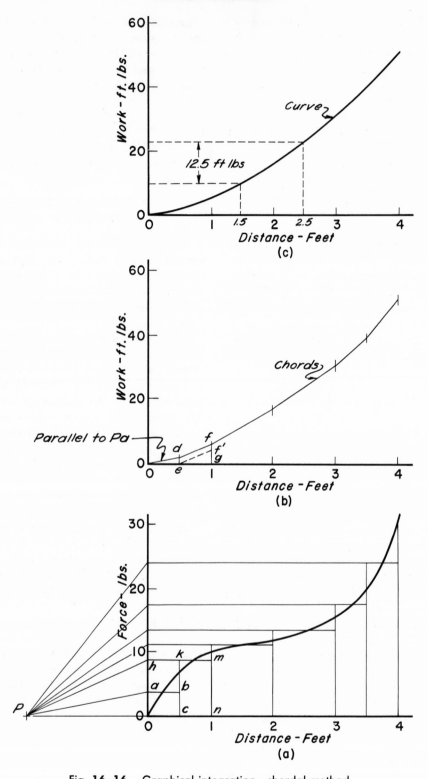

Fig. 16–16. Graphical integration—chordal method.

of the axes of the integral graph the line $0d$ is drawn parallel to the ray Pa and extending over the x-axis interval 0 to 0.5. To satisfy the area relationship, the ordinate de must equal the area of the rectangle $0abc$. This is accomplished through the proper location of the pole point P.

Attention must now be directed to the precise location of point P. Triangle $P0a$ is similar to triangle $0ed$ by construction. Since corresponding parts of similar triangles are proportional, then

$$\frac{de}{0e} = \frac{a0}{P0}$$

and

$$de = \frac{(a0)(0e)}{P0}.$$

Since de is the difference in ordinates of the higher order curve and $(a0)(0e)$ is the area under the lower order curve, the area relationship is satisfied only if $P0$ equals one. Note that $0e = ab$. As discussed in Art. 16-4, this condition is not desirable. Therefore, the scale multiplier is again introduced as:

$$de = (a0)(0e)\frac{SM}{P0},$$

and the area relationship is obeyed if $SM = P0$. In this example $SM = 20/10 = 2$. Therefore point P must be located two abscissa units from the origin.

This construction is now repeated for the next interval (in this example from $x = 0.5$ to $x = 1.0$) and the line ef' is drawn. The ordinate of $f'g$ represents the area under the rectangle $ckmn$. Since the area under the integral curve is cumulative, the line df is drawn from point d parallel to ray Ph. The method is now repeated for the remaining intervals until the original curve is traversed. One feature of this method is that intervals along the x-axis need not be of equal width.

To complete the integral graph the straight-line segments are assumed to be chords of the integral curve, and the corresponding curve is drawn. Fig. 16-16(c) shows this final curve. Inspection of this final curve shows that when the object has moved four feet, the total work done on the object is 54 ft.-lb. Also, in moving the object from $x = 1.5$ to $x = 2.5$, the work done on the object is the difference in corresponding ordinates or 12.5 ft.-lb.

Thus total work or the work done over any interval may be readily determined.

In reviewing the method, it should be remembered that the intervals selected need not be of equal width. Steep or rapidly changing curves necessitate closely spaced intervals, while flat portions of the curve permit more widely spaced intervals. Accuracy of this solution is limited by the accuracy of the given data, the size of the interval selected, and the drafting accuracy.

16-7. GRAPHICAL INTEGRATION BY DISTANCE TRANSFER METHOD

Another method for graphical integration, the distance transfer method, also depends on the area relationship as the basis for construction. The example of the previous article is again solved utilizing this second method. (For construction details refer to Fig. 16-17.)

Initial steps of construction are similar to those of the chordal method, and include establishment of the axes and assignment of the scale values. Then, the original curve is divided into intervals of equal width. In this example an interval width of 0.5 is used. For the first interval from $x = 0$ to $x = 0.5$, a rectangle $0abc$ is drawn approximating the area under that segment of the curve. This rectangle is constructed by the method of Fig. 16-11. For the area relationship to be true the ordinate de on the integral curve must equal the area of the rectangle $0abc$ which is (4) (0.5) or 2.

Again, as with the distance transfer method for differentiation (Art. 16-5), a simple method is desirable for determining the ordinate heights on the integral curve. Such a method will eliminate the tedious arithmetic involved. Referring to rectangle $0abc$, in order for the area relationship to hold, the equation $D_1 = (0c)(0a)$ must be satisfied. In this example the vertical scale of the integral curve is twice that of the original curve. This ratio, in general, is called the scale multiplier and is designated as SM. Thus to compensate for such differences in the scales, the previous equation must be modified to read

$$D_1 = \frac{(0c)(0a)}{SM}.$$

Substituting the numerical values for this problem

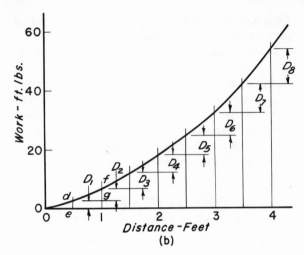

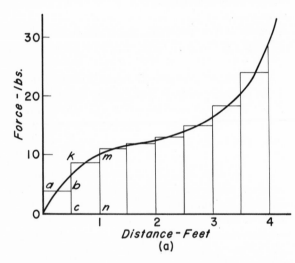

Fig. 16–17. Graphical integration—distance transfer method.

In reviewing this method of graphical integration, the width of the interval along the x-axis is selected which will give a convenient value in the equation $D = (a)(x)/SM$, where a is the ordinate of the approximating rectangle and x is the interval width. If, for greater accuracy, the width of the interval is changed for any portion of the curve, the ratio of the distance transferred must be correspondingly altered. Accuracy of this method is limited by the accuracy of the basic data and the graphical accuracy in transferring distances.

16–8. CONSTANT OF INTEGRATION

In the example of Arts. 16–6 and 16–7 the integral curve begins at zero, but this is not always true in every case. The area relationship states that the area under a given curve between two ordinates equals the difference in length of the corresponding ordinates on the integral curve. Thus integration of a curve provides the shape of the integral curve but does not position it vertically. To determine the position of the curve with respect to the x-axis, the constant of integration must be known. Usually this constant is determined by knowing either the relationship between the original and the integral values of the variable, or by knowing one point on the integral curve.

16–9. NUMERICAL METHODS OF INTEGRATION

The numerical methods of integration use formulas based on calculus to determine the area under a curve. With formal calculus, if the equation of the curve to be integrated is known, x- and y-coordinates for certain specified points are calculated and substituted into the formula. The solution may be made partially graphical in that the curve may be plotted and the necessary data scaled from the graph and then substituted into the formula. This semigraphical procedure has the advantage that it may be applied to experimental data where the equation representing the data is unknown. In the following two articles, two methods of numerical integration, the *trapezoidal rule* and *Simpson's rule*, are described. Each of these methods is simply a means of approximating the area under a curve.

of the interval $x = 0.5$ and $SM = 2$, the equation reduces to $D_1 = (0a)/4$. Therefore, if one-fourth of the distance $0a$ is transferred and laid off as the ordinate de, the area relationships will be satisfied.

This process is repeated for the rectangle $ckmn$, and the distance fg equal to D_2 is laid off as one-fourth of the distance ck. As in the chordal method, these distances are cumulative. After the remaining distances D_3 through D_8 have been laid off for all the intervals, a smooth curve is drawn as shown. Values for work done may then be read from the integral curve as they were with the chordal method.

16–10. TRAPEZOIDAL RULE

Fig. 16–18 shows a curve under which the area is to be found between the limits a and b by means of the trapezoidal rule.

First, divide the interval between the limits a and b into n parts of equal width Δx. By replacing the curved top of each segment of the curve with a straight line (shown dotted on the figure), the area is divided into a series of trapezoids whose area can be summed up as follows:

$$A_T = \tfrac{1}{2}(y_0 + y_1)\Delta x + \tfrac{1}{2}(y_1 + y_2)\Delta x$$
$$+ \tfrac{1}{2}(y_2 + y_3)\Delta x + \cdots + \tfrac{1}{2}(y_{(n-1)} + y_n)\Delta x$$

or

$$A_T = \Delta x\,[\tfrac{1}{2}(y_0 + y_n) + y_1 + y_2 + y_3 + \cdots$$
$$+ y_{(n-1)}].$$

By scaling the graph for values of Δx, y_1, y_2, y_3, etc., substituting into the formula, and solving, the approximate area is determined. If Δx is assumed small enough, the error introduced by replacing the curve with a series of straight lines is quite small.

16–11. SIMPSON'S RULE

Referring again to Fig. 16–18, the small area is to be obtained by means of Simpson's rule. First, the interval from a to b is divided into an even number of equal parts by means of ordinates. Then, the following formula is used as an approxi-mation of the area under the curve for the first two parts:

$$A = \frac{\Delta x}{3}(y_0 + 4y_1 + y_2).$$

This is actually the area under a parabola, $y = Ax^2 + Bx + C$, which passes through the three points on the curve determined by three adjacent ordinates. Proof for this formula may be found in any standard calculus text. Thus, Simpson's rule substitutes segments of the actual curve with arcs of parabolas and determines the area under these arcs. The total area can be found by repeating the process for each of the remaining groups of two segments and finding the total. The mathematical equation for Simpson's rule is derived as follows:

$$A_T = \frac{\Delta x}{3}(y_0 + 4y_1 + y_2) + \frac{\Delta x}{3}(y_2 + 4y_3 + y_4)$$
$$+ \cdots + \frac{\Delta x}{3}(y_{(n-2)} + 4y_{(n-1)} + y_n)$$

$$A_T = \frac{\Delta x}{3}[(y_0 + 4y_1 + y_2) + (y_2 + 4y_3 + y_4)$$
$$+ \cdots + (y_{(n-2)} + 4y_{(n-1)} + y_n)]$$

$$A_T = \frac{\Delta x}{3}[y_0 + 4y_1 + 2y_2 + 4y_3 + 2y_4 + \cdots$$
$$+ 4y_{(n-1)} + y_n]$$

$$A_T = \frac{\Delta x}{3}[(y_0 + y_n) + 4(y_1 + y_3 + y_5 + \cdots$$
$$+ y_{(n-1)}) + 2(y_2 + y_4 + y_6 + \cdots + y_{(n-2)})].$$

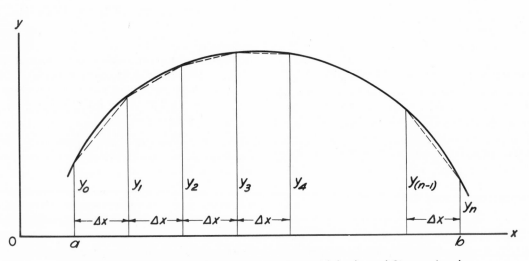

Fig. 16–18. Semigraphical integration—trapezoidal rule and Simpson's rule.

Thus the area under a curve as found by Simpson's rule is equal to the sum of the end ordinates plus four times the sum of the odd-numbered ordinates, plus two times the sum of the even-numbered ordinates, all multiplied by $\Delta x/3$.

16–12. MECHANICAL INTEGRATION

Devices exist which will mechanically integrate a curve. While such devices are beyond the scope of this text, one such instrument, the planimeter, is briefly described to indicate its potential. The planimeter determines the area contained within any boundary, and since it thus accomplishes a summation it is essentially a mechanical integrator. To use a planimeter, its tracing point is moved around the area in a clockwise direction until the perimeter of the area is traversed. During the tracing, a calibrated wheel, through a combination motion of slipping and rolling, records the area to some scale.

Problems

In the following problems, perform the graphical differentiation or integration utilizing any of the methods described in this chapter or that method assigned by the instructor.

DIFFERENTIATION

16–1. Plot the following data, and draw a smooth curve through the points. Construct the derivative curve.

x	y	x	y
0	0	4.5	4.47
0.5	1.00	5.0	4.60
1.0	1.70	5.5	4.64
1.5	2.30	6.0	4.60
2.0	2.80	6.5	4.40
2.5	3.27	7.0	4.00
3.0	3.65	7.5	3.45
3.5	4.00	8.0	2.80
4.0	4.25		

16–2. Plot the following data, and draw a smooth curve through the points. Construct the derivative curve.

x	y	x	y
0	−2.00	4.0	1.10
1.0	−1.52	5.0	2.00
2.0	−1.00	6.0	2.60
2.5	−0.60	7.0	2.83
3.0	0	8.0	2.56
3.5	0.60	9.0	1.00

16–3. Plot the curve, $y = \sin \theta$, for one complete cycle. (θ varies from 0 to 2π radians.) Determine the curve, $y = \cos \theta$, by graphical differentiation.

16–4. The following data were obtained during performance tests on an automobile. Draw the curve representing these data. Construct the acceleration (miles per hour per second) vs. time (seconds) graph.

Velocity (Miles per Hour)									
0	12	28	46	58	68	74	77	79	80
0	3	5	10	15	20	25	30	35	40
Time (Seconds)									

16–5. The following data represent work performed over a specified time interval. Plot the curve representing these data, and then construct the power curve. Express the power in horsepower. (1 hp. = 33,000 ft.-lb./min.) Power is defined as the rate of performing work.

Work (Foot-Pounds)	Time (Minutes)	Work (Foot-Pounds)	Time (Minutes)
100,000	1	42,000	6
96,500	2	33,000	7
86,000	3	26,000	8
70,000	4	22,000	9
54,000	5	20,000	10

16–6. A simply supported beam has a span of 10 feet, and supports a uniform load of 2,000 pounds per foot. Establish a curve which will show the deflection at any point along the beam. The modulus of elasticity, E, is 30×10^6 psi, and the moment of inertia, I, is 100 in.^{4}

16–7. A cantilever beam has a length of 10 feet, and supports a uniform load of 2,000 pounds per foot. The modulus of elasticity, E, is 30×10^6 psi, and the moment of inertia, I, is 100 in.^{4} Establish a curve which will show the deflection at any point along the beam. Determine the maximum deflection of the beam. At what point on the beam is the slope one-half the slope at the free end?

INTEGRATION

16–8. Using the data from Problem 16–1, draw the smooth curve representing the data. Determine the integral curve.

16–9. Using the data from Problem 16–2, draw the smooth curve representing the data. Determine the integral curve.

16–10. For the equation, $xy = 10$, determine the area bounded by the x-axis and the curve between the values of $x = 1$ and $x = 10$.

16–11. Using the data from Problem 16–4, draw the smooth curve representing the data. Determine the displacement vs. time curve for the automobile.

16–12. A force, acting on an object moving in a straight line, varies according to the following data. Graph these data, using force as the ordinate and distance as the abscissa. Construct the curve showing the total work, in foot-pounds, vs. the distance moved.

Force (Pounds)								
12.0	9.6	8.0	5.7	4.4	3.5	2.8	2.4	2.2
0	0.5	1.0	2.0	3.0	4.0	5.0	6.0	7.0
Distance (Feet)								

16–13. The acceleration of an object moving in a straight line is given by the equation $a = t + 1$, where a is the acceleration in feet per second^2 and t is the time in seconds. When $t = 0$, the velocity, v, is two feet per second and the distance traveled is zero. Plot the acceleration vs. time curve for the period from zero to six seconds. Construct the velocity vs. time and distance vs. time curves for the object.

16–14. The vertical displacement of a cam follower for one revolution of the cam is given by the following data. The cam makes one revolution every three seconds. Plot the smooth curve showing displacement vs. time. Construct the velocity vs. time curve and the acceleration vs. time curve for the follower during one revolution of the cam.

Rotation (Degrees)	Displacement (Inches)	Rotation (Degrees)	Displacement (Inches)
0	0	195	1.45
15	0.10	210	1.30
30	0.25	225	1.07
45	0.48	240	0.75
60	0.75	255	0.48
75	1.07	270	0.25
90	1.30	285	0.10
105	1.45	300	0
120	1.50	315	0
135	1.50	330	0
150	1.50	345	0
165	1.50	360	0
180	1.50		

17

NOMOGRAPHS—
GRAPHIC ANALOG
COMPUTERS

17-1. INTRODUCTION

A nomograph, in the broadest sense, is a graphic representation of numerical relations. Using this definition, the plot of any curve is a nomograph, since the plot graphically shows a direct numerical relationship. However, by common usage, the term "nomograph" is applied only to those graphs or diagrams which are primarily designed to enable the user actually to solve the numerical relationship.

Basically, a nomograph is a diagram upon which are drawn three graphic scales representing three related variables. These scales are positioned in such a manner that a straight line drawn between values of any two of the variables will intersect the third variable at the corresponding value. When more than three variables are involved, the answer is determined by using two variables to find a subresultant, combining that subresultant with a third variable to find a new subresultant, and continuing this procedure until the final result is determined. Fig. 17-1 shows an interesting nomograph involving five variables. Note how pairs of variables are combined to find subresultants. Note, also, that the scales of these subresultants are not identified by name or unit since the values are unimportant in the overall problem.

An analog computer is a device in which definite numbers are represented by measurable physical quantities. These quantities are continuous in effect, rather than discontinuous as are the actual numbers. Since the nomograph uses continuous graphic scales (as discussed in Art. 17-2), the nomograph is also a graphic form of an analog computer.

Since the construction of a nomograph for the solution of a numerical relationship is often more time-consuming than the solution by the use of conventional mathematics, the two most valuable uses of the nomograph occur (a) when the numerical relationship must be solved repeatedly, or (b) when the relationship must be solved by one lacking the mathematical background to handle the analytical solution. The use of nomographs has increased rapidly in recent years in engineering, science, and business because of the time saved under either of the two conditions of use listed above. The engineer and scientist should be familiar with nomog-

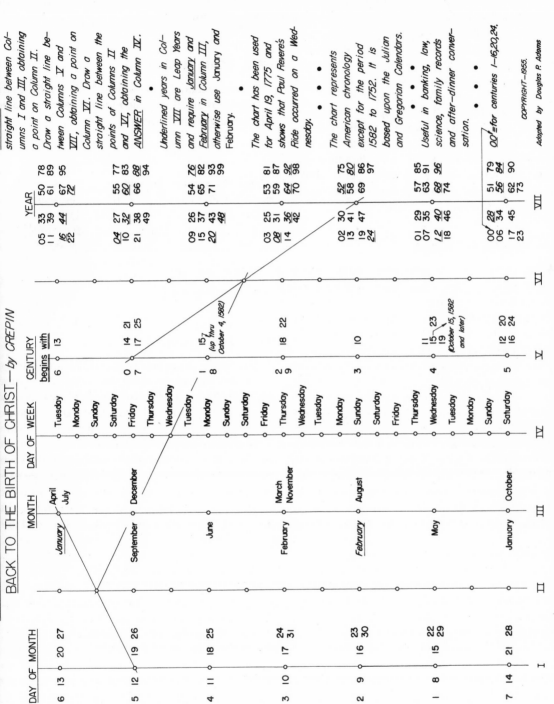

Fig. 17-1. Day of the week for any date of history. (By permission of Professor Douglas P. Adams, Massachusetts Institute of Technology.)

raphy so that they can know when the nomograph is the most appropriate of the various methods for problem solution and so that they can more effectively use an existing nomograph.

This chapter discusses the basic forms of the most common nomographs or graphic analog computers: the alignment diagram and special-purpose slide rules. The alignment diagram is so widely used that many people think that nomographs and alignment diagrams are synonymous. While it is true that all alignment diagrams are nomographs, it is not true that all nomographs are alignment diagrams. For a complete discussion of all the types of nomographs, the student should consult one of the standard texts on nomography.

17-2. FUNCTIONAL SCALES

A functional scale, in general, is simply a line along which are plotted values of a variable according to some system of measurement as in Fig. 17–2. Since nomography involves the graphical representation of numerical relations, the use of functional scales to represent a given numerical relation or function is required in any nomograph. Examples of functional scales exist everywhere in the world around us. A thermometer, a gasoline gage in an automobile, a measuring scale, and a slide rule are but a few examples. These scales may be either uniform or non-uniform. The common inch scale used in drawing is an example of a uniform scale, while the C- and D-scales of the slide rule are examples of non-uniform scales. Uniform and non-uniform scales are frequently referred to as linear and non-linear respectively. In any functional

scale, a given range of values of a variable, u, plotted along a given length of line according to th value of the function, $f(u)$.

17-3. SCALE MODULUS

The scale modulus, M, is merely the length on th scale for a unit value of the function of the variable The equation for the scale modulus is:

$$M_u = \frac{L}{f(u)_{max} - f(u)_{min}}, \qquad (17-\mathbf{1}$$

where M_u = the scale modulus of the u-scale, L = the scale length, $f(u)_{max}$ = the highest value of th function of u, and $f(u)_{min}$ = the lowest value c the function of u. It is important to understan that these are the highest and lowest values of th function of u, and that these values do not nece sarily correspond to the highest and lowest value of the variable itself.

17-4. SCALE EQUATION

The scale equation is the equation used t determine distances along the scale for variou values of the variable, where the distances ar measured from one end of the line. If the range c values of the variable u started at the value whic yields a zero value of the function, the scale equa tion would be only the scale modulus multiplied b the value of the function. However, in some case the range of values might start at a positive c negative value. Under this condition, the physic zero end of the line coincides with the location c

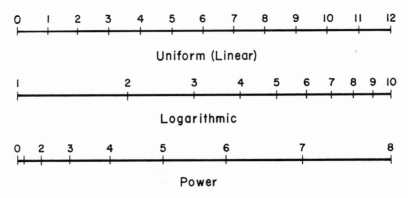

Fig. **17–2.** Functional scales.

ome real value of the variable. Hence the scale equation must be written as:

$$S_u = M_u \left[f(u) - f(u)_{min} \right], \qquad (17\text{-}2)$$

where S_u = distance along the scale to any value of the variable u.

17–5. LAYOUT OF FUNCTIONAL SCALES

The actual layout or construction of a functional scale is best illustrated by an example. Consider the case of $f(u) = u^2$ where u ranges from 1 through 7. It is desired to plot this range of values on a line 6″ long.

The first step in the construction of the functional scale is to determine the scale modulus using Eq. 17–1 (see Art. 17–3):

$$M_u = \frac{L}{f(u)_{max} - f(u)_{min}}.$$

In the case being considered, $f(u)_{max} = 49$ at $u = 7$, and $f(u)_{min} = 1$ at $u = 1$. Therefore the scale modulus is:

$$M_u = \frac{6}{49 - 1} = \frac{6}{48} = 0.125 \text{ inch per unit.}$$

Next, the scale equation is determined using Eq. 17–2, shown in Art. 17–4:

$$S_u = M_u \left[f(u) - f(u)_{min} \right].$$

In the case being considered, this equation becomes:

$$S_u = 0.125 \left[u^2 - 1 \right].$$

Using this equation, distances along the scale are calculated. When determining these distances, it is common to use tables as shown in Fig. 17–3. When all desired S_u distances (or distances along the scale for various values of u) are determined, then the functional scale can be laid out as in Fig. 17–4.

Among those who are experienced in the design of functional scales, it is common procedure to assume a convenient scale modulus first and then determine the scale length. However, beginners frequently find that they end with scale lines that are too long for the paper on which they are working. It is for this reason that the examples in this chapter start with the assumption of a scale length.

17–6. GRAPHICAL CONSTRUCTION OF FUNCTIONAL SCALES

While previously described methods can be used in the construction of any functional scale, there are shortcuts that can be used for certain functions. As can be seen in the examples throughout this chap-

u	u^2	u^2-1	S_u $0.125\,(u^2-1)$
1	1	0	0.000″
2	4	3	0.375″
3	9	8	1.000″
4	16	15	1.875″
5	25	24	3.000″
6	36	35	4.375″
7	49	48	6.000″

Fig. 17–3.   Table for calculating scale distances for $f(u) = u^2$.

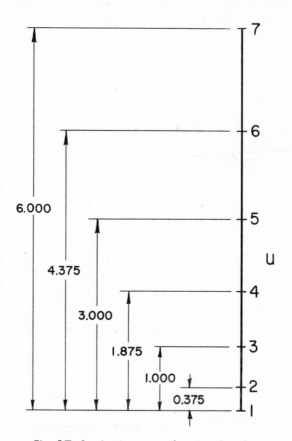

Fig. 17–4.   Laying out a functional scale.

ter, the majority of the functional scales used are either uniform, logarithmic, power, or trigonometric functions. The first three of these scales can be easily constructed by graphical means. It should be remembered, however, that graphical construction has more inherent sources of error than the method of calculating distances and then laying them off along the scale as described in Art. 17-5. In the method of calculating the required distances, the only inherent source of error is in marking off the exact distance. When graphical construction is used, there are additional sources of error; i.e., the lines used to project values onto the scale might not be precisely parallel. However, theoretically the graphical methods are just as accurate as the mathematical, and, if the designer exercises due care, they will give very acceptable results.

The easiest system of graphically laying out a functional scale is to adjust the scale length so that the divisions of commercially prepared graph sheets can be directly transferred to the scale length. However, when designing a functional

scale to fit within a given space, this is sometime not a practical solution. When this situation oc curs, the method of graphically dividing a line int proportional parts can be used.

The theory of graphically dividing a line int proportional parts is based on similar triangles an is illustrated in Fig. 17-5. Fig. 17-5(a) shows a lin AB. It is desired to divide the line AB into tw parts so that the ratio of the whole length to one o the parts is in the ratio of X : Y. The length of A is such that direct measurements cannot easily b made. The first step in the solution is shown i Fig. 17-5(b). A second line is drawn at any angl to the first line and direct measurements of value X and Y are laid off along this second line establish ing points M and N. Now points M and A are con nected by a straight line and then a line is draw through point N parallel to line MA, establishin point C as in Fig. 17-5(c). Triangle ABM is simila to triangle CBN and hence:

$$\frac{BA}{BC} = \frac{BM}{BN} = \frac{X}{Y}.$$

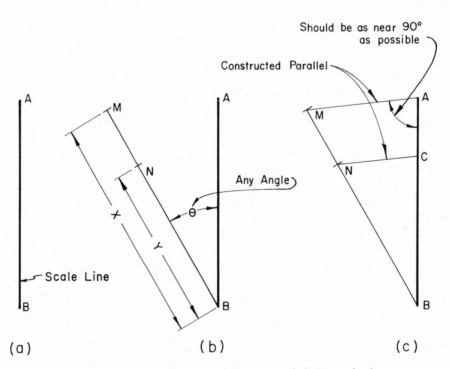

Fig. **17-5.** Theory of graphical proportional division of a line.

The line AB is therefore divided as originally desired.

The greatest accuracy in this construction is attained when the angles between the rays MA and NC (Fig. 17-5) and the scale line AB are close to $90°$. Angle θ and the scale used to measure the distances X and Y should be varied so as to achieve this perpendicular or nearly perpendicular relationship between the rays and the scale line.

The graphical construction to make a functional scale for $f(u) = \log u$ where u varies from 2 to 25 is shown in Fig. 17-6. First, a scale line is drawn at any length desired. A sheet of commercial log paper is then placed at some angle to the scale line and positioned so that the 2 in one cycle coincides with one end of the scale line. Next, a line is drawn from 25 (in the next cycle) to the other end of the

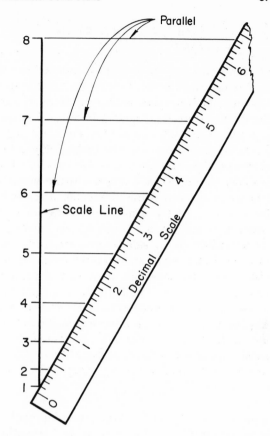

Fig. **17-7.** Graphical construction of a power scale.

scale line. All other desired values are projected onto the scale line with projectors parallel to the first projector. The result is a functional scale with values of u plotted according to $\log u$.

Often a functional scale is needed to represent some power function such as $f(u) = u^2$ where u varies from 1 to 8. Such a scale is shown in Fig. 17-7. Again the first step is to lay off a scale line of any desired length. Next, a decimal scale is placed at some angle to the scale line and positioned so that the 0.1″ (representing the square of 1) on the scale coincides with one end of the scale. Distances representing the square of the desired values of u are now marked off along the decimal scale as shown. The 6.4″ (representing the square of 8) is projected to the end of the scale line and all other desired values are then projected in a parallel direction. The result is a functional scale with values of u plotted according to the square of u.

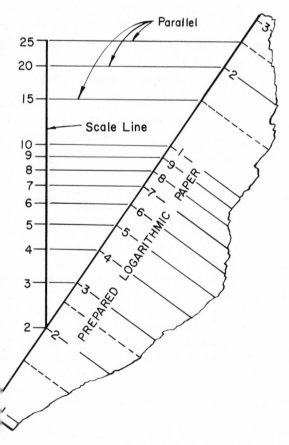

Fig. **17-6.** Graphical construction of a logarithmic scale.

17–7. ADJACENT SCALE CONVERSION DIAGRAMS

A functional scale is in itself of little value. It is only when one functional scale is used in conjunction with other functional scales or with some index that the scales are of any practical value. The dial of a voltmeter is an example of the use of a single functional scale, but it would be useless without the indexing needle to show what value to read. The adjacent scale conversion diagram is the simplest example of the actual use of functional scales in nomography. As the name implies, the adjacent scale conversion diagram is simply two functional scales placed side by side so as to maintain the integrity of some mathematical relationship. In so doing, it becomes possible to convert a quantity measured in one set of units to the same quantity measured in a different set of units. A common example is the conversion of temperature from degrees Fahrenheit to degrees Centigrade. The mathematical conversion formula is:

$$C° = \frac{F° - 32}{1.8}.$$

A conversion diagram for this relationship, with F varying from 0° to 140°, can be set up mathematically. The high and low values of C can be calculated:

$$C_{max} = \frac{140 - 32}{1.8} = 60.000°$$

$$C_{min} = \frac{0 - 32}{1.8} = -17.778°.$$

Therefore the values of F, to be plotted on one side of the scale, will range from 0° to 140° and the values of C, to be plotted on the other side of the scale, will range from -17.778° to 60.000°.

Since C ranges from a negative to a positive value, subsequent calculations will be simplified by first determining the modulus of the C-scale using Eq. 17–1. If a scale length of 8″ is assumed, then:

$$M_C = \frac{8}{60.000 - (-17.778)} = \frac{8}{77.778}$$
$$= 0.1028 \text{ inch per unit.}$$

This is not a convenient value for M_C since every calculation of a scale distance involves multiplying by M_C. Therefore, in order to simplify multiplication, assume $M_C = 0.100$. This assumption

means that the scale length of the maximum valu is no longer 8.00″, and a new value must b calculated:

$$L = 0.100 (77.778) = 7.778″,$$

which is reasonably close to 8.00″. The scal equation (17–2) now becomes:

$$S_C = 0.100 [C - (-17.778)]$$
$$= 0.100(C + 17.778$$

Distances along the scale line for various values c C can now be determined as in Fig. 17–8(a).

Since values of F are also to be plotted along thi same scale line, the modulus of the F-scale is:

$$M_F = \frac{7.778}{140 - 0} = 0.05556 \text{ inch per unit.}$$

This modulus cannot be adjusted because the C and F-scales are related and the scale length ha been determined through the calculations for th C-scale. In other words, C was chosen as the inde pendent variable and therefore F is the dependen variable. Hence the scale equation is:

$$S_F = 0.05556 (F - 0) = 0.05556 F.$$

Distances along the scale line for various values c F can now be determined as in Fig. 17–8(b). Th completed adjacent scale conversion diagram i shown in Fig. 17–9.

17–8. GRAPHICAL CONSTRUCTION OF ADJACENT SCALE DIAGRAMS

A faster way to construct the same conversior diagram as in the previous article is to determine both scales graphically as discussed in Art. 17–6 Again, it must be remembered that care in plotting and construction must be exercised in order to achieve comparable accuracy with the mathemati cal method. The first step is shown in Fig. 17–10 where a vertical line is drawn at any convenient length. Then a construction line is drawn at some arbitrary angle with the vertical line. This con struction line is then divided into twenty-eight equal lengths (140° in 5° increments) by the use of some convenient scale. In Fig. 17–10(a) a con struction line 7″ long is used, since 7″ can be thought of as being twenty-eight $\frac{1}{4}$″ increments. The twenty-eighth division is connected with the end of the vertical line and the other divisions are

F	S_F
F	0.05556F
0	0.000
10	0.556
20	1.111
30	1.667
40	2.222
50	2.778
60	3.334
70	3.889
80	4.445
90	5.000
100	5.556
110	6.112
120	6.667
130	7.223
140	7.778

C	C+17.778	S_C 0.100(C+17.778)
-10	7.778	0.778
0	17.778	1.778
10	27.778	2.778
20	37.778	3.778
30	47.778	4.778
40	57.778	5.778
50	67.778	6.778
60	77.778	7.778

(a)

(b)

Fig. 17–8. Tables calculating scale distances for converting Fahrenheit to Centigrade.

projected by parallel projectors to the vertical line. Thus the vertical line is divided into twenty-eight equal lengths. These graduations are for temperature in degrees Fahrenheit from 0° to 140° in increments of 5°.

To determine points on the Centigrade scale, two conversions must be calculated. These points should be far enough apart to insure accuracy. One should be in the upper range of values and the other in the lower range. It is an advantage, but not a requirement, to choose conversion points that convert to whole values. The points chosen are F = 140° and F = 40°. At F = 40°,

$$C = \frac{40 - 32}{1.8} = \frac{8}{1.8} = 4.444° \text{ C};$$

and at F = 140°,

$$C = \frac{140 - 32}{1.8} = 60.000° \text{ C}.$$

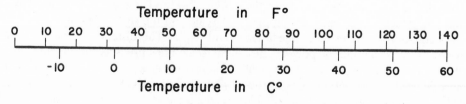

Fig. 17–9. Adjacent scale conversion diagram for converting Fahrenheit to Centigrade.

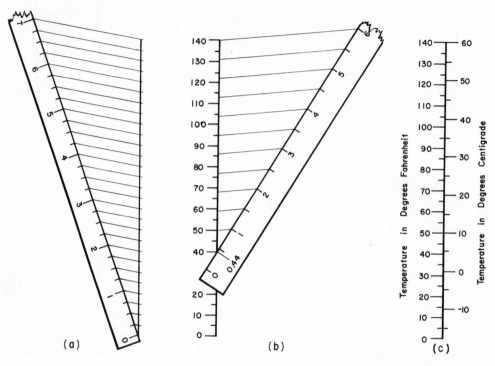

Fig. 17–10. Graphical construction of an adjacent scale conversion diagram.

A decimal scale is then placed at some angle with the conversion scale [Fig. 17–10(b)] with 0.444″ (to correspond to 4.44°) on the scale aligned with 40° F on the conversion scale. Then 6.00″ (to correspond to 60°) is projected to 140° F on the conversion scale and all other points projected parallel to this projector. In this case, every 0.50″ mark is projected giving a Centigrade scale reading to the nearest 5°. The portion of the Centigrade scale lying below 40° F can be located by extending the decimal scale to the left and projecting back to the right, or by using dividers to step off the required divisions. The complete adjacent scale conversion diagram is shown in Fig. 17–10(c).

In this example, both scales have been uniformly divided. That this is true can be seen from the given formula in which both variables appear linearly. Other equations could result in one linear and one power scale, or both might be power scales. An examination of the equations reveals the type of scale that must be used. The method of construction would be the same for any two-variable equation.

17–9. PARALLEL SCALE ALIGNMENT DIAGRAMS

The parallel scale alignment diagram is a nomograph that will solve any relationship involving the sum (or difference) of two variables; i.e., $f(x) \pm f(y) = f(z)$. Since multiplication becomes a process of addition when the variables are written in logarithmic form, the parallel scale alignment diagram can also solve relationships of the form $f(x) \cdot f(y) = f(z)$ if the relationship is rewritten as $\log f(x) + \log f(y) = \log f(z)$. The theory of these diagrams is based on the use of similar triangles. Two parallel functional scales of different moduli are drawn an arbitrary distance apart as in Fig. 17–11. These are named the X-scale and the Y-scale and the scale markings show values of $f(x)$ and $f(y)$. The distance between the divisions on the scale lines presents the modulus of each scale. A third scale, Z, is to be drawn such that $f(z) = f(x) + f(y)$. Here X and Y are the independent variables and Z is the dependent variable. The first step is to draw lines between two sets of values or x and y that result in the same value of z. In this case, lines are drawn between sets $f(x) = 3$, $f(y) = 7$ and $f(x) = 4$, $f(y) = 6$ giving $f(z) = 10$ for both sets. The intersection of these two lines must be a point on the Z-scale. If this process is repeated for other values of $f(z)$, the Z-scale will be found to be a line parallel to the X- and Y-scales. The distance between 3 and 4 on the X-scale represents the modulus of the X-scale, and the distance between 6 and 7 on the Y-scale represents the modulus of the Y-scale. Calling the distance between the X- and Z-scales a and the distance between the Y- and Z-scales b, by similar triangles:

$$\frac{M_x}{M_y} = \frac{a}{b}, \text{ or } a = \frac{M_x b}{M_y}. \qquad (17\text{–}3)$$

Now consider the lines joining sets $f(x) = 0$, $f(y) = 0$ and $f(x) = 1$, $f(y) = 0$. These would give values of $f(z)$ of 0 and 1. Again the distance between 0 and 1 on the X-scale represents the modulus of the X-scale and the distance between 0 and 1 on the Z-scale represents the modulus of the Z-scale. By similar triangles:

$$\frac{M_z}{M_x} = \frac{b}{a + b}, \text{ or } M_z = \frac{M_x b}{a + b}. \qquad (17\text{–}4)$$

Substitute for a in Eq. 17–4 the value found in Eq. 17–3,

$$M_z = \frac{M_x b}{\frac{M_x b}{M_y} + b}, \qquad (17\text{–}5)$$

$$M_z = \frac{M_x b}{\frac{M_x b + M_y b}{M_y}} \qquad (17\text{–}6)$$

$$= \left[\frac{M_x b}{1} \right] \left[\frac{M_y}{b(M_x + M_y)} \right], \qquad (17\text{–}7)$$

and finally:

$$M_z = \frac{M_x M_y}{M_x + M_y}. \qquad (17\text{–}8)$$

The use of Eqs. 17–3 and 17–8 makes possible the construction of parallel scale alignment diagrams to handle any equation of the form $f(z) = f(x) \pm f(y)$. If the equation were $f(z) = f(x) - f(y)$, the functional scale representing values of y would be inverted as in Fig. 17–12. In either case, the scale for the dependent variable (z) is the middle scale.

Although many alignment diagrams are drawn with all scale lines of equal length, this is not a necessary condition. Each scale line can be selected for the length that will make the scale readable to the precision desired. One reason that many alignment diagrams are drawn with equal-length scale lines is the desire for eye-pleasing symmetry. However, a nomograph is a problem-solving device; readability should not be sacrificed for symmetry.

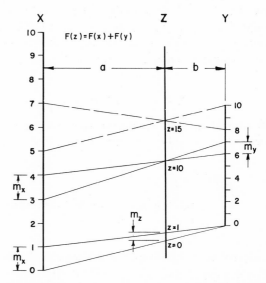

Fig. **17–11.** The theory of parallel scale alignment diagrams.

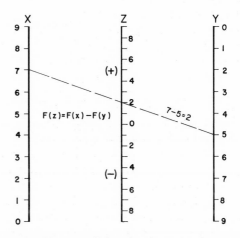

Fig. **17–12.** Parallel scale alignment diagram for $f(z) = f(x) - f(y)$.

Many equations in the engineering-science areas involve multiplication rather than addition. An equation of the form $f(z) = f(x) \cdot f(y)$ can be handled by the parallel scale alignment diagram if the equation is first transformed into logarithmic form: $\log f(z) = \log f(x) + \log f(y)$. A specific example of this type of equation is:

$$I = Ak^2,$$

where I = moment of inertia in inches^4, A = area in square inches, and k = radius of gyration in inches. The values of both A and k are to range from 1 to 10, with scale lengths of 8". With this range of A and k, the range of I is from 1 to 1,000. The first step in the construction of the parallel scale alignment diagram is to rewrite the equation as:

$$\log I = \log A + 2 \log k.$$

The moduli of the scales for the independent variables can now be determined using Eq. 17-1:

$$M_A = \frac{8}{\log 10 - \log 1} = \frac{8}{1 - 0}$$
$$= 8.000 \text{ inches/cycle.}$$

$$M_k = \frac{8}{2(\log 10 - \log 1)} = \frac{8}{2}$$
$$= 4.000 \text{ inches/cycle.}$$

Then, using Eq. 17-8, the modulus of the dependent variable is:

$$M_I = \frac{M_A M_k}{M_A + M_k} = \frac{(4)(8)}{4 + 8} = \frac{32}{12} =$$
$$2.667 \text{ inches/cycle.}$$

Even though the calculated modulus of the I-scale is not as convenient to use in multiplication as would be a whole number, this modulus cannot be changed because I, in this example, is the dependent variable. However, the moduli of the two outside scales (A and k) can be changed, if desired, prior to the determination of the modulus of the dependent (I) scale since they are the scales for the independent variables.

The relative position of the I-scale can be determined by using Eq. 17-3:

$$\frac{M_A}{M_k} = \frac{8}{4} = \frac{2}{1} = \frac{a}{b}$$

In other words, the distance from the A-scale to the I-scale will be twice the distance from the k-scale to the I-scale. If the distance between the A- and k-scales is 6", the I-scale will be 4" from the A-scale and 2" from the k-scale.

Now, using Eq. 17-2, scale equations can be set up for each scale and distances along the scale calculated for desired values of each variable. The three scale equations are:

$$S_A = 8 [\log A - \log 1] = 8 [\log A - 0]$$
$$= 8 \log A.$$
$$S_k = 4 [2 \log k - 2 \log 1] = 8 [\log k - 0]$$
$$= 8 \log k.$$
$$S_I = 2.667 [\log I - \log 1] = 2.667 [\log I - 0]$$
$$= 2.667 \log I.$$

These calculations would probably best be accomplished in tabular form as in Fig. 17-13. Note that, though the actual moduli of the A- and k-scales are different, the scale equations for both variables show the same effective modulus. (The effective

$$S_A = 8 \log A$$
$$S_k = 8 \log k$$

$$S_I = 2.667 \log I$$

A & k	log	S
1.0	0.00000	0.000"
1.5	0.17609	1.409"
2.0	0.30103	2.408"
2.5	0.39794	3.184"
. . .	. . . . . .	. . . .
10.0	1.00000	8.000"

I	log	S_I
1.0	0.00000	0.000"
1.5	0.17609	0.470"
2.0	0.30103	0.803"
2.5	0.39794	1.061"
. . . .	. . . . . .	. . . .
1000	3.00000	8.000"

Fig. **17-13.** Tables for calculating scale distances, $I = Ak^2$.

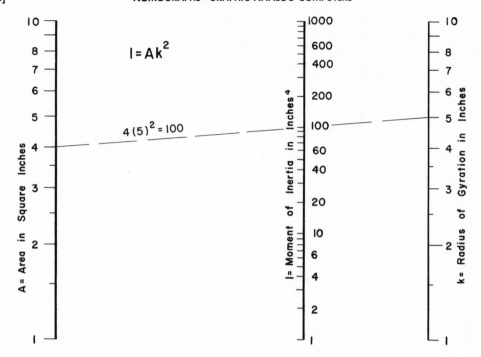

Fig. **17-14.** A parallel scale alignment diagram for $I = Ak^2$.

modulus is the actual modulus multiplied by any constants in the scale equation.)   When this occurs it must be remembered that the actual scale moduli, not the effective moduli, are used in calculating the modulus and position of the third (in this case, I) scale through the use of Eqs. 17–3 and 17–8.

The completed nomograph (a parallel scale alignment diagram) is shown in Fig. 17–14.   Of particular importance is the fact that the unit of measure for each scale is labeled along the scale both by letter symbol and words describing what the letter symbol means, to include the unit of measure.   Also, the formula for which the nomograph is a solution must be included somewhere on the drawing together with a sample solution line for a specific case.   The nomograph is valueless without this information.

Note that this nomograph could be used to solve numerically any equation of the form: $Z = XY^2$. This is true only because all the variables are expressed in terms of the same units (inches). However, if the variables had been expressed in units that differed (e.g., inches and feet or feet and meters), the effect would be to introduce a hidden

constant into the equation.   (The effect of a constant is discussed in the next article, Art. 17–10.) Therefore, it is good practice not to use a given nomograph for any solution other than its intended application.

If the equation to be solved were of the form $f(z) = f(x)/f(y)$, it could be handled in two ways. First, the equation could be rewritten as $f(z) \cdot f(y) = f(x)$, and the nomograph designed as previously discussed.   Secondly, leaving the equation in its given form, the nomograph can be designed as follows.   Write the equation in logarithmic form: $\log f(z) = \log f(x) - \log f(y)$.   The negative sign indicates an inversed scale for $f(y)$ and the nomograph would then appear as in Fig. 17–15.

17-10. EFFECT OF A CONSTANT ON A PARALLEL SCALE ALIGNMENT DIAGRAM

The effect on a nomograph of the addition of a constant in the given equation is a vertical displacement of the dependent (middle) scale.   This can best be illustrated by an example.   Suppose that

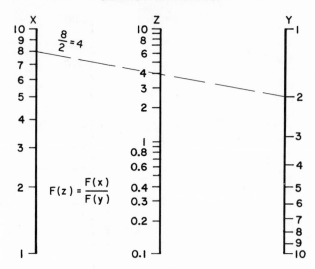

Fig. 17-15. A parallel scale alignment diagram for $f(z) = f(x)/f(y)$.

the equation just considered ($I = Ak^2$) had, instead, been:

$$I = \frac{Ak^2}{2}.$$

The range of A and k is again to be from 1 to 10 with scale lengths of 8″, as in the previous example. However, the range of I is now from 0.5 to 500.

In designing a nomograph it is customary to associate the constant with the dependent variable. Hence, the given equation would be rewritten as $2I = Ak^2$, and in logarithmic form would be:

$$\log I + \log 2 = \log A + 2\log k.$$

Since the right-hand side of this equation is identical to the right-hand side of the logarithmic form of the equation previously discussed ($I = Ak^2$), the moduli of the A- and k-scales are the same in both examples and hence the modulus of the I-scale is the same. Therefore the scale equations of the A- and k-scales would also be unchanged from those in the previous example and the relative distances of the I-scale from the A- and k-scales would remain unchanged. However, the scale equation of the I-scale would be changed because $f(I) = \log I + \log 2$. Hence:

$$S_I = 2.667\,[(\log I + \log 2) - (\log 0.5 + \log 2)]$$

or

$$S_I = 2.667\,[\log I + \log 2 - \log 0.5 - \log 2]$$
$$= 2.667\,[\log I - \log 0.5]$$
$$= 2.667\,[\log \frac{I}{0.5}].$$

The various distances along the I-scale could be determined and the completed nomograph would appear as in Fig. 17-16. Compare Figs. 17-14 and 17-16. Note that in Fig. 17-16 the scales are not identified as to units. This identification is purposely omitted because the equation $I = Ak^2/2$ is meaningless except as an example. The only effect of a given constant is on the scale equation of the dependent (middle) scale. A constant (placed as in the given equation) whose value is less than one displaces the dependent scale upward; while a constant whose value is greater than one, displaces the dependent scale downward.

17-11. GRAPHICAL CONSTRUCTION FOR PARALLEL SCALE ALIGNMENT DIAGRAMS

Just as a functional scale or an adjacent scale diagram can be constructed graphically, so can parallel scale alignment diagrams be constructed graphically. Again consider the equation:

$$I = Ak^2,$$

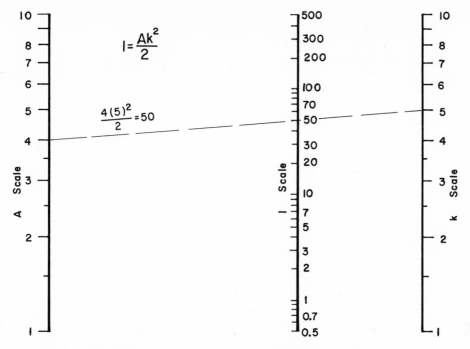

Fig. **17-16.** Effect of a constant on a parallel scale alignment diagram.

where I = moment of inertia in inches^4 and ranges from 1 to 1,000, A = area in square inches and ranges from 1 to 10, and k = radius of gyration and also ranges from 1 to 10. Rewriting in logarithmic form:

$$\log I = \log A + 2 \log k,$$

it can be seen that all scales are logarithmic. All scales are graduated in the same direction since there are no negative signs. The first step is to draw two parallel lines of any length and any distance apart. Project logarithmic scales onto these lines as discussed in Art. 17-6, and name one line the A-scale, and the other line the k-scale. In Fig. 17-17(a), both the A- and k-scales are graduated from 1 to 10. Dependent upon the conditions desired to be covered by the nomograph, the A- and k-scales could each have a different range of values. The next step is to draw in some "solution lines" which represent solutions of the given equation. At least two "solution lines" must represent the same solution. In Fig. 17-17(b), two "solution lines" are drawn representing the solution $I = 100$.

Other "solution lines" are drawn for I = 1,000, 10, and 1. Since the form of the nomograph is to be a parallel scale alignment diagram, the direction of the I-scale is known. The intersection of the two "solution lines" for $I = 100$ fixes the position of the I-scale and one "solution point" on it. The line that is to be the I-scale can now be drawn and its intersections with the other "solution lines" marked as in Fig. 17-17(b). Since the I-scale is a logarithmic scale, there is now a check on the accuracy of construction, because the distances from 1 to 10, from 10 to 100, and from 100 to 1,000 must be identical. This is true because these distances are all one complete logarithmic cycle, measured on the same scale. After these distances are checked for accuracy, the logarithmic scale divisions can be projected graphically onto the I-scale, all scales properly identified, and the nomograph is complete as in Fig. 17-17(c).

While in this example the "solution points" located on the dependent scale (I-scale) are one full logarithmic cycle apart, this is not necessary and sometimes not even possible. It is advantageous

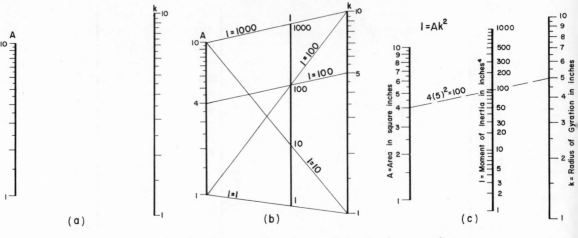

Fig. **17–17.** Graphical construction of a parallel scale alignment diagram.

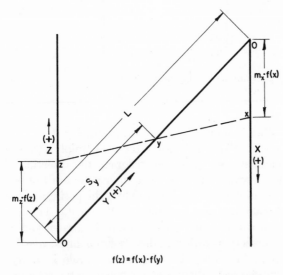

Fig. **17–18.** Theory of the N-scale alignment diagram.

because of the simplicity of the check. However, points that are not a full cycle apart are checked when the logarithmic divisions are projected onto the scale. Three points on the scale are required in any case to check the accuracy of construction.

The advantages of this method are its rapidity and simplicity. Very few calculations need be performed. There is no need for scale equations or scale moduli. The position of the third scale need not be calculated, and there is an early accuracy check.

The disadvantages are the inherent human inaccuracies that occur in any graphic construction. Unless great care is maintained, the results will not be satisfactory. Hence the construction must be executed with great care, using sharp, fine lines drawn with a hard (preferably 6H or harder), well-sharpened pencil.

17–12. N-SCALE ALIGNMENT DIAGRAMS

Another form of nomograph commonly used for the solution of the three-variable relationship, $f(z) = f(x) \cdot f(y)$, is the N-scale alignment diagram (sometimes called the Z-scale alignment diagram). The theory of this form of nomograph is based on the use of similar triangles and is developed as follows.

Assume that, as in Fig. 17–18, two parallel lines are drawn any distance apart and functional scales for $f(z)$ and $f(x)$ are laid off in opposite directions. The only restriction is that both scales must start from zero in order to simplify the scale equation of each scale. These two zero points are to be connected by a line which is to be graduated according to $f(y)$ such that: $f(z) = f(x) \cdot f(y)$. The scale equations of the Z- and X-scales, since they start at zero, are simply $S_z = M_z \cdot f(z)$ and $S_x = M_x \cdot f(x)$. However, the scale equation of the Y-scale must be determined. Suppose that a straight line joins points $f(z)$ and $f(x)$ in Fig. 17–18 and intersects the diagonal at a point $f(y)$ so that the equation $f(z) = f(x) \cdot f(y)$ is satisfied. Then by similar triangles:

$$\frac{S_y}{L - S_y} = \frac{M_z \cdot f(z)}{M_x \cdot f(x)} . \qquad (17\text{-}9)$$

If

$$f(z) = f(x) \cdot f(y), \qquad (17\text{-}10)$$

then

$$\frac{f(z)}{f(x)} = f(y) . \qquad (17\text{-}11)$$

By substitution of Eq. 17–11 into Eq. 17–9:

$$\frac{S_y}{L - S_y} = \frac{M_z \cdot f(y)}{M_x} . \qquad (17\text{-}12)$$

Inverting Eq. 17–12 and adding 1 to both sides,

$$\frac{L - S_y}{S_y} + \frac{S_y}{S_y} = \frac{M_x}{M_z \cdot f(y)} + \frac{M_z \cdot f(y)}{M_z \cdot f(y)} . \qquad (17\text{-}13)$$

Then

$$\frac{L}{S_y} = \frac{M_x + M_z \cdot f(y)}{M_z \cdot f(y)} . \qquad (17\text{-}14)$$

Solving for S_y,

$$S_y = \frac{L \cdot M_z \cdot f(y)}{M_x + M_z \cdot f(y)} . \qquad (17\text{-}15)$$

Using this scale equation, distances along the Y-scale (diagonal) can be determined for any value of y. Note that, although Eq. 17–15 involves a number of terms, the equation would be much more complicated if the X- and Z-scales started at some value other than zero.

Certain features of the N-scale alignment diagram must be remembered. The two parallel scales can be either linear or power scales according to the function of the variable that they represent, since the nomograph is designed to perform multiplication without the necessity of resorting to logarithms. Because of the development of the N-scale nomograph, as just presented, the following statements are true.

1. One of the parallel scales is always the product scale, $f(z)$.
2. Both parallel scales must include the zero point (at least in the design of the graph).
3. The two parallel scales are always graduated in opposite directions.
4. The diagonal scale always connects the zero point of the product scale with the zero point of the other parallel scale.
5. The zero point of the diagonal scale always coincides with the zero point of the product scale.

Other configurations for the N-scale alignment diagram are shown in Fig. 17–19. Actually, Fig. 17–19(b) is merely Fig. 17–18 held upside down, and the only accomplishment in so doing is to move the dependent variable scale to the right side of the nomograph. The form shown in Fig. 17–19(a) can

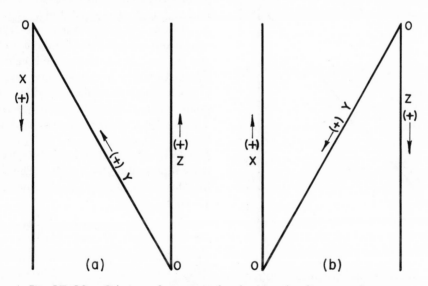

Fig. 17–19. Other configurations for the N-scale alignment diagram.

also be held upside down and, again, the only effect is to move the location of the scale for the dependent variable.

17–13. GRAPHICAL CONSTRUCTION FOR N-SCALE ALIGNMENT DIAGRAMS

The difficulty with the method just discussed is the complexity of calculations for distances along the diagonal scale. This can be simplified by the following device which, again, is developed through the use of similar triangles.

Assume, as in Fig. 17–20, that the two parallel scales have been laid out for the variables Z and X. Select a fixed point on the multiplier scale (X-scale) whose distance is measured in inches from the zero point of the scale. Then assume that a false Y-scale is superimposed on the product scale (Z-scale) in such a manner that a line joining some y' on the false scale will intersect the diagonal scale at the true position of y. Then by similar triangles,

$$\frac{S'_y}{P} = \frac{S_y}{L - S_y}. \qquad (17\text{--}16)$$

From Eq. 17–12 of Art. 17–12,

$$\frac{S_y}{L - S_y} = \frac{M_z \cdot f(y)}{M_x},$$

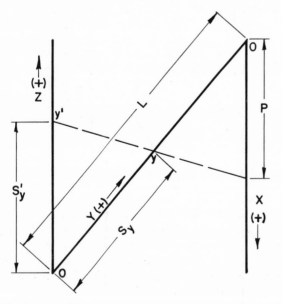

Fig. 17–20. Theory of the graphical construction of an N-scale alignment diagram.

and by substitution

$$\frac{S'_y}{P} = \frac{M_z}{M_x} \cdot f(y), \qquad (17\text{--}17)$$

or

$$S'_y = \left[P \cdot \frac{M_z}{M_x} \right] f(y). \qquad (17\text{--}18)$$

The simplicity of this method should be apparent through a comparison of Eqs. 17–15 and 17–18. The value of the expression within the brackets in Eq. 17–18 becomes a constant and the scale equation for the false scale becomes simply a constant times the function of the variable. Now the determination of scale distances on the diagonal scale becomes a matter of constructing a simple false scale superimposed on the product scale. Then the divisions of the false scale are connected by rays to a fixed point P selected on the other parallel scale. The intersections of the rays and the diagonal scale mark the actual divisions on the diagonal scale. In some cases the false scale may run off the paper, or may cause poor intersections (intersections at too small an angle) with the diagonal scale. In such an instance, choose a new distance P and determine a new constant for the false scale. Increasing the distance to the fixed point increases the distance between divisions on the false scale; decreasing the distance has the opposite effect.

Fig. 17–21 illustrates the above method applied to the construction of an N-scale alignment diagram for the equation $I = Ak^2$. This is the equation of Art. 17–9 where A and k range from 1 to 10 and I from 1 to 1,000. First, two parallel lines are drawn and graduated for I and A as in Fig. 17–21(a) and the modulus of each scale is calculated. Note that both scales are linear since each variable has a linear function in the equation. Then a fixed point on the A-scale is arbitrarily selected and the distance from the zero end of the A-scale is measured as P inches as in Fig. 17–21(b). Next, a false k-scale is calculated and plotted on the line originally representing the I-scale. The scale equation for this false k-scale, as determined using Eq. 17–18, is:

$$S'_k = \left[P \cdot \frac{M_I}{M_A} \right] k^2.$$

This false scale is also shown in Fig. 17–21(b). After plotting this false k-scale, rays are drawn from the points on the false scale to the fixed point on the

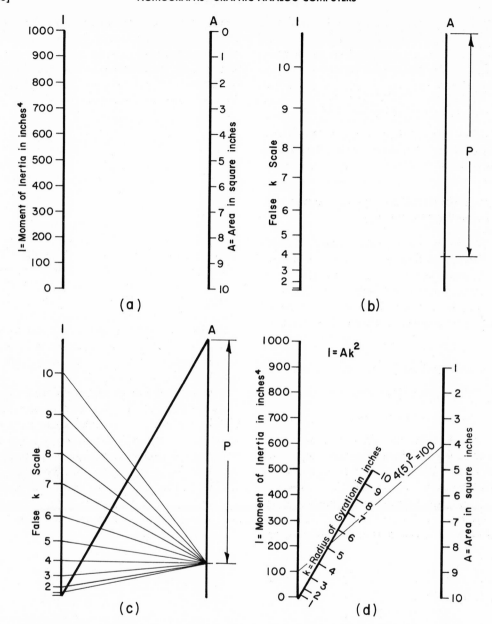

Fig. **17–21.** An N-scale alignment diagram for $I = Ak^2$ (graphical construction).

A-scale as in Fig. 17–21(c). The points where these rays intersect the diagonal scale are marked and labeled, fixing the real k-scale. The completed nomograph is shown in Fig. 17–21(d). Note that the unused portion of the diagonal and the zero point on the A-scale have been omitted since they were not required for the range of values specified. This is common practice and often results in a nomograph which causes the uninitiated to wonder how the scales were derived. However, to the nomographer the N-scale nomograph is as understandable as the parallel scale nomograph. Compare the nomograph of Fig. 17–21(d) with that of Fig. 17–17(c) or Fig. 17–14.

There is no great advantage in using an N-scale nomograph to solve a three-variable relationship, except for the fact that the two parallel scales do not have to be logarithmically graduated. Actually, there is some disadvantage in that the diagonal scale is often harder to interpret between divisions. Also, if the range of the variables plotted on the two parallel scales is between two relatively high values, a large portion of the scales will be unusable. However, in certain types of equations there is a definite advantage in using this form of nomograph, as is discussed in the next article.

17–14. ALIGNMENT DIAGRAMS FOR MORE THAN THREE VARIABLES

When an equation has more than three variables, the equation can be changed into a series of equations, each having three variables. Then, by combining alignment diagrams to solve each of a series of equations, the solution of the original equation is attained. For example, consider the equation

$$f(u) \cdot f(v) \cdot f(w) = f(z). \quad (17\text{–}19)$$

This can be changed into a pair of equations:

$$f(u) \cdot f(v) = T; \quad (17\text{–}20)$$

$$T \cdot f(w) = f(z). \quad (17\text{–}21)$$

These can be solved by two parallel scale alignment diagrams as in Fig. 17–22 where line 1 represents a solution of Eq. 17–20 and line 2 represents the corresponding solution of Eq. 17–21. Taken as a whole, the diagram represents a solution of the original equation. All scales in Fig. 17–22 would be logarithmic. The T-scale is called a turning line

and is usually not graduated in the finished nomograph as its value is meaningless in the original context. However, during the construction of the nomograph, the modulus of the turning line must be determined and sufficient values plotted to tie the two basic nomographs together.

Another type of equation is

$$f(u) \cdot f(v) + f(w) = f(z). \quad (17\text{–}22)$$

This can be separated into

$$f(u) \cdot f(v) = T; \quad (17\text{–}23)$$

$$T + f(w) = f(z). \quad (17\text{–}24)$$

Eq. 17–23 could be solved by a parallel scale alignment diagram with logarithmic scales. Eq. 17–24 could be solved by a parallel scale alignment diagram with uniform or power scales. However, to tie the two nomographs together would require a special conversion scale to convert from logarithmic divisions to the corresponding non-logarithmic divisions. (Such a scale is illustrated in the middle fixed scale of Fig. 17–32.)

A better solution to this problem is to use an N-scale alignment diagram for the solution of Eq. 17–23. Since the two parallel scales have uniform or power divisions, this form of nomograph directly leads into the parallel scale alignment diagram used to solve Eq. 17–24. This is illustrated in Fig. 17–23. In this situation the ability to construct an N-scale alignment diagram has definite advantage over the ability to construct only parallel scale alignment diagrams.

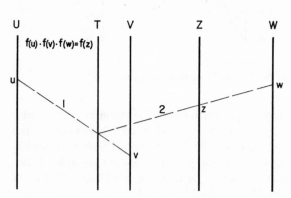

Fig. 17–22. Combined alignment diagrams for $f(u) \cdot f(v) \cdot f(w) = f(z)$.

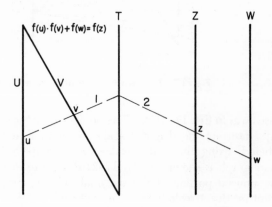

Fig. 17–23. Combined alignment diagrams for $f(u) \cdot f(v) + f(w) = f(z)$.

Equations of any number of variables can be handled in a similar manner. The best form of alignment diagram must be chosen for each subequation so that it will lead into the next subequation. A sample solution must be included as part of the information on any nomograph. This sample solution may be given directly on the nomograph itself or may be given as a small diagram in the marginal information.

17-15. OTHER FORMS OF NOMOGRAPHS

It is the intent here to illustrate only some of the other forms of nomographs. For a discussion of these and other forms, the student should consult a text on nomography. Fig. 17-24 illustrates four different nomographs and the types of equations that they solve. The circular nomograph, as shown in Fig. 17-24(d) is included because, although it handles the same type of equation as does the parallel and N-scale alignment diagrams, the circular form is particularly advantageous in working with trigonometric functions.

17-16. THE GENERAL-PURPOSE SLIDE RULE

A functional scale representing $f(u) = \log u$ can be used for multiplication by adding distances. In Fig. 17-25(a), the distance a represents the logarithm of 2. In Fig. 17-25(b), the distance a has been added to a distance b which represents the logarithm of 3. The combined distance reaches 6 on the functional scale. Hence, the adding of distances has represented the multiplication of two numbers.

This process can be more readily performed when two logarithmic functional scales are used that can slide along each other. Fig. 17-26 shows the same multiplication performed by using two sliding logarithmic scales. When only one scale is

used, the distances are added by some method of transfer; but when two sliding scales are used, the addition of the distances is done by the scales themselves. In this sense, the C- and D-scales of the slide rule are another form of a graphic analog computer. It should be noted here that, because a distance on one scale is being added to a distance

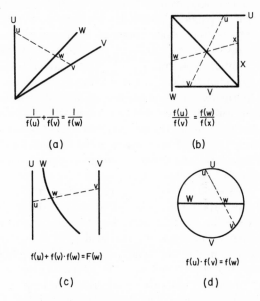

$$\frac{1}{f(u)} + \frac{1}{f(v)} = \frac{1}{f(w)}$$

(a)

$$\frac{f(u)}{f(v)} = \frac{f(w)}{f(x)}$$

(b)

$$f(u) + f(v) \cdot f(w) = F(w)$$

(c)

$$f(u) \cdot f(v) = f(w)$$

(d)

Fig. **17-24.**   Other forms of nomographs.

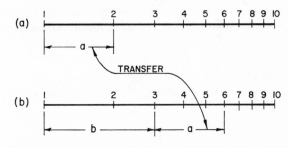

Fig. **17-25.**   Multiplication on a functional scale.

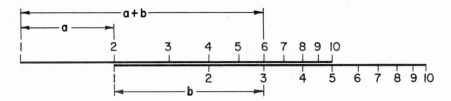

Fig. **17-26.**   Multiplication by sliding scales.

on a second scale and the result is being read on the first scale, the same modulus must be used for both scales. This is the basis upon which the general-purpose slide rule is constructed.

17-17. SPECIAL-PURPOSE SLIDE RULES FOR THREE AND FOUR VARIABLES

The nomographs previously discussed are usually drawn on paper. When the nomograph is used repeatedly, the paper becomes worn, dirty, and often disfigured with pencil marks left from previous solutions. A transparent plastic cover could be used, but this can become scratched with use. Furthermore, the nomograph may not be convenient to carry around without folding, which would decrease the life of the paper. To avoid these conditions, it is often advantageous to construct another form of graphic analog computer, the special-purpose slide rule.

The special-purpose slide rule differs from the general-purpose slide rule in that: (a) it is designed for a specific equation of three or more variables; (b) each variable has its own scale; (c) the independent variables are matched against each other across the slide rule; and (d) all constants and adjustments for units are incorporated in the placement of the scales. The special-purpose slide rule operates by the addition of distances as does the general-purpose slide rule, but in contrast it is limited to the solution of one specific equation. However, it solves that equation faster and easier than a general-purpose slide rule. This together with its greater convenience when compared with nomographs drawn on paper, are the principal reasons for the increasing use of special-purpose slide rules.

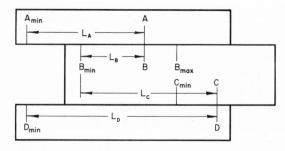

Fig. **17-27.** The theory of the special-purpose slide rule.

The theory of the special-purpose slide rule for the solution of $f(A) + f(B) + f(C) = f(D)$ is illustrated in Fig. 17-27. Scales are plotted according to the function of each variable on the fixed and sliding portions of the slide rule. In order to match the variables against each other, the scales are so located that in the closed position the minimum values of A, B, and D are aligned along the left end of the slide rule and the minimum value of C is aligned with the maximum value of B. All scales increase from left to right and all scales must have the same modulus since a distance on one scale is to be added to a distance on another scale. Fig. 17-27 shows the slide rule set for a particular solution with values of the two independent variables A and B aligned with each other and a value of the third independent variable C aligned with the corresponding value of the dependent variable D. Thus, one movement of the slide to align desired values of A and B enables the user to read the corresponding value of D for any desired value of C. In this position, the indicated lengths have the relationship:

$$L_A - L_B = L_D - L_C, \qquad (17\text{-}25)$$

or,

$$L_A - L_B + L_C - L_D = 0. \qquad (17\text{-}26)$$

Since the lengths on the scale represent the function of each variable, Eq. 17-26 can be rewritten as:

$$f(A) - f(B) + f(C) - f(D) = 0. \qquad (17\text{-}27)$$

This equation will be called the *type equation* for the special-purpose slide rule.

The above information can be used to design a special-purpose slide rule for any specific equation involving three or four variables. The scale equations, determined according to Eq. 17-2, of each of the variables are:

$$S_A = M\,[f(A) - f(A)_{\min}], \qquad (17\text{-}28)$$

$$S_B = M\,[f(B) - f(B)_{\min}], \qquad (17\text{-}29)$$

$$S_C = M\,[f(C) - f(C)_{\min}], \qquad (17\text{-}30)$$

$$S_D = M\,[f(D) - f(D)_{\min}]. \qquad (17\text{-}31)$$

For an example of designing a four-variable special-purpose slide rule, consider the equation:

$$WXY = Z,$$

where W, X, and Y all range from 1 to 10 and hence Z ranges from 1 to 1,000. The equation involves multiplication and, since the special-purpose slide rule operates by the addition of variables, the equation must be rewritten in logarithmic form:

$$\log W + \log X + \log Y = \log Z.$$

Here $\log W$ corresponds to $f(A)$, $\log X$ to $f(B)$, $\log Y$ to $f(C)$, and $\log Z$ to $f(D)$ of Eq. 17-27.

The modulus for all scales will be determined by the scale with the greatest range of values. Hence the Z-scale is the scale that determines the modulus. Since the range of Z (1 to 1,000) is three full logarithmic cycles, and assuming a scale length of 9″, the modulus to be used for all scales is:

$$M = 9/3 = 3 \text{ inches/cycle.}$$

Scale distances for all variables can now be calculated using Eqs. 17-28 through 17-31, or the scales could be graphically constructed if the direction of the scales were known. In either case, the direction of the scales must be determined before the slide rule can be completed. The placement of the scales will always correspond to the placement of the scales on the theoretical slide rule.

In determining the direction of the scales, the specific equation being considered is compared with the type equation:

Type equation:

$$f(A) - f(B) + f(C) - f(D) = 0 \quad (17\text{-}27)$$

Specific equation:

$$\log W + \log X + \log Y - \log Z = 0.$$

Since the first term of each agrees in sign, the W-scale increases from left to right and the lowest value is at the left end of the slide rule. In other words, the direction of the W-scale corresponds to the direction of the A-scale on the theoretical slide rule, Fig. 17-27.

The second terms of the two equations differ in sign and hence the X-scale must be inverted to account for the difference in sign. The position of the scale is the same as the position of the B-scale on the theoretical slide rule, but, because of the inversion, the maximum value of X will be at the left end of the scale.

The third terms of the two equations agree in sign and hence the Y-scale corresponds to the C-scale in direction. However, the minimum value of Y will be aligned with the minimum value of X because of the inversion of the X-scale.

The fourth (and last) terms of each equation also agree in sign. The direction of the Z-scale, therefore, corresponds to the direction of the D-scale. The minimum value of Z is aligned at the left end of the slide rule and the maximum value falls at the right end. The scales could be drawn and the slide rule completed as in Fig. 17-28.

This is the same form of equation as discussed in Art. 17-14 and solved by alignment diagrams in Fig. 17-22 where the determination of a solution required two operations. Note that the four-variable equation can now be solved by one movement of the slide. Also, other combinations of variables giving the same results are readily apparent. This is a valuable asset for the design engineer.

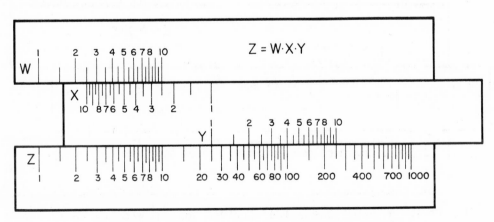

Fig. **17-28.** A special-purpose slide rule of four variables.

In the case just considered, the ranges of all variables are full logarithmic cycles. When this is not true, there is an apparent difficulty in locating the position of the scales. However, this difficulty is eliminated if the scales of all variables are aligned using as locators the scale divisions whose values are multiples of 10, starting with the longest scale as a base. Fig. 17–29 illustrates the special-purpose slide rule for the same equation, $Z = WXY$, where W and Y range from 5 to 15, X ranges from 10 to 100, and Z ranges from 250 to 22,500. Here, the 10 value of the W-scale is aligned with the 1,000 value of the Z-scale. The 100 value of the X-scale is aligned with the 10 value of the W-scale. (Note that, as before, the X-scale is inverted.) Finally, the 10 value of the Y-scale is aligned with the 10 value of the X-scale.

When the specific equation involves only three variables, one of the independent variables of the type equations becomes the constant 1 and appears on the slide rule only as an index or fiducial mark. Consider the equation used as an example throughout this chapter: $I = Ak^2$, where I is the moment of inertia in inches^4 and ranges from 1 to 1,000, A is the area in square inches and ranges from 1 to 10, and k is the radius of gyration in inches and ranges from 1 to 10. Rewriting the specific equation and comparing it to the type equation:

Type equation:

$$f(A) - f(B) + f(C) - f(D) = 0; \quad (17-27)$$

Specific equation:

$$\log A + 2 \log k \qquad - \log I = 0,$$

we find that the third independent variable is missing. By comparing signs, it is found that the A- and I-scales increase from left to right and the k-scale increases from right to left. Since the third independent variable is missing in the specific equation, it will appear only as an index mark aligned, in this case, under the minimum value of k. (If the k-scale did not have to be inverted, the index mark would have been aligned with the maximum value.)

Again assuming a scale length of 9″, the modulus of the slide rule is determined using the values of the I-scale because it has the greatest range of values.

$$M = \frac{9}{\log 1{,}000 - \log 1} = \frac{9}{3} = 3 \text{ inches/cycle.}$$

The scale equations are:

$$S_I = 3 \, (\log I - \log 1) = 3 \log I,$$
$$S_A = 3 \, (\log A - \log 1) = 3 \log A,$$
$$S_k = 3 \, (2 \log k - 2 \log 1) = 6 \log k.$$

The completed special-purpose slide rule is shown in Fig. 17–30. Note the effect on the scale when a variable is raised to some power. Note, also, that all scales are identified as to units of the scale and the specific equation is shown. A special-purpose slide rule is not complete without these data.

The effect of a constant in the specific equation is merely to shift the position of one of the scales. Fig. 17–31 shows the special-purpose slide rule for $I = Ak^2/2$. Note that the only difference between Figs. 17–30 and 17–31 is in the I-scale.

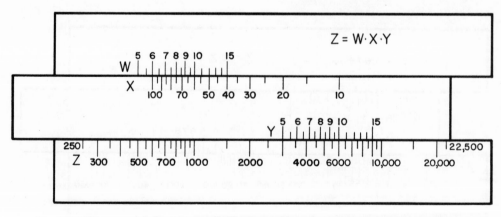

Fig. **17–29.** A special-purpose slide rule of four variables where the variables are not complete log cycles.

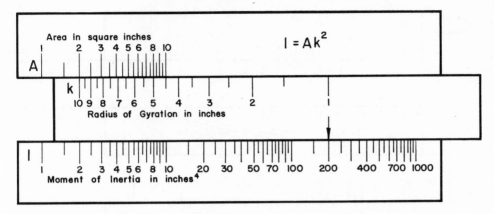

Fig. **17-30.** A special-purpose slide rule of three variables.

Equations sometimes involve both multiplication and addition. In such a case, the equation must be solved in two parts with a fixed center scale which converts from logarithmic to linear values. Fig. 17-32 illustrates a special-purpose slide rule for an equation of the form $vw = x + y$. The two parts of the solution are $vw = k$ and $k = x + y$. This same type equation is shown in alignment diagram form in Fig. 17-23 where an N-scale and a parallel scale alignment diagram have been combined to give the solution. In this type equation, two settings or operations are required by either method of solution.

17-18. SPECIAL-PURPOSE SLIDE RULES FOR FIVE OR MORE VARIABLES

The design of special-purpose slide rules for five or more variables is merely an extension of the dis-

cussion in Art. 17-17. The addition of a second slide increases to six the number of variables that can be handled, while the addition of a third slide increases the possible variables to eight. The type equation for a two-slide slide rule becomes:

$$f(A) - f(B) + f(C) - f(D) + f(E) - f(F) = 0,$$
$$(17\text{-}32)$$

and the type equation for the three-slide slide rule is extended similarly. The actual design and positioning of the scales are done in the same manner as in Art. 17-17.

17-19. PHYSICAL CONSTRUCTION OF SLIDE RULES

The simplest answer as to how to physically set up a special-purpose slide rule is to draw the scales on paper and then glue the scales onto a discarded

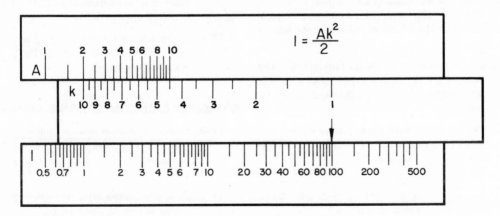

Fig. **17-31.** Effect of a constant on a special-purpose slide rule.

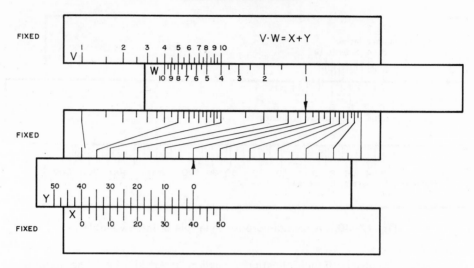

Fig. 17–32. A special-purpose slide rule combining multiplication and addition.

general-purpose slide rule. Of course, this does not answer the requirement when there is no discarded general-purpose slide rule available, or when the equation being solved has more than four variables. In these cases, strips can be cut from a high grade paper drawing board, the scales drawn on these strips, and the strips mounted on a stiff backing of wood or paper. A cover of acetate or thin plexiglass will prevent the slide or slides from falling out of the slide rule. All parts should be thoroughly lacquered after marking and assembly in order to provide increased resistance to wear. A third solution is to construct the slide rule of preprinted graph and log paper. This has the advantage that the scale distances need not be plotted. It also has the disadvantage of limiting the designer to the few moduli available in commercial paper. Slide rules made of paper must be folded and heavily lacquered to attain rigidity and resistance to wear. A fourth solution is to purchase the materials for the slide rules. At least one commercial source is available, the Dyna-Slide Company of Chicago, Illinois.

Problems

FUNCTIONAL SCALES

17–1. Design a functional scale for $f(u) = u^2 + 3$. The value of u varies from 0 to 5 and the scale length is to be 5″. Show calculations in tabular form.

17–2. Design a functional scale for $f(u) = u^{2/3}$. The value of u varies from 0 to 9. Select a suitable scale length and show calculations in tabular form.

17–3. Design a functional scale $f(u) = \log u$. The value of u ranges from 1 to 50. Use a scale length of approximately 6″.

17–4. Design a functional scale for $f(u) = (u + 1)^2$. The value of u varies from -5 to $+6$. Use a scale length of approximately 6″.

17–5. Design a functional scale for $f(u) = \sin u$. The value of u varies from 0° to 180°. Use a scale length of approximately 6″.

17–6. Design a functional scale for $f(u) = \tan u$. The value of u varies from 0° to 180°. Select a suitable scale length.

ADJACENT SCALE CONVERSION DIAGRAMS

17–7. Design a nomograph to solve: $A = 640M$, where A is in acres and M is in square miles. M varies from 0 to 10. Use a scale length of 10″.

17–8. Design a nomograph to solve: $W = 550P$, where W is in foot-pounds per second and P is in horsepower. P varies from 0 to 15. Use a scale length of 10″.

17–9. Design the nomograph to solve: $P = 14.22k$, where P is in pounds per square inch and k is in kilograms per square centimeter. P varies from 10,000 psi to 70,000 psi. Select a suitable scale length.

17–10. Design a nomograph to solve: $K = 737.56W$, where K is in kilowatts and W is in foot-pounds per second. K varies from 1 to 50. Select a suitable scale.

17–11. Design a nomograph to solve: $V = (2gH)^{1/2}$, where V is velocity in feet per second, H is the velocity head in feet, and g is gravity (use 32.17 feet per second per second). Let V vary from 10 to 30. Select a suitable scale.

17–12. Design a nomograph to solve: $A = \dfrac{\pi D^2}{4}$, where A is the area in square inches and D is the diameter of a circle in inches. Let D vary from 1″ to 12″. Select a suitable scale.

PARALLEL SCALE ALIGNMENT DIAGRAMS

17–13. Design a nomograph to solve: $E = IR$, where E is the electromotive force in volts, I is the current in amperes, and R is the resistance in ohms. Let E vary from 1 to 300 and R vary from 1 to 30. Select suitable scales.

17–14. Design a nomograph to solve: $P = I^2R$, where P is the power in watts, I is the current in amperes, and R is the resistance in ohms. Let P vary from 10 to 160 and R vary from 0.10 to 0.30. Select suitable scales.

17–15. Design a nomograph to solve the Pythagorian Theorem.

17–16. Design a nomograph to determine the volume of right circular cylindrical tanks where the diameter varies from 5 to 30 feet and the height varies from 5 to 15 feet.

17–17. Design a nomograph to solve: $D = V_o t \cos \theta$, where D is the horizontal distance traveled in feet, V_o is the initial velocity in feet per second, t is the time in seconds, and θ is the angle with the horizontal in degrees. Let V_o vary from 500 to 5,000; t vary from 60 to 600 seconds; and θ vary from 10° to 70°.

17–18. Design a nomograph to solve: $s = \dfrac{Mc}{I}$, where s is the stress in pounds per square inch, M is the moment in inch-pounds, c is the distance from the neutral axis in inches, and I is the moment of inertia with respect to the neutral axis in inches to the fourth power. Let s vary from 1 to 10,000; c vary from 1 to 10; and I vary from 100 to 1,000.

N-SCALE ALIGNMENT DIAGRAMS

17–19. Design a nomograph to solve: $W = T\theta$, where W is the work in foot-pounds, T is the torque in pound-feet, and θ is the twist angle in radians. Let T vary from 0 to 1,000 and θ vary from 0 to 2π.

17–20. Design a nomograph to solve: $KE = \dfrac{MV^2}{2g}$, where KE is the kinetic energy in foot-pounds, M is the weight in pounds, and V is the velocity in feet per second. Let M vary from 5 to 500 and V vary from 10 to 100. ($g = 32.2$ ft./sec./sec.)

17–21. Design a nomograph to determine the volume of rectangular boxes where the height varies from 5″ to 30″, the width varies from 5″ to 15″, and the depth varies from 5″ to 10″.

17–22. Design a nomograph to solve: $V_L = V_G - IR$, where V_L is the voltage at the load end of a transmission line, V_G is the voltage at the generator end, I is the current in amperes, and R is the total resistance in ohms. Let V_G vary from 110 to 1,100; I vary from 10 to 1,000; and R vary from 0.1 to 10.

SPECIAL-PURPOSE SLIDE RULES

17–23. Design a slide rule to solve the equation of Problem 17–13.

17–24. Design a slide rule to solve the equation of Problem 17–18.

17–25. Design a slide rule to solve the equation of Problem 17–17.

17–26. Design a slide rule to solve the equation of Problem 17–22.

18

EMPIRICAL
EQUATIONS

18-1. INTRODUCTION

The engineer and scientist make constant use of equations in their work. Such equations may be categorized into two general types, rational and empirical. The rational equation is one developed by logical reasoning, such as deriving, from Newton's Law, the equation relating the work done on a moving object to the change in kinetic energy of the object. The empirical equation is developed either from data obtained experimentally or from observations made of natural phenomena. Any relationship expressed as an empirical equation should be considered valid only within the range of the experimental or observed data. Extrapolation beyond this range should be treated with extreme caution. Empirical equations are very useful in the design of machines, structures, and systems. A typical empirical equation might express the relationship between the horsepower developed by an engine and the accompanying gasoline consumption. This chapter presents the fundamental techniques for deriving empirical equations from experimental or observed data.

Additional information on empirical equations may be found in Chapter 20.

18-2. PRESENTATION OF EXPERIMENTAL DATA

Most experiments are performed to determine the relationship between variable quantities. In the majority of such experiments, two quantities are permitted to vary while all other factors are held as constant as possible.

The results of experiments may be presented in any of three ways. First, they may be presented in a tabular form. However, tabled data are difficult to interpret, and interpolation of values is inconvenient. Another method of presenting experimental data is by the use of graphs. Graphs provide a superior means for visual comparison of data, and readily permit interpolation. The third method of data presentation is to record the data in the form of an empirical equation. Such an equation, if not too complex, is a more precise method of presenting data, and readily permits interpolation. It also presents the data in a form acceptable for use with desk calculators, special-purpose slide rules, or computers. This latter use is especially important when the data are to be used repeatedly.

It is this third method, the use of empirical equations in the presentation of data, which is of primary interest in this chapter. However, it will be shown that determination of the empirical equation usually requires either the tabular data, or the graph of the data, or both, as preliminary steps.

18-3. SELECTION OF APPROPRIATE TYPE OF EQUATION

To select the appropriate type of equation to represent experimentally obtained data, first plot the data on rectilinear coordinate paper. Then, draw a smooth curve which will best fit the plotted points. The techniques presented in Arts. 14–5 through 14–11 should be followed when plotting the data. Visual inspection of the resulting curve will often indicate a possible equation form, i.e., straight line, exponential, hyperbolic, parabolic, etc. If the rectilinear plot is other than a straight line, the data are replotted on appropriately ruled paper (usually logarithmic or semilogarithmic) to determine if a straight-line plot is feasible. If it does plot as a straight line on some particular type of graph paper, the type of equation is established and the empirical equation may be determined. If, in replotting the data, the curve still has a slight bend, the data can often be converted to a straight-line plot by inserting a constant into the relationship. Chapter 20 analyzes in detail the types of equations containing such constants. In this chapter, the discussion is restricted to basic types of equations without such constants.

18-4. COMMON TYPES OF EQUATIONS

There are many types of equations available for fitting data, and they range from simple to extremely complex. However, most engineering and scientific data fit a relatively few of the simpler types. In this chapter the discussion is limited to the three most widely used types, each containing only two constants.

Type I: $y = mx + b$. This is the equation for a straight line. Fig. 18–1 shows a typical family of such equations for varying values of m, when $b = 2$. In this type of equation, m represents the slope of the curve while b is the y-axis intercept.

Type II: $y = ax^m$. In this equation, often referred to as a power equation, a and m are constants. When plotted on rectilinear graph paper, positive values of m result in parabolas, while negative values give hyperbolas. Fig. 18–2 presents several parabolas for varying positive values of m when $a = 5$. All these curves pass through the origin. In Fig. 18–3 several hyperbolas are shown based on the same equation, but with varying negative values for m.

If this type of equation is transformed by taking logarithms of both sides, it becomes

$$\log y = \log a + m \log x.$$

This form indicates that $\log y$ is linear with $\log x$, and if $\log y$ is plotted against $\log x$ on a rectilinear grid a straight line will result. However, this is equivalent to plotting the original equation, $y = ax^m$, on a logarithmic grid. Fig. 18–4 shows the same curves of Fig. 18–2 and Fig. 18–3 replotted on logarithmic paper, where they appear as straight lines. On this grid positive values of m result in positive slopes, while negative values of m result in negative slopes.

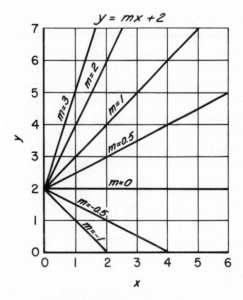

Fig. **18-1.** Linear equations.

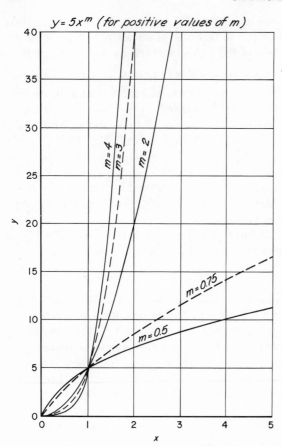

Fig. **18-2.** Power equations of parabolic form.

paper, where they appear as straight lines. Positive values of m result in positive slopes while negative values of m give a negative slope.

If, in attempting to plot Type III data as a straight line on a semilogarithmic grid, the resulting curve is not a straight line, then try reversal of the coordinates so the equation is in the form $x = ae^{my}$. This may result in a straight line.

18-5. METHODS FOR DETERMINING EQUATIONS

Once experimental data have been plotted as a straight line on some particular type of graph paper, thus establishing the type of empirical equation, the constants in the equation must be evaluated.

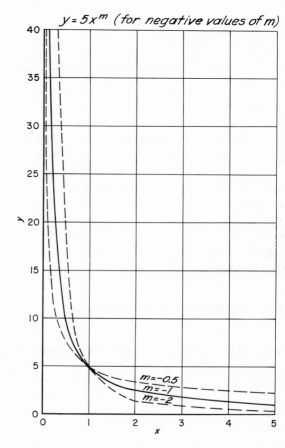

Fig. **18-3.** Power equations of hyperbolic form.

Type III: $y = ae^{mx}$. In this equation, commonly referred to as an exponential equation, a and m are constants, while e is equal to 2.718. Fig. 18–5 shows the resulting curve form if this equation is plotted on rectilinear graph paper. In the figure several curves have been drawn for varying values of m, when $a = 5$.

If this type of equation is transposed by taking logarithms of both sides, it becomes

$$\log y = \log a + mx \log e.$$

This indicates that the log y is linear with x, and if log y is plotted against x on a rectilinear grid a straight line will result. This is, however, equivalent to plotting the original equation, $y = ae^{mx}$, on a semilogarithmic grid. In Fig. 18–6 the curves of Fig. 18–5 have been replotted on semilogarithmic

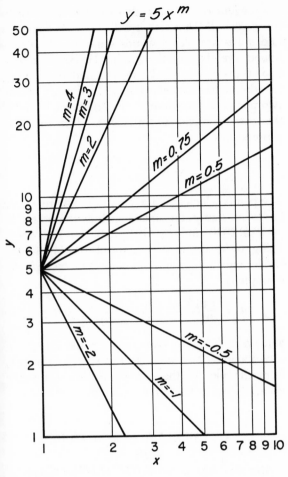

Fig. **18-4.** Power equations on logarithmic paper.

18-6. EMPIRICAL EQUATIONS—TYPE I:
$y = mx + b$

A study was made to determine the insulating quality of a certain wall construction. This was done by maintaining the inside room temperature at a uniform 70° F, while recording various outside air temperatures. The experiment resulted in the data shown in Table 18–1.

An empirical equation is to be fitted to these data. As the initial step, the data are plotted on rectilinear graph paper as shown in Fig. 18–7. After drawing an average line through these data, it is apparent that the plot is a straight line, and is therefore of the general form $y = mx + b$. The actual equation is $T_i = mT_o + b$, where T_o is out-side air temperature and T_i is inside wall tempera-

There are five methods for determining these constants. These methods, ranked in order of increasing difficulty (amount of work involved), are as follows:

1. Slope and intercept method
2. Method of selected points
3. Method of averages
4. Method of moments
5. Method of least squares

In this text only the first three methods are presented. The following articles, utilizing the results of various experiments, will apply these methods to the three types of empirical equations discussed in Art. 18–4.

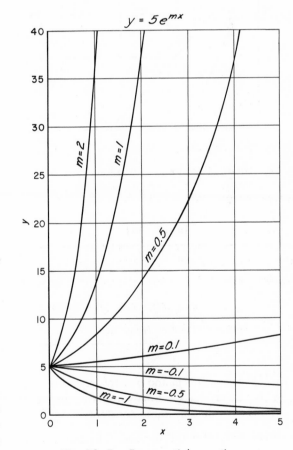

Fig. **18-5.** Exponential equations.

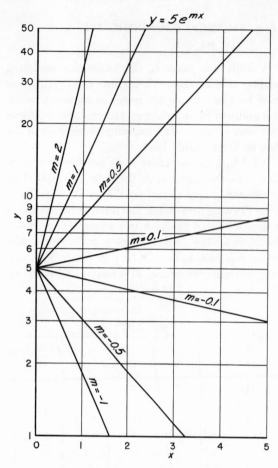

Fig. **18-6.** Exponential equations on semilogarithmic paper.

TABLE 18-1

Outside Air Temperature, °F.							
−20.0	−11.0	−4.0	3.0	11.0	20.0	29.0	39.0
11.5	17.5	24.0	28.0	33.0	40.0	45.0	52.2
Inside Wall Surface Temperature, °F.							

ture. The constants m and b of this equation must now be determined. Following are the three methods of evaluating these constants.

Slope and Intercept Method. In the general equation, $y = mx + b$, m is the slope of the line, and b is the y-axis intercept. Slope is expressed as the tangent of the angle that the line makes with the x-axis. If the scales of units for both the x-axis and y-axis are identical, this slope may be determined directly from the graph. However, in general, the slope is usually determined by dividing the difference between the y-coordinates of any two points on the curve by the difference between the corresponding x-coordinates. This may be expressed as

$$m = \frac{y_2 - y_1}{x_2 - x_1}.$$

The points selected on the curve should preferably be taken fairly far apart, such as the points P_1 (−10.0, 18.8) and P_2 (30.0, 46.3) on Fig. 18–7. Using these coordinates and substituting in the above equation, the slope, m, for this specific example is

$$m = \frac{46.3 - 18.8}{30.0 - (-10.0)} = \frac{27.5}{40.0} = 0.688.$$

Since b is the y-axis intercept, it is the value of y corresponding to $x = 0$. In this specific example, from the plot of the data, $b = 25.7$. In some instances where the curve representing the experi-

OUTSIDE AIR TEMPERATURE
VS
INSIDE WALL SURFACE TEMPERATURE
(ROOM TEMPERATURE = 70°F)

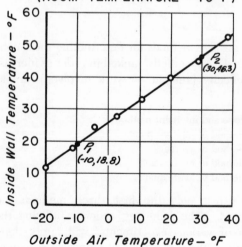

Fig. **18-7.** Experimental data which plot as a straight line on rectilinear coordinate paper.

mental data does not cross the y-axis, it is necessary to extend the curve and extrapolate a value for b. However this is a dangerous procedure since a slight error of judgment in the slope of the line could cause a larger error in the value of the intercept.

Now that values have been determined for both m and b, the empirical equation representing these data may be written as

$$T_i = 0.688T_o + 25.7,$$

where T_o represents the outside air temperature and T_i represents the inside wall surface temperature.

To check the accuracy with which the empirical equation fits the experimental data, residuals are frequently determined. *Residuals* are defined as the difference between observed experimental ordinate values and those calculated from the equation. If the observed value is greater than the calculated one, the residual is positive; while if the observed value is less than the calculated one, the result is a negative residual. If the sum of the residuals is fairly small it is indicative of a good correlation between data and equation. If most of the residuals are negative it indicates that the curve could be shifted to a slightly lower position. A predominance of positive values indicates that an upward shifting of the curve would give a better fit. Table 18–2 shows the residuals for the slope intercept method, as well as for the other two

methods to be discussed. In this table, y' represents the calculated ordinate values, based on the empirical equation, corresponding to observed x-values.

Analysis of the calculated residuals shows that the residuals are relatively small. However, there are more negative than positive ones, and their sum is also negative. This indicates that while the curve fits the data quite well, a slight lowering of the curve might result in a better fit.

Method of Selected Points. In this method the two unknown constants are determined through the simultaneous solution of two equations containing the unknown constants. To do this, two widely separated points which lie on the curve are selected, and the respective values of x and y for each point are substituted into the general equation.

The two points P_1 $(-10.0, 18.8)$ and P_2 $(30.0, 46.3)$ of Fig. 18–7 are selected, and substitution into the general equation results in the equations

$$18.8 = -10.0m + b$$
$$46.3 = 30.0m + b.$$

Solving these simultaneously results in the values $m = 0.688$ and $b = 25.675$. Thus, the resulting empirical equation is

$$T_i = 0.688T_o + 25.675.$$

The residuals resulting from this method of selected

TABLE 18–2

Experimental Data		Calculated Residuals					
		Slope and Intercept Method		Method of Selected Points		Method of Averages	
T_o (x)	T_i (y)	y'	Residual	y'	Residual	y'	Residual
−20.0	11.5	11.94	−.44	11.92	−.42	12.08	−.58
−11.0	17.5	18.13	−.63	18.11	−.61	18.21	−.71
−4.0	24.0	22.95	+1.05	22.92	+1.08	22.97	+1.03
3.0	28.0	27.76	+.24	27.74	+.26	27.74	+.26
11.0	33.0	33.27	−.27	33.24	−.24	33.19	−.19
20.0	40.0	39.46	+.54	39.44	+.56	39.32	+.68
29.0	45.0	45.65	−.65	45.63	−.63	45.45	−.45
39.0	52.2	52.53	−.33	52.51	−.31	52.26	−.06
			Sum = −.49		Sum = −.31		Sum = −.02

points have been calculated and tabulated in Table 18–2. The same observations made for the slope and intercept method apply to this method also. However, the smaller sum of the residuals is indicative of an empirical equation which fits the data better than that resulting from the slope and intercept method.

Method of Averages. This method holds one primary advantage over the two previous methods. The determination of the empirical equation is based on the original experimental data, and not on the line drawn through the data. Thus, the empirical equation is not dependent on a visual interpretation of the data. The only reason for plotting the data with this method is to determine the proper form for the equation.

As previously shown, some of the plotted points lie above the average line, while others lie below the line. However, they tend to balance one another. The equation that best fits the data is obtained when the sum of the residuals equals zero. This observation forms the basis for the method of averages. The residuals are the difference between the observed ordinate values, y, and the calculated values, y', based on the empirical equation. Any one residual may be stated as $y - y'$. Since the sum of all the residuals should equal zero, this may be expressed mathematically as

$$\Sigma y - \Sigma y' = 0.$$

For the general equation under consideration, $y' = mx + b$, and the summation of all the y'-values is $\Sigma y' = m\Sigma x + nb$. The constant, n, represents the number of y'-values being summed. This expression for $\Sigma y'$ may be substituted into the previous equation to obtain

$$\Sigma y - m\Sigma x - nb = 0$$

or

$$\Sigma y = m\Sigma x + nb.$$

Since the two constants, m and b, must be determined, it is necessary to obtain two equations for simultaneous solution. This is accomplished by dividing the given data into two equal or nearly equal groups, and summing each group. The data may be divided into two groups in any manner, but usually they simply are divided into an upper and lower group. In the specific example under consideration, there are eight sets of readings, so the data may be divided into two equal groups. For the first four sets of readings, $\Sigma T_i = 81$ and $\Sigma T_o = -32$. The remaining readings yield $\Sigma T_i = 170.2$ and $\Sigma T_o = 99.0$. The value $n = 4$ applies to both groups since each contains four sets of data. Substitution of these values in the equation $\Sigma y = m\Sigma x + nb$ results in the simultaneous equations

$$81.0 = -32.0m + 4b$$
$$170.2 = 99.0m + 4b.$$

Solution of these equations results in values of $m = 0.681$ and $b = 25.698$. Thus, the empirical equation is

$$T_i = 0.681T_o + 25.698.$$

The calculated values of the residuals for this method are also given in Table 18–2. The low value for the sum of the residuals indicates that this empirical equation is probably the one which best fits the data.

In the foregoing discussions of the three methods of determining the constants, each has been calculated, in most cases, to three decimal places. This was done so that an academic discussion of residuals could be presented. However, an empirical equation cannot have a greater precision than the precision of the data used in determining the equation. From Table 18–1 it can be seen that the data are precise to the nearest tenth. Hence the constants, as determined by each method, should be rounded-off to the same precision. Therefore, in practice, the equation determined by all three methods is identical:

$$T_i = 0.7T_o + 25.7.$$

18–7. EMPIRICAL EQUATIONS—TYPE II:
$y = ax^m$

In a study of flow through copper tubing, the friction loss in head was determined for various flow rates. The information presented in Table 18–3 gives the data resulting from studies on $1\frac{1}{4}''$-diameter smooth copper tubing. An empirical equation is required which will represent these data.

First, the data are plotted on a rectilinear grid as in Fig. 18–8. Visual inspection seems to indicate that this curve is similar to the parabolas shown in Fig. 18–2, where the constant m is positive but has a value less than one. This indicates that the data will appear as a straight line if they are replotted on a logarithmic grid. Replotting of the data on a logarithmic grid, Fig. 18–9, does result in a straight-line plot, which verifies the decision. Thus the general type of empirical equation is $y = ax^m$. Now that the type of equation has been decided, the constants m and a must be evaluated. Again, for comparison they will be determined using the three methods—slope and intercept, selected points, and averages.

Slope and Intercept Method. In plotting data on logarithmic graph paper the x- and y-coordinates are proportional to the logarithms of the actual numbers plotted. Thus, for obtaining the empirical equation the logarithmic form of the general equation is used, and $y = ax^m$ becomes

$$\log y = \log a + m \log x.$$

The constants may now be evaluated using this logarithmic form.

The slope, m, may be obtained directly from the graphical plot on logarithmic paper, provided the cycle lengths in both the x-axis and y-axis directions are identical. The slope angle may be measured directly on the graph and its tangent obtained from appropriate tables, or the x- and y-distances between any two points on the line can be measured in inches and the slope is the ratio, y/x. The latter is the more accurate of the two methods. Fig. 18–9 shows the logarithmic plot of the data of Table 18–3. On Fig. 18–9 the two arbitrary distances BC and CD are laid off and the ratio of $CD:BC$ is the slope. In this example, $CD = 1.16''$ and $BC = 2.00''$. (These were measured on the

TABLE 18–3

Friction Loss in Head (lb./sq.in./100 ft. length)									
0.1	0.19	0.3	0.55	0.8	1.4	2.5	4.0	6.4	9.0
2.5	3.5	4.8	6.6	8.2	12.0	15.0	21.0	27.0	33.0
Flow—Gallons of Water per Minute									

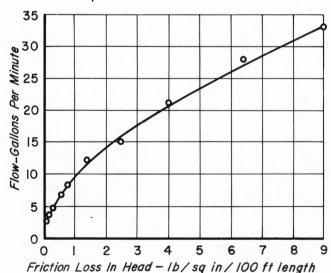

Fig. 18–8. Experimental data which plot in parabolic form on rectilinear coordinate paper.

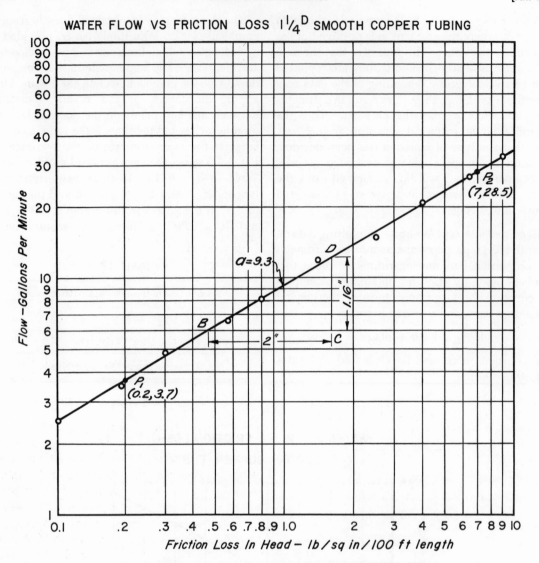

Fig. **18–9.** Data from Fig. 18–8 plotted on logarithmic paper.

original graph before reduction to a size appropriate for use in this text.) Therefore

$$m = \frac{CD}{BC} = \frac{1.16}{2.00} = 0.58.$$

If BC were made equal to 1 unit, then the value of m would equal the value of CD. Another convenient value of BC would be 10 units.

The constant, a, may also be determined directly from the graph. In the general equation, $y = ax^m$, a is the y-intercept when $x = 1$. In this specific example, $a = 9.3$.

Thus, the specific empirical equation is $G = 9.3f^{0.58}$, where G is the gallons per minute and f is the friction loss in head. In Table 18–4 the calculated values of the residuals for this method have been listed, along with their sum, for comparison with the other methods.

Method of Selected Points. To obtain the empirical equation by this method, the general equation in logarithmic form, $\log y = \log a + m \log x$, is again used. Two points are selected which lie on the curve as drawn on the logarithmic plot.

TABLE 18–4

Experimental Data		Calculated Residuals					
		Slope and Intercept Method		Method of Selected Points		Method of Averages	
f (x)	G (y)	y'	Residual	y'	Residual	y'	Residual
0.1	2.5	2.45	+.05	2.49	+.01	2.48	+.02
0.19	3.5	3.55	−.05	3.60	−.10	3.59	−.09
0.3	4.8	4.62	+.18	4.78	+.02	4.67	+.13
0.55	6.6	6.58	+.02	6.62	−.02	6.63	−.03
0.8	8.2	8.17	+.03	8.21	−.01	8.22	−.02
1.4	12.0	11.31	+.69	11.31	+.69	11.35	+.65
2.5	15.0	15.81	−.81	15.78	−.78	15.85	−.85
4.0	21.0	20.79	+.21	20.67	+.33	20.78	+.22
6.4	27.0	27.34	−.34	27.07	−.07	27.24	−.24
9.0	33.0	33.29	−.25	32.92	+.08	33.14	−.14
			Sum = −.27		Sum = +.13		Sum = −.35

The respective x- and y-coordinate values for each of these points are substituted into the logarithmic form of the general equation to obtain two equations. Each equation contains the unknowns m and a. These equations are then solved simultaneously to obtain values of m and a.

The two points P_1 (0.2, 3.7) and P_2 (7.0, 28.5) of Fig. 18–9 are selected and substituted into

$$\log y = \log a + m \log x$$

to obtain the two simultaneous equations

$$\log 28.5 = \log a + m \log 7.0$$
$$\log 3.7 = \log a + m \log 0.2$$

or

$$1.4548 = \log a + 0.8451m$$
$$0.5682 = \log a - 0.6990m.$$

Solving these equations, $m = 0.574$ and $a = 9.326$, and the specific empirical equation is

$$G = 9.326f^{0.574}.$$

The residuals resulting from this method are shown in Table 18–4.

Method of Averages. This method is also appropriate for determining an empirical equation for data which plot as a straight line on logarithmic graph paper. Again the general equation is used in the logarithmic form. In this solution the sum of the residuals should be zero, or

$$\Sigma \log y - \Sigma \log y' = 0$$

where

$$\Sigma \log y' = m\Sigma \log x + n \log a.$$

Substituting the latter equation into the former, and transposing,

$$\Sigma \log y = m\Sigma \log x + n \log a.$$

Since there are two constants, m and a, to be determined, the two simultaneous equations are obtained by dividing the given data into two equal groups, determining the logarithms of the data in each group, and then summing the logarithms. Summing the logarithms for the first five sets of readings results in $\Sigma \log y = 3.3565$ and $\Sigma \log x = -2.6006$. The result of summing the last five is $\Sigma \log y = 6.5274$ and $\Sigma \log x = 2.9065$. Since there are five readings in each group, $n = 5$. These values result in two simultaneous equations:

$$3.3565 = -2.6006m + 5 \log a$$
$$6.5274 = 2.9065m + 5 \log a.$$

Solving these equations yields the results $m = 0.576$ and $a = 9.352$. Therefore, the empirical equation is

$$G = 9.352f^{0.576}.$$

The residuals based on this equation are also listed in Table 18–4. Comparison of residuals for the three methods indicates that the method of selected points in this example yields the best result. However, comparison of the values of m and a for these three methods shows little variation, and any of the three equations may suitably represent the data.

The statement in Art. 18-6 regarding the practical limits on the precision of solution for the constants generally holds true here also. The constant a is meaningless beyond the first decimal place. However, the constant m is different when used as an exponent in a power equation. There is a great difference in the two values of any number raised to two powers that differ by only one-tenth. Hence, to achieve a precision in the final result comparable to the precision of the given data, a constant used as an exponent must be determined to at least three significant figures. Therefore, using the constants determined by the method of selected points, the specific equation would be:

$$G = 9.3f^{0.574}.$$

18-8. EMPIRICAL EQUATIONS—TYPE III:
$y = ae^{mx}$.

Table 18-5 gives the barometric pressure, in inches of mercury, for various heights above sea level. It is desired to obtain an empirical equation to represent these data.

The first step is, as usual, to plot the data on a rectilinear grid as in Fig. 18-10. Visual inspection shows that the curve is similar to the exponential plots of Fig. 18-5, with m a negative number. Since this type of equation plots as a straight line on a semilogarithmic grid, the data are replotted (Fig. 18-11) using such a grid. The resulting straight-line plot indicates that the general equation best fitting these data is $y = ae^{mx}$. Having decided on the type of equation, the constants a and m can now be evaluated.

Slope and Intercept Method. In plotting the data of Table 18-5 on semilogarithmic graph paper,

the y-coordinates are proportional to the logarithms of the actual values plotted while the x-coordinates are directly proportional to the values plotted. Thus, in determining the empirical equation, the logarithmic form of the general equation is used, and $y = ae^{mx}$ becomes $\log y = \log a + mx \log e$. Since $e = 2.718$, $\log e = 0.434$ (to three decimal places), and the equation may be written as $\log y = \log a + 0.434mx$. The constants a and m may now be evaluated.

When the general equation is written in logarithmic form the slope of the curve is $0.434m$, and is equal to the actual slope of the line divided by the ratio of the modulus of the y-scale to the modu-

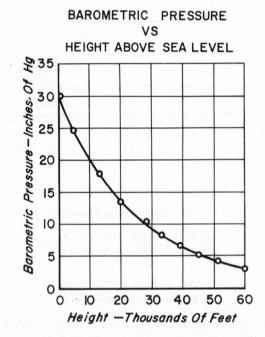

Fig. **18-10.** Experimental data which plot in exponential form on rectilinear coordinate paper.

TABLE 18-5

Height (Feet)									
0	5,000	13,000	20,000	28,000	33,000	39,000	45,000	51,000	60,000
30.0	24.7	18.0	13.5	10.5	8.4	6.7	5.2	4.3	3.0
Pressure (Inches of Mercury)									

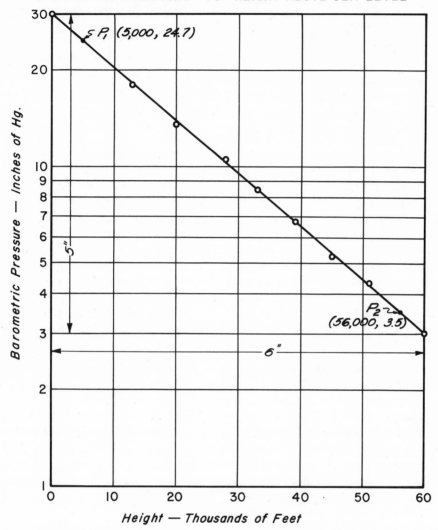

BAROMETRIC PRESSURE VS HEIGHT ABOVE SEA LEVEL

Fig. **18–11.** Data from Fig. 18–10 plotted on semilogarithmic paper.

us of the x-scale. This may be expressed mathe-matically as

$$0.434m = \dfrac{\dfrac{y}{x}}{\dfrac{m_y}{m_x}}.$$

Visual inspection shows the slope to be negative in this case. The values of x and y can be scaled from direct measurements on the plot, Fig. 18–11. (The values of 6″ and 5″ were measured on the original graph before reduction for use in the text.)

The y-scale modulus is 5″ per unit (cycle), and the x-axis modulus is 0.0001″ per unit. Therefore

$$0.434m = \dfrac{\dfrac{-5}{6}}{\dfrac{5}{0.0001}} = -0.0000167$$

or

$$m = -0.000037.$$

The value of the constant a is read directly from the graph as the y-value corresponding to $x = 0$. In this example $a = 30$. Therefore, the empirical equation, based on the slope and intercept method is

$$P = 30e^{-0.000037H},$$

where P is the pressure in inches of mercury, and H is the height in thousands of feet. Table 18–6 indicates the residuals resulting from this equation. An analysis of these residuals indicates that all are negative. A slightly smaller value of a would help correct this condition and result in a better fitting equation.

Method of Selected Points. The logarithmic form, $\log y = \log a + 0.434mx$, is used when determining the empirical equation by this method. Two points are selected which lie some distance apart on the curve, and the x, y values for each point are substituted into the logarithmic form of the equation. This results in two equations which may be solved simultaneously for the constants a and m.

The selected points are P_1 (5,000, 24.7) and P_2 (56,000, 3.5), and the resulting simultaneous equations are

$$\log 3.5 = \log a + m\,(56,000)\,(0.434)$$
$$\log 24.7 = \log a + m\,(5,000)\,(0.434)$$

or

$$0.54407 = \log a + 24,304m.$$
$$1.39270 = \log a + 2,170m.$$

Solving these equations, $m = -0.0000383$ and $a = 29.91$. Thus the empirical equation is

$$P = 29.91e^{-0.0000383H}.$$

The residuals resulting from this method are also shown in Table 18–6, and indicate a better fit than the previous solution by the slope and intercept method.

Method of Averages. This method also utilizes the logarithmic form of the equation, $\log y = \log a + 0.434mx$. As in the previous examples (Arts. 18–6 and 18–7), the data are divided into two groups and summed. Summing the logarithms of the first five y-values results in $\Sigma \log y = 6.27661$ while the sum of the corresponding x-values is $\Sigma x = 66,000$. For the remaining values, $\Sigma \log y = 3.57694$, while the corresponding $\Sigma x = 228,000$. Substituting each of these sets of sums into the logarithmic form of the general equation, and knowing $n = 5$, the resulting simultaneous equations are

$$6.27661 = 5 \log a + m\,(0.434)\,(66,000)$$
$$3.57694 = 5 \log a + m\,(0.434)\,(228,000)$$

or

$$6.27661 = 5 \log a + 28,644m$$
$$3.57694 = 5 \log a + 98,452m.$$

TABLE 18–6

Experimental Data		Calculated Residuals					
		Slope and Intercept Method		Method of Selected Points		Method of Averages	
H (x)	P (y)	y'	Residual	y'	Residual	y'	Residual
0	30.0	30.00	0	29.91	+.09	29.88	+.12
5,000	24.7	24.94	−.24	24.70	0	24.66	+.04
13,000	18.0	18.55	−.55	18.19	−.19	18.14	−.14
20,000	13.5	14.32	−.82	13.91	−.41	13.87	−.37
28,000	10.5	10.65	−.15	10.24	+.26	10.20	+.30
33,000	8.4	8.85	−.45	8.46	−.06	8.42	−.02
39,000	6.7	7.09	−.39	6.72	−.02	6.69	+.01
45,000	5.2	5.68	−.48	5.34	−.14	5.31	−.11
51,000	4.3	4.55	−.25	4.25	+.05	4.22	+.08
60,000	3.0	3.26	−.26	3.01	−.01	2.99	+.01
			Sum = −3.59		Sum = −.43		Sum = −.08

olving these equations results in $m = -0.0000384$, and $a = 29.875$. The empirical quation is

$$P = 29.875e^{-0.0000384H}.$$

[T]he residuals for this method are listed in Table [1]8–6. Since their sum is almost zero, this method [p]rovides the best empirical equation to fit the data.

However, any of the three equations determined in this article is acceptable.

The practical considerations are the same as in the previous discussions. The constant a would probably be expressed as 29.9, while m must be expressed to at least three significant figures. Hence, the practical form of the empirical equation is

$$P = 29.9e^{-0.0000384H}.$$

Problems

In each of the following problems plot the data on [r]ectilinear coordinate paper. Then replot, if necessary, on [a]ppropriate graph paper (logarithmic or semilogarithmic) [s]o data are represented as a straight line. Determine an [e]mpirical equation to represent the data, using the method [s]pecified by the instructor.

18–1.

x	0	0.9	1.8	3.0	4.1	5.3	6.0	7.3	8.8
y	5.0	6.2	7.6	9.2	10.7	12.5	13.4	15.2	17.3

18–2.

x	0	1.8	3.9	5.0	6.4	7.8	9.5	11.3	13.0	15.5
y	18.0	16.1	13.6	12.3	10.7	9.3	7.3	5.3	3.4	0.6

18–3.

x	0.10	0.30	0.50	0.70	2.2	3.6	5.0	8.5	20	60
y	0.20	0.58	0.95	1.30	4.0	6.5	9.0	15	34	100

18–4.

x	10	17	25	40	80	150	270	400	680	900
y	60	37	26	17	9.0	5.1	3.0	2.1	1.3	1.0

18–5.

x	0	10	20	30	40	50	60	70
y	2.0	3.3	5.5	9.2	15.2	25.3	42.0	70.0

18–6.

x	0	1.0	2.0	3.0	4.0	5.0	6.0
y	3.0	1.95	1.26	0.85	0.56	0.37	0.26

18–7. Centrifugal fan capacity. Q is the air flow in thousands of cubic feet per minute; R is the fan revolutions per minute.

Q	5	8	13	18	20	25	28
R	250	400	700	950	1,100	1,350	1,500

18–8. Friction loss in 10″-diameter galvanized duct. F is friction loss in inches of water per 100 feet; Q is the air flow in cubic feet per minute.

F	0.02	0.04	0.10	0.30	0.80	4.00	10.00
Q	180	260	425	750	1,250	3,000	4,700

18–9. Water discharge over a sharp crested weir. H is the depth of the water in feet; Q is the discharge in cubic feet per second.

H	1	2	3	4	5	6	7
Q	3.35	9.30	16.8	25.5	36.0	46.4	58.5

18–10. Relationship between absolute pressure and specific volume of saturated steam. P is the pressure in pounds per square inch, absolute; V is the specific volume in cubic feet per pound.

P	0.113	0.720	1.101	3.280	29.82
V	2,632	454.9	305.0	109.3	13.83

18–11. Electrical conductivity of material "A" for various temperatures. C is the conductivity in mho meters; T is the temperature in °F.

C	.002	.004	.007	.014	.020	.035	.058	.090
T	0	44	78	120	144	180	212	240

18–12. Oscillation of a pendulum. A is the amplitude of swing in inches; T is the elapsed time in minutes.

A	4.0	2.4	1.5	0.89	0.58	0.33	0.20	0.12
T	0	2	4	6	8	10	12	14

18–13. Fatigue strength of stainless steel which has been heated for ten hours at 1,800°F. S is the stress in thousands of pounds per square inch; N is the cycles to failure.

S	34.50	38.10	40.15	42.00	43.55
N	9,000,000	1,650,000	630,000	260,000	125,000

18–14. Tensile strength for various diameters of A.S. 5 music wire. D is the wire diameter in inches; S is the tensile strength in thousands of pounds per square inch.

D	.010	.018	.024	.036	.055	.080	.120
S	389	360	350	330	310	290	270

18–15. A sample of plastic was exposed to intens nuclear radiation, and after removal the deca of induced radioactivity was observed with Geiger counter at one-hour intervals. T is th elapsed time in hours; cpm is the Geiger count reading in counts per minute.

cpm	450	210	140	105	94	88	84	81	79	76	74	7
T	1	2	3	4	5	6	7	8	9	10	11	1

Determine:
a. The number of radioactive components
b. The law of decay
c. Initial intensity of the radiation
d. The "half-life" of each component

V
APPLICATIONS

19

DRAWINGS FOR DESIGN AND PRODUCTION

19-1. INTRODUCTION

Graphical representations or drawings emerge from *ideas* intended to aid, check, or preserve calculations and from *ideas* used to develop design concepts for the purpose of communication. Design usually starts with preliminary planning and sketches; seldom with details. The design is developed to the stage where, from the preliminary sketching and planning, the project can be incorporated into layout drawings, sometimes called design assembly drawings. It is from these drawings that the individual elements or parts are developed, designed, and recorded as detail drawings which delineate each controlling feature affecting the design.

Drawings which convey information usually follow a distinguishable style evolved by the area of specialty in which the engineering is done. For example, the drawings prepared for architecture, civil engineering, and industrial engineering all follow the basic concepts of graphics; however, the style of each is recognizable as originating from the demands of a particular area of engineering specialty.

To prepare design sketches, layout assembly drawings, and detail drawings, it is necessary to have a knowledge of accepted pertinent graphical standards and to know common methods used in dimensioning, fastening, and fabricating the parts or elements of the structure being designed. Before sketches and formal drawings are prepared, a suitable system of symbols and notation as used in engineering must be recognized. The topics of the next two sections—Dimensioning, and Fasteners—are essential to the preparation of sketches and formal drawings for use in engineering and manufacturing, as presented in the final section of the chapter, Working Drawings.

Dimensioning

19–2. GENERAL

Dimensioning is the procedure that is used in indicating the sizes, locations, and related information regarding the features comprising some device or a component part of the device. This also includes those notes, specifications, and symbols which provide information not shown graphically. Dimensioning style is influenced by what is considered to be good practice in engineering design, structural work, or architectural practices. Standardized dimensioning practices have been developed by such organizations as the American Standards Association, The Society of Automotive Engineers, and the technical branches of the military establishment in their drafting manuals. When industrial companies develop standards for their own specific needs, they usually design those standards so as to conform as closely as possible to the general standards proposed by the ASA, SAE, and other standards groups.

19–3. DIMENSIONING RULES

Applying the rules of dimensioning requires experience and judgment. Often, rules supersede each other in the interest of clarity, hence a thorough knowledge of the design intent and the processes to be employed in production assists in recognizing dimensioning needs and in applying rules. The following are the most generally accepted dimensioning rules.

1. Enough dimensions should be shown so that all sizes can be determined and relative locations established without scaling the drawing. Superfluous dimensions should be avoided.
2. A dimension should be placed between points, lines, or surfaces which have a specific relation to each other so that the dimension can be interpreted in only one way.
3. Dimensions should not be repeated on separate views.
4. Each dimension should be placed on the view which shows the best contour of the feature and only where the dimension appears in true size.
5. Each dimension carries a tolerance indicated or understood. A *tolerance* is the maximum amount of variation to be permitted in the size of a single

dimension. A general tolerance is indicated by a note on the drawing. The general tolerance notation may be superseded by a specific tolerance in the dimension figures.

6. Choose dimensions in such a manner as to avoid or minimize accumulation of tolerances.
7. Do not specify manufacturing methods such as "drill," "ream," "bore," etc., in design drawings. However, such methods must be specified in process drawings.
8. Linear dimensions are commonly expressed in inches or in feet and inches. The inch-mark symbol is omitted from all dimensions when every dimension is in inches, except where the dimension might be misunderstood in a notation. Feet and inches are expressed as $8'-7\frac{1}{2}$ or as $8'-0\frac{1}{4}$.
9. Angular dimensions are commonly expressed in degrees, minutes, and seconds as required.
10. When common fractions are used, only the increments $\frac{1}{2}$, $\frac{1}{4}$, $\frac{1}{8}$, $\frac{1}{16}$, $\frac{1}{32}$, $\frac{1}{64}$ are acceptable. When a tolerance of less than $\pm\frac{1}{64}$ is required, decimal dimensions must be used. The division bar of the fraction should be horizontal and numerals should be placed clearly away from the bar.
11. Decimal dimensions may be used to replace common fractions altogether. Two-place decimals are used for dimensions where the tolerance can be $\pm.01$ or more; three-place decimals where the tolerance is less than $\pm.010$. The last place in a two-place or three-place decimal dimension for a diameter should preferably be chosen as an even digit, as .32, .054, etc., so that when halved it remains a two-place or three-place decimal. When dimensioning, no cipher should be placed to the left of the decimal point for decimal dimensions of less than one inch. All decimal dimensions showing tolerance should be expressed in the same number of decimal places as the tolerance.

19–4. SIZE AND LOCATION DIMENSIONS

It should be understood that determination of size and location is the desired objective for dimensioning regardless of techniques. To accomplish this, it is essential that there be a clear understanding of the shape to be dimensioned. This is best done by identifying and defining the geometric characteristics of the object represented. Complicated parts, when analyzed, can generally be visual-

ed as composed of cylinders, prisms, cones, or
ther geometric forms as in Fig. 19–1. Each geometric feature must be dimensioned for size and be
ositioned by location dimensions as in Fig. 19–2.
Dimensions are placed so that they locate from
dges, datum planes, or from center lines. Refer-
nce dimensions (Fig. 19–2) are theoretical values
ot necessary for construction, but they preserve
alculations or design data. All reference dimen-
ions should be accompanied by the notation
REF). Being theoretical, they carry no tolerance.

If used as regular dimensions, they would usually
cause duplication and accumulation of tolerance.

19–5. DIMENSIONING METHODS

A typical dimensioned view is illustrated in Fig.
19–3. A complete *dimension* consists of a dimension value indicating size or magnitude and a
dimension line terminated by arrowheads. A complete dimension may be placed between extension
lines. The *extension lines* "extend" from the view

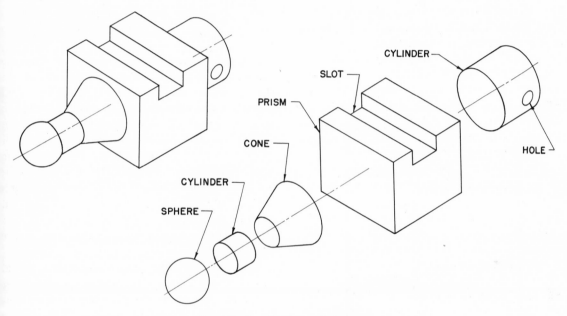

Fig. **19–1.** Analysis of shapes.

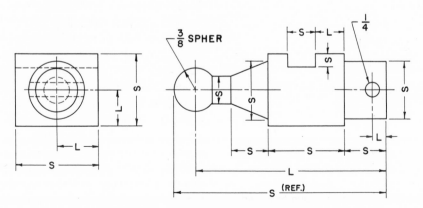

Fig. **19–2.** Size and location dimensions.

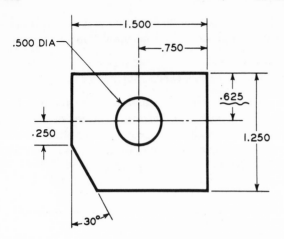

Fig. **19-3.** Leaders, dimension and extension lines. (Courtesy of ASA Y14.5–1957.)

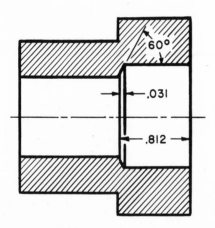

Fig. **19-4.** Dimensions within outlines. (Courtesy of ASA Y14.5–1957.)

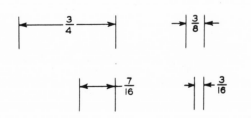

Fig. **19-5.** Optional placement due to crowding. (Courtesy of ASA Y14.5–1957.)

perpendicular to the distance being dimensioned. Both extension and dimension lines are fine lines to contrast with medium-weight object lines. Angular *leader lines* are used, with an appropriate notation, to specify the sizes of certain types of features, such as holes and chamfers. The leader and its associated notation is called a *note* or "call out." Dimensions may be in fractions or in decimals as required by a particular industrial practice. Dimension figures always indicate full size regardless of the scale of the drawing. The .625 dimension with wavy underlining, in Fig. 19–3, indicates that this particular dimension is not drawn to scale. Such dimensions result from revisions and save redrawing when only a few size changes are made.

It is generally preferable to place the dimension lines about ½″ away from and outside the view so that dimension figures are clearly readable. Additional parallel dimension lines should be spaced about ⅜″ apart. Dimensions are preferably placed outside the view, but may be placed on the view as in Fig. 19–4, where appropriate. Note that space is provided in the crosshatching to accommodate dimension figures on the view in a sectioned area. When features to be dimensioned are small and crowded dimensions would result, the arrowhead may be placed outside the extension lines as illustrated in Fig. 19–5.

Fig. 19–6 shows that extension lines do not touch the view and that they extend beyond the dimension line. Extension lines should cross each other without breaks except for small features as illustrated in Fig. 19–7. Extension lines should be used rather than placing dimensions and arrowheads at intersections or corners, as illustrated in Fig. 19–8. Arrowheads and dimension lines should not be the continuation of object lines. It should be noted, as in Fig. 19–3, that center lines may be used as extension lines. Fig. 19–9 illustrates that intermediate dimension lines, such as the two .60 dimensions, should be aligned as recommended and that it is preferred to place the 1.80 overall dimension on the same side of the object as the intermediate dimensions. When several dimensions are parallel as in Fig. 19–10, it is common to stagger the dimension values to make them more readable, instead of placing them in line. The parallel dimension lines are spaced uniformly apart.

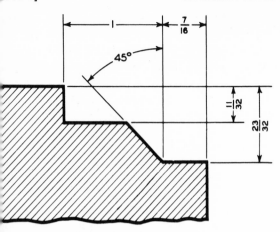

Fig. **19-6.** Crossing extension lines. (Courtesy of SA Y14.5-1957.)

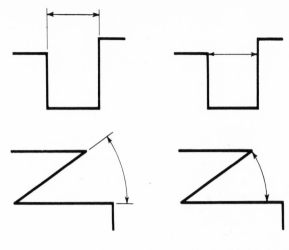

Recommended   Not Recommended

Fig. **19-8.** Use of extension lines. (Courtesy of ASA Y14.5-1957.)

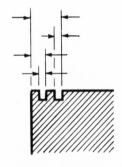

Fig. **19-7.** Breaks in extension lines. (Courtesy f ASA Y14.5-1957.)

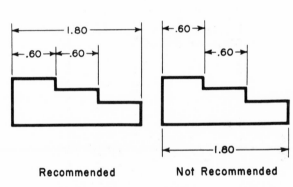

Recommended   Not Recommended

Fig. **19-9.** Placing intermediate dimensions. (Courtesy of ASA Y14.5-1957.)

In Fig. 19-3, all of the dimension figures—ertical, horizontal, and angular, as well as nota-ons—are placed to read from the bottom. This lacement is called the *unidirectional system* of imensioning. This system is universally used in e aero-space industry and is most convenient for rge drawings. In Fig. 19-6, all vertical dimen-ons are placed to read from the right side of the rawing while all horizontal dimensions, angular imensions, and notes read from below. This lacement is called the *aligned system.* Notations ould be placed to read from the bottom on all rawings. Figs. 19-11 and 19-12 illustrate posi-oning the dimension figures for the unidirectional nd aligned systems.

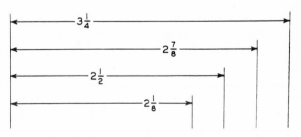

Fig. **19-10.** Staggered numerals. (Courtesy of ASA Y14.5-1957.)

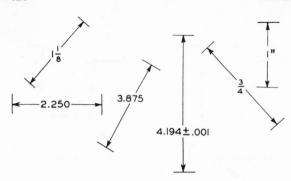

Fig. 19-11. Unidirectional dimensioning. (Courtesy of ASA Y14.5-1957.)

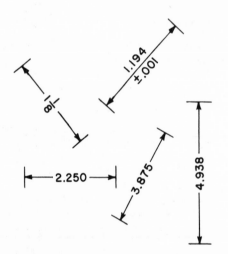

Fig. 19-12. Aligned dimensioning. (Courtesy of ASA Y14.5-1957.)

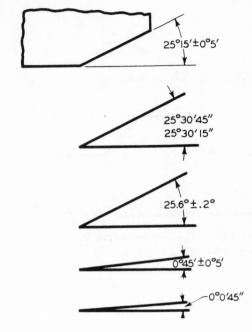

Fig. 19-13. Angular dimensions. (Courtesy of ASA Y14.5-1957.)

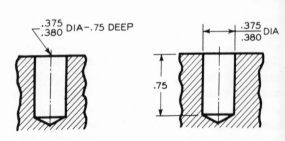

Fig. 19-14. Dimensioning holes. (Courtesy of ASA Y14.5-1957.)

Angular dimensions are expressed as in Fig. 19-13. The dimension line arc for the arrowheads has its center at the intersection of the sides of the angle dimensioned. All angular dimensions are written horizontally except for very large angles in which the dimension figures may be placed radially in a break in the dimension line arc.

All circular holes (negative cylinders) are dimensioned by their diameters—never by their radii. Small holes are preferably dimensioned by placing a size note on a leader in the view which shows the hole as a circle, as in Fig. 19-14. Alternate methods of dimensioning small holes are illustrated in this figure.

Cylinders are dimensioned by placing the length and diameter off the rectangular view, as in Fig. 19-15. The end view of a cylinder, which shows as a circle, is preferably not used in dimensioning its diameter.

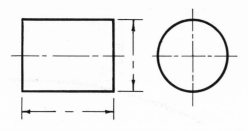

Fig. **19–15.** Length and diameter off the rectangular view.

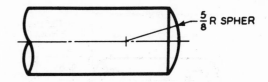

Fig. **19–17.** Spherical radius. (Courtesy of ASA Y14.5–1957.)

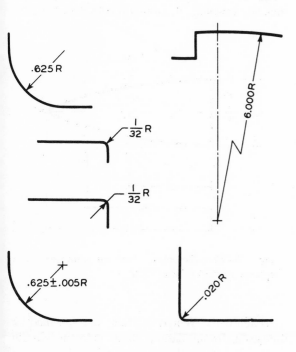

A radius may be dimensioned as:

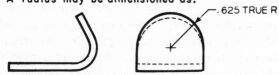

Fig. **19–16.** Dimensioning circle arcs. (Courtesy of ASA Y14.5–1957.)

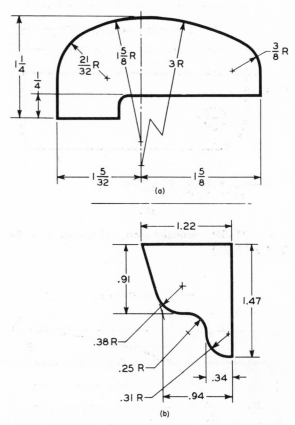

Fig. **19–18.** Curves composed of circle arcs. (Courtesy of ASA Y14.5–1957.)

Methods for dimensioning circle arcs are illustrated in Fig. 19–16. The abbreviation *R* for radius should accompany all radial dimensions. Except for small radii, the center of the arc should be indicated.

Features having spherical ends are dimensioned as a spherical radius, illustrated in Fig. 19–17. Fig.

19–18 shows the controlling of contours by the use of circle arcs. Parts with rounded ends may be controlled as in Fig. 19–19. In Fig. 19–19(a), it will be noted that the shape of the end of the piece is indicated without a numeral by the radius *R*. It is important to include the *R* to verify that the ends are arcs and to indicate their center. It would be considered duplication of dimensioning to give the size of the radius when the .926 and 1.852 dimensions are given.

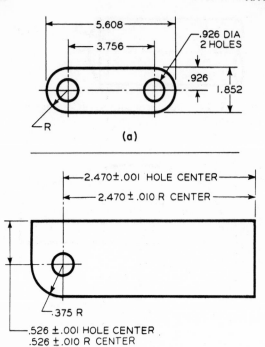

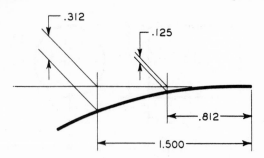

Fig. **19-21.** Non-circular curves where dimensions are crowded. (Courtesy of ASA Y14.5-1957.)

Fig. **19-19.** Rounded ends. (Courtesy of ASA Y14.5-1957.)

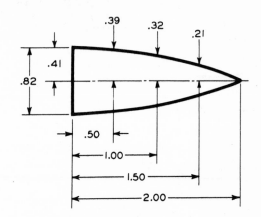

Fig. **19-22.** Dimension lines as extension lines. (Courtesy of ASA Y14.5-1957.)

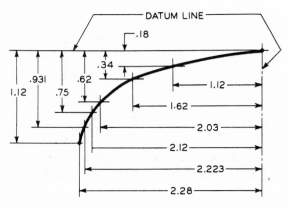

Fig. **19-20.** Non-circular curves. (Courtesy of ASA Y14.5-1957.)

Irregular curves are commonly dimensioned by plotting points which are located from datum lines by coordinates. "Datum points, lines or surfaces are features of a part which are assumed to be exact for purposes of computation or reference, and from which the location of other features of the part may

be established. Where positions are specified by dimensions from a datum, different features of the part are located with respect to these datums and not with respect to one another. Features which are selected to serve as datums must be clearly identified and easily recognizable."[1] The datum line may be a center line or a line in the surface of the object. Fig. 19-20 shows a typical application in dimensioning irregular curves, using datum lines and coordinates. Where the change of direction in the curve would create crowding, angularly placed extension lines may be used to indicate the coordinate distance, as in Fig. 19-21. Another method of dimensioning an irregular curve by coordinates is shown in Fig. 19-22 in which the dimension lines for the vertical coordinates are used as extension lines for the horizontal distances.

[1] ASA Y14. 5-1957.

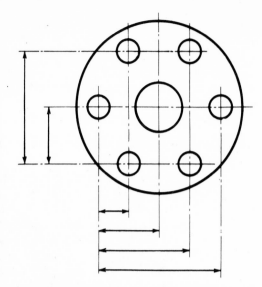

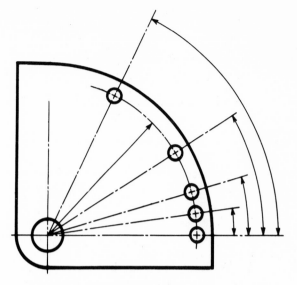

Fig. **19–23.** Locating holes by rectangular coordinates. (Courtesy of ASA Y14.5–1957.)

Fig. **19–24.** Locating holes by polar coordinates. (Courtesy of ASA Y14.5–1957.)

Rectangular coordinates are often used for accurate hole location as in Fig. 19–23. When a series of holes are equally spaced radially from a common center, they may be located on a circular center line by polar coordinates as in Fig. 19–24. Holes located by rectangular coordinates are generally considered to be more accurately located than by the radial method. Holes equally spaced on a common circular center line may be located as in Fig. 19–25. In a situation such as this the circular center line is sometimes referred to as a bolt circle.

19–6. DIMENSIONING FOR INTERCHANGE-ABILITY AND QUALITY CONTROL

Modern manufacturing methods require that any given part be interchangeable with any other like part. For example, a cam shaft designed for engine "X" must fit any engine "X" that is manufactured. This requirement has resulted in the development and use of limit dimensions.

As previously stated, all dimensions are subject to some tolerance, or permissible variation in size, that is specified directly or indirectly on the drawing. *Limits* are the maximum and minimum permissible sizes of a part. In determining the limits, two terms defining *size* are used. The *nominal size* is the designation used for general identification,

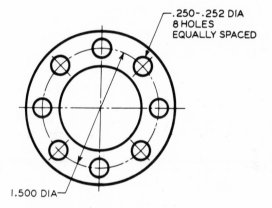

Fig. **19–25.** Locating holes on a bolt circle. (Courtesy of ASA Y14.5–1957.)

and is commonly expressed in fractional terms. For example: for a part with the limits of 1.498″ and 1.502″, the nominal size would be $1\frac{1}{2}$″. The *basic size* is the designation used for the size from which the limits are derived, and is expressed decimally to the number of places required by the tolerance used. For example: for a part whose nominal size is $1\frac{1}{2}$″ and which has a tolerance of ±.002″, the basic size would be 1.500″.

Another term encountered in connection with limit dimensioning is allowance. This refers to the

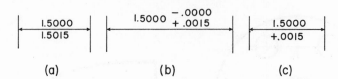

Fig. **19–26.** Expressing tolerance dimensions.

intentional variations of the limits of mating parts. *Allowance* is the desired minimum clearance or maximum interference between two mating parts. For example: consider a piston whose limits are 1.4987″ and 1.4982″ and which fits into a cylinder whose limits are 1.5015″ and 1.5000″. The largest allowable piston is 1.4987″ and the smallest allowable cylinder is 1.5000″. Hence the allowance is a *clearance* of .0013″. In another example, a valve insert has for the outside diameter limits of 1.5022″ and 1.5011″ and is to be placed in a hole which has the limits 1.5007″ and 1.5000″. Here the largest valve seat is 1.5022″ and the smallest hole is 1.5000″. Hence the allowance is an *interference* of .0022″. One method of assembling such parts is to chill the valve insert in order to reduce, temporarily, its diameter sufficiently to fit into the hole.

Limit dimensions may be written according to a variety of methods. Fig. 19–26 illustrates some of these methods. In Fig. 19–26(a), the most common method, the size is indicated by the actual limits. In Fig. 19–26(b), the size is indicated by giving the basic size together with its tolerance, while Fig. 19–26(c) shows only the basic size and

one tolerance value. In this latter case, the second tolerance is always taken as zero.

The order in which limits are lettered on the drawing depends upon the general machining process used. When using the method of Fig. 19–26(a), the upper dimension is always the first limit attained in machining. The machining of a hole essentially consists of removing material from the inside. Hence the smallest hole would be the first limit attained, and Fig. 19–26(a) is the correct dimensioning of a hole. In the case of the piston, the machining process is essentially one of removing material from the outside. Hence for a piston, or shaft, the largest limit would be the upper one shown on the drawing.

Choosing tolerances to satisfy specific design functions and to control fits and products for interchangeability is accomplished through the use of tables and formulae. Also important is experience and company policy. An adequate study of this detailed and constantly changing procedure is a function of more advanced design courses and will not be treated further here.

Fasteners

19–7. GENERAL

The components of a device or machine must be fastened together in some manner. The fastening may be permanent as in riveting or welding or it may be removable for disassembly as is possible with such fastening devices as screws, bolts, nuts, keys, pins, and various other locking devices. Special fasteners are continuously being devised to meet specific conditions which constantly arise in the design of new products. Standardized fasteners are used whenever possible and their specifications are available in handbooks and manufacturers'

catalogs. Innumerable types of fasteners are used in assembling hardware. In this section only a few of the more common standardized fasteners will be discussed.

19–8. THREADS

Screw threads have three general uses: fastening, adjusting, and transmitting power. Different types of threads have been developed to meet specific uses. Screw threads employ leverage or mechanical advantage based on the principle of the inclined plane; the plane, or thread, is wrapped around a cylinder in the form of a helix to give a climbing action (Fig. 19–27). The helix angle determines the rate of advance on the axis of the screw.

Screw thread terminology is illustrated in Fig. 19–28. External (male) threads are cut on the cylinder and any threaded shaft is called a screw. Internal (female) threads are cut in a hole, as in a *nut*. A nut in many instances may be considered to be a threaded hole in a machine part. The *major diameter* is the largest diameter of the thread and is the *nominal* or naming size. The *pitch diameter* is useful in accurately checking threads. The *minor diameter* is the smallest diameter of the thread. From the figure it will be seen that the *tap drill diameter* is the actual size of the hole in the nut. The specification of tap drill size controls the per cent of thread depth, which varies with design requirements and the hardness of the material being threaded. The *pitch* of a thread is the distance measured axially from a point on one thread to a corresponding point on the next thread. The pitch in inches is equal to the inverse of the number of threads per inch. The *lead* is the distance a screw advances axially in one revolution and, on single threads, is equal to the pitch. *Multiple threads* (Fig. 19–29) may be designed to provide rapid travel along the axis of the screw. On such threads the lead is increased so that on double threads it is twice the pitch, on triple threads it is three times the pitch, etc.

Either *right-hand* or *left-hand* threads may be produced. Left-hand threads must be so specified, otherwise the thread is understood to be right-hand. Generally, left-hand threads are used on bolt and nut combinations where inertia would tend to loosen the nut if a right-hand thread were used.

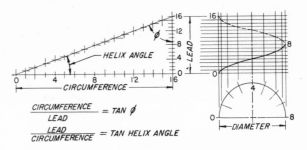

$$\frac{CIRCUMFERENCE}{LEAD} = TAN\ \phi$$

$$\frac{LEAD}{CIRCUMFERENCE} = TAN\ HELIX\ ANGLE$$

Fig. **19–27.** Development of a helix.

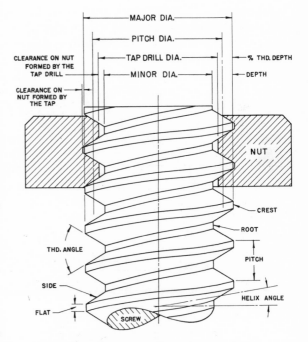

Fig. **19–28.** Screw thread terminology.

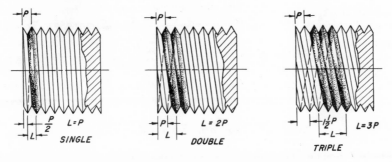

Fig. **19–29.** Single and multiple threads.

The threads used on fasteners, on shafts for transmitting power, and for adjusting are known as *straight threads*. They are cut, rolled, or otherwise produced parallel with the axis of the cylinder, and since they generally require clearance between the nut and screw, they do not form a leak-proof seal. When threads are expected to provide a seal, a standardized taper pipe thread may be specified which tapers in a ratio of 16 to 1.

19-9. THREAD FORMS

The *Unified* thread series is the accepted design for threads commonly used in fastening and adjusting (Fig. 19–30). It was adapted from the American National and British Whitworth forms (Fig. 19–31) to provide interchangeability and ease of manufacture. *Sharp* V threads are sometimes used on set screws. Where great strength is required

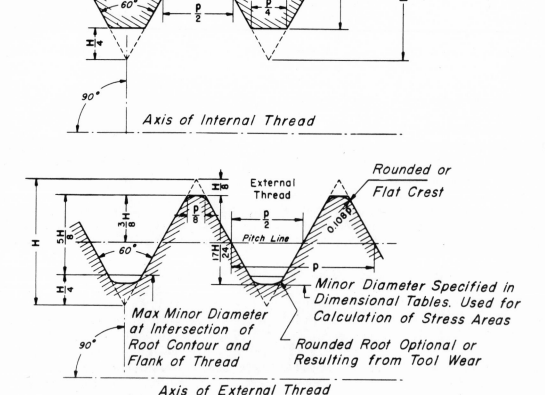

Fig. **19–30.** Unified and American screw thread forms. (Courtesy of ASA Y14.6–1957.)

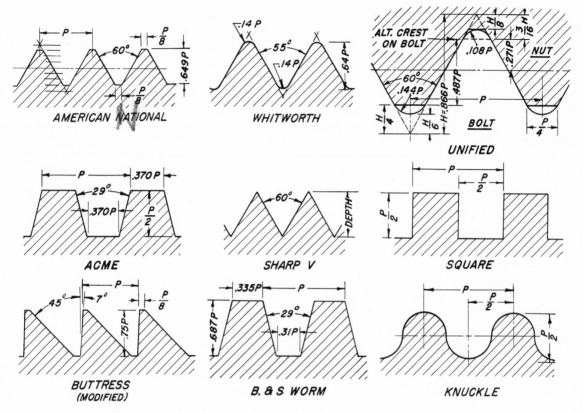

Fig. **19–31.** Thread forms in common use.

for transmission of power, as in jacks and vises, a *square* thread may be used. The *Acme* thread, having an included thread angle of 29°, was designed to transmit power and has a wide variety of uses. It will permit the use of a half or split nut to grip the screw in providing transverse motion on machines, whereas the square thread will not.

The *worm* thread is a modified form of the Acme thread and is used primarily in connection with gearing.

The *knuckle* thread form has many modifications, being useful in rough machinery, screw tops for jars, electric light bulb sockets, and other similar fittings.

Buttress threads are a combination of the square and V thread and are designed to withstand thrust in one direction. They are in common use by the military in breechblocks of artillery pieces which must withstand the pressures generated by the

propellent charge and then must be easily opened once that pressure has been dissipated.

19–10. THREAD SERIES

The American National (N) and the Unified (UN) thread forms have many features in common, as described in the ASA B1.1–1960 and ASA Y14.6–1957 Standards.

Unified and American National thread forms are divided into coarse, fine, extra fine, 8 pitch, 12 pitch, and 16 pitch thread series. The coarse thread series (NC or UNC) is commonly used for soft metals and where quick or easy assembly is desirable. Close fits may be obtained with coarse as well as with fine threads by controlling the tolerances. It is also preferred that coarse threads be used with the numbered screw sizes which are below $\frac{1}{4}''$ diameter. The fine thread series (NF or

UNF) is commonly used in aircraft and engine manufacture and other situations where vibration is a considerable factor. Extra fine series threads (NEF or UNEF) may be used where close adjustments are desired, where thin-walled materials are to be threaded, where the height of nuts must be held to a minimum, and where a maximum number of threads is desired to give a maximum strength within a given thread length. It may be noted that fine threads provide greater holding power than coarse threads, all other considerations being equal. Coarse threads, however, are preferred where the design function permits because they are cheaper to manufacture.

The 8 pitch, 12 pitch, and 16 pitch thread series are uniform pitch series which may be used for larger diameters. The 8 pitch series is often a substitute for coarse threads for diameters larger than 1″; the 12 pitch, as a continuation of fine threads larger than 1.5″; the 16 pitch, as a continuation of extra fine threads for diameters larger than 2″.

19-11. THREAD CLASSES

Classes of thread indicate the amount of tolerance permissible in thread manufacture. The specific tolerances represented by the class notations are available from the American Standard Unified and American Screw Threads, ASA B1.1-1960. Three classes of threads are in common use, classes 1, 2, and 3. Class 1 provides the greatest tolerance, class 3 the least. Classes 1A, 2A, and 3A are applied to external threads only; classes 1B, 2B, and 3B are applied to internal threads. These classes of fit may be selected for any thread diameters and identify the tolerance limits specified in the tables for the diameter noted. It is necessary to specify class A or class B tolerances for mating parts since the class A tolerance on the shaft or screw is generally somewhat closer than the class B tolerance on threaded holes. This compensates for limitations in manufacture of threads. Classes 2A and 2B are commonly used for commercial products such as general-purpose threads for bolts, nuts, screws, and normal applications in the mechanical field where lead and angle error can be permitted. In some cases they may be used for aeronautical purposes on non-structural parts where loads are considered to be minor or insignificant. Classes 3A and 3B have been generally adopted by the aeronautical industry for most threading applications.

19-12. SPECIFYING THREADS

Thread specifications are placed on drawings in the form of a notation with an angular leader to the threaded shaft or threaded hole. The thread size is designated by listing in consecutive order the nominal size, the number of threads per inch, the thread series, and the class of tolerance, as in Fig. 19-32. In the illustration the decimal fraction is used to indicate the nominal size. A common fraction or a numbered size may be used instead. The thread form and series UNC indicates a Unified National coarse thread. If the thread series were changed to a fine (F) or extra fine (EF) series, there would be a corresponding change in the number of threads per inch for the given size. Any one of the three classes of tolerance could be used with this thread, but class 2A is specified. The "A" indicates the tolerance for an external thread. Were this same thread to be used in a nut, the class of tolerance would be 2B. Note that the placement of dashes is only after the nominal size and before the class of tolerance. This is a right-hand thread because no indication of left-hand is made. Were a left-hand thread desired, a dash and the letters LH would be added to the right of the class of tolerance. The spacing of the written notation would be .750-10 UNC-2A-LH. The thread specified in Fig. 19-32 is also a single thread because there is no indication of multiplicity. A multiple thread would be specified by adding a dash and the word DOUBLE, TRIPLE, etc., as required, at the end of the specification.

The type of designation explained above is used for threads on manufactured products where a

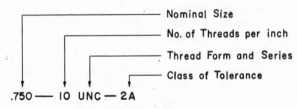

Fig. **19-32.** Thread specification. (Courtesy of SAE Aero Space Drafting Manual—1963.)

tolerance is desired. The tolerance limits control the fit that will result. To write a specification in such a manner as $\frac{1}{4}$–20 UNC tap (or thread) in no way insures that a controlled fit will be produced. The designer is leaving the fit to whatever results from the machine tools used. Special and modified threads sometimes require information regarding the pitch diameter, major diameter, and minor diameter tolerances. This requires a form of notation available from standards manuals.

The thread notation indicated in Fig. 19–32 is used to specify threads only. A more complete description, illustrated later, is used to specify fasteners.

Screw thread diameters and corresponding threads per inch are shown in the Screw Thread Series table, Fig. 19–33. It will be noted that when specifying threads in fractional sizes all diameters under $\frac{1}{4}''$ are given by numbered screw size. The table identifies the standard number of threads per inch for each screw thread series. In writing a thread notation, the designer obtains information regarding diameter, number of threads per inch, and thread series from the table, but must add to the notation a class of tolerance to satisfy the intended design function of the thread.

19–13. THREAD REPRESENTATION

Threads are represented conventionally with symbols which modify the true picture of the thread. The American Standards show threads represented as in Fig. 19–34. It will be noted that the detailed thread representation [Fig. 19–34(a)] shows the thread outline with crest and root lines simulating the thread. The schematic representation [Fig. 19–34(b)] eliminates the groove outlines of the thread, but is suggestive of crest and root outlines. The simplified representation [Fig. 19–34(c)] is most commonly used. In the simplified representation the major diameter of the thread is a measured size with the minor diameter approximated to illustrate the thread. It will be noted that threaded shafts or screws are chamfered on the ends. It is preferable that threaded holes be threaded (tapped) all the way through the material. When this is impractical or undesirable for reasons of appearance, blind holes are tapped part way through the material. The hole made by the drill

point must be included since it affects the strength of the piece. Generally, holes are illustrated as threaded to a depth of approximately twice the diameter of the screw with the drilled hole showing beyond the threads to a convenient distance (approximately one-half the diameter of the screw). In the assembled representation of Fig. 19–34(d), detail and schematic representation are shown. Simplified representation could have been used. To prevent stripping in hard metals, a threaded shaft should enter the hole a minimum of one and one-half times the diameter of the thread. To design a threaded shaft to enter a hole to excessive length is considered wasteful. Note that the threaded end of the hexagonal-head cap screw shows three things: the chamfered end of the screw, the end of the threaded hole, and the drilled hole.

The aero-space industry recommends the use of simplified thread representation and for some time has used phantom lines instead of dashes to represent thread roots, as illustrated in Fig. 19–35. Phantom lines are thin, broken lines with two short dashes located in each break. The figure also illustrates tapered pipe threads which actually taper in a ratio of 16 to 1 as opposed to straight threads without taper. When it is necessary to use detailed representation for threads, it is common practice to use a template for constructing the outlines. Templates are available for Unified, Acme, Square, and other thread forms.

19–14. FASTENER USAGE

The many varieties of fasteners and the number of manufacturers of fastener products are legion. A complete classification in this text would be impractical. New fasteners are designed and patented for each new condition that arises. They are made up on special order in large or small quantities and perform their function by clipping, pinning, interlocking, riveting, keying, and most commonly by the use of engaged screw threads.

Many bolts, nuts, cap screws, machine screws, set screws, washers, and keys have been standardized. The specifications for their manufacture are set up in tables by the ASA and other standards organizations and, where design conditions permit, it is both logical and economical to specify such standard purchased fasteners.

Size	Basic Major Dia	Coarse (UNC or NC)*	Fine (UNF or NF)*	Extra Fine (UNEF or NEF)*	8 Thread Series (UN, N or NS)*	12 Thread Series (UN or N)*	16 Thread Series (UN or N)*	Size
		Threads Per Inch						
0	0.0600	—	80	—	—	—	—	0
1	0.0730	64	72	—	—	—	—	1
2	0.0860	56	64	—	—	—	—	2
3	0.0990	48	56	—	—	—	—	3
4	0.1120	40	48	—	—	—	—	4
5	0.1250	40	44	—	—	—	—	5
6	0.1380	32	40	—	—	—	—	6
8	0.1640	32	36	—	—	—	—	8
10	0.1900	24	32	—	—	—	—	10
12	0.2160	24	28	32	—	—	—	12
1/4	0.2500	20	28	32	—	—	—	1/4
5/16	0.3125	18	24	32	—	—	—	5/16
3/8	0.3750	16	24	32	—	—	—	3/8
7/16	0.4375	14	20	28	—	—	—	7/16
1/2	0.5000	13	20	28	—	12	—	1/2
9/16	0.5625	12	18	24	—	12	—	9/16
5/8	0.6250	11	18	24	—	12	—	5/8
11/16	0.6875	—	—	24	—	12	—	11/16
3/4	0.7500	10	16	20	—	12	16	3/4
13/16	0.8125	—	—	20	—	12	16	13/16
7/8	0.8750	9	14	20	—	12	16	7/8
15/16	0.9375	—	—	20	—	12	16	15/16
1	1.0000	—	14 **	—	—	—	—	1
1	1.0000	8	12	20	8	12	16	1
1- 1/16	1.0625	—	—	18	—	12	16	1- 1/16
1- 1/8	1.1250	7	12	18	8	12	16	1- 1/8
1- 3/16	1.1875	—	—	18	—	12	16	1- 3/16
1- 1/4	1.2500	7	12	18	8	12	16	1- 1/4
1- 5/16	1.3125	—	—	18	—	12	16	1- 5/16
1- 3/8	1.3750	6	12	18	8	12	16	1- 3/8
1- 7/16	1.4375	—	—	18	—	12	16	1- 7/16
1- 1/2	1.5000	6	12	18	8	12	16	1- 1/2
1- 9/16	1.5625	—	—	18	—	—	16	1- 9/16
1- 5/8	1.6250	—	—	18	8	12	16	1- 5/8
1-11/16	1.6875	—	—	18	—	—	16	1-11/16
1- 3/4	1.7500	5	—	16	8	12	16	1- 3/4
1-13/16	1.8125	—	—	—	—	—	16	1-13/16
1- 7/8	1.8750	—	—	—	8	12	16	1- 7/8
1-15/16	1.9375	—	—	—	—	—	16	1-15/16
2	2.0000	4 ½	—	16	8	12	16	2
2- 1/16	2.0625	—	—	—	—	—	16	2- 1/16
2- 1/8	2.1250	—	—	—	8	12	16	2- 1/8
2- 3/16	2.1875	—	—	—	—	—	16	2- 3/16
2- 1/4	2.2500	4 ½	—	—	8	12	16	2- 1/4
2- 5/16	2.3125	—			—	—	16	2- 5/16
2- 3/8	2.3750	—			—	12	16	2- 3/8
2- 7/16	2.4375	—			—	—	16	2- 7/16
2- 1/2	2.5000	4			8	12	16	2- 1/2
2- 5/8	2.6250	—			—	12	16	2- 5/8
2- 3/4	2.7500	4			8	12	16	2- 3/4
2- 7/8	2.8750	—			—	12	16	2- 7/8
3	3.0000	4			8	12	16	3
3- 1/8	3.1250	—			—	12	16	3- 1/8
3- 1/4	3.2500	4			8	12	16	3- 1/4
3- 3/8	3.3750	—			—	12	16	3- 3/8
3- 1/2	3.5000	4			8	12	16	3- 1/2
3- 5/8	3.6250	—			—	12	16	3- 5/8
3- 3/4	3.7500	4			8	12	16	3- 3/4
3- 7/8	3.8750	—			—	12	16	3- 7/8
4	4.0000	4			8	12	16	4
4- 1/4	4.2500	—			8	12	16	4- 1/4
4- 1/2	4.5000	—			8	12	16	4- 1/2
4- 3/4	4.7500	—			8	12	16	4- 3/4
5	5.0000	—	—	—	8	12	16	5
5- 1/4	5.2500	—	—	—	8	12	16	5- 1/4
5- 1/2	5.5000	—	—	—	8	12	16	5- 1/2
5- 3/4	5.7500	—	—	—	8	12	16	5- 3/4
6	6.0000	—	—	—	8	12	16	6

* For Series Symbols applying to a particular thread, see dimensional tables ASA B1.1
** NS

Extracted from ASA Y14.6—1957.

Fig. **19-33.** Screw Thread Series table. (Courtesy of ASA Y14.6–1957.)

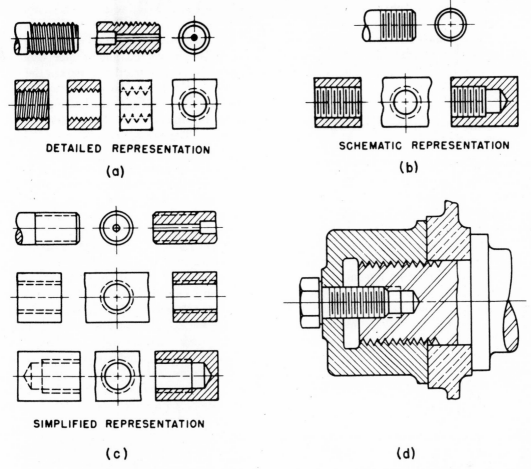

DETAILED REPRESENTATION

(a)

SCHEMATIC REPRESENTATION

(b)

SIMPLIFIED REPRESENTATION

(c)

(d)

Fig. **19-34.** Thread representation. (Courtesy of ASA Y14.6–1957.)

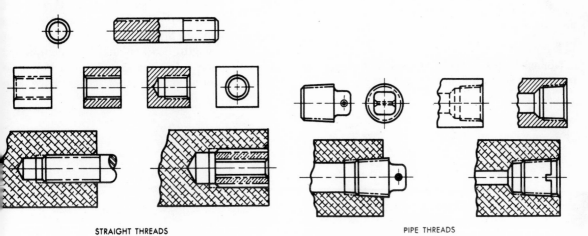

STRAIGHT THREADS

PIPE THREADS

Fig. **19-35.** Straight and pipe threads. (Courtesy of SAE Aero Space Drafting Manual—1963.)

It is common practice to alter standard fasteners or design new ones for special purposes when required. It will be found that many seemingly common fasteners are not standardized and their specifications must be obtained from or submitted to the manufacturer.

19-15. SQUARE AND HEXAGONAL BOLTS AND NUTS

Specifications for square and hexagonal bolts and nuts are available from the American Standard ASA B18.2–1960. This standard lists three series for bolts and nuts. The *Regular Series* bolt heads and nuts are for general use. *Heavy Series* bolt heads and nuts are for use where greater bearing service is necessary. *Light Series* nuts have smaller dimensions across the flats than the regular series nuts. In addition to the use classification, the finish or machining on bolts or nuts varies with each series and must be checked with the standards. Unfinished bolts and nuts are not finished (machined) on any surface. Semifinished bolts and nuts are processed to have a flat bearing surface under the head only. Finished bolts and nuts are machined only to the extent that they conform to specified tolerance. In finished bolts and nuts, "finished" refers to the quality and does not indicate that all surfaces are completely machined except as they must conform to specified tolerances.

American Standards tables (see Appendix) are available which specify the recommended sizes for regular and heavy, square and hexagonal, semifinished and finished, bolt head and nut combinations.

Nomenclature. The following definitions are from the American Standard ASA B18.2–1960.

Washer Face. The washer face is a circular boss turned or otherwise produced on the bearing surface of a bolt head or nut to relieve the corners. A similar circular bearing surface can also be produced by chamfering the corners of the nut.

Height of Head. The height of head is the overall distance from the top to the bearing surface and includes the thickness of the washer face where provided. (The washer face is usually $\frac{1}{64}''$ thick for all sizes.)

Thickness of Nut. The thickness of nut is the overall distance from the top to the bearing surface and includes the thickness of the washer face where provided.

Thread Length. Thread length is the distance from the extreme point (end of the fastener) to the last complete thread.

Bolt Length. Bolt length is the distance from the bearing surface of the head to the extreme point.

Thread Tolerance. Current standards specify class 2A for external threads. Unless otherwise agreed by manufacturer and user, class 2 may be substituted by the manufacturer for an indefinite period to permit exhaustion of existing stock and practical replacement of material, tools, and gages.

Dimensions. All dimensions in the ASA Standard are in inches unless otherwise stated.

Fig. 19–36 illustrates some of the features in nut shapes. In addition to finished and unfinished square and hexagonal nuts, there are other standard variations. *Jam nuts* are thinner than regular nuts and may be beveled on both sides or with a washer face. They are used principally in pairs as locking devices. Standard *thick nuts* have excessive height for added strength. Locking may be accomplished by slotting the nuts to receive a cotter key as in *slotted nuts* or as in *castle nuts*. These have been

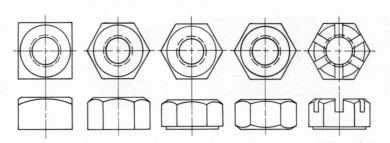

Fig. **19–36.** Nut shapes.

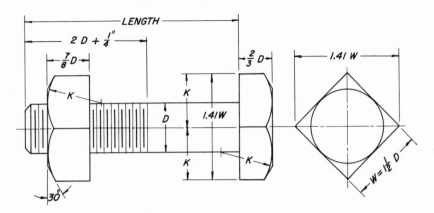

Fig. **19–37.** Square bolt and nut proportions.

standardized. An infinite number of now standard patented locking devices have been developed for special uses. Some of these are designed as special locking nuts while others are used in conjunction with lock washers.

19–16. DRAWING BOLT HEADS AND NUTS

General size formulas for bolt head and nut shapes are available in the Standards. More accurate specifications for bolts and nuts should be obtained from the tables when clearance is important in designing. Bolt and nut proportions may be used on drawings as illustrated in Figs. 19–37 and 19–38. The general proportions are based on the shank diameter *D*.

It is common practice when drawing hexagonal and square heads and nuts in profile to show the outline across the corners regardless of true projec-

tion from the end view of the head or nut. That is, two flats will always show in the profile view of a square head or nut regardless of projection, and three flats will always show in every profile of a hexagonal head or nut. Washer faces are generally omitted from the drawing since it is understood that a bearing surface must be provided in the manufacture of the fastener.

19–17. SPECIFYING BOLTS AND NUTS

Bolt specifications for ordering and for parts lists are given by stating in order the diameter and thread specification including class of fit, length of bolt, finish, and type of head, followed by the name of the fastener, bolt.

Example: $\frac{1}{2}$–13 UNC–2A $\times$ $1\frac{3}{4}$ SEMI-FIN. HEX HEAD BOLT

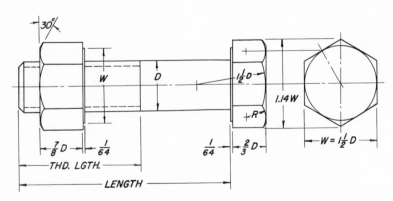

Fig. **19–38.** Hexagonal bolt and nut proportions.

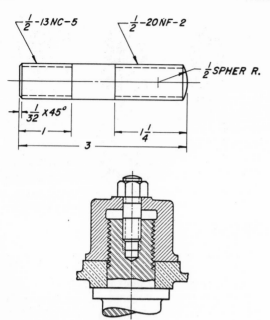

Fig. **19–39.** (Top) A stud. (Bottom) A stud in assembly.

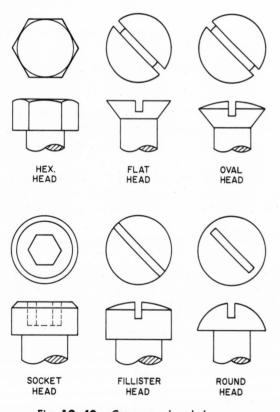

Fig. **19–40.** Cap screw head shapes.

Remember, in writing specifications, nuts or other headless fasteners do not have heads.

Example: ¾–10 UNC–2B REGULAR HEX NUT

Abbreviated and non-standard fastener specifications are often used carelessly or for convenience, but in ordering or specifying the fastener, notation must be complete to include threads and materials. If other than steel the material must be noted in the specification.

Bolt lengths have not been standardized by the ASA or by all the manufacturers. However, for the Regular Series Bolts shown in the Appendix, the length increments can be assumed to be ⅛″ for bolts from ¼″ to ¾″ long; ¼″ for bolts from ¾″ to 3″ long; and ½″ for bolts from 3″ to 6″ long.

19–18. STUDS

Of the common fasteners, *studs* or *stud bolts* provide the strongest holding power (Fig. 19–39). They are used in practically all forms of construction and machine design, notably on cylinder heads. They have threads on both ends with the stud end being screwed semipermanently into the material the full depth of the threads by means of a special stud wrench. It is quite common to use coarse threads on the stud end and fine threads on the nut end because the final tightening is accomplished with the nut. Studs are designed to meet a specific need and are not purchased as standard parts. Since threads and thread lengths are available on drawings, it is common practice to refer to the stud by its nominal diameter and overall length as: ½ × 3 STUD.

19–19. CAP SCREWS

Cap screws are the most common fasteners in machine construction. They are used to draw parts tightly together by passing through a clearance hole in the first member and threading into a tapped hole in the second member. Standardized head shapes are hexagonal, socket, flat, oval, fillister, and round (Fig. 19–40). The hexagonal and socket heads provide greatest holding power because they can be tightened with wrenches. Slotted heads, tightened with a screw driver, are used only in light construction where holding power is secondary. A bearing surface for the underside of the head is usually provided on parts to be held by cap screws by counterboring, spotfacing, or countersinking, as illustrated in Fig. 19–41.

It is common practice to show the screw threaded into the second member one to one and one-half times the major diameter, except in softer metals where the screw should enter to a depth of twice the diameter. Excessive lengths are undesirable. In the end views, screwdriver slots are drawn diagonally across the circle regardless of projection and center lines. Cap and machine screw specifications should be complete, including thread specification, length, type of head, name of fastener, and other data regarding material (if other than steel) and finish.

19–20. MACHINE SCREWS

Machine screws are similar to cap screws, but are limited to a smaller size range, the largest being $\frac{3}{4}''$ in diameter. The four most common head shapes are flat, oval, round, and fillister. All four shapes may have slotted or recessed heads. The threaded ends may be chamfered or unchamfered. Whereas cap screws are intended to be used without nuts, machine screws are furnished with hexagonal or square nuts as ordered.

19–21. SET SCREWS

Set screws are used to prevent relative movement between parts and for adjusting. They should be used for light-duty applications and are not intended for heavy duty or where sudden loads may develop. It is desirable to provide machined flats or recesses on shafts to make better bearing surfaces for set screw points. Set screws are made with flat, oval, cone, cup, and dog points. Square head, screwdriver slot, and socket head types are standard. It is mandatory that screwdriver or headless socket types be used and set flush with or under the surface of parts which revolve in order to prevent accidents. The head shapes may be obtained in any combination with any of the points, in either coarse or fine thread series. The point and head shape must be included in the specification, as well as the threads and name of the fastener, as:

$\frac{3}{8}$–16 $\times$ $\frac{3}{4}$ CUP PT. SOC. HD. SET SCR.

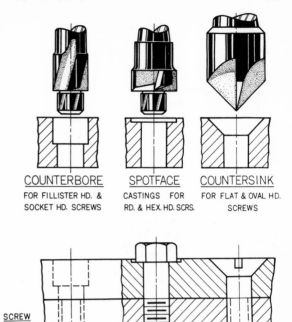

Fig. **19–41.** Counterboring, spotfacing, and countersinking.

19–22. KEYS

Keys are used to carry thrust or torque and prevent relative motion between machined parts, as in pulleys, gears, or cranks mounted on shafts. There are many types of keys and consequently considerable overlapping in their features, usefulness, and classification. Standard sizes and recommended tolerances are available in handbooks. The rectangular, Gib head, Pratt and Whitney, and Woodruff keys, shown in Fig. 19–42, are common types. The Pratt and Whitney keys are rectangular with rounded ends fitted in a key seat. The Woodruff key is useful in light-duty construction, having less strength than square-type keys and requiring less exact fitting.

19–23. PINS

Taper pins are often used to fix gears, pulleys, collars, and handwheels to shafts where relatively light holding is required. The taper reamed hole

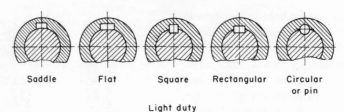

Saddle   Flat   Square   Rectangular   Circular or pin

Light duty

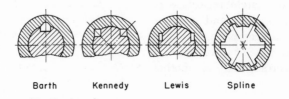

Barth   Kennedy   Lewis   Spline

Heavy duty

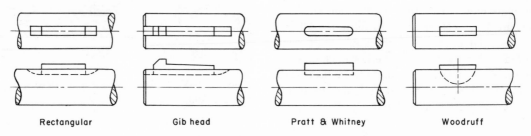

Rectangular   Gib head   Pratt & Whitney   Woodruff

Fig. 19–42. Key shapes.

($\frac{1}{4}$″ per foot) to receive the pin is generally made after the parts have been assembled. Steel dowel pins are commonly used where parts must be kept from lateral movement as in fastening metal plates. When fastening metal plates, screws or bolts hold the parts together but do not positively prevent lateral movement. Two dowel pins pressed in reamed holes located near opposite edges of the plates are used in addition to screws to guarantee no relative movement between the parts.

19–24. WELDED CONSTRUCTION, RIVETED JOINTS, AND PIPING

Many joints are made permanent through the use of welding and riveting. Piping involves a detailed study of fittings and assembly techniques. Each of these types of fastening requires much specialized study in the areas of strength of materials, machine design, and mechanics, and will not be treated here.

Working Drawings

19–25. GENERAL INFORMATION

Working drawings are made to provide the necessary information for the manufacture or construction of parts, objects, or structures. Working drawings include: detail drawings which completely describe the details of a single part, and assembly drawings which show all the parts of a complete machine or structure, or portion thereof, assembled in their relative working positions.

Generally there are two classes of working drawings made during the total manufacturing process. The first is usually made during the engineering or design phase and is concerned only with the creation of the engineering concept and with the experimental work required in developing new products or in improving products already being manufactured. The working drawings made during this phase most frequently start as sketches (Fig. 19–43) and are then refined into accurate, carefully constructed instrumental drawings. These drawings completely control the size, shape, and function of parts irrespective of production methods.

The second class, on the other hand, is primarily concerned with production methods. The detail drawings created during this phase of production are often known as process or operation drawings. A process drawing is one that only provides the information for a particular operation in the fabrication of a single part. These drawings might show such operations as forging, casting, and machining. A forging drawing is illustrated in Fig. 19–44 and a machining drawing is illustrated in Fig. 19–45. In quantity production, a separate machining drawing is made for each individual setup. In this case the drawing is called an operation drawing. The preparation of process drawings requires detailed knowledge of shop operations and is not considered to be within the scope of this text.

Some confusion exists concerning the terms "assembly drawing" and "layout drawing." They look alike, but the intent is different. A layout drawing is usually thought of as being the initial drawing made in developing a product. It shows the interrelation of the component parts of the product and shows important dimensions and notes. It is used as a reference for the detail drawings. An assembly drawing, on the other hand, is generally considered as being made after detailing has been completed. An assembly drawing shows only dimensions (usually overall dimensions) of interest to the user and the part numbers of the components. A layout drawing is shown in Fig. 19–46 and an assembly drawing is shown in Fig. 19–47.

19–26. DETAIL DRAWINGS

The class of detail drawings to be presented here is the one which shows completely the size and shape of a single part. Normally, only one part is described on each sheet. In preparing the detail drawing, much time can be saved if the part is sketched first in order to determine how the views will best fit on the sheet and where the dimensions should be located. Full scale is desirable in detailing, but obviously, very small parts, such as watch parts, must be enlarged, and excessively large parts must be reduced. The scale of the drawing is always shown in the title block.

Title blocks and record strips are included on working drawings for the purpose of supplying general information. Title blocks are normally located in the lower right corner of the drawing. On small sheets they may cover the entire bottom or side of the sheet. Fig. 19–48 shows a typical title block and record strip. The record strip is used to show any revisions and the dates that they occurred. The user of the drawing will first look for general information in the title block and record strip. Information which is too voluminous for the blanks in the title should be entered in suitable areas of the drawing in the form of general notations, and the statement "See Note" or "Noted" entered in the space provided in the title.

The views used to describe an object in a detail drawing are chosen by following the principles discussed in Chapter 6, Orthographic View Construction. Only sufficient principal views, sections, and auxiliary views to describe the shape completely should be used. Views which do not add to the shape description or clarify the dimensioning should be omitted. In the selection of views, some consideration should be given to the normal working position of the part. However, it is more important that the front view on the drawing show the best picture of the contour of the object, and that hidden lines be reduced to a minimum.

When the required views of the object are completed, the dimensions necessary to control completely the size and shape are added according to the rules established in the first section of this chapter. Fig. 19–49 shows a completed detail drawing. Note that the dimensions do not specify a method of machining.

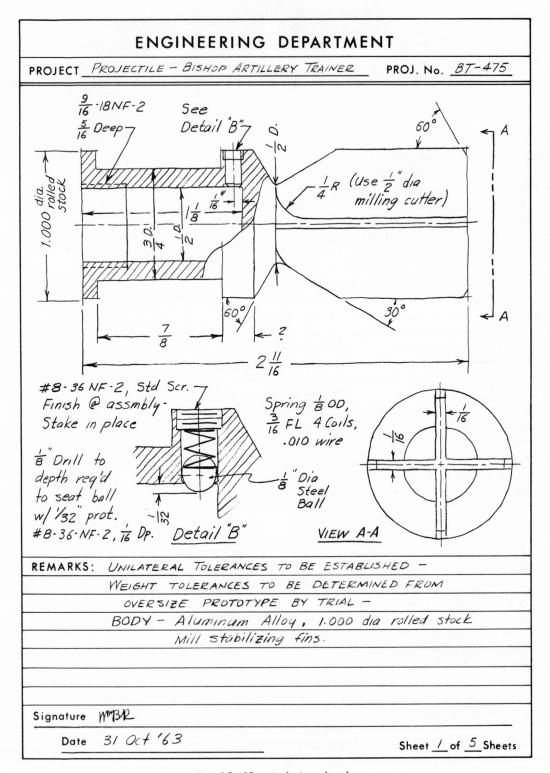

Fig. **19-43.** A design sketch.

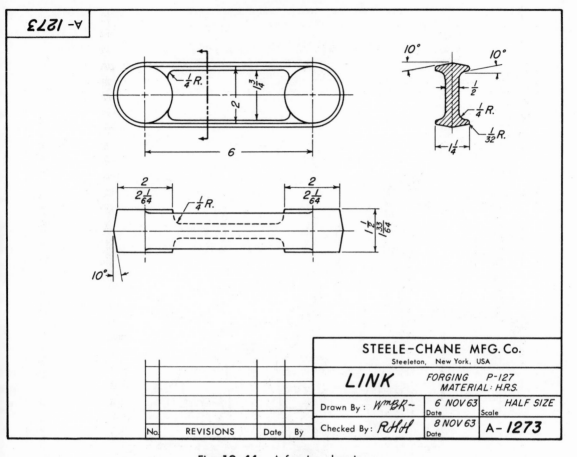

Fig. **19–44.** A forging drawing.

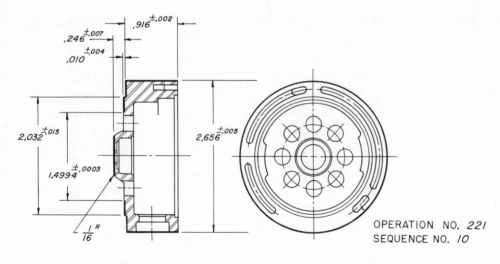

OPERATION NO. *221*
SEQUENCE NO. *10*

ISSUED BY *B.J.C.* DATE *1-1-64* PART NAME *CAP* SHEET *2* OF *15* PART NO. *97426*

Fig. **19–45.** A machining drawing.

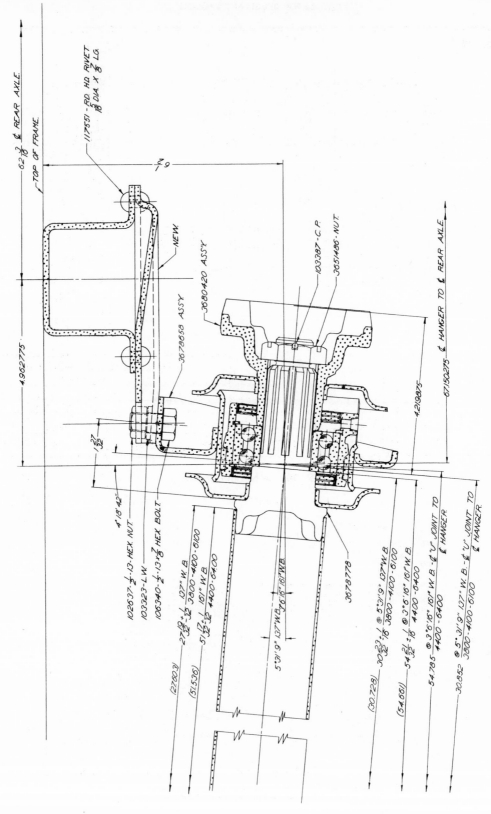

Fig. 19-46. A layout drawing. (Courtesy of Chevrolet Motor Division, General Motors Corporation.)

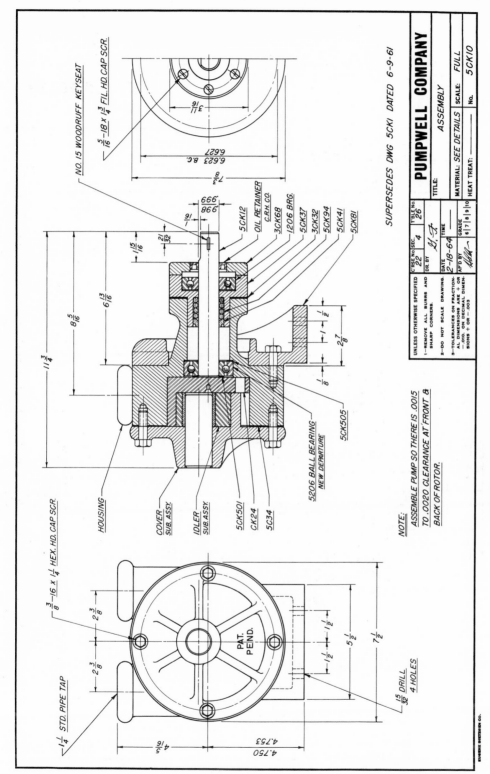

Fig. **19–47.** A general assembly drawing.

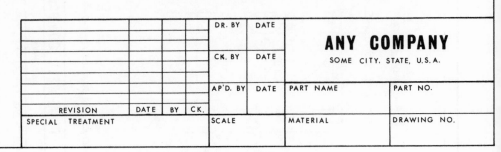

Fig. **19–48.** A title block and record strip.

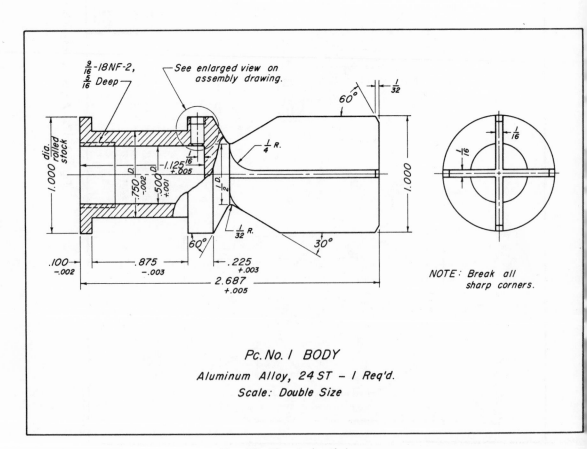

Fig. **19–49.** A detail drawing.

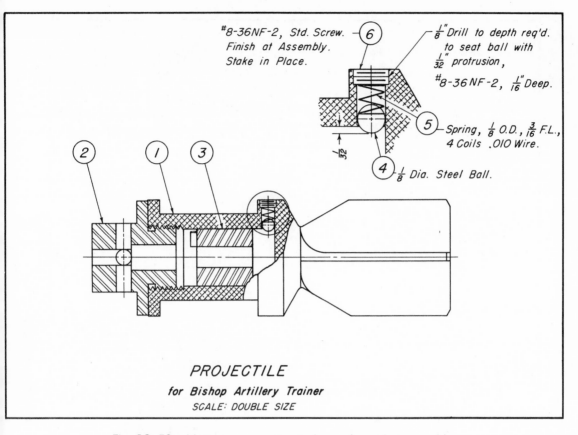

Fig. **19–50.** Noting an operation to be performed at assembly.

9–27. ASSEMBLY DRAWINGS

An assembly drawing is made when it is desirable to show the relative positions of more than one part of a machine or structure. In addition to showing the relationship of component parts, an assembly drawing is useful in supplying information concerning how the components are put together or assembled as well as to give the overall size and appearance of the completed assembly.

A general assembly drawing may serve to identify parts, furnish location dimensions, and show information for assembly. Fig. 19–47 shows such an assembly. A general assembly drawing may contain a parts list, but usually the parts list is supplied separately on a parts list specification sheet.

A subassembly drawing is used to show the relationships of small groups of parts of a complete assembly. Such a subassembly is often used to

show how parts are pressed, crimped, brazed, or otherwise fastened together. Another use for a subassembly drawing occurs when it is desirable to assemble a group of parts before some machining operation is performed. Close tolerances and expensive machining can sometimes be avoided by this procedure. Fig. 19–50 illustrates this technique. In the illustration, a screw is to be staked in place and then finished off flush with the surface of the body. The detail drawings do not show this (see Fig. 19–49). However, the subassembly, shown to an enlarged scale in Fig. 19–50, provides the necessary information.

An outline assembly drawing is made to show only the visible outlines of the assembly. Such a drawing is useful in giving installation instructions and showing clearance requirements. Catalog data are often accompanied by an outline assembly drawing.

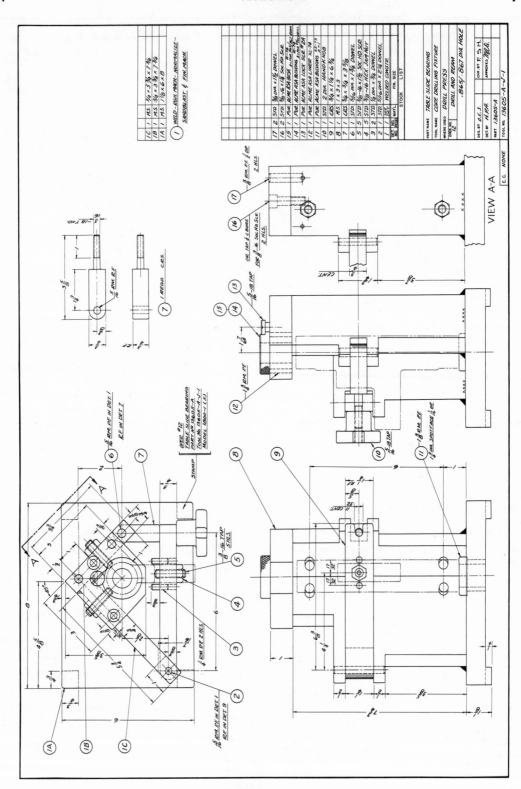

Fig. 19-51. An assembly working drawing.

An assembly working drawing, though not in common use by engineering departments, can be used when the component parts can be clearly detailed on the assembly drawing. Fig. 19-51 is a typical working assembly drawing.

Problems

19-1. Prepare detail drawings of objects as assigned from Chapter 6.

19-2. Answer the following questions with the word or phrase that describes the fastener element shown in Fig. 19-52.

    1-14. Give the technical terminology for each fastener element shown by letters *A* through *O*.

    15. What does *P* represent?

    16. What does *Q* represent?

    17. What is *S*?

    18. What is the recess represented by *T*?

    19. What type of thread representation is used on the bolt?

    20. What type of thread representation is used on the oval head screw?

19-3. Answer the following questions concerning Fig. 19-53.

1. What does the dimension *O* represent with regard to the fastened part?
2. What does *P* represent?
3. At what included angle is *R* drawn?
4. What does *M* represent?
5. What does *L* represent?
6. What does *J* represent?
7. What does *K* represent?
8. Should *F* be a solid or dashed line?
9. Should the crosshatch lines extend through line *H*?
10. Should *E* be a solid or dashed line?
11. What is the recommended relationship of *A* to *D* when the material is steel?
12. What is the recommended relationship of *A* to *D* when the material is aluminum?
13. How is *C* determined?
14. Write a suitable specification for the fastener shown in hidden outline.
15. Write a suitable specification for the fastener shown in the sectioned view.

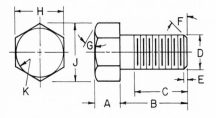
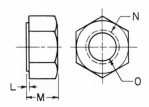
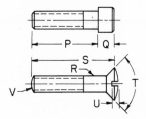

Fig. **19-52.**

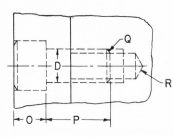
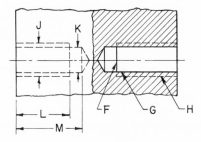
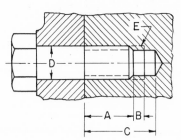

Fig. **19-53.**

19–4. Make a full-scale, one-view drawing of a 2″ diameter by 3″ long semifinished hexagonal head regular bolt. Show thread in detailed representation. Letter the complete specification below the drawing.

19–5. Make a two-view drawing of a hexagonal nut to fit the bolt of the previous problem. Show the profile view in full section. Use detailed thread representation. Letter the full specification of the nut below the drawing.

19–6. Show front and top views of the two pieces of steel in Fig. 19–54, held together with the following fasteners:

1. $\frac{3}{8}$–16 UNC–2A $\times$ $\frac{3}{4}$ Slotted Head Cap Screw.
2. $\frac{1}{2}$–20 UNF–2A $\times$ $1\frac{1}{4}$ Hexagon Head Cap Screw.
3. $\frac{3}{8}$–24 UNF–2A $\times$ $1\frac{1}{4}$ Slotted Oval Head Machine Screw.
4. $\frac{1}{2}$–13 UNC–2A $\times$ 2 Square Head Bolt.
5. $\frac{3}{8}$–16 UNC–2A $\times$ 1 Slotted Round Head Cap Screw.
6. $\frac{3}{8}$–16 UNC–2A $\times$ 3 Semifinished Hexagon Head Bolt and Nut.
7. $\frac{1}{2}$–13 UNC–2A $\times$ 1 Slotted Fillister Head Cap Screw.
8. $\frac{5}{8}$–11 UNC–2A $\times$ 1 Slotted Flat Head Machine Screw.

19–7. Make a detail drawing of the bearing bracket shown in Fig. 19–55. Material is cast iron.

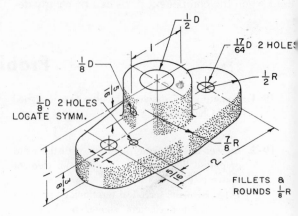

Fig. **19–55.** Bearing bracket.

19–8. Make a detail drawing of the segment lever shown in Fig. 19–56. The material is SAE No. 62 bronze.

19–9. Make a detail drawing of the extractor cam lever shown in Fig. 19–57. The material is cast iron. The angling sides are tangent to the central boss.

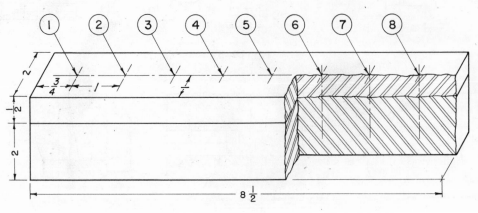

Fig. **19–54.**

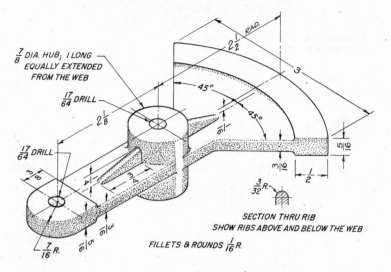

$\frac{7}{8}$ DIA. HUB; I LONG
EQUALLY EXTENDED
FROM THE WEB

$\frac{17}{64}$ DRILL

$2\frac{1}{8}$

$\frac{17}{64}$ DRILL

$2\frac{1}{2}$ RAD.

3

45°

45°

$\frac{3}{16}$

$\frac{1}{2}$

$\frac{5}{16}$

$\frac{3}{32}$ R.

SECTION THRU RIB
SHOW RIBS ABOVE AND BELOW THE WEB

FILLETS & ROUNDS $\frac{1}{16}$ R.

$\frac{7}{16}$ R.

$\frac{3}{16}$

$\frac{5}{16}$

Fig. **19–56.** Segment lever.

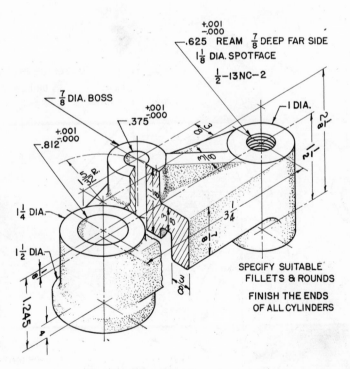

$.625$ REAM $^{+.001}_{-.000}$ $\frac{7}{8}$ DEEP FAR SIDE
$1\frac{1}{8}$ DIA. SPOTFACE

$\frac{1}{2}$-13NC-2

$\frac{7}{8}$ DIA. BOSS

$.375$ $^{+.001}_{-.000}$

$.812$ $^{+.001}_{-.000}$

I DIA.

$2\frac{1}{8}$

$1\frac{1}{2}$

$1\frac{1}{4}$ DIA.

$3\frac{1}{4}$

$1\frac{1}{2}$ DIA.

1.245

SPECIFY SUITABLE
FILLETS & ROUNDS

FINISH THE ENDS
OF ALL CYLINDERS

Fig. **19–57.** Extractor cam lever.

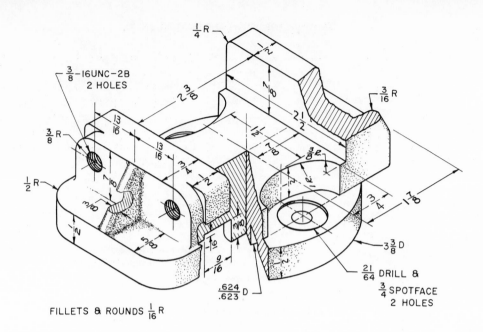

$\frac{1}{4}$ R

$\frac{3}{8}$-16UNC-2B
2 HOLES

$\frac{3}{16}$ R

$2\frac{3}{8}$

$\frac{7}{8}$

$2\frac{1}{2}$

$\frac{3}{8}$ R

$\frac{13}{16}$

$\frac{13}{16}$

$\frac{3}{4}$

$\frac{1}{2}$

$\frac{7}{8}$

$\frac{3}{8}$ R

$\frac{1}{2}$ R

$\frac{7}{8}$

$\frac{3}{16}$

2

$\frac{3}{16}$

$1\frac{7}{8}$

$\frac{3}{4}$

2

$\frac{5}{8}$

$\frac{9}{16}$

$\frac{.624}{.623}$ D

$3\frac{3}{8}$ D

$\frac{21}{64}$ DRILL &
$\frac{3}{4}$ SPOTFACE
2 HOLES

FILLETS & ROUNDS $\frac{1}{16}$ R

Fig. **19-58.** Vise jaw.

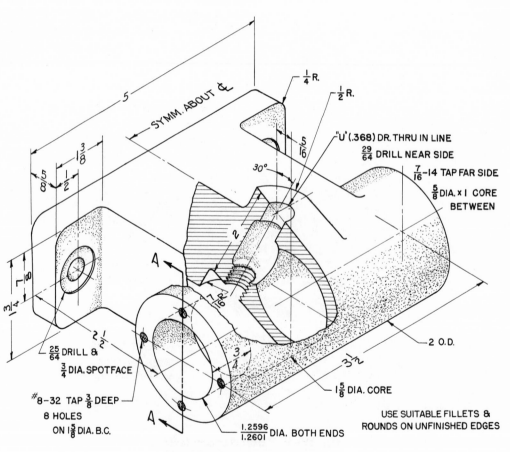

SYMM. ABOUT ℄

5

$1\frac{3}{8}$

$\frac{5}{8}$

$\frac{1}{2}$

$\frac{1}{4}$ R.

$\frac{1}{2}$ R.

$\frac{5}{16}$

30°

"U"(.368) DR. THRU IN LINE
$\frac{29}{64}$ DRILL NEAR SIDE
$\frac{7}{16}$-14 TAP FAR SIDE
$\frac{5}{8}$ DIA. x 1 CORE
BETWEEN

2

$\frac{7}{16}$ R

A

$\frac{7}{8}$

$1\frac{3}{4}$

$2\frac{1}{2}$

$\frac{3}{4}$

2 O.D.

$3\frac{1}{2}$

$\frac{25}{64}$ DRILL &
$\frac{3}{4}$ DIA. SPOTFACE

A

#8-32 TAP $\frac{3}{8}$ DEEP
8 HOLES
ON $1\frac{3}{8}$ DIA. B.C.

$\frac{1.2596}{1.2601}$ DIA. BOTH ENDS

$1\frac{5}{8}$ DIA. CORE

USE SUITABLE FILLETS &
ROUNDS ON UNFINISHED EDGES

Fig. **19-59.** Tool post support.

19–10. Make a detail drawing of the cast iron vise jaw shown in Fig. 19–58.

19–11. Make a detail drawing of the cast iron tool post support shown in Fig. 19–59. Show necessary views with a section view, *A–A*, as one of the principal views.

19–12. Make detail drawings of the parts of the apparatus stand shown in Fig. 19–60. The pad is loosely fitted to turn independently of the screw. The pad is located on the same vertical center line as the upper boss. The tip of the screw is peened after the parts have been assembled. Devise a method for holding the handle in place.

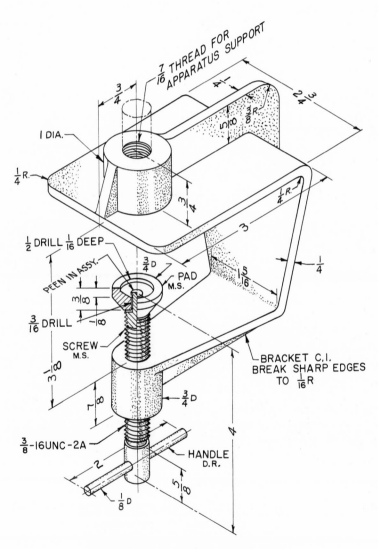

Fig. **19–60.** Apparatus stand clamp.

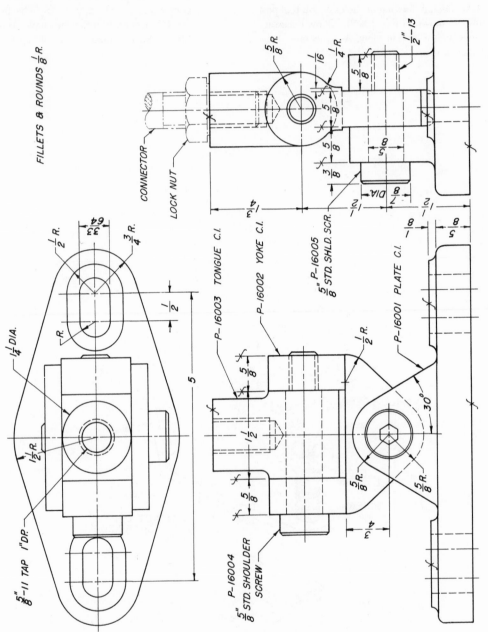

Fig. 19–61. Flexible anchor plate.

19-13. Make detail drawings of the parts of the flexible anchor plate shown in Fig. 19-61.

19-14. Make detail drawings of the parts of the adjustable clamping bracket shown in Fig. 19-62. By tightening a hexagon nut on the $\frac{1}{4}''$ screw shown between the posts, a clamping action is obtained. The posts are $\frac{1}{2}''$ in diameter and $2\frac{1}{2}''$ apart. The two holes in the bracket support are for $\frac{1}{4}''$ screws and must be outside the ends of the clamp. Make all parts of #18 U.S.S. Ga. steel (0.0500'' thick).

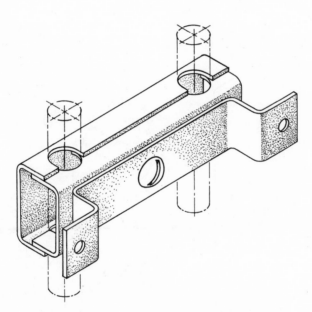

Fig. **19-62.** Adjustable clamping bracket.

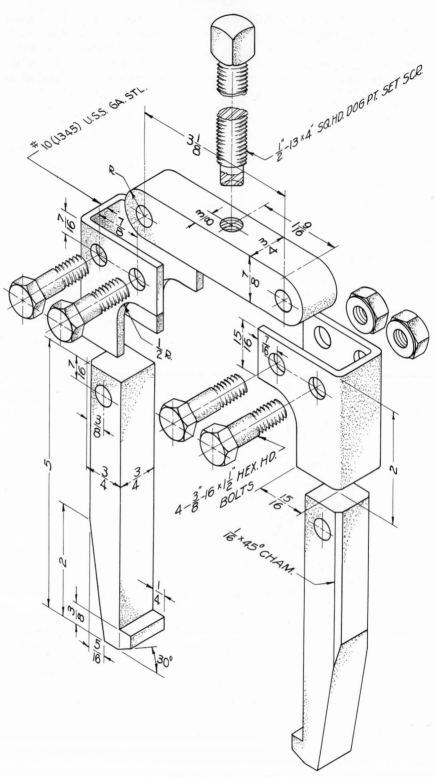

Fig. **19–63.** Gear puller.

19-15. Make a two-view assembly drawing of the gear puller shown in Fig. 19-63. The head of the setscrew is $\frac{1}{2}''$ wide across flats and is $\frac{3}{8}''$ high.

19-16. Make a layout drawing from the pictorial illustration shown in Fig. 19-64. The surface for the camera mounting should be $1\frac{3}{4}'' \times 2''$ and fitted with a special $\frac{1}{4}''$-20 thumb screw as shown in the removed section, lower right. The base is $3''$ in diameter with a $\frac{1}{4}$-20 threaded hole.

Panning and tilting action is controlled by the handle and parts P-14201 and P-14202. Locking of both pan and tilt is accomplished by expanding parts P-14204 and P-14205. Machine screws of suitable size hold the locking ring to the base and restrain the expansion of P-14202 which contains a sawed slot. Part P-14206 of C.R.S. is inserted in the plastic handle. Suitable sizes for parts and any alteration in construction will necessarily be the responsibility of the layout man.

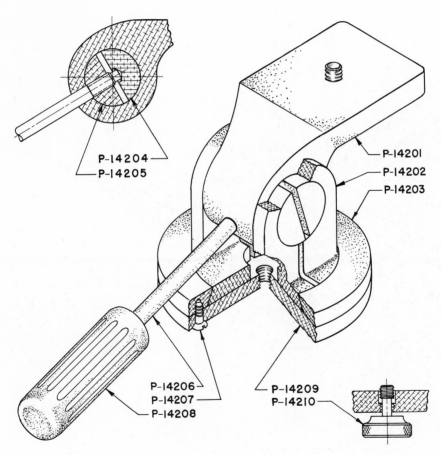

Fig. **19-64.** Tripod pan head—an adaptor for camera mount.

19-17. Referring to Fig. 19-65, and using the details of Fig. 19-66, make a general assembly drawing of the micrometer stop. Three principal views should be sufficient to describe the stop. Assume the front view to be taken looking toward the end of part 3802, in the exploded view. Remove a portion of the front view by a broken-out section to show parts 3809 and 3810 and show a removed view of the upper surface of

part 3805. A cutting plane, as used for a removed section, is suitable for identifying the removed view. A spring-ball oil cup may be substituted for part 3811 if desired.

19-18. Make an assembly drawing showing the construction of the surface gage illustrated in Fig 19-67. Use suitable sections and hidden lines to show detail.

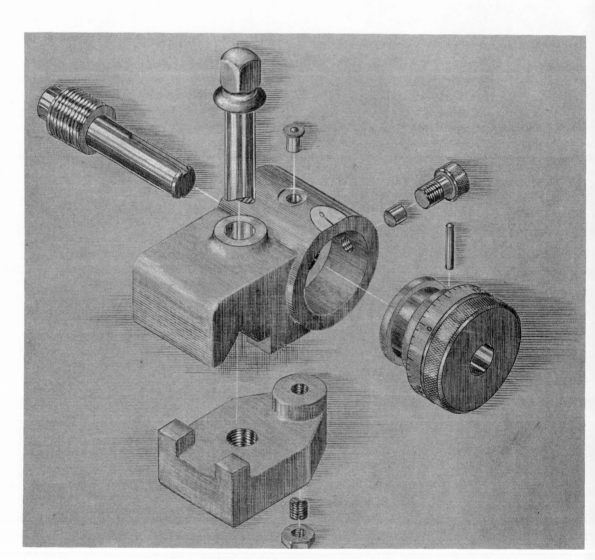

Fig. **19-65.** Exploded view of micrometer stop.

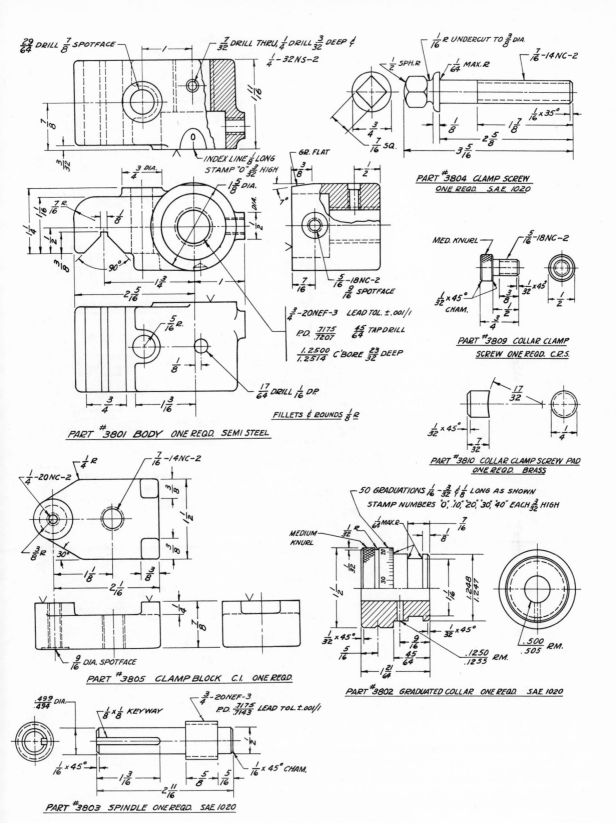

Fig. **19-66.** Details of micrometer stop.

455

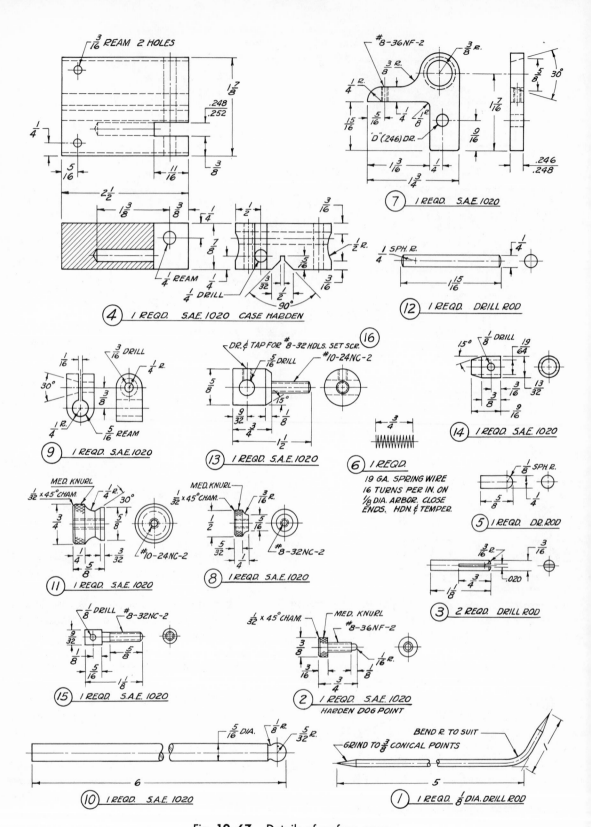

Fig. **19–67.** Details of surface gage.

20

ADDITIONAL
APPLICATIONS

20-1. GENERAL INTRODUCTION

Applications of graphical methods in design and analysis are too numerous to consider completely or in detail here, and new applications are continually being uncovered. The graphical approach is now being utilized in many fields because the visualization of a whole concept is made easier when that concept is expressed graphically. Visual methods are readily followed and offer the opportunity for observing the effects of varying the parameters of a problem.

A working knowledge in the area of graphical communication is widely recognized as a most desirable capability on the part of the engineer-scientist. The fundamentals of this area were discussed in Parts II and III, and some of the applications were presented in Chapter 19. Other applications occur in many fields (i.e., structural drawings, map projections, and patent office drawings, to name but a few).

Part III presented the fundamentals of graphical analysis of spatial conditions and Part IV presented

the fundamentals of graphical analysis of various mathematical procedures. (It is interesting to note that the material in Part III can be considered as either communications or analysis, depending upon the purpose of the drawing.) The greatest use of graphic solutions is in the conceptual and analytical phases of a design process. They are not exact solutions in most cases; their purpose is to offer a quick method of establishing parameters and answers within practical limits of accuracy. Should a problem be programmed for computer solution, the graphical solution offers a check on the program.

Four additional applications in the area of graphic solutions having the most general use will be discussed in this chapter. The first two of these —periodic functions and projective geometry— are subjects not previously discussed in this text and only the introductory concepts will be presented here. The other two subjects, differential equations and empirical equations, are extensions of Chapters 16 and 18 respectively.

Periodic Functions

20-2. NOMENCLATURE

Periodic functions are those whose magnitudes are repeated at constant time intervals. They are utilized in such areas as vibrations, electrical currents, and light waves, among others. Fig. 20-1 shows the general case of a periodic function. The *period* (P) of the function is the time interval at which the curve repeats itself. Normally, the period is measured between corresponding crests; however, it can be measured between any two comparable points on the curve. The simplest periodic motion is that known as simple harmonic motion.

20-3. SIMPLE HARMONIC MOTION

Simple harmonic motion is defined as the projections on a straight line (diameter) of a point which is rotating with constant velocity around the center of the line. The rotating point can be thought of as the tip of a rotating vector, AB, whose tail is at the center of rotation as in Fig. 20-2(a). The plot of the displacement (AB' projected to B'', for example) for various amounts of rotation is shown in Fig. 20-2(b). This plot shows that simple harmonic motion plots as a sine curve, and hence the general equation for harmonic motion is $y = a \sin (\theta + \alpha)$. Note that the horizontal axis, graduated in terms of rotation, could also be graduated in terms of time. The distance along the x-axis representing a

cycle is an arbitrary length. It should be chosen so as to open out the curve sufficiently to allow easy reading of values on the x-axis. In simple harmonic motion, the rate of rotation is called the *frequency* (f), measured in cycles per unit time and is the inverse of the period which is measured in time per cycle. The *amplitude* of a simple harmonic curve is equal to the distance from the x-axis to the highest point of the curve or from the x-axis to the lowest point of the curve. The amplitude is equal to the true length of the rotating vector. All sliding parts driven by a crankshaft (e.g., pistons) and many parts driven by cams (e.g., valves) utilize entirely, or partially, harmonic motions.

20-4. ADDITION OF HARMONIC FUNCTIONS OF EQUAL FREQUENCY

Fig. 20-3(a) shows two vectors of different amplitudes but the same frequency. The angle α between the two vectors is known as the *phase angle* and is the amount that one vector precedes the other vector (or the amount that the two vectors are out of phase with each other). The curve generated by each vector can be plotted as in Fig. 20-3(a). The resultant curve can be found by adding corresponding ordinates. The result is another simple harmonic curve of the same frequency but different amplitude.

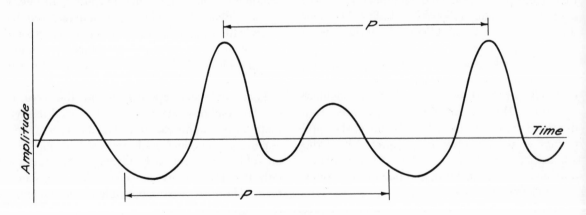

Fig. **20-1.** A periodic function.

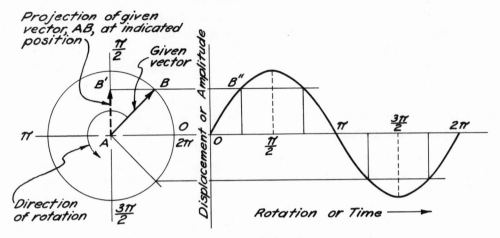

Fig. **20-2.** Harmonic motion.

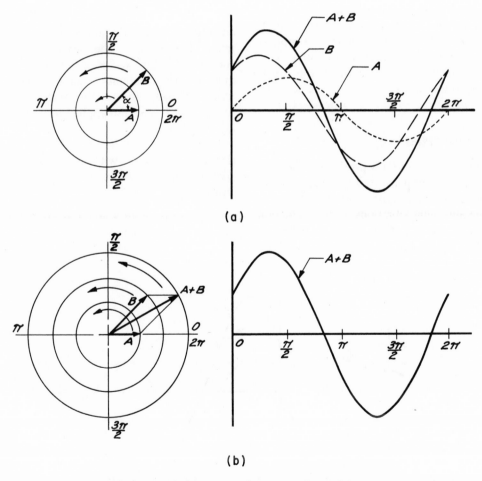

(a)

(b)

Fig. **20-3.** Added harmonic functions of equal frequency.

A simpler method of determining the resultant curve is to add vectorially (refer to Chapter 12) the two vectors and then plot the desired curve using the resultant. This is illustrated in Fig. 20–3(b).

20–5. ADDITION OF HARMONIC FUNCTIONS OF UNEQUAL FREQUENCIES

The addition of harmonic functions of unequal frequencies is a more common problem than the addition of harmonic functions of equal frequencies. When the frequencies vary, the angular velocity of each vector is different and the vectors cannot be added as in Fig. 20–3(b). Instead, the curves for each vector must be constructed and the resultant curve plotted by adding corresponding ordinates as in Fig. 20–4. The resultant curve is no longer a simple harmonic function, but it is still a periodic function. Any periodic curve can be derived by adding harmonic functions of properly related frequencies. Even when the curve is not periodic, a selected interval of the curve can be similarly reproduced.

20–6. FOURIER SERIES

A common procedure for reproducing the curve of some function over a selected interval is the use of a Fourier series. This type of series is often used in problems involving vibrations, heat conduction, and electricity, among others. The general case of a Fourier series is the summation of an infinite number of related sine and cosine curves as in Eq. 20–1:

$$f(x) = \frac{b_o}{2} + \sum_{n=1}^{\infty} a_n \sin \frac{n\pi x}{L} + \sum_{n=1}^{\infty} b_n \cos \frac{n\pi x}{L}, \quad (20\text{–}1)$$

where $0 < x < 2L$. The trigonometric terms in the series have periods of $2L/n$ and hence the interval to be considered is the common period, $2L$. The mathematical determination of the constants a_n and b_n depends upon the fact that trigonometric functions have orthogonal properties. The graphical development of the evaluation of these constants is presented later in this Article.

In many actual problems, one set of constants often is found to be zero, and the series becomes the summation of sine curves or cosine curves. Under this condition, the series could be written as:

$$f(x) = a_1 \sin \theta + a_2 \sin 2\theta + \dots a_n \sin n\theta, \quad (20\text{–}2)$$

and represents the addition of sine curves of various related frequencies. The period, or interval to be considered in Eq. 20–2 is from 0 to 2π. These frequencies are commonly called *harmonics*. This term originally meant the science of musical sounds, but is now also applied to problems involving frequency.

Many periodic curves are made up of harmonics that are not in phase with each other. In order to account for this condition, Eq. 20–2 can be re-written as:

$$\begin{aligned} f(x) = {} & a_1 \sin (\theta + \alpha_1) + a_2 \sin (2\theta + \alpha_2) \\ & + a_3 \sin (3\theta + \alpha_3) \\ & + \dots a_n \sin (n\theta + \alpha_n). \end{aligned} \quad (20\text{–}3)$$

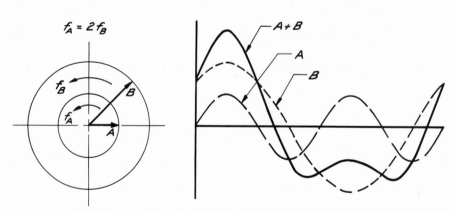

Fig. **20–4.** Added harmonic functions of unequal frequency.

This equation allows each harmonic to be out of phase with the basic frequency, θ. By solving for the amplitude constants, a_n, and the phase constants, α_n, it is possible to replace any periodic curve with a series of simple harmonic curves. The graphical solution for these constants is developed below.

When solving the general Fourier series (Eq. 20–1) by the calculus, the equation for a_n is found to be:

$$a_n = \frac{1}{\pi} \int_0^{2\pi} y \sin n\theta \, d\theta. \qquad (20\text{–}4)$$

The period of any given periodic curve can be considered as 2π radians or 360°. If this period is divided into n uniformly spaced strips, the area of each strip is the mean ordinate multiplied by $2\pi/n$. The value of the amplitude of a particular harmonic, k, can be approximated by multiplying the area of each strip by $\sin k\theta$, adding all areas, and multiplying the total by $1/\pi$. Using this concept, Eq. 20–4 can be rewritten as:

$$a_k = \frac{2}{n}(y_1 \sin k\theta + y_2 \sin k\theta + \ldots). \qquad (20\text{–}5)$$

Fig. 20–5 shows one period of a curve. The first step in the graphical determination of the harmonics that comprise the given curve is to select a set of axes as in Fig. 20–5, such that all ordinates to the curve are positive. Then divide the period (or interval) of the curve into uniformly spaced strips, in this case 12 strips. Hence the width of each strip is 30°. The left-hand ordinate of each strip is assumed to be the mean ordinate of the strip. The construction to determine the amplitude and phase angle of the first harmonic, or fundamental, is shown in Fig. 20–6(a). Starting at the origin, each of the 12 ordinates is laid out as a vector. The right-hand ordinate (ordinate number 1) is not used as it is in reality only the start of the next period. The vectors are joined tip to tail. The first vector is always laid out along the x-axis and the angle of each succeeding vector with the preceding vector is $k\theta$. Since k for the first harmonic is one, the angle in this case is 30°. That the vector polygon has the effect of multiplying by $\sin k\theta$ can be seen when the projections of each vector on the y-axis are considered.

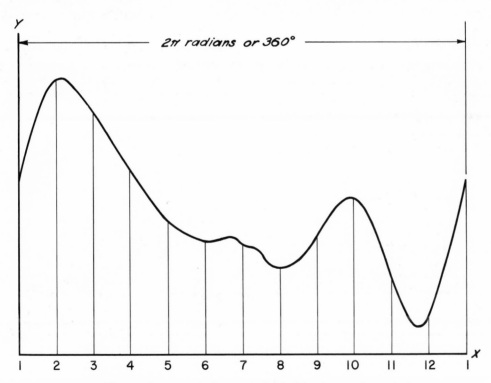

Fig. 20–5. Given periodic curve divided for harmonic analysis.

The resultant vector $0A$ is drawn to close the vector polygon. From Eq. 20-5,

$$a_1 = \frac{2}{n}(0A) = \frac{1}{6}(0A).$$

The phase angle, α_1, can also be measured on the vector polygon. It is the angle between the y-axis and the resultant vector $0A$, with the positive direction a clockwise direction from the y-axis. If, in the determination of some particular harmonic, the tip of the vector representing the last ordinate falls on the origin, the resultant of the

system is zero and that harmonic is missing from the given periodic curve.

The determination of the constants for the second, third, and fourth harmonics are shown in Fig. 20-6(b), (c), and (d) respectively. These harmonics are laid out and added together to form the resulting curve in Fig. 20-7. The closeness by which this constructed curve duplicates the given curve demonstrates the validity of this construction. In engineering problems, seldom are more than four harmonics required to duplicate the given curve within acceptable limits of accuracy.

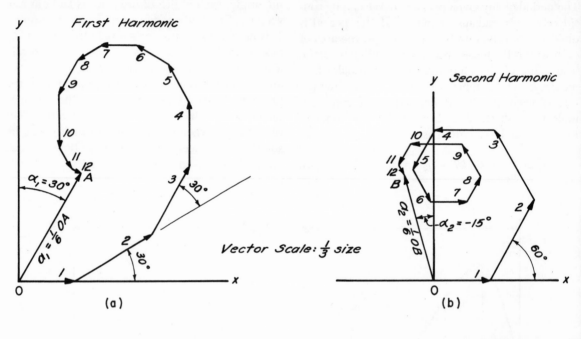

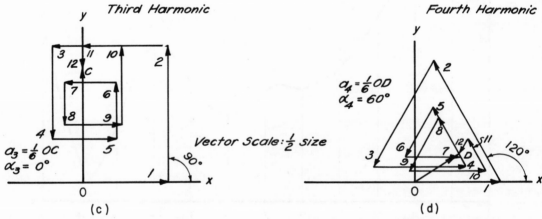

Fig. **20-6.** Determination of amplitude and phase angle of harmonics.

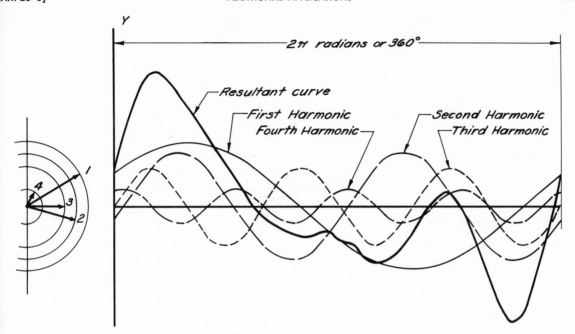

Fig. **20-7.** Construction of resultant curve.

Utilizing the methods just presented, any periodic curve, or a selected interval of any other curve, can be analyzed and reproduced through the addition of selected harmonics. There are two advantages to the graphic method. One is that, if the given curve results from experimental data, no time need be spent trying to develop a formula for the curve. The second advantage is that the point beyond which the higher harmonics fail to affect the curve appreciably is easier to visualize.

Projective Geometry

20-7. DEVELOPMENT

Throughout this text, figures have been projected onto planes by orthographic projection (Chapter 5) and by central projection as in perspective drawings (Chapter 8). Gaspard Mongé is generally credited as the founder of present-day descriptive geometry. A student of Mongé's, Jean Poncelet, developed the idea that the properties of one figure could be extended to another by changes accomplished through the use of projection, especially central projection. Hence the name: projective geometry. This subject has been taught by mathematicians since 1822. Many of the basic concepts can be demonstrated graphically and are then easier to visualize. The accelerated use of aerial photography in surveying and mapping has caused an increased interest in the graphic solution of problems involving projective geometry. The following Articles will introduce some of the basic graphic concepts of projective geometry as they apply to photo data. There are many other practical uses of projective geometry. For a comprehensive treatment, the student is referred to the standard texts on projective geometry.

20-8. GEOMETRICAL RULES AND NOMENCLATURE

A simple perspective drawing illustrates many of the basic rules of projective geometry. Fig. 20-8 shows a perspective view made on a frontal picture plane using central projection. The center of pro-

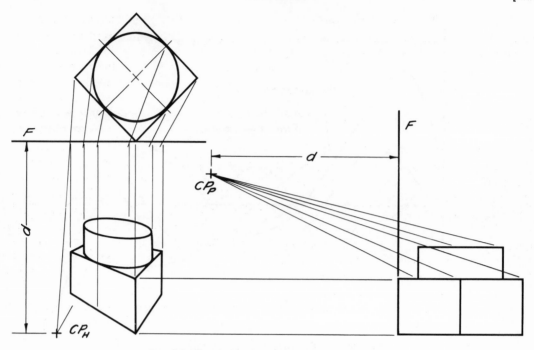

Fig. **20-8.**   Central (perspective) projection.

jection (C.P.) is shown in the given horizontal and profile views. A study of this perspective view reveals the relationships which are the bases of projective geometry. These are:

1. In using central projection to project one figure onto another (in this case the surfaces of the object onto the perspective plane), certain changes in the figure always occur.
   a. Angles and lengths are changed.
   b. Parallel lines become convergent.
   c. The ratios of lengths and angles are altered. (The plane faces of the object are square; but in the perspective, the angles are not equal to each other and the lengths of the sides are all different.)
   d. The shape of curved lines is changed. (The circle becomes egg-shaped.)
2. There are also some properties that do not change.
   a. Straight lines remain straight lines.
   b. Intersecting lines remain intersecting.
   c. All points on a line remain on that line.
   d. A tangency between a curve and a straight line remains a tangency.

There are two terms used in projective geometry whose definition should be known. The first of these is a *pencil of rays* which means a group of lines which intersect at a common point (or are concurrent). The other is a *point row* which means a set of points, all of which lie on the same straight line. These are also shown in Fig. 20–8.

20-9. CROSS RATIO IN PHOTOGRAMMETRY

One basic rule of projective geometry that is widely used in photogrammetry is that the ratio into which a pencil of rays divides a point row is a constant as the pencil and point row are projected onto different surfaces by the use of central projection. This is illustrated in Fig. 20–9 where a pencil of rays and a point row are projected onto two different surfaces. The pencil of rays which is concurrent at point A intersects the point row MN at points $1, 2, 3,$ and 4 in Fig. 20–9(a). The cross ratio of these points can be expressed as:

$$\frac{\dfrac{12}{23}}{\dfrac{13}{34}} = K.$$

There are actually six distinct cross ratios that may be written for a group of four points; however, for the purposes of this example, it is immaterial which cross ratio is used. Fig. 20–9(b) shows the same pencil of rays and point row projected onto another surface. Therefore, since the cross ratio is a constant, it can be said that:

$$\frac{\dfrac{1'2'}{2'3'}}{\dfrac{1'3'}{3'4'}} = K = \frac{\dfrac{12}{23}}{\dfrac{13}{34}}.$$

The fact that the cross ratios are equal is used to transfer information from a photograph to a map (or vice versa). Fig. 20–10(a) depicts a photograph which shows a highway junction, a railroad junction, a building, and a possible missile site of the underground silo type. The highway and railroad junctions and the building can be identified on a map of the same area, but the missile site, being new, does not show on the map. The first step in locating it on the map is to draw, on the photograph, rays from a known point to the missile site and at least three other known points. In Fig. 20–10(b), rays are drawn on the photograph from the highway junction to the railroad junction, the building, the missile site, and along the highway. On the map, rays are drawn from the highway junc-

tion to the railroad junction, the building, and along the highway. Since the location of the missile site is unknown on the map, that ray cannot now be drawn. However, from the theory of projective geometry, it is known that the cross ratio of the rays on both the photograph and the map must be a constant. Therefore, a strip of paper is laid across the rays on the photograph and the point row of intersections ticked off as in Fig. 20–10(b). Then the strip of paper is placed on the map and oriented so that the marked points fall on top of the corresponding rays. The point on the strip of paper that corresponds to the missile site ray now locates the same ray on the map, as in Fig. 20–10(c). To complete the location on the map, the process is repeated, drawing the rays on the photograph from a different vertex as in Fig. 20–10(c). When this ray to the missile site is located on the map, the intersection of the two rays pinpoints the missile site on the map. This procedure will work regardless of the tilt of the camera. However, when the terrain photographed is very hilly, other geometric constructions must be performed first in order to correct for the relief distortion.

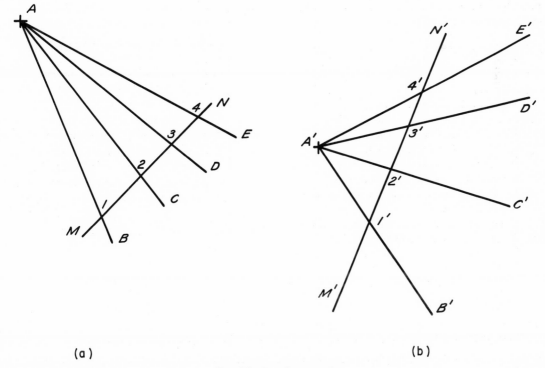

(a)   (b)

Fig. **20–9.** Cross ratio.

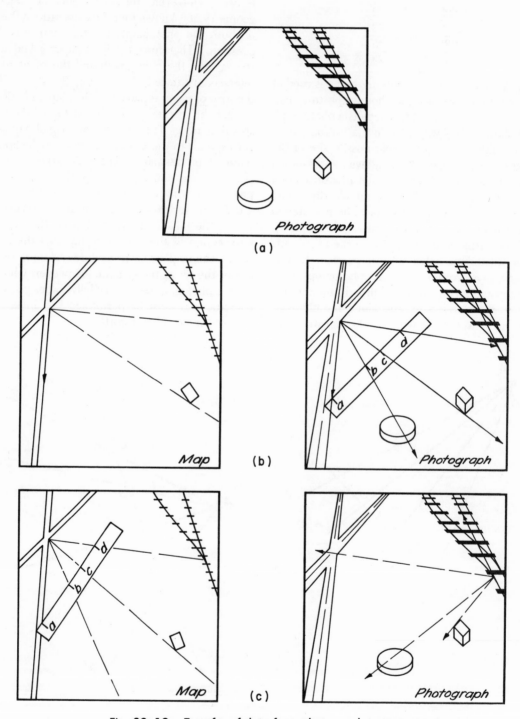

Fig. **20-10.** Transfer of data from photograph to map.

Differential Equations

20-10. SLOPE LINE INTEGRATION

Chapter 16 presented the usual methods of graphical integration. Another method of graphical integration has been developed[1] using the relationship of similar triangles. This new method, called *slope line integration*, adapts itself well for the solution of differential equations.

[1] Prof. H. M. Paynter, *Journal of the Boston Society of Civil Engineers*, Vol. 39, April, 1952.

The theory of slope line integration is based on an increment of area, such as $A_1 = y_1 \Delta x$ in Fig. 20–11(a). To develop this theory, an isosceles triangle is constructed with a base proportional to the increment of area as in Fig. 20–11(a). For this construction, the altitude of the triangle is made equal to the ordinate of the increment of area, and the slope of the two equal sides of the triangle may be any desired slope.

However, the slope is ordinarily chosen so as to avoid too small an angle at the apex of the triangle.

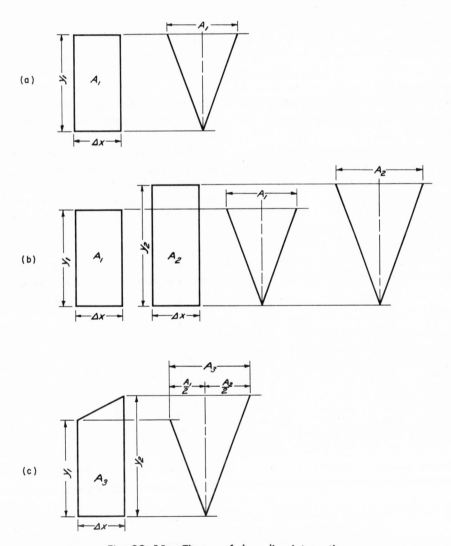

Fig. **20–11.** Theory of slope line integration.

A scale is then established so that the base, when measured to this scale, is numerically equal to the area of the increment. The establishment of this scale will be discussed later in this Article.

With the relation between the triangle and the increment of area known, a second increment with a different area but with the same width (Δx) could be represented by the base of a second triangle similar to the first triangle and, therefore, drawn with sides of the same slope as the first triangle, as in Fig. 20–11(b). The two areas are $A_1 = y_1\Delta x$ and $A_2 = y_2\Delta x$ and, hence, the ratio of the areas is the same as the ratios of the ordinates. Since the triangles are similar, the bases are in proportion to the altitudes. The altitude of each triangle is made equal to the ordinate of the corresponding increment of area; hence, the bases of the triangles are in the same proportion as the areas. The base of the first triangle, measured to the proper scale, was numerically equal to the first increment of area. Therefore, the base of the second triangle, measured to the same scale, would be equal to the second increment of area.

This same concept can be extended to a trapezoidal increment of area. In Fig. 20–11(c) the area of the trapezoid is:

$$A_3 = \frac{(y_1 + y_2)\Delta x}{2} = \frac{y_1\Delta x + y_2\Delta x}{2} = \frac{A_1 + A_2}{2}.$$

Hence, the area of the trapezoid can be represented by the two slope lines as shown in Fig. 20–11(c).

The area under a curve can be divided into a series of trapezoidal increments of area. Since integration is essentially measuring the area under a curve, the slope line construction is a method of constructing (or measuring) the integral of a curve. This construction is applied to the integration of the area under a curve consisting of straight lines connecting successive points as shown in Fig. 20–12(a). The areas under successive lines are therefore trapezoids. The integral, Fig. 20–12(b), is determined by points located by successive triangles representing the areas of successive trapezoids.

An important difference in this method of graphical integration is that the integral is a plot of the increase in area against corresponding values of y instead of values of x. This is not the purely mathematical concept of an integral curve, but it is an integral in the sense that it represents a summation of areas. The methods discussed in Chapter 16 resulted in integral curves where the increase in area was plotted against values of x. If this type of plot were desired, the curve of Fig. 20–12(b), for example, would have to be replotted. However, the plot of area versus y leads into the solution of

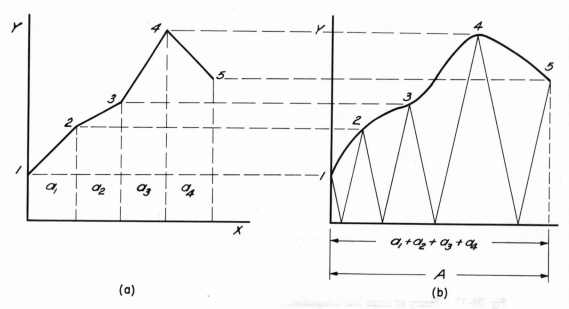

(a)   (b)

Fig. **20–12.** Slope line integration.

differential equations, which is the principal reason for discussing this particular method.

The establishment of a scale and the slope of the construction lines are best explained through an example. Fig. 20–13(a) shows the given curve. The average ordinate is estimated by eye and the approximate area (600 square units) under the given curve determined as shown. Next, an abscissa (area) scale is selected for the integral curve such that values up to 600 may be shown. Then a small area (ΔA) of the original plot is established as shown in Fig. 20–13(b). Here the ordinate was

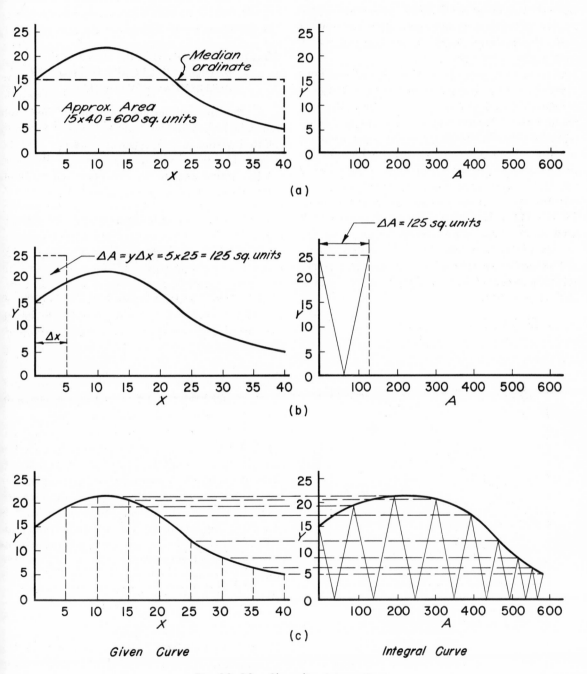

Fig. **20–13.** Slope line integration.

arbitrarily chosen to be 25 and the abscissa to be 5, hence the increment of area is 125. On the integral plot an isosceles triangle is drawn with an altitude of 25 y-units and a base of 125 area units as shown in Fig. 20–13(b). All slope lines used in the process of integration must be parallel to the sides of this triangle. In most problems the slope should be approximately 1 inch horizontally per 5 inches vertically. Lesser slopes tend to result in poor intersections, while steeper slopes result in unnecessary construction.

Finally, the given curve is divided into uniform intervals with a Δx width equal to that of the assumed base rectangle of 5 units [Fig. 20–13(c)]. Each interval is now thought of as being a trapezoidal increment of area. After the given curve is divided into intervals, the ordinate values are projected over to the integral plot as shown in Fig. 20–13(c). Then the slope lines are zigzagged, as shown, from ordinate value to ordinate value. When a smooth curve is drawn from vertex to vertex, the integral curve is completed.

Fig. 20–14 shows that, unless the sloping edge of the trapezoid closely conforms to the given curve, inaccuracies result and the resulting area will be measurably less than the true area. Hence, for acceptable accuracy, the width of the interval must be carefully considered so as to find the value where the trapezoids give the best possible fit over the entire curve.

20–11. EXTENSION OF THE SLOPE LINE METHOD TO CERTAIN FIRST-ORDER DIFFERENTIAL EQUATIONS

In the integration just presented, the result could be considered as A plotted against y or as y plotted against A. Disregarding the fact that the trapezoidal increment of area was not the same as the actual area under the curve, the relation between variables can be expressed as:

$$dA = y \, dx \qquad (20\text{--}6)$$

or

$$\frac{dA}{dx} = y. \qquad (20\text{--}7)$$

If y is considered as a function of A, the previous example determined A as the result of integrating A' with respect to the independent variable x, or:

$$A' = f(A). \qquad (20\text{--}8)$$

This equation shows that this discussion is limited to the special type of differential equations where the independent variable is missing.

If we were to start with a plot of A' as a function of A and were to reverse the process described in Art. 20–10, the result would be A as a function of x. This would be a solution of Eq. 20–8, a simple, first-order, differential equation. Fig. 20–15 illustrates this procedure. The given plot of A' versus A is shown in Fig. 20–15(a). The first step in the solution is illustrated in Fig. 20–15(b) where the construction to determine the x-interval (Δx) and the direction of the slope lines are shown. From our previous work it is known that:

$$\Delta A = A' \Delta x. \qquad (20\text{--}9)$$

If it is desired to plot x at intervals of one unit in the solution, then $\Delta x = 1$. If A' is arbitrarily selected

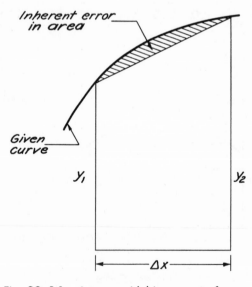

Fig. 20–14. A trapezoidal increment of area.

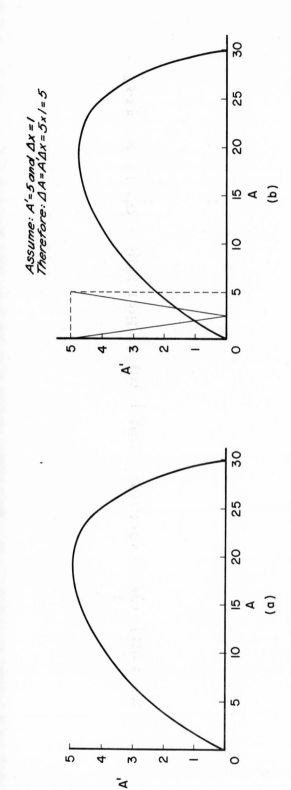

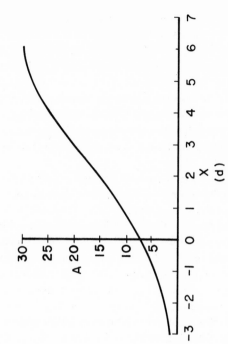

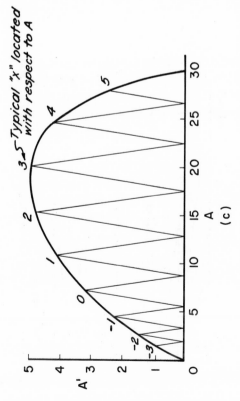

Fig. **20–15.** Graphic solution of $A' = f(A)$.

as 5, then by substitution in Eq. 20-9 the value of ΔA can be calculated:

$$\Delta A = A'\Delta x = 5 \cdot 1 = 5.$$

Therefore, an isosceles triangle drawn as in Fig. 20–15(b) with an altitude of $A' = 5$ and a base of $A = 5$ establishes the direction of the slope lines necessary to determine a solution with an x interval of one unit.

The next step in the solution is either to plot a known value of x if the boundary conditions are known or, as in this example, assume a point on the curve where $x = 0$, as in Fig. 20–15(c). The assumption of different initial values of x merely means different constants of integration. Starting from this point, the zigzags are drawn with lines parallel to the sides of the isosceles triangle, locating other positions of x along the curve. Now, if it is desired, A could be replotted as a function of x, as in Fig. 20–15(d), which means that we have a solution of the original differential equation, 20–8. Other intervals of x could have been chosen as well

as other values of A', or values of ΔA and A' could have been arbitrarily selected and the value of Δx determined from those choices.

To demonstrate this method further, a solution will be found for two differential equations for which the answer is known. The first of these equations is $y' = 1$ and the solution is demonstrated in Fig. 20–16. Here, a Δx of 1 was desired. Hence, constructing the isosceles triangle with an altitude of $y' = 2$ would require a base of $\Delta y = 2$. It is also assumed that the constant of integration is zero, or that $x = 0$ at $y = 0$. This initial condition is located and the zigzag construction locates successive values of x. From a study of Fig. 20–16 it can be seen that $y = x$, which is the known solution of $y' = 1$ when $x = 0$ at $y = 0$. Therefore, the validity of the method is demonstrated.

A second demonstration involving another familiar differential equation is the solution of $y' = y$ where $x = 0$ at $y = 1$. The solution is shown in Fig. 20–17 where x values at intervals of $\frac{1}{4}$ unit are obtained. A plot of values of y versus x would show the familiar plot of the exponential $y = e^x$.

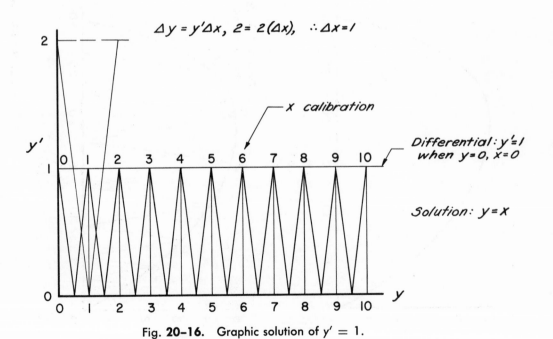

Fig. 20–16. Graphic solution of $y' = 1$.

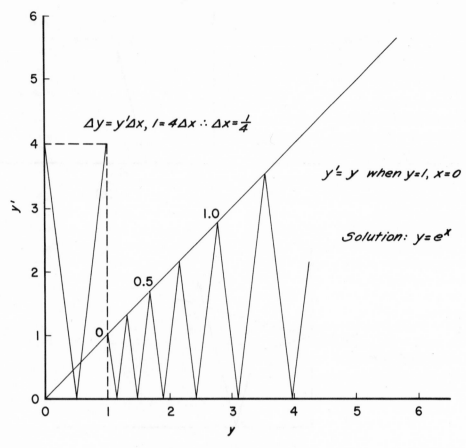

$\Delta y = y'\Delta x,\ 1 = 4\Delta x \therefore \Delta x = \frac{1}{4}$

$y' = y$ when $y=1,\ x=0$

Solution: $y=e^x$

Fig. **20–17.** Graphic solution of $y' = y$.

20–12. THE SLOPE LINE METHOD IN CERTAIN SECOND-ORDER DIFFERENTIAL EQUATIONS

The second-order differential equation where the independent variable is missing is:

$$A'' = f(A). \qquad (20\text{-}10)$$

This equation can be solved through the simultaneous solution of two other equations:

$$A'' = g(A') \qquad (20\text{-}11)$$

$$A' = h(A). \qquad (20\text{-}12)$$

Fig. 20–18(a) shows the start of the solution of Eq. 20–11 when one point on the solution is known. Since the location of the second point on the solution is unknown, the construction can go no further. Fig. 20–18(b) shows the start of the solution of Eq. 20–12. Again the construction can go no further. However, if A and A'' were plotted on the same axis, as in Fig. 20–18(c), the solution of Eq. 20–12 is turned from its previous position and the two solutions combine to actually locate point 2 by their intersection. Therefore, the location of one point in the solution of this type of second-order differential equation leads to the location of other

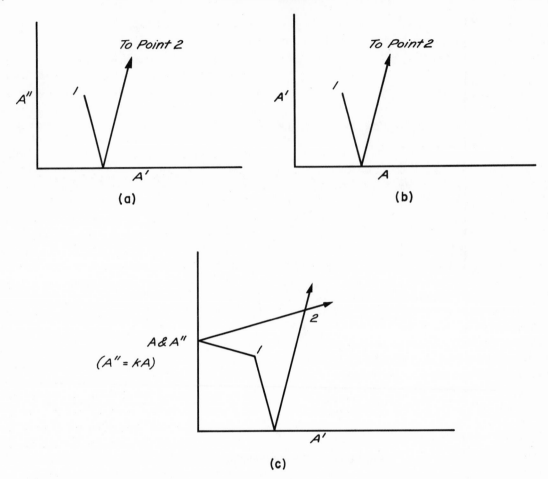

Fig. **20-18.** The slope line method in second-order differential equations.

successive points in the graphical solution. However, the solution of a second-order differential equation is harder and requires more thought because there is nothing known about the position of each point until the slope lines locate the point. This is in contrast to the solution of first-order differential equations where each successive point was known to be on the differential curve. A major difficulty is which of the two possible slopes to use in starting the zigzag construction from the initial conditions (or the first known point). If the general solution is known, the slope is chosen that leads to that general solution. This will be demonstrated later in this Article. When the general solution is

unknown, other points in the specific solution must be known in order to select the slope that will lead to those solutions (points). This is often the case in experimental work when it is known that a differential relationship exists, but the type of relationship is unknown.

Another important consideration is the fact that both the A and A'' scales coincide. In Fig. 20-18(c), point 1 is actually two coincident points: A versus A' and A'' versus A'. Therefore the ordinates for both A and A'' must be the same physical length. This imposes the additional restriction that $A'' = kA$. When the known initial values of A'' and A are equal, A'' and A can be plotted to the same scale on the same axis. However, when the initial values of A and A'' differ, the scales for plotting each value must be adjusted according to $A'' = kA$ in order that the initial values of A'' and A will coincide.

To illustrate these difficulties and to demonstrate the solution of a second-order differential equation, the equation $y'' = -y$, with the initial conditions of $x = 0$, $y = 0$, $y' = 1$, and $y'' = 0$, will be solved. It is well known that the solution of this equation is $y = \sin x$ where x is expressed in radians. The axes for the graphical solution are laid out as in Fig. 20–19(a) where y'' and y are plotted to the same scale on the same axis since the initial values of both y'' and y are equal. According to the given equation, positive values of y'' coincide with negative values of y. Hence, the positive direction for these two scales is as shown. The other axis shows y'. The first step in the solution is to determine the direction of the slope lines. It is important to realize that if y'' and y had been plotted with different scales, the slopes of the two parts of the solution would be different. Since in this example y'' and y are plotted to the same scale, the same slope can be used for both parts of the solution. In either case, the same method is used in the determination of the slope. The slope is determined as in Fig. 20–19(a) where an isosceles triangle is constructed with an altitude (y) of 1.0 and a base $(\Delta y')$ of 0.2. Using Eq. 20–6, the value of Δx is calculated as shown in the illustration. The point $x = 0$ is plotted at $y'' = y = 0$ and $y' = 1$. From this point slope lines representing a solution of $y' = h(y)$ are drawn about a horizontal axis and slope lines representing a solution of $y'' = g(y')$ are drawn about a vertical axis. The fact that y'' is negative requires that they be drawn below the y'-axis, as shown. From the general solution $(y = \sin x)$ it is known that x increases as y increases and as y' decreases. The slope lines originating at the initial point are chosen so that they will produce this situation. The intersection of these two sets of slope lines locates $x = 0.2$ [Fig. 20–19(a)] since Δx was determined to be 0.2. From this point the set of slope lines representing solutions of $y'' = g(y')$ are drawn so that they bounce off the y'-axis and the set of slope lines representing solutions of $y' = h(y)$ are drawn so that they bounce off the y'',

y-axis. The intersection of this next set locates $x = 0.4$.

The solution is carried on with each set of slope lines bouncing off its respective axis to the new solution point until the solution $x = 1.4$ is reached. The slope line representing solutions of $y'' = g(y')$, as drawn from point $x = 1.4$, crosses over the y'', y-axis as it progresses from $x = 1.4$ to the y'-axis and back again to $x = 1.6$, as in Fig. 20–19(b). Hence, the solution $x = 1.6$ must be on the left side of the y'', y-axis. The slope lines representing solutions of $y' = h(y)$ have previously been drawn from a solution point to the y'', y-axis and back again to the next solution. However, in this special case, because the next point $(x = 1.6)$ is on the left side of the y'', y-axis, this particular slope line must cross the axis. The manner in which this is accomplished is as follows. The slope line representing a solution of $y' = h(y)$ bounces off the y'', y-axis in its customary path as shown in Fig. 20–19(b). Then, realizing that this direction is leading in the wrong direction, the direction is reversed and the slope line is extended to the intersection of $x = 1.6$. Hence, the actual path is as shown in Fig. 20–19(b). This is an important and critical point to remember. It occurs every time either set of slope lines crosses an axis from which it should bounce. Follow the complete solution as shown in Fig. 20–19(c) and determine what happens as the solution crosses over an axis.

With the solution completed [Fig. 20–19(c)], values of y could be plotted against values of x and the normal sine curve would result. Also, a plot of y' versus x would show a cosine curve and a plot of y'' versus x would show a negative sine curve as in Fig. 20–20. This demonstrates that the graphical construction just discussed does result in the solution of a second-order differential equation.

20–13. THE SLOPE LINE METHOD IN OTHER DIFFERENTIAL EQUATIONS

The slope-line method can be extended for the solution of ordinary differential equations of any order. The methods are similar to the methods in previous discussions. However, such applications are beyond the scope of this text.

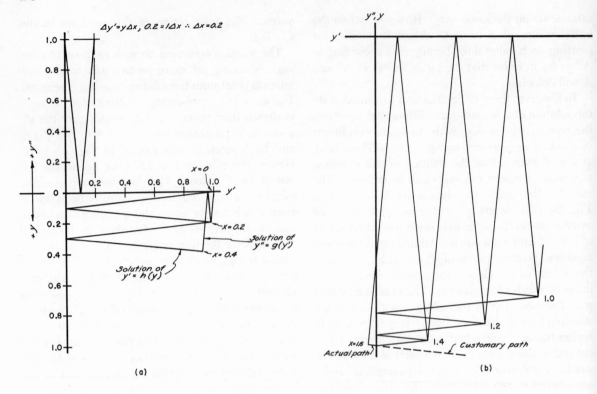

(a)

(b)

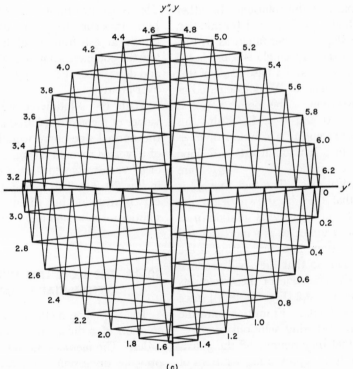

(c)

Fig. 20-19. Graphic solution of $y'' = -y$.

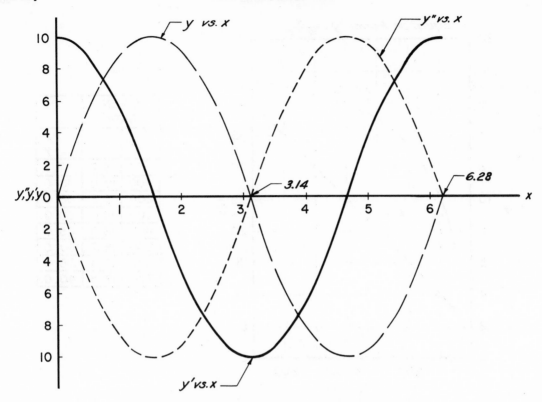

Fig. **20–20.** Normal plot of the solution of $y'' = -y$.

Other Empirical Equations

20–14. INTRODUCTION

Methods of determining which of the three basic forms of empirical equations would best fit the data on hand are presented in Chapter 18. However, sometimes data do not fit any of those three forms and some other solution is desirable. This section will discuss briefly some of these other solutions. This is not meant to be an exhaustive treatment; some material will be left for the student to explore in further detail elsewhere.

20–15. HYPERBOLIC CURVES OF TWO CONSTANTS

The curves of some data become asymptotic to axes (or other lines) when plotted on rectilinear

grid paper. When this occurs, the equation of the data may be of the form:

$$y = \frac{x}{a + bx}. \qquad (20\text{–}13)$$

This curve may be changed so as to plot as a straight line by rearranging it as:

$$\frac{x}{y} = a + bx$$

which will plot as a straight line on rectilinear paper when x/y is plotted against x. The two constants can now be determined from the straight line plot as discussed in Chapter 18. Fig. 20–21 illustrates this case. The plot of x versus y appears to be of the hyperbolic form, so a plot of x/y versus x is

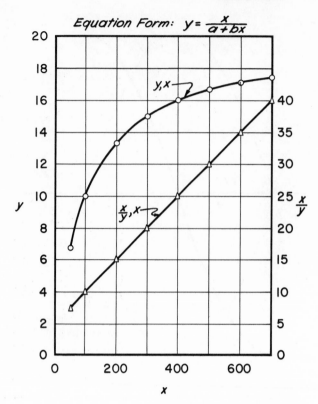

Fig. 20-21. Equation of the form: $y = \dfrac{x}{a + bx}$.

made. This plot is a straight line which verifies the fact that the data are hyperbolic.

20-16. PARABOLIC OR HYPERBOLIC CURVES OF THREE CONSTANTS

Equations of the type:

$$y = ax^b + c \qquad (20\text{-}14)$$

are parabolic if b is positive and hyperbolic if b is negative. This equation can be changed so as to plot as a straight line by rewriting it as:

$$y - c = ax^b$$

and then:

$$\log (y - c) = \log a + b \log x$$

which will plot as a straight line when the variables $(y - c)$ and x are plotted on log paper. However, the constant c must be evaluated before the test plot can be made. To evaluate c, select any two points (x_1, y_1) and (x_2, y_2) on the rectilinear plot of the data, Fig. 20-22(a). Assuming that the curve is of the form of Eq. 20-14, locate x_3 so that $x_3 = \sqrt{x_1 x_2}$ and measure the corresponding y_3. By substituting these three points into Eq. 20-14, we obtain:

$$x_1 = \left(\frac{y_1 - c}{a}\right)^{1/b}$$

$$x_2 = \left(\frac{y_2 - c}{a}\right)^{1/b}$$

$$y_3 = a(x_1 x_2)^{b/2} + c$$

Therefore:

$$y_3 - c = a\left[\left(\frac{y_1 - c}{a}\right)^{1/b}\left(\frac{y_2 - c}{a}\right)^{1/b}\right]^{b/2}$$

$$= [(y_1 - c)(y_2 - c)]^{1/2}$$

Hence:

$$y_3{}^2 - 2y_3 c + c^2 = y_1 y_2 - y_1 c - y_2 c + c^2$$

or:

$$y_1 c + y_2 c - 2y_3 c = y_1 y_2 - y_3^2$$

and:

$$c = \frac{y_1 y_2 - y_3^2}{y_1 + y_2 - 2y_3} \qquad (20\text{-}15)$$

Having the value of c, the variables $y - c$ and x are plotted on log paper. If these variables plot as a straight line, the data are of the form of Eq. 20-14 and the constants a and b can be evaluated by the

methods of Chapter 18. This form of equation is illustrated in Fig. 20-22(b).

20-17. PARABOLIC CURVES OF THREE CONSTANTS

The general equation of a parabola in the second degree of x is:

$$y = a + bx + cx^2. \qquad (20\text{-}16)$$

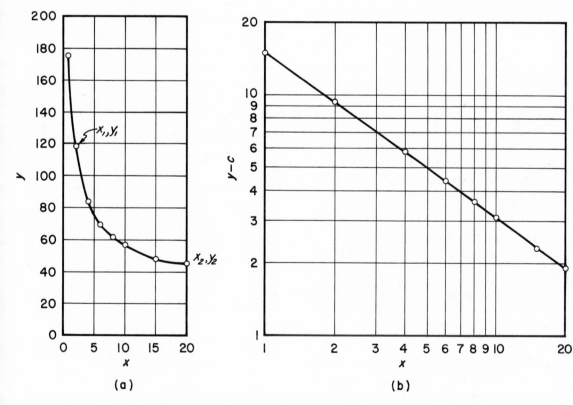

x	y
1	175
2	119
4	84
6	70
8	62
10	57
15	49
20	45

Assume: $y = ax^b + c$

$x_3 = \sqrt{2(20)} = 6.33$

y_3 (measured) $= 68$

$c = \dfrac{(119)(45) - (68)^2}{119 + 45 - 2(68)} = 26.1$

x	y	$y-c$
1	175	149
2	119	93
4	84	58
6	70	44
8	62	36
10	57	31
15	49	23
20	45	19

(a)

(b)

Fig. 20-22. Equation of the form: $y = ax^b + c$.

This equation can be changed so as to plot as a straight line by selecting some point (x_1, y_1) from the plot of the data. It is preferable that this point be one set of the original data. Substitute these values into Eq. 20–16:

$$y_1 = a + bx_1 + cx_1^2,$$

and subtract from Eq. 20–16:

$$(y - y_1) = b(x - x_1) + c(x^2 - x_1^2).$$

Factoring:

$$(y - y_1) = b(x - x_1) + c(x - x_1)(x + x_1),$$

and dividing by $(x - x_1)$:

$$\frac{(y - y_1)}{(x - x_1)} = b + c(x + x_1),$$

and finally:

$$\frac{(y - y_1)}{(x - x_1)} = (b + cx_1) + cx.$$

Since the term $(b + cx_1)$ is a constant, this last equation can be rewritten as:

$$\frac{(y - y_1)}{(x - x_1)} = A + Bx. \qquad (20–17)$$

This is the equation for a straight line in terms of x and

$$\frac{(y - y_1)}{(x - x_1)}.$$

From this plot the constants A and B can be determined and substituted back into Eq. 20–17. Then multiplying by $(x - x_1)$ and collecting like terms will yield an equation of the form of Eq. 20–16.

20–18. EXPONENTIAL CURVES OF THREE CONSTANTS

Chapter 18 discussed the exponential curve of two constants. Sometimes those curves are shifted upward or downward and the equation becomes:

$$y = ae^{bx} + c. \qquad (20–18)$$

This curve can be changed so as to plot as a straight line by rewriting it as:

$$(y - c) = ae^{bx},$$

and putting it into logarithmic form:

$$\log (y - c) = \log a + bx \log e,$$

and since the logarithm of e (to three places) is 0.434:

$$\log (y - c) = \log a + 0.434\, bx.$$

This equation will plot as a straight line on semilog paper when the variables are x and $(y - c)$. The constant c must be evaluated prior to this test plot and the method of evaluation is similar to that discussed in Art. 20–16. Choose any two points on the rectilinear plot of the data such as (x_1, y_1) and (x_2, y_2). Determine x_3 such that $x_3 = \frac{1}{2}(x_1 + x_2)$ and measure the corresponding y_3. The constant c can now be evaluated by Eq. 20–15:

$$c = \frac{y_1 y_2 - y_3^2}{y_1 + y_2 - 2y_3} \qquad (20–15)$$

The proof of this condition is similar to the proof developed in Art. 20–16, but the details are left to the student. Having the values of c, the values of $(y - c)$ and x can be plotted on semi-log paper. If the plot is a straight line, the assumption as to the form of the equation is verified and the constants a and b can be evaluated as in Chapter 18.

Another form of exponential curve is:

$$y = e^{a + bx + cx^2}. \qquad (20–19)$$

This equation is changed so as to plot as a straight line by rewriting it in logarithmic form:

$$\log y = (a + bx + cx^2) \log e,$$

or

$$\log y = 0.434(a + bx + cx^2).$$

This equation is now of a form similar to the equation discussed in Art. 20–17 and the constants are evaluated in the same manner. Choose a point (x_1, y_1) in the initial data and make a test plot for x and

$$\frac{(\log y - \log y_1)}{0.434(x - x_1)}.$$

This test plot cannot be made on semi-log paper because of the mixture of terms in the variable:

$$\frac{(\log y - \log y_1)}{0.434(x - x_1)}.$$

Perhaps the most direct method for evaluating this variable is to change it to:

$$\frac{\log\left(\dfrac{y}{y_1}\right)}{0.434(x - x_1)}.$$

When this variable is evaluated and plotted versus x on rectilinear paper, the points will plot as a straight line if the original data fit Eq. 20–19. The constants are then determined as in Art. 20–17.

20–19. OTHER EMPIRICAL EQUATIONS

There are many other equations that can be used when determining the equation of some test or empirical data. Some of these equations are:

$$y = a + bx + e^{c+dx} \tag{20–20}$$

$$y = ae^{bx} + ce^{dx} \tag{20–21}$$

$$y = a + bx + cx^d \tag{20–22}$$

$$y = ax^b + cx^d \tag{20–23}$$

$$y = a + bx + cx^2 + dx^3 \tag{20–24}$$

These equations (except for Eq. 20–24) are actually combinations of equations previously discussed. They are handled by finding, through test plots, the equation which best fits each range of data.

Equations of the type of Eq. 20–24 are seldom used because of the great amount of labor involved in determining the constants. Usually, a simpler form of curve can be found that will closely fit the data and this is the equation used. If this equation is the only one that will fit the data, the constants can be determined by selecting four points and substituting their coordinates into Eq. 20–24. This will yield four equations which can be solved simultaneously to evaluate the constants.

Problems

20–1. Construct the harmonic curve of the function whose period is one second and whose amplitude is two units.

20–2. Construct the resultant curve of two functions whose periods are equal. The amplitude of one function is twice that of the other function and the larger function precedes the smaller function by 30°.

20–3. Show the result of the first four terms of the equation:

$$y = 3 + 4 \sin \theta + 3 \sin \frac{\theta}{2} + 2 \sin \frac{\theta}{4} + \cdots .$$

20–4. Show the result of the equation:

$$y = 0 + 3 \sin \theta + 1\tfrac{1}{2} \sin 2\theta + \tfrac{3}{4} \sin 3\theta.$$

When a point is defined in the following problems as $A(1, 5)$, the first number refers to the numbers of inches to the right of the left edge of the paper and the second

number refers to the number of inches above the bottom edge of the paper.

20–5. Four points can be located on a map, $A(1, 9)$, $B(2, 6)$, $C(3, 8)$, and $D(4, 7)$. Six points can be located on a photograph, $A'(1, 5)$, $B'(3, 1)$, $C'(4, 4)$, $D'(5, 2)$, $E'(5, 5)$ and $F'(7, 6)$. Locate points E and F on the map.

20–6. Points $A(1\tfrac{1}{4}, 6\tfrac{1}{2})$, $B(1\tfrac{1}{4}, 9\tfrac{1}{2})$, $C(7\tfrac{1}{4}, 9\tfrac{1}{2})$ and $D(7\tfrac{1}{4}, 6\tfrac{1}{2})$ mark the four corners of the playing area of a football field. The home team is defending the right goal line. A photograph, taken at the start of a play, shows the two ends of the home team's goal line at $(3, 4)$ and $(6, 6)$; the two ends of the thirty-yard line at $(1, 4)$ and $(2\tfrac{1}{2}, 6)$. The ball is spotted at $(2\tfrac{1}{2}, 5)$. Another photograph taken after the runner was tackled shows the two ends of the 50- and the opponent's 20-yard lines at $(7\tfrac{1}{2}, 1)$ $(6, 3)$ and $(5\tfrac{1}{2}, 1)$ $(3\tfrac{1}{2}, 3)$ respectively. The runner is at $(4, 2\tfrac{3}{4})$. How far did the ball advance?

20-7. Solve the differential equation: $y' = 2y$ where y ranges from 0 to 10 and where $y = 1, x = 0$.

20-8. Solve the differential equation: $y' = 1 - y^2$ where y ranges from 0 to 6 and when $y = 0$, $x = 0$.

20-9. Solve the differential equation: $y'' = y$ where when $x = 0, y = y' = y'' = 1$.

20-10. Determine the equations of the following sets of empirical data:

a.

L	10	20	30	40	50	60	70
W	1.7	4.0	7.1	11.8	19.2	33.3	70.0

b.

R	1.0	1.5	2.0	3.0	5.0	10.0	15.0	20.0
S	40	30	25	20	16	13	12	11.5

c.

Q	1	2	3	4	5	6	7	8
R	6	11	18	27	38	51	66	83

d.

S	0	0.1	0.2	0.3	0.4	0.5	0.6	0.7	0.8
D	20.1	24.7	31.1	39.9	52.3	69.9	95.4	132.5	188.0

APPENDIX

APPENDIX

Contents

PLOTTING PROBLEMS

In some problems a point is designated as: $A(2\frac{1}{2}, 1, 3)$. This is interpreted as follows:

1st number—the distance in inches of the FRONT and TOP views of point A to the right of the left edge of the paper.

2nd number—the distance in inches of the FRONT view above the lower edge of the paper.

3rd number—the distance in inches of the TOP view above the lower edge of the paper.

Thus the FRONT view of $A(2\frac{1}{2}, 1, 3)$, shown in the illustration at the right, is $2\frac{1}{2}$ inches to the right of the left edge and 1 inch above the lower edge; the TOP view is $2\frac{1}{2}$ inches to the right of the left edge and 3 inches above the lower edge. Note that the FRONT and TOP views are in vertical alignment as is always true in orthographic projection.

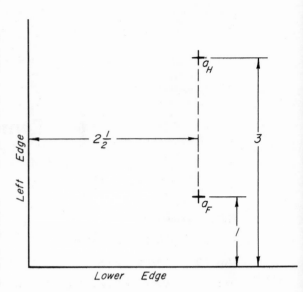

TABLE 1

Useful Constants

$\pi = 3.1416$	$\log \pi = 0.4971$
$\pi^2 = 9.8696$	$\log \pi^2 = 0.9943$
$\pi^3 = 31.0063$	$\log \pi^3 = 1.4914$
$\sqrt{\pi} = 1.7725$	$\log \sqrt{\pi} = 0.2486$
$\sqrt[3]{\pi} = 1.4646$	$\log \sqrt[3]{\pi} = 0.1657$
$e = 2.7183$	$\log e = 0.4343$
$e^2 = 7.3891$	$\log e^2 = 0.8686$
$\sqrt{e} = 1.6487$	$\log \sqrt{e} = 0.2171$

1°	= 0.017453 radian	1′ = 0.000291 radian
1 cm.	= 0.3937 in.	1 in. = 2.5400 cm.
1 ft.	= 0.3048 meter	3.2808 ft. = 1 meter

1 knot   = 1.15078 statute miles/hr.
1 acre   = 43,560 sq. ft.
1 U.S.
  gallon = 231 cu. in.
1 gravity = 32.174 ft./sec./sec.
1 mile/hr. = 88 ft./min.
30 mile/hr. = 44 ft./sec.

TABLE 2

Chord Values

(Values shown are the chord lengths of arcs of unit radius subtending the given angles.)

Degrees	Minutes					
	0'	10'	20'	30'	40'	50'
0	0.0000	0.0029	0.0058	0.0087	0.0116	0.0145
1	0.0175	0.0204	0.0233	0.0262	0.0291	0.0320
2	0.0349	0.0378	0.0407	0.0436	0.0465	0.0494
3	0.0524	0.0553	0.0582	0.0611	0.0640	0.0669
4	0.0698	0.0727	0.0756	0.0785	0.0814	0.0843
5	0.0872	0.0901	0.0931	0.0960	0.0989	0.1018
6	0.1047	0.1076	0.1105	0.1134	0.1163	0.1192
7	0.1221	0.1250	0.1279	0.1308	0.1337	0.1366
8	0.1395	0.1424	0.1453	0.1482	0.1511	0.1540
9	0.1569	0.1598	0.1627	0.1656	0.1685	0.1714
10	0.1743	0.1772	0.1801	0.1830	0.1859	0.1888
11	0.1917	0.1946	0.1975	0.2004	0.2033	0.2062
12	0.2091	0.2119	0.2148	0.2177	0.2206	0.2235
13	0.2264	0.2293	0.2322	0.2351	0.2380	0.2409
14	0.2437	0.2466	0.2495	0.2524	0.2553	0.2582
15	0.2611	0.2639	0.2668	0.2697	0.2726	0.2755
16	0.2783	0.2812	0.2841	0.2870	0.2899	0.2927
17	0.2956	0.2985	0.3014	0.3042	0.3071	0.3100
18	0.3129	0.3157	0.3186	0.3215	0.3244	0.3272
19	0.3301	C.3330	0.3358	0.3387	0.3416	0.3444
20	0.3473	0.3502	0.3530	0.3559	0.3587	0.3616
21	0.3645	0.3673	0.3702	0.3730	0.3759	0.3788
22	0.3816	0.3845	0.3873	0.3902	0.3930	0.3959
23	0.3987	0.4016	0.4044	0.4073	0.4101	0.4130
24	0.4158	0.4187	0.4215	0.4244	0.4272	0.4300
25	0.4329	0.4357	0.4386	0.4414	0.4442	0.4471
26	0.4499	0.4527	0.4556	0.4584	0.4612	0.4641
27	0.4669	0.4697	0.4725	0.4754	0.4782	0.4810
28	0.4838	0.4867	0.4895	0.4923	0.4951	0.4979
29	0.5008	0.5036	0.5064	0.5092	0.5120	0.5148
30	0.5176	0.5204	0.5233	0.5261	0.5289	0.5317
31	0.5345	0.5373	0.5401	0.5429	0.5457	0.5485
32	0.5513	0.5541	0.5569	0.5597	0.5625	0.5652
33	0.5680	0.5708	0.5736	0.5764	0.5792	0.5820
34	0.5847	0.5875	0.5903	0.5931	0.5959	0.5986
35	0.6014	0.6042	0.6070	0.6097	0.6125	0.6153
36	0.6180	0.6208	0.6236	0.6263	0.6291	0.6319
37	0.6346	0.6374	0.6401	0.6429	0.6456	0.6484
38	0.6511	0.6539	0.6566	0.6594	0.6621	0.6649
39	0.6676	0.6704	0.6731	0.6758	0.6786	0.6813
40	0.6840	0.6868	0.6895	0.6922	0.6950	0.6977
41	0.7004	0.7031	0.7059	0.7086	0.7113	0.7140
42	0.7167	0.7195	0.7222	0.7249	0.7276	0.7303
43	0.7330	0.7357	0.7384	0.7411	0.7438	0.7465
44	0.7492	0.7519	0.7546	0.7573	0.7600	0.7627
45	0.7654	0.7681	0.7707	0.7734	0.7761	0.7788

TABLE 3
Decimal Equivalents of Fractions of an Inch

Fraction					Decimal Equivalent	Three-Place Decimal	Two-Place Decimal
				$\frac{1}{64}$	.015625	.016	.02
			$\frac{1}{32}$		.03125	.031	.03
				$\frac{3}{64}$	.046875	.047	.05
		$\frac{1}{16}$			.0625	.062	.06
				$\frac{5}{64}$	.078125	.078	.08
			$\frac{3}{32}$		.09375	.094	.09
				$\frac{7}{64}$	.109375	.109	.11
	$\frac{1}{8}$				.125	.125	.12
				$\frac{9}{64}$	.140625	.141	.14
			$\frac{5}{32}$		.15625	.156	.16
				$\frac{11}{64}$	.171875	.172	.17
		$\frac{3}{16}$			.1875	.188	.19
				$\frac{13}{64}$	.203125	.203	.20
			$\frac{7}{32}$		.21875	.219	.22
				$\frac{15}{64}$	.234375	.234	.23
$\frac{1}{4}$					.250	.250	.25
				$\frac{17}{64}$	.265625	.266	.27
			$\frac{9}{32}$		.28125	.281	.28
				$\frac{19}{64}$	.296875	.297	.30
		$\frac{5}{16}$			.3125	.312	.31
				$\frac{21}{64}$	.328125	.328	.33
			$\frac{11}{32}$		.34375	.344	.34
				$\frac{23}{64}$	.359375	.359	.36
	$\frac{3}{8}$				.375	.375	.38
				$\frac{25}{64}$	.390625	.391	.39
			$\frac{13}{32}$		.40625	.406	.41
				$\frac{27}{64}$	.421875	.422	.42
		$\frac{7}{16}$			.4375	.438	.44
				$\frac{29}{64}$	.453125	.453	.45
			$\frac{15}{32}$		.46875	.469	.47
				$\frac{31}{64}$	.484375	.484	.48
$\frac{1}{2}$					.500	.500	.50

TABLE 3 (Continued)

Decimal Equivalents of Fractions of an Inch

Fraction						Decimal Equivalent	Three-Place Decimal	Two-Place Decimal
					$\frac{33}{64}$	.515625	.516	.52
				$\frac{17}{32}$		.53125	.531	.53
					$\frac{35}{64}$	.546875	.547	.55
			$\frac{9}{16}$			.5625	.562	.56
					$\frac{37}{64}$	.578125	.578	.58
				$\frac{19}{32}$		.59375	.594	.59
					$\frac{39}{64}$	.609375	.609	.61
	$\frac{5}{8}$					.625	.625	.62
					$\frac{41}{64}$	.640625	.641	.64
				$\frac{21}{32}$		.65625	.656	.66
					$\frac{43}{64}$	.671875	.672	.67
			$\frac{11}{16}$			.6875	.688	.69
					$\frac{45}{64}$	.703125	.703	.70
				$\frac{23}{32}$		.71875	.719	.72
					$\frac{47}{64}$	.734375	.734	.73
$\frac{3}{4}$						.750	.750	.75
					$\frac{49}{64}$	.765625	.766	.77
				$\frac{25}{32}$		.78125	.781	.78
					$\frac{51}{64}$	.796875	.797	.80
			$\frac{13}{16}$			.8125	.812	.81
					$\frac{53}{64}$	.828125	.828	.83
				$\frac{27}{32}$		.84375	.844	.84
					$\frac{55}{64}$	.859375	.859	.86
	$\frac{7}{8}$					.875	.875	.88
					$\frac{57}{64}$	.890625	.891	.89
				$\frac{29}{32}$		.90625	.906	.91
					$\frac{59}{64}$	.921875	.922	.92
			$\frac{15}{16}$			.9375	.938	.94
					$\frac{61}{64}$	.953125	.953	.95
				$\frac{31}{32}$		.96875	.969	.97
					$\frac{63}{64}$	.984375	.984	.98
1						1.000	1.000	1.00

TABLE 4
Functions of Numbers

No.	Square	Cube	Square Root	Cube Root	1000 × Reciprocal	No. = Diameter	
						Circum.	Area
1	1	1	1.0000	1.0000	1000.000	3.142	0.7854
2	4	8	1.4142	1.2599	500.000	6.283	3.1416
3	9	27	1.7321	1.4422	333.333	9.425	7.0686
4	16	64	2.0000	1.5874	250.000	12.566	12.5664
5	25	125	2.2361	1.7100	200.000	15.708	19.6450
6	36	216	2.4495	1.8171	166.667	18.850	28.2743
7	49	343	2.6458	1.9129	142.857	21.991	38.4845
8	64	512	2.8284	2.0000	125.000	25.133	50.2655
9	81	729	3.0000	2.0801	111.111	28.274	63.6173
10	100	1000	3.1623	2.1544	100.000	31.416	78.5398
11	121	1331	3.3166	2.2240	90.9091	34.558	95.0332
12	144	1728	3.4641	2.2894	83.3333	37.699	113.097
13	169	2197	3.6056	2.3513	76.9231	40.841	132.732
14	196	2744	3.7417	2.4101	71.4286	43.982	153.938
15	225	3375	3.8730	2.4662	66.6667	47.124	176.715
16	256	4096	4.0000	2.5198	62.5000	50.265	201.062
17	289	4913	4.1231	2.5713	58.8235	53.407	226.980
18	324	5832	4.2426	2.6207	55.5556	56.549	254.469
19	361	6859	4.3589	2.6684	52.6316	59.690	283.529
20	400	8000	4.4721	2.7144	50.0000	62.832	314.159
21	441	9261	4.5826	2.7589	47.6190	65.973	346.361
22	484	10648	4.6904	2.8020	45.4545	69.115	380.133
23	529	12167	4.7958	2.8439	43.4783	72.257	415.476
24	576	13824	4.8990	2.8845	41.6667	75.398	452.389
25	625	15625	5.0000	2.9240	40.0000	78.540	490.874
26	676	17576	5.0990	2.9625	38.4615	81.681	530.929
27	729	19683	5.1962	3.0000	37.0370	84.823	572.555
28	784	21952	5.2915	3.0366	35.7143	87.965	615.752
29	841	24389	5.3852	3.0723	34.4828	91.106	660.520
30	900	27000	5.4772	3.1072	33.3333	94.248	706.858
31	961	29791	5.5678	3.1414	32.2581	97.389	754.768
32	1024	32768	5.6569	3.1748	31.2500	100.531	804.248
33	1089	35937	5.7446	3.2075	30.3030	103.673	855.299
34	1156	39304	5.8310	3.2396	29.4118	106.814	907.920
35	1225	42875	5.9161	3.2711	28.5714	109.956	962.113
36	1296	46656	6.0000	3.3019	27.7778	113.097	1017.88
37	1369	50653	6.0828	3.3322	27.0270	116.239	1075.21
38	1444	54872	6.1644	3.3620	26.3158	119.381	1134.11
39	1521	59319	6.2450	3.3912	25.6410	122.522	1194.59
40	1600	64000	6.3246	3.4200	25.0000	125.66	1256.64
41	1681	68921	6.4031	3.4482	24.3902	128.81	1320.25
42	1764	74088	6.4807	3.4760	23.8095	131.95	1385.44
43	1849	79507	6.5574	3.5034	23.2558	135.09	1452.20
44	1936	85184	6.6332	3.5303	22.7273	138.23	1520.53
45	2025	91125	6.7082	3.5569	22.2222	141.37	1590.43
46	2116	97336	6.7823	3.5830	21.7391	144.51	1661.90
47	2209	103823	6.8557	3.6088	21.2766	147.65	1734.94
48	2304	110592	6.9282	3.6342	20.8333	150.80	1809.56
49	2401	117649	7.0000	3.6593	20.4082	153.94	1885.74
50	2500	125000	7.0711	3.6840	20.0000	157.08	1963.50

TABLE 4 (Continued)

Functions of Numbers

No.	Square	Cube	Square Root	Cube Root	1000 × Reciprocal	No. = Diameter	
						Circum.	Area
51	2601	132651	7. 1414	3. 7084	19. 6078	160. 22	2042. 82
52	2704	140608	7. 2111	3. 7325	19. 2308	163. 36	2123. 72
53	2809	148877	7. 2801	3. 7563	18. 8679	166. 50	2206. 18
54	2916	157464	7. 3485	3. 7798	18. 5185	169. 65	2290. 22
55	3025	166375	7. 4162	3. 8030	18. 1818	172. 79	2375. 83
56	3136	175616	7. 4833	3. 8259	17. 8571	175. 93	2463. 01
57	3249	185193	7. 5498	3. 8485	17. 5439	179. 07	2551. 76
58	3364	195112	7. 6158	3. 8709	17. 2414	182. 21	2642. 08
59	3481	205379	7. 6811	3. 8930	16. 9492	185. 35	2733. 97
60	3600	216000	7. 7460	3. 9149	16. 6667	188. 50	2827. 43
61	3721	226981	7. 8102	3. 9365	16. 3934	191. 64	2922. 47
62	3844	238328	7. 8740	3. 9579	16. 1290	194. 78	3019. 07
63	3969	250047	7. 9373	3. 9791	15. 8730	197. 92	3117. 25
64	4096	262144	8. 0000	4. 0000	15. 6250	201. 06	3216. 99
65	4225	274625	8. 0623	4. 0207	15. 3846	204. 20	3318. 31
66	4356	287496	8. 1240	4. 0412	15. 1515	207. 35	3421. 19
67	4489	300763	8. 1854	4. 0615	14. 9254	210. 49	3525. 65
68	4624	314432	8. 2462	4. 0817	14. 7059	213. 63	3631. 68
69	4761	328509	8. 3066	4. 1016	14. 4928	216. 77	3739. 28
70	4900	343000	8. 3666	4. 1213	14. 2857	219. 91	3848. 45
71	5041	357911	8. 4261	4. 1408	14. 0845	223. 05	3959. 19
72	5184	373248	8. 4853	4. 1602	13. 8889	226. 19	4071. 50
73	5329	389017	8. 5440	4. 1793	13. 6986	229. 34	4185. 39
74	5476	405224	8. 6023	4. 1983	13. 5135	232. 48	4300. 84
75	5625	421875	8. 6603	4. 2172	13. 3333	235. 62	4417. 86
76	5776	438976	8. 7178	4. 2358	13. 1579	238. 76	4536. 46
77	5929	456533	8. 7750	4. 2543	12. 9870	241. 90	4656. 63
78	6084	474552	8. 8318	4. 2727	12. 8205	245. 04	4778. 36
79	6241	493039	8. 8882	4. 2908	12. 6582	248. 19	4901. 67
80	6400	512000	8. 9443	4. 3089	12. 5000	251. 33	5026. 55
81	6561	531441	9. 0000	4. 3267	12. 3457	254. 47	5153. 00
82	6724	551368	9. 0554	4. 3445	12. 1951	257. 61	5281. 02
83	6889	571787	9. 1104	4. 3621	12. 0482	260. 75	5410. 61
84	7056	592704	9. 1652	4. 3795	11. 9048	263. 89	5541. 77
85	7225	614125	9. 2195	4. 3968	11. 7647	267. 04	5674. 50
86	7396	636056	9. 2736	4. 4140	11. 6279	270. 18	5808. 80
87	7569	658503	9. 3274	4. 4310	11. 4943	273. 32	5944. 68
88	7744	681472	9. 3808	4. 4480	11. 3636	276. 46	6082. 12
89	7921	704969	9. 4340	4. 4647	11. 2360	279. 60	6221. 14
90	8100	729000	9. 4868	4. 4814	11. 1111	282. 74	6361. 73
91	8281	753571	9. 5394	4. 4979	10. 9890	285. 88	6503. 88
92	8464	778688	9. 5917	4. 5144	10. 8696	289. 03	6647. 61
93	8649	804357	9. 6437	4. 5307	10. 7527	292. 17	6792. 91
94	8836	830584	9. 6954	4. 5468	10. 6383	295. 31	6939. 78
95	9025	857375	9. 7468	4. 5629	10. 5263	298. 45	7088. 22
96	9216	884736	9. 7980	4. 5789	10. 4167	301. 59	7238. 23
97	9409	912673	9. 8489	4. 5947	10. 3093	304. 73	7389. 81
98	9604	941192	9. 8995	4. 6104	10. 2041	307. 88	7542. 96
99	9801	970299	9. 9499	4. 6261	10. 1010	311. 02	7697. 69
100	10000	1000000	10. 0000	4. 6416	10. 0000	314. 16	7853. 98

APPENDIX

TABLE 5
Common Logarithms of Numbers

N	0	1	2	3	4	5	6	7	8	9
10	0000	0043	0086	0128	0170	0212	0253	0294	0334	0374
11	0414	0453	0492	0531	0569	0607	0645	0682	0719	0755
12	0792	0828	0864	0899	0934	0969	1004	1038	1072	1106
13	1139	1173	1206	1239	1271	1303	1335	1367	1399	1430
14	1461	1492	1523	1553	1584	1614	1644	1673	1703	1732
15	1761	1790	1818	1847	1875	1903	1931	1959	1987	2014
16	2041	2068	2095	2122	2148	2175	2201	2227	2253	2279
17	2304	2330	2355	2380	2405	2430	2455	2480	2504	2529
18	2553	2577	2601	2625	2648	2672	2695	2718	2742	2765
19	2788	2810	2833	2856	2878	2900	2923	2945	2967	2989
20	3010	3032	3054	3075	3096	3118	3139	3160	3181	3201
21	3222	3243	3263	3284	3304	3324	3345	3365	3385	3404
22	3424	3444	3464	3483	3502	3522	3541	3560	3579	3598
23	3617	3636	3655	3674	3692	3711	3729	3747	3766	3784
24	3802	3820	3838	3856	3874	3892	3909	3927	3945	3962
25	3979	3997	4014	4031	4048	4065	4082	4099	4116	4133
26	4150	4166	4183	4200	4216	4232	4249	4265	4281	4298
27	4314	4330	4346	4362	4378	4393	4409	4425	4440	4456
28	4472	4487	4502	4518	4533	4548	4564	4579	4594	4609
29	4624	4639	4654	4669	4683	4698	4713	4728	4742	4757
30	4771	4786	4800	4814	4829	4843	4857	4871	4886	4900
31	4914	4928	4942	4955	4969	4983	4997	5011	5024	5038
32	5051	5065	5079	5092	5105	5119	5132	5145	5159	5172
33	5185	5198	5211	5224	5237	5250	5263	5276	5289	5302
34	5315	5328	5340	5353	5366	5378	5391	5403	5416	5428
35	5441	5453	5465	5478	5490	5502	5514	5527	5539	5551
36	5563	5575	5587	5599	5611	5623	5635	5647	5658	5670
37	5682	5694	5705	5717	5729	5740	5752	5763	5775	5786
38	5798	5809	5821	5832	5843	5855	5866	5877	5888	5899
39	5911	5922	5933	5944	5955	5966	5977	5988	5999	6010
40	6021	6031	6042	6053	6064	6075	6085	6096	6107	6117
41	6128	6138	6149	6160	6170	6180	6191	6201	6212	6222
42	6232	6243	6253	6263	6274	6284	6294	6304	6314	6325
43	6335	6345	6355	6365	6375	6385	6395	6405	6415	6425
44	6435	6444	6454	6464	6474	6484	6493	6503	6513	6522
45	6532	6542	6551	6561	6571	6580	6590	6599	6609	6618
46	6628	6637	6646	6656	6665	6675	6684	6693	6702	6712
47	6721	6730	6739	6749	6758	6767	6776	6785	6794	6803
48	6812	6821	6830	6839	6848	6857	6866	6875	6884	6893
49	6902	6911	6920	6928	6937	6946	6955	6964	6972	6981
50	6990	6998	7007	7016	7024	7033	7042	7050	7059	7067
51	7076	7084	7093	7101	7110	7118	7126	7135	7143	7152
52	7160	7168	7177	7185	7193	7202	7210	7218	7226	7235
53	7243	7251	7259	7267	7275	7284	7292	7300	7308	7316
54	7324	7332	7340	7348	7356	7364	7372	7380	7388	7396

TABLE 5 (Continued)

Common Logarithms of Numbers

N	0	1	2	3	4	5	6	7	8	9
55	7404	7412	7419	7427	7435	7443	7451	7459	7466	7474
56	7482	7490	7497	7505	7513	7520	7528	7536	7543	7551
57	7559	7566	7574	7582	7589	7597	7604	7612	7619	7627
58	7634	7642	7649	7657	7664	7672	7679	7686	7694	7701
59	7709	7716	7723	7731	7738	7745	7752	7760	7767	7774
60	7782	7789	7796	7803	7810	7818	7825	7832	7839	7846
61	7853	7860	7868	7875	7882	7889	7896	7903	7910	7917
62	7924	7931	7938	7945	7952	7959	7966	7973	7980	7987
63	7993	8000	8007	8014	8021	8028	8035	8041	8048	8055
64	8062	8069	8075	8082	8089	8096	8102	8109	8116	8122
65	8129	8136	8142	8149	8156	8162	8169	8176	8182	8189
66	8195	8202	8209	8215	8222	8228	8235	8241	8248	8254
67	8261	8267	8274	8280	8287	8293	8299	8306	8312	8319
68	8325	8331	8338	8344	8351	8357	8363	8370	8376	8382
69	8388	8395	8401	8407	8414	8420	8426	8432	8439	8445
70	8451	8457	8463	8470	8476	8482	8488	8494	8500	8506
71	8513	8519	8525	8531	8537	8543	8549	8555	8561	8567
72	8573	8579	8585	8591	8597	8603	8609	8615	8621	8627
73	8633	8639	8645	8651	8657	8663	8669	8675	8681	8686
74	8692	8698	8704	8710	8716	8722	8727	8733	8739	8745
75	8751	8756	8762	8768	8774	8779	8785	8791	8797	8802
76	8808	8814	8820	8825	8831	8837	8842	8848	8854	8859
77	8865	8871	8876	8882	8887	8893	8899	8904	8910	8915
78	8921	8927	8932	8938	8943	8949	8954	8960	8965	8971
79	8976	8982	8987	8993	8998	9004	9009	9015	9020	9025
80	9031	9036	9042	9047	9053	9058	9063	9069	9074	9079
81	9085	9090	9096	9101	9106	9112	9117	9122	9128	9133
82	9138	9143	9149	9154	9159	9165	9170	9175	9180	9186
83	9191	9196	9201	9206	9212	9217	9222	9227	9232	9238
84	9243	9248	9253	9258	9263	9269	9274	9279	9284	9289
85	9294	9299	9304	9309	9315	9320	9325	9330	9335	9340
86	9345	9350	9355	9360	9365	9370	9375	9380	9385	9390
87	9395	9400	9405	9410	9415	9420	9425	9430	9435	9440
88	9445	9450	9455	9460	9465	9469	9474	9479	9484	9489
89	9494	9499	9504	9509	9513	9518	9523	9528	9533	9538
90	9542	9547	9552	9557	9562	9566	9571	9576	9581	9586
91	9590	9595	9600	9605	9609	9614	9619	9624	9628	9633
92	9638	9643	9647	9652	9657	9661	9666	9671	9675	9680
93	9685	9689	9694	9699	9703	9708	9713	9717	9722	9727
94	9731	9736	9741	9745	9750	9754	9759	9763	9768	9773
95	9777	9782	9786	9791	9795	9800	9805	9809	9814	9818
96	9823	9827	9832	9836	9841	9845	9850	9854	9859	9863
97	9868	9872	9877	9881	9886	9890	9894	9899	9903	9908
98	9912	9917	9921	9926	9930	9934	9939	9943	9948	9952
99	9956	9961	9965	9969	9974	9978	9983	9987	9991	9996

TABLE 6
Trigonometric Functions

Angle Degrees	Angle Radians	Sine Nat.	Sine Log.	Cosine Nat.	Cosine Log.	Tangent Nat.	Tangent Log.	Cotangent Nat.	Cotangent Log.	Degrees	Radians
0° 00'	0	.0000	∞	1.0000	0.0000	.0000	∞	∞	∞	90° 00'	1.5708
10'	0.0029	.0029	7.4637	1.0000	0000	.0029	7.4637	343.77	2.5363	50'	1.5679
20'	0.0058	.0058	7648	1.0000	0000	.0058	7648	171.89	2352	40'	1.5650
30'	0.0087	.0087	9408	1.0000	0000	.0087	9409	114.59	0591	30'	1.5621
40'	0.0116	.0116	8.0658	.9999	0000	.0116	8.0658	85.940	1.9342	20'	1.5592
50'	0.0145	.0145	1627	.9999	0000	.0145	1627	68.750	8373	10'	1.5563
1° 00'	0.0175	.0175	8.2419	.9998	9.9999	.0175	8.2419	57.290	1.7581	89° 00'	1.5533
10'	0.0204	.0204	3088	.9998	9999	.0204	3089	49.104	6911	50'	1.5504
20'	0.0233	.0233	3668	.9997	9999	.0233	3669	42.964	6331	40'	1.5475
30'	0.0262	.0262	4179	.9997	9999	.0262	4181	38.188	5819	30'	1.5446
40'	0.0291	.0291	4637	.9996	9998	.0291	4638	34.368	5362	20'	1.5417
50'	0.0320	.0320	5050	.9995	9998	.0320	5053	31.242	4947	10'	1.5388
2° 00'	0.0349	.0349	8.5428	.9994	9.9997	.0349	8.5431	28.636	1.4569	88° 00'	1.5359
10'	0.0378	.0378	5776	.9993	9997	.0378	5779	26.432	4221	50'	1.5330
20'	0.0407	.0407	6097	.9992	9996	.0407	6101	24.542	3899	40'	1.5301
30'	0.0436	.0436	6397	.9990	9996	.0437	6401	22.904	3599	30'	1.5272
40'	0.0465	.0465	6677	.9989	9995	.0466	6682	21.470	3318	20'	1.5243
50'	0.0494	.0494	6940	.9988	9995	.0495	6945	20.206	3055	10'	1.5213
3° 00'	0.0524	.0523	8.7188	.9986	9.9994	.0524	8.7194	19.081	1.2806	87° 00'	1.5184
10'	0.0553	.0552	7423	.9985	9993	.0553	7429	18.075	2571	50'	1.5155
20'	0.0582	.0581	7645	.9983	9993	.0582	7652	17.169	2348	40'	1.5126
30'	0.0611	.0610	7857	.9981	9992	.0612	7865	16.350	2135	30'	1.5097
40'	0.0640	.0640	8059	.9980	9991	.0641	8067	15.605	1933	20'	1.5068
50'	0.0669	.0669	8251	.9978	9990	.0670	8261	14.924	1739	10'	1.5039
4° 00'	0.0698	.0698	8.8436	.9976	9.9989	.0699	8.8446	14.301	1.1554	86° 00'	1.5010
10'	0.0727	.0727	8613	.9974	9989	.0729	8624	13.727	1376	50'	1.4981
20'	0.0756	.0756	8783	.9971	9988	.0758	8795	13.197	1205	40'	1.4952
30'	0.0785	.0785	8946	.9969	9987	.0787	8960	12.706	1040	30'	1.4923
40'	0.0815	.0814	9104	.9967	9986	.0816	9118	12.251	0882	20'	1.4893
50'	0.0844	.0843	9256	.9964	9985	.0846	9272	11.826	0728	10'	1.4864
Radians Degrees (Cosine)		Nat. Log. (Cosine)		Nat. Log. (Sine)		Nat. Log. (Cotangent)		Nat. Log. (Tangent)		Degrees Radians	Angle

Angle		Sine		Cosine		Tangent		Cotangent		Angle	
Degrees	Radians	Nat.	Log.	Nat.	Log.	Nat.	Log.	Nat.	Log.	Degrees	Radians
5° 00'	0.0873	.0872	8.9403	.9962	9.9983	.0875	8.9420	11.430	1.0580	85° 00'	1.4835
10'	0.0902	.0901	9545	.9959	9982	.0904	9563	11.059	0437	50'	1.4806
20'	0.0931	.0929	9682	.9957	9981	.0934	9701	10.712	0299	40'	1.4777
30'	0.0960	.0958	9816	.9954	9980	.0963	9836	10.385	0164	30'	1.4748
40'	0.0989	.0987	9945	.9951	9979	.0992	9966	10.078	0034	20'	1.4719
50'	0.1018	.1016	9.0070	.9948	9977	.1022	9.0093	9.7882	0.9907	10'	1.4690
6° 00'	0.1047	.1045	9.0192	.9945	9.9976	.1051	9.0216	9.5144	0.9784	84° 00'	1.4661
10'	0.1076	.1074	0311	.9942	9975	.1080	0336	9.2553	9664	50'	1.4632
20'	0.1105	.1103	0426	.9939	9973	.1110	0453	9.0098	9547	40'	1.4603
30'	0.1134	.1132	0539	.9936	9972	.1139	0567	8.7769	9433	30'	1.4574
40'	0.1164	.1161	0648	.9932	9971	.1169	0678	8.5555	9322	20'	1.4544
50'	0.1193	.1190	0755	.9929	9969	.1198	0786	8.3450	9214	10'	1.4515
7° 00'	0.1222	.1219	9.0859	.9925	9.9968	.1228	9.0891	8.1443	9.9109	83° 00'	1.4486
10'	0.1251	.1248	0961	.9922	9966	.1257	0995	7.9530	9005	50'	1.4457
20'	0.1280	.1276	1060	.9918	9964	.1287	1096	7.7704	8904	40'	1.4428
30'	0.1309	.1305	1157	.9914	9963	.1317	1194	7.5958	8806	30'	1.4399
40'	0.1338	.1334	1252	.9911	9961	.1346	1291	7.4287	8709	20'	1.4370
50'	0.1367	.1363	1345	.9907	9959	.1376	1385	7.2687	8615	10'	1.4341
8° 00'	0.1396	.1392	9.1436	.9903	9.9958	.1405	9.1478	7.1154	0.8522	82° 00'	1.4312
10'	0.1425	.1421	1525	.9899	9956	.1435	1569	6.9682	8431	50'	1.4283
20'	0.1454	.1449	1612	.9894	9954	.1465	1658	6.8269	8342	40'	1.4254
30'	0.1484	.1478	1697	.9890	9952	.1495	1745	6.6912	8255	30'	1.4224
40'	0.1513	.1507	1781	.9886	9950	.1524	1831	6.5606	8169	20'	1.4195
50'	0.1542	.1536	1863	.9881	9948	.1554	1915	6.4348	8085	10'	1.4166
9° 00'	0.1571	.1564	9.1943	.9877	9.9946	.1584	9.1997	6.3138	0.8003	81° 00'	1.4137
10'	0.1600	.1593	2022	.9872	9944	.1614	2078	6.1970	7922	50'	1.4108
20'	0.1629	.1622	2100	.9868	9942	.1644	2158	6.0844	7842	40'	1.4079
30'	0.1658	.1650	2176	.9863	9940	.1673	2236	5.9758	7764	30'	1.4050
40'	0.1687	.1679	2251	.9858	9938	.1703	2313	5.8708	7687	20'	1.4021
50'	0.1716	.1708	2324	.9853	9936	.1733	2389	5.7694	7611	10'	1.3992
		Nat.	Log.	Nat.	Log.	Nat.	Log.	Nat.	Log.	Degrees	Radians
		Cosine		Sine		Cotangent		Tangent		Angle	

TABLE 6 (Continued)
Trigonometric Functions

Angle Degrees	Angle Radians	Sine Nat.	Sine Log.	Cosine Nat.	Cosine Log.	Tangent Nat.	Tangent Log.	Cotangent Nat.	Cotangent Log.	Degrees	Radians
10° 00'	0.1745	.1736	9.2397	.9848	9.9934	.1763	9.2463	5.6713	0.7537	80° 00'	1.3963
10'	0.1774	.1765	2468	.9843	9931	.1793	2536	5.5764	7464	50'	1.3934
20'	0.1804	.1794	2538	.9838	9929	.1823	2609	5.4845	7391	40'	1.3904
30'	0.1833	.1822	2606	.9833	9927	.1853	2680	5.3955	7320	30'	1.3875
40'	0.1862	.1851	2674	.9827	9924	.1883	2750	5.3093	7250	20'	1.3846
50'	0.1891	.1880	2740	.9822	9922	.1914	2819	5.2257	7181	10'	1.3817
11° 00'	0.1920	.1908	9.2806	.9816	9.9919	.1944	9.2887	5.1446	0.7113	79° 00'	1.3788
10'	0.1949	.1937	2870	.9811	9917	.1974	2953	5.0658	7047	50'	1.3759
20'	0.1978	.1965	2934	.9805	9914	.2004	3020	4.9894	6980	40'	1.3730
30'	0.2007	.1994	2997	.9799	9912	.2035	3085	4.9152	6915	30'	1.3701
40'	0.2036	.2022	3058	.9793	9909	.2065	3149	4.8430	6851	20'	1.3672
50'	0.2065	.2051	3119	.9787	9907	.2095	3212	4.7729	6788	10'	1.3643
12° 00'	0.2094	.2079	9.3179	.9781	9.9904	.2126	9.3275	4.7046	0.6725	78° 00'	1.3614
10'	0.2124	.2108	3238	.9775	9901	.2156	3336	4.6382	6664	50'	1.3584
20'	0.2153	.2136	3296	.9769	9899	.2186	3397	4.5736	6603	40'	1.3555
30'	0.2182	.2164	3353	.9763	9896	.2217	3458	4.5107	6542	30'	1.3526
40'	0.2211	.2193	3410	.9757	9893	.2247	3517	4.4494	6483	20'	1.3497
50'	0.2240	.2221	3466	.9750	9890	.2278	3576	4.3897	6424	10'	1.3468
13° 00'	0.2269	.2250	9.3521	.9744	9.9887	.2309	9.3634	4.3315	0.6366	77° 00'	1.3439
10'	0.2298	.2278	3575	.9737	9884	.2339	3691	4.2747	6309	50'	1.3410
20'	0.2327	.2306	3629	.9730	9881	.2370	3748	4.2193	6252	40'	1.3381
30'	0.2356	.2334	3682	.9724	9878	.2401	3804	4.1653	6196	30'	1.3352
40'	0.2385	.2363	3734	.9717	9875	.2432	3859	4.1126	6141	20'	1.3323
50'	0.2414	.2391	3786	.9710	9872	.2462	3914	4.0611	6086	10'	1.3294
14° 00'	0.2443	.2419	9.3837	.9703	9.9869	.2493	9.3968	4.0108	0.6032	76° 00'	1.3265
10'	0.2473	.2447	3887	.9696	9866	.2524	4021	3.9617	5979	50'	1.3235
20'	0.2502	.2476	3937	.9689	9863	.2555	4074	3.9136	5926	40'	1.3206
30'	0.2531	.2504	3986	.9681	9859	.2586	4127	3.8667	5873	30'	1.3177
40'	0.2560	.2532	4035	.9674	9856	.2617	4178	3.8208	5822	20'	1.3148
50'	0.2589	.2560	4083	.9667	9853	.2648	4230	3.7760	5770	10'	1.3119
		Cosine Nat.	Cosine Log.	Sine Nat.	Sine Log.	Cotangent Nat.	Cotangent Log.	Tangent Nat.	Tangent Log.	Degrees	Radians
										Angle	

Angle Degrees	Angle Radians	Sine Nat.	Sine Log.	Cosine Nat.	Cosine Log.	Tangent Nat.	Tangent Log.	Cotangent Nat.	Cotangent Log.	Degrees	Radians
15° 00'	0.2618	.2588	9.4130	.9659	9.9849	.2679	9.4281	3.7321	0.5719	75° 00'	1.3090
10'	0.2647	.2616	4177	.9652	9846	.2711	4331	3.6891	5669	50'	1.3061
20'	0.2676	.2644	4223	.9644	9843	.2742	4381	3.6470	5619	40'	1.3032
30'	0.2705	.2672	4269	.9636	9839	.2773	4430	3.6059	5570	30'	1.3003
40'	0.2734	.2700	4314	.9628	9836	.2805	4479	3.5656	5521	20'	1.2974
50'	0.2763	.2728	4359	.9621	9832	.2836	4527	3.5261	5473	10'	1.2945
16° 00'	0.2793	.2756	9.4403	.9613	9.9828	.2867	9.4575	3.4874	0.5425	74° 00'	1.2915
10'	0.2822	.2784	4447	.9605	9825	.2899	4622	3.4495	5378	50'	1.2886
20'	0.2851	.2812	4491	.9596	9821	.2931	4669	3.4124	5331	40'	1.2857
30'	0.2880	.2840	4533	.9588	9817	.2962	4716	3.3759	5284	30'	1.2828
40'	0.2909	.2868	4576	.9580	9814	.2994	4762	3.3402	5238	20'	1.2799
50'	0.2938	.2896	4618	.9572	9810	.3026	4808	3.3052	5192	10'	1.2770
17° 00'	0.2967	.2924	9.4659	.9563	9.9806	.3057	9.4853	3.2709	0.5147	73° 00'	1.2741
10'	0.2996	.2952	4700	.9555	9802	.3089	4898	3.2371	5102	50'	1.2712
20'	0.3025	.2979	4741	.9546	9798	.3121	4943	3.2041	5057	40'	1.2683
30'	0.3054	.3007	4781	.9537	9794	.3153	4987	3.1716	5013	30'	1.2654
40'	0.3083	.3035	4821	.9528	9790	.3185	5031	3.1397	4969	20'	1.2625
50'	0.3113	.3062	4861	.9520	9786	.3217	5075	3.1084	4925	10'	1.2595
18° 00'	0.3142	.3090	9.4900	.9511	9.9782	.3249	9.5118	3.0777	0.4882	72° 00'	1.2566
10'	0.3171	.3118	4939	.9502	9778	.3281	5161	3.0475	4839	50'	1.2537
20'	0.3200	.3145	4977	.9492	9774	.3314	5203	3.0178	4797	40'	1.2508
30'	0.3229	.3173	5015	.9483	9770	.3346	5245	2.9887	4755	30'	1.2479
40'	0.3258	.3201	5052	.9474	9765	.3378	5287	2.9600	4713	20'	1.2450
50'	0.3287	.3228	5090	.9465	9761	.3411	5329	2.9319	4671	10'	1.2421
19° 00'	0.3316	.3256	9.5126	.9455	9.9757	.3443	9.5370	2.9042	0.4630	71° 00'	1.2392
10'	0.3345	.3283	5163	.9446	9752	.3476	5411	2.8770	4589	50'	1.2363
20'	0.3374	.3311	5199	.9436	9748	.3508	5451	2.8502	4549	40'	1.2334
30'	0.3403	.3338	5235	.9426	9743	.3541	5491	2.8239	4509	30'	1.2305
40'	0.3432	.3365	5270	.9417	9739	.3574	5531	2.7980	4469	20'	1.2276
50'	0.3462	.3393	5306	.9407	9734	.3607	5571	2.7725	4429	10'	1.2246
		Cosine Nat.	Cosine Log.	Sine Nat.	Sine Log.	Cotangent Nat.	Cotangent Log.	Tangent Nat.	Tangent Log.	Degrees	Radians

TABLE 6 (Continued)
Trigonometric Functions

Angle Degrees	Angle Radians	Sine Nat.	Sine Log.	Cosine Nat.	Cosine Log.	Tangent Nat.	Tangent Log.	Cotangent Nat.	Cotangent Log.	Angle Degrees	Angle Radians
20° 00'	0.3491	.3420	9.5341	.9397	9.9730	.3640	9.5611	2.7475	0.4389	70° 00'	1.2217
10'	0.3520	.3448	5375	.9387	9725	.3673	5650	2.7228	4350	50'	1.2188
20'	0.3549	.3475	5409	.9377	9721	.3706	5689	2.6985	4311	40'	1.2159
30'	0.3578	.3502	5443	.9367	9716	.3739	5727	2.6746	4273	30'	1.2130
40'	0.3607	.3529	5477	.9356	9711	.3772	5766	2.6511	4234	20'	1.2101
50'	0.3636	.3557	5510	.9346	9706	.3805	5804	2.6279	4196	10'	1.2072
21° 00'	0.3665	.3584	9.5543	.9336	9.9702	.3839	9.5842	2.6051	0.4158	69° 00'	1.2043
10'	0.3694	.3611	5576	.9325	9697	.3872	5879	2.5826	4121	50'	1.2014
20'	0.3723	.3638	5609	.9315	9692	.3906	5917	2.5605	4083	40'	1.1985
30'	0.3752	.3665	5641	.9304	9687	.3939	5954	2.5386	4046	30'	1.1956
40'	0.3782	.3692	5673	.9293	9682	.3973	5991	2.5172	4009	20'	1.1926
50'	0.3811	.3719	5704	.9283	9677	.4006	6028	2.4960	3972	10'	1.1897
22° 00'	0.3840	.3746	9.5736	.9272	9.9672	.4040	9.6064	2.4751	0.3936	68° 00'	1.1868
10'	0.3869	.3773	5767	.9261	9667	.4074	6100	2.4545	3900	50'	1.1839
20'	0.3898	.3800	5798	.9250	9661	.4108	6136	2.4342	3864	40'	1.1810
30'	0.3927	.3827	5828	.9239	9656	.4142	6172	2.4142	3828	30'	1.1781
40'	0.3956	.3854	5859	.9228	9651	.4176	6208	2.3945	3792	20'	1.1752
50'	0.3985	.3881	5889	.9216	9646	.4210	6243	2.3750	3757	10'	1.1723
23° 00'	0.4014	.3907	9.5919	.9205	9.9640	.4245	9.6279	2.3559	0.3721	67° 00'	1.1694
10'	0.4043	.3934	5948	.9194	9635	.4279	6314	2.3369	3686	50'	1.1665
20'	0.4072	.3961	5978	.9182	9629	.4314	6348	2.3183	3652	40'	1.1636
30'	0.4102	.3987	6007	.9171	9624	.4348	6383	2.2998	3617	30'	1.1606
40'	0.4131	.4014	6036	.9159	9618	.4383	6417	2.2817	3583	20'	1.1577
50'	0.4160	.4041	6065	.9147	9613	.4417	6452	2.2637	3548	10'	1.1548
24° 00'	0.4189	.4067	9.6093	.9135	9.9607	.4452	9.6486	2.2460	0.3514	66° 00'	1.1519
10'	0.4218	.4094	6121	.9124	9602	.4487	6520	2.2286	3480	50'	1.1490
20'	0.4247	.4120	6149	.9112	9596	.4522	6553	2.2113	3447	40'	1.1461
30'	0.4276	.4147	6177	.9100	9590	.4557	6587	2.1943	3413	30'	1.1432
40'	0.4305	.4173	6205	.9088	9584	.4592	6620	2.1775	3380	20'	1.1403
50'	0.4334	.4200	6232	.9075	9579	.4628	6654	2.1609	3346	10'	1.1374
Degrees	Radians	Nat.	Log.	Nat.	Log.	Nat.	Log.	Nat.	Log.	Degrees	Radians
Angle		Cosine		Sine		Cotangent		Tangent		Angle	

Angle		Sine		Cosine		Tangent		Cotangent		Angle	
Degrees	Radians	Nat.	Log.	Nat.	Log.	Nat.	Log.	Nat.	Log.	Degrees	Radians
25° 00'	0.4363	.4226	9.6259	.9063	9.9573	.4663	9.6687	2.1445	0.3313	65° 00'	1.1345
10'	0.4392	.4253	6286	.9051	9567	.4699	6720	2.1283	3280	50'	1.1316
20'	0.4422	.4279	6313	.9038	9561	.4734	6752	2.1123	3248	40'	1.1286
30'	0.4451	.4305	6340	.9026	9555	.4770	6785	2.0965	3215	30'	1.1257
40'	0.4480	.4331	6366	.9013	9549	.4806	6817	2.0809	3183	20'	1.1228
50'	0.4509	.4358	6392	.9001	9543	.4841	6850	2.0655	3150	10'	1.1199
26° 00'	0.4538	.4384	9.6418	.8988	9.9537	.4877	9.6882	2.0503	0.3118	64° 00'	1.1170
10'	0.4567	.4410	6444	.8975	9530	.4913	6914	2.0353	3086	50'	1.1141
20'	0.4596	.4436	6470	.8962	9524	.4950	6946	2.0204	3054	40'	1.1112
30'	0.4625	.4462	6495	.8949	9518	.4986	6977	2.0057	3023	30'	1.1083
40'	0.4654	.4488	6521	.8936	9512	.5022	7009	1.9912	2991	20'	1.1054
50'	0.4683	.4514	6546	.8923	9505	.5059	7040	1.9768	2960	10'	1.1025
27° 00'	0.4712	.4540	9.6570	.8910	9.9499	.5095	9.7072	1.9626	0.2928	63° 00'	1.0996
10'	0.4742	.4566	6595	.8897	9492	.5132	7103	1.9486	2897	50'	1.0966
20'	0.4771	.4592	6620	.8884	9486	.5169	7134	1.9347	2866	40'	1.0937
30'	0.4800	.4617	6644	.8870	9479	.5206	7165	1.9210	2835	30'	1.0908
40'	0.4829	.4643	6668	.8857	9473	.5243	7196	1.9074	2804	20'	1.0879
50'	0.4858	.4669	6692	.8843	9466	.5280	7226	1.8940	2774	10'	1.0850
28° 00'	0.4887	.4695	9.6716	.8829	9.9459	.5317	9.7257	1.8807	0.2743	62° 00'	1.0821
10'	0.4916	.4720	6740	.8816	9453	.5354	7287	1.8676	2713	50'	1.0792
20'	0.4945	.4746	6763	.8802	9446	.5392	7317	1.8546	2683	40'	1.0763
30'	0.4974	.4772	6787	.8788	9439	.5430	7348	1.8418	2652	30'	1.0734
40'	0.5003	.4797	6810	.8774	9432	.5467	7378	1.8291	2622	20'	1.0705
50'	0.5032	.4823	6833	.8760	9425	.5505	7408	1.8165	2592	10'	1.0676
29° 00'	0.5061	.4848	9.6856	.8746	9.9418	.5543	9.7438	1.8040	0.2562	61° 00'	1.0647
10'	0.5091	.4874	6878	.8732	9411	.5581	7467	1.7917	2533	50'	1.0617
20'	0.5120	.4899	6901	.8718	9404	.5619	7497	1.7796	2503	40'	1.0588
30'	0.5149	.4924	6923	.8704	9397	.5658	7526	1.7675	2474	30'	1.0559
40'	0.5178	.4950	6946	.8689	9390	.5696	7556	1.7556	2444	20'	1.0530
50'	0.5207	.4975	6968	.8675	9383	.5735	7585	1.7437	2415	10'	1.0501
Degrees	Radians	Nat.	Log.	Nat.	Log.	Nat.	Log.	Nat.	Log.	Degrees	Radians
Angle		Cosine		Sine		Cotangent		Tangent		Angle	

TABLE 6 (Continued)
Trigonometric Functions

Angle Degrees	Angle Radians	Sine Nat.	Sine Log.	Cosine Nat.	Cosine Log.	Tangent Nat.	Tangent Log.	Cotangent Nat.	Cotangent Log.	Degrees	Radians
30° 00'	0.5236	.5000	9.6990	.8660	9.9375	.5774	9.7614	1.7321	0.2386	60° 00'	1.0472
10'	0.5265	.5025	7012	.8646	9368	.5812	7644	1.7205	2356	50'	1.0443
20'	0.5294	.5050	7033	.8631	9361	.5851	7673	1.7090	2327	40'	1.0414
30'	0.5323	.5075	7055	.8616	9353	.5890	7701	1.6977	2299	30'	1.0385
40'	0.5352	.5100	7076	.8601	9346	.5930	7730	1.6864	2270	20'	1.0356
50'	0.5381	.5125	7097	.8587	9338	.5969	7759	1.6753	2241	10'	1.0327
31° 00'	0.5411	.5150	9.7118	.8572	9.9331	.6009	9.7788	1.6643	0.2212	59° 00'	1.0297
10'	0.5440	.5175	7139	.8557	9323	.6048	7816	1.6534	2184	50'	1.0268
20'	0.5469	.5200	7160	.8542	9315	.6088	7845	1.6426	2155	40'	1.0239
30'	0.5498	.5225	7181	.8526	9308	.6128	7873	1.6319	2127	30'	1.0210
40'	0.5527	.5250	7201	.8511	9300	.6168	7902	1.6212	2098	20'	1.0181
50'	0.5556	.5275	7222	.8496	9292	.6208	7930	1.6107	2070	10'	1.0152
32° 00'	0.5585	.5299	9.7242	.8480	9.9284	.6249	9.7958	1.6003	0.2042	58° 00'	1.0123
10'	0.5614	.5324	7262	.8465	9276	.6289	7986	1.5900	2014	50'	1.0094
20'	0.5643	.5348	7282	.8450	9268	.6330	8014	1.5798	1986	40'	1.0065
30'	0.5672	.5373	7302	.8434	9260	.6371	8042	1.5697	1958	30'	1.0036
40'	0.5701	.5398	7322	.8418	9252	.6412	8070	1.5597	1930	20'	1.0007
50'	0.5730	.5422	7342	.8403	9244	.6453	8097	1.5497	1903	10'	0.9977
33° 00'	0.5760	.5446	9.7361	.8387	9.9236	.6494	9.8125	1.5399	0.1875	57° 00'	0.9948
10'	0.5789	.5471	7380	.8371	9228	.6536	8153	1.5301	1847	50'	0.9919
20'	0.5818	.5495	7400	.8355	9219	.6577	8180	1.5204	1820	40'	0.9890
30'	0.5847	.5519	7419	.8339	9211	.6619	8208	1.5108	1792	30'	0.9861
40'	0.5876	.5544	7438	.8323	9203	.6661	8235	1.5013	1765	20'	0.9832
50'	0.5905	.5568	7457	.8307	9194	.6703	8263	1.4919	1737	10'	0.9803
34° 00'	0.5934	.5592	9.7476	.8290	9.9186	.6745	9.8290	1.4826	0.1710	56° 00'	0.9774
10'	0.5963	.5616	7494	.8274	9177	.6787	8317	1.4733	1683	50'	0.9745
20'	0.5992	.5640	7513	.8258	9169	.6830	8344	1.4641	1656	40'	0.9716
30'	0.6021	.5664	7531	.8241	9160	.6873	8371	1.4550	1629	30'	0.9687
40'	0.6051	.5688	7550	.8225	9151	.6916	8398	1.4460	1602	20'	0.9657
50'	0.6080	.5712	7568	.8208	9142	.6959	8425	1.4370	1575	10'	0.9628
Degrees	Radians	Nat.	Log.	Nat.	Log.	Nat.	Log.	Nat.	Log.	Degrees	Radians
		Cosine		Sine		Cotangent		Tangent		Angle	

Angle Degrees	Radians	Sine Nat.	Sine Log.	Cosine Nat.	Cosine Log.	Tangent Nat.	Tangent Log.	Cotangent Nat.	Cotangent Log.	Degrees	Radians
35° 00'	0.6109	.5736	9.7586	.8192	9.9134	.7002	9.8452	1.4281	0.1548	55° 00'	0.9599
10'	0.6138	.5760	7604	.8175	9125	.7046	8479	1.4193	1521	50'	0.9570
20'	0.6167	.5783	7622	.8158	9116	.7089	8506	1.4106	1494	40'	0.9541
30'	0.6196	.5807	7640	.8141	9107	.7133	8533	1.4019	1467	30'	0.9512
40'	0.6225	.5831	7657	.8124	9098	.7177	8559	1.3934	1441	20'	0.9483
50'	0.6254	.5854	7675	.8107	9089	.7221	8586	1.3848	1414	10'	0.9454
36° 00'	0.6283	.5878	9.7692	.8090	9.9080	.7265	9.8613	1.3764	0.1387	54° 00'	0.9425
10'	0.6312	.5901	7710	.8073	9070	.7310	8639	1.3680	1361	50'	0.9396
20'	0.6341	.5925	7727	.8056	9061	.7355	8666	1.3597	1334	40'	0.9367
30'	0.6370	.5948	7744	.8039	9052	.7400	8692	1.3514	1308	30'	0.9338
40'	0.6400	.5972	7761	.8021	9042	.7445	8718	1.3432	1282	20'	0.9308
50'	0.6429	.5995	7778	.8004	9033	.7490	8745	1.3351	1255	10'	0.9279
37° 00'	0.6458	.6018	9.7795	.7986	9.9023	.7536	9.8771	1.3270	0.1229	53° 00'	0.9250
10'	0.6487	.6041	7811	.7969	9014	.7581	8797	1.3190	1203	50'	0.9221
20'	0.6516	.6065	7828	.7951	9004	.7627	8824	1.3111	1176	40'	0.9192
30'	0.6545	.6088	7844	.7934	8995	.7673	8850	1.3032	1150	30'	0.9163
40'	0.6574	.6111	7861	.7916	8985	.7720	8876	1.2954	1124	20'	0.9134
50'	0.6603	.6134	7877	.7898	8975	.7766	8902	1.2876	1098	10'	0.9105
38° 00'	0.6632	.6157	9.7893	.7880	9.8965	.7813	9.8928	1.2799	0.1072	52° 00'	0.9076
10'	0.6661	.6180	7910	.7862	8955	.7860	8954	1.2723	1046	50'	0.9047
20'	0.6690	.6202	7926	.7844	8945	.7907	8980	1.2647	1020	40'	0.9018
30'	0.6720	.6225	7941	.7826	8935	.7954	9006	1.2572	0994	30'	0.8988
40'	0.6749	.6248	7957	.7808	8925	.8002	9032	1.2497	0968	20'	0.8959
50'	0.6778	.6271	7973	.7790	8915	.8050	9058	1.2423	0942	10'	0.8930
39° 00'	0.6807	.6293	9.7989	.7771	9.8905	.8098	9.9084	1.2349	0.0916	51° 00'	0.8901
10'	0.6836	.6316	8004	.7753	8895	.8146	9110	1.2276	0890	50'	0.8872
20'	0.6865	.6338	8020	.7735	8884	.8195	9135	1.2203	0865	40'	0.8843
30'	0.6894	.6361	8035	.7716	8874	.8243	9161	1.2131	0839	30'	0.8814
40'	0.6923	.6383	8050	.7698	8864	.8292	9187	1.2059	0813	20'	0.8785
50'	0.6952	.6406	8066	.7679	8853	.8342	9212	1.1988	0788	10'	0.8756
Degrees Radians		Nat.	Log.	Nat.	Log.	Nat.	Log.	Nat.	Log.	Degrees	Radians
Angle		Cosine		Sine		Cotangent		Tangent		Angle	

TABLE 6 (Continued)
Trigonometric Functions

Angle Degrees	Angle Radians	Sine Nat.	Sine Log.	Cosine Nat.	Cosine Log.	Tangent Nat.	Tangent Log.	Cotangent Nat.	Cotangent Log.	Angle Degrees	Angle Radians
40° 00'	0.6981	.6428	9.8081	.7660	9.8843	.8391	9.9238	1.1918	0.0762	50° 00'	0.8727
10'	0.7010	.6450	8096	.7642	8832	.8441	9264	1.1847	0736	50'	0.8698
20'	0.7040	.6472	8111	.7623	8821	.8491	9289	1.1778	0711	40'	0.8668
30'	0.7069	.6494	8125	.7604	8810	.8541	9315	1.1708	0685	30'	0.8639
40'	0.7098	.6517	8140	.7585	8800	.8591	9341	1.1640	0659	20'	0.8610
50'	0.7127	.6539	8155	.7566	8789	.8642	9366	1.1571	0634	10'	0.8581
41° 00'	0.7156	.6561	9.8169	.7547	9.8778	.8693	9.9392	1.1504	0.0608	49° 00'	0.8552
10'	0.7185	.6583	8184	.7528	8767	.8744	9417	1.1436	0583	50'	0.8523
20'	0.7214	.6604	8198	.7509	8756	.8796	9443	1.1369	0557	40'	0.8494
30'	0.7243	.6626	8213	.7490	8745	.8847	9468	1.1303	0532	30'	0.8465
40'	0.7272	.6648	8227	.7470	8733	.8899	9494	1.1237	0506	20'	0.8436
50'	0.7301	.6670	8241	.7451	8722	.8952	9519	1.1171	0481	10'	0.8407
42° 00'	0.7330	.6691	9.8255	.7431	9.8711	.9004	9.9544	1.1106	0.0456	48° 00'	0.8378
10'	0.7359	.6713	8269	.7412	8699	.9057	9570	1.1041	0430	50'	0.8349
20'	0.7389	.6734	8283	.7392	8688	.9110	9595	1.0977	0405	40'	0.8319
30'	0.7418	.6756	8297	.7373	8676	.9163	9621	1.0913	0379	30'	0.8290
40'	0.7447	.6777	8311	.7353	8665	.9217	9646	1.0850	0354	20'	0.8261
50'	0.7476	.6799	8324	.7333	8653	.9271	9671	1.0786	0329	10'	0.8232
43° 00'	0.7505	.6820	9.8338	.7314	9.8641	.9325	9.9697	1.0724	0.0303	47° 00'	0.8203
10'	0.7534	.6841	8351	.7294	8629	.9380	9722	1.0661	0278	50'	0.8174
20'	0.7563	.6862	8365	.7274	8618	.9435	9747	1.0599	0253	40'	0.8145
30'	0.7592	.6884	8378	.7254	8606	.9490	9772	1.0538	0228	30'	0.8116
40'	0.7621	.6905	8391	.7234	8594	.9545	9798	1.0477	0202	20'	0.8087
50'	0.7650	.6926	8405	.7214	8582	.9601	9823	1.0416	0177	10'	0.8058
44° 00'	0.7679	.6947	9.8418	.7193	9.8569	.9657	9.9848	1.0355	0.0152	46° 00'	0.8029
10'	0.7709	.6967	8431	.7173	8557	.9713	9874	1.0295	0126	50'	0.7999
20'	0.7738	.6988	8444	.7153	8545	.9770	9899	1.0235	0101	40'	0.7970
30'	0.7767	.7009	8457	.7133	8532	.9827	9924	1.0176	0076	30'	0.7941
40'	0.7796	.7030	8469	.7112	8520	.9884	9949	1.0117	0051	20'	0.7912
50'	0.7825	.7050	8482	.7092	8507	.9942	9975	1.0058	0025	10'	0.7883
45° 00'	0.7854	.7071	9.8495	.7071	9.8495	1.0000	0.0000	1.0000	0.0000	45° 00'	0.7854
Angle Degrees	Angle Radians	Cosine Nat.	Cosine Log.	Sine Nat.	Sine Log.	Cotangent Nat.	Cotangent Log.	Tangent Nat.	Tangent Log.	Angle Degrees	Angle Radians

TABLE 7

Screw Thread Series

Size	Basic Major Dia	Threads Per Inch						Size
		Coarse (UNC or NC)*	Fine (UNF or NF)*	Extra Fine (UNEF or NEF)*	8 Thread Series (UN, N or NS)*	12 Thread Series (UN or N)*	16 Thread Series (UN or N)*	
0	0.0600		80	—	—	—	—	0
1	0.0730	64	72	—	—	—	—	1
2	0.0860	56	64	—	—	—	—	2
3	0.0990	48	56	—	—	—	—	3
4	0.1120	40	48	—	—	—	—	4
5	0.1250	40	44	—	—	—	—	5
6	0.1380	32	40	—	—	—	—	6
8	0.1640	32	36	—	—	—	—	8
10	0.1900	24	32	—	—	—	—	10
12	0.2160	24	28	32	—	—	—	12
1/4	0.2500	20	28	32	—	—	—	1/4
5/16	0.3125	18	24	32	—	—	—	5/16
3/8	0.3750	16	24	32	—	—	—	3/8
7/16	0.4375	14	20	28	—	—	—	7/16
1/2	0.5000	13	20	28	—	12	—	1/2
9/16	0.5625	12	18	24	—	12	—	9/16
5/8	0.6250	11	18	24	—	12	—	5/8
11/16	0.6875	—	—	24	—	12	—	11/16
3/4	0.7500	10	16	20	—	12	16	3/4
13/16	0.8125	—	—	20	—	12	16	13/16
7/8	0.8750	9	14	20	—	12	16	7/8
15/16	0.9375	—	—	20	—	12	16	15/16
1	1.0000	—	14 **	—	—	—	—	1
1	1.0000	8	12	20	8	12	16	1
1- 1/16	1.0625	—	—	18	—	12	16	1- 1/16
1- 1/8	1.1250	7	12	18	8	12	16	1- 1/8
1- 3/16	1.1875	—	—	18	—	12	16	1- 3/16
1- 1/4	1.2500	7	12	18	8	12	16	1- 1/4
1- 5/16	1.3125	—	—	18	—	12	16	1- 5/16
1- 3/8	1.3750	6	12	18	8	12	16	1- 3/8
1- 7/16	1.4375	—	—	18	—	12	16	1- 7/16
1- 1/2	1.5000	6	12	18	8	12	16	1- 1/2
1- 9/16	1.5625	—	—	18	—	—	16	1- 9/16
1- 5/8	1.6250	—	—	18	8	12	16	1- 5/8
1-11/16	1.6875	—	—	18	—	—	16	1-11/16
1- 3/4	1.7500	5	—	16	8	12	16	1- 3/4
1-13/16	1.8125	—	—	—	—	—	16	1-13/16
1- 7/8	1.8750	—	—	—	8	12	16	1- 7/8
1-15/16	1.9375	—	—	—	—	—	16	1-15/16
2	2.0000	4 ½	—	16	8	12	16	2
2- 1/16	2.0625	—	—	—	—	—	16	2- 1/16
2- 1/8	2.1250	—	—	—	8	12	16	2- 1/8
2- 3/16	2.1875	—	—	—	—	—	16	2- 3/16
2- 1/4	2.2500	4 ½	—	—	8	12	16	2- 1/4
2- 5/16	2.3125	—			—	—	16	2- 5/16
2- 3/8	2.3750	—			—	12	16	2- 3/8
2- 7/16	2.4375	—			—	—	16	2- 7/16
2- 1/2	2.5000	4			8	12	16	2- 1/2
2- 5/8	2.6250	—			—	12	16	2- 5/8
2- 3/4	2.7500	4			8	12	16	2- 3/4
2- 7/8	2.8750	—			—	12	16	2- 7/8
3	3.0000	4			8	12	16	3
3- 1/8	3.1250	—			—	12	16	3- 1/8
3- 1/4	3.2500	4			8	12	16	3- 1/4
3- 3/8	3.3750	—			—	12	16	3- 3/8
3- 1/2	3.5000	4			8	12	16	3- 1/2
3- 5/8	3.6250	—			—	12	16	3- 5/8
3- 3/4	3.7500	4			8	12	16	3- 3/4
3- 7/8	3.8750	—			—	12	16	3- 7/8
4	4.0000	4			8	12	16	4
4- 1/4	4.2500	—			8	12	16	4- 1/4
4- 1/2	4.5000	—			8	12	16	4- 1/2
4- 3/4	4.7500	—			8	12	16	4- 3/4
5	5.0000	—	—	—	8	12	16	5
5- 1/4	5.2500	—	—	—	8	12	16	5- 1/4
5- 1/2	5.5000	—	—	—	8	12	16	5- 1/2
5- 3/4	5.7500	—	—	—	8	12	16	5- 3/4
6	6.0000	—	—	—	8	12	16	6

* For Series Symbols applying to a particular thread, see dimensional tables ASA B1.1
** NS

Extracted from ASA Y14.6—1957.

TABLE 8
Tap Drills for Various Threads

Thread Nominal Size	Tap Drill					
	UNC NC	UNF NF	UNEF NEF	8UN 8N	12UN 12N	16UN 16N
0	—	$\frac{3}{64}$	—	—	—	—
1	No. 53	No. 53	—	—	—	—
2	No. 50	No. 50	—	—	—	—
3	No. 47	No. 45	—	—	—	—
4	No. 43	No. 42	—	—	—	—
5	No. 38	No. 37	—	—	—	—
6	No. 36	No. 33	—	—	—	—
8	No. 29	No. 29	—	—	—	—
10	No. 25	No. 21	—	—	—	—
12	No. 16	No. 14	No. 13	—	—	—
$\frac{1}{4}$	No. 7	No. 3	$\frac{7}{32}$	—	—	—
$\frac{5}{16}$	F	I	$\frac{9}{32}$	—	—	—
$\frac{3}{8}$	$\frac{5}{16}$	Q	$\frac{11}{32}$	—	—	—

Extracted from ASA B1.1–1960.

* NS.

TABLE 8 (Continued)
Tap Drills for Various Threads

Thread Nominal Size	Tap Drill					
	UNC NC	UNF NF	UNEF NEF	8UN 8N	12UN 12N	16UN 16N
$\frac{7}{16}$	U	$\frac{25}{64}$	$\frac{13}{32}$	—	—	—
$\frac{1}{2}$	$\frac{27}{64}$	$\frac{29}{64}$	$\frac{15}{32}$	—	$\frac{27}{64}$	—
$\frac{9}{16}$	$\frac{31}{64}$	$\frac{33}{64}$	$\frac{33}{64}$	—	$\frac{31}{64}$	—
$\frac{5}{8}$	$\frac{17}{32}$	$\frac{37}{64}$	$\frac{37}{64}$	—	$\frac{35}{64}$	—
$\frac{11}{16}$	—	—	$\frac{41}{64}$	—	$\frac{39}{64}$	—
$\frac{3}{4}$	$\frac{21}{32}$	$\frac{11}{16}$	$\frac{45}{64}$	—	$\frac{43}{64}$	$\frac{11}{16}$
$\frac{13}{16}$	—	—	$\frac{49}{64}$	—	$\frac{47}{64}$	$\frac{3}{4}$
$\frac{7}{8}$	$\frac{49}{64}$	$\frac{13}{16}$	$\frac{53}{64}$	—	$\frac{51}{64}$	$\frac{13}{16}$
$\frac{15}{16}$	—	—	$\frac{57}{64}$	—	$\frac{55}{64}$	$\frac{7}{8}$
1	—	$\frac{15^*}{16}$	—	—	—	—
1	$\frac{7}{8}$	$\frac{59}{64}$	$\frac{61}{64}$	$\frac{7}{8}$	$\frac{59}{64}$	$\frac{15}{16}$
$1\frac{1}{16}$	—	—	1	—	$\frac{63}{64}$	1
$1\frac{1}{8}$	$\frac{63}{64}$	$1\frac{3}{64}$	$1\frac{5}{64}$	1	$1\frac{3}{64}$	$1\frac{1}{16}$

TABLE 8 (Continued)
Tap Drills for Various Threads

Thread Nominal Size	Tap Drill					
	UNC NC	UNF NF	UNEF NEF	8UN 8N	12UN 12N	16UN 16N
$1 \frac{3}{16}$	—	—	$1 \frac{9}{64}$	—	$1 \frac{7}{64}$	$1 \frac{1}{8}$
$1 \frac{1}{4}$	$1 \frac{7}{64}$	$1 \frac{11}{64}$	$1 \frac{3}{16}$	$1 \frac{1}{8}$	$1 \frac{11}{64}$	$1 \frac{3}{16}$
$1 \frac{5}{16}$	—	—	$1 \frac{17}{64}$	—	$1 \frac{15}{64}$	$1 \frac{1}{4}$
$1 \frac{3}{8}$	$1 \frac{7}{32}$	$1 \frac{19}{64}$	$1 \frac{5}{16}$	$1 \frac{1}{4}$	$1 \frac{19}{64}$	$1 \frac{5}{16}$
$1 \frac{7}{16}$	—	—	$1 \frac{3}{8}$	—	$1 \frac{23}{64}$	$1 \frac{3}{8}$
$1 \frac{1}{2}$	$1 \frac{11}{32}$	$1 \frac{27}{64}$	$1 \frac{7}{16}$	$1 \frac{3}{8}$	$1 \frac{27}{64}$	$1 \frac{7}{16}$
$1 \frac{9}{16}$	—	—	$1 \frac{1}{2}$	—	—	$1 \frac{1}{2}$
$1 \frac{5}{8}$	—	—	$1 \frac{9}{16}$	$1 \frac{1}{2}$	$1 \frac{35}{64}$	$1 \frac{9}{16}$
$1 \frac{11}{16}$	—	—	$1 \frac{5}{8}$	—	—	$1 \frac{5}{8}$
$1 \frac{3}{4}$	$1 \frac{9}{16}$	—	$1 \frac{11}{16}$	$1 \frac{5}{8}$	$1 \frac{43}{64}$	$1 \frac{11}{16}$
$1 \frac{13}{16}$	—	—	—	—	—	$1 \frac{3}{4}$
$1 \frac{7}{8}$	—	—	—	$1 \frac{3}{4}$	$1 \frac{51}{64}$	$1 \frac{13}{16}$
$1 \frac{15}{16}$	—	—	—	—	—	$1 \frac{7}{8}$
2	$1 \frac{25}{32}$	—	$1 \frac{15}{16}$	$1 \frac{7}{8}$	$1 \frac{59}{64}$	$1 \frac{15}{16}$

TABLE 8 (Continued)
Tap Drills for Various Threads

Thread Nominal Size	Tap Drill					
	UNC NC	UNF NF	UNEF NEF	8UN 8N	12UN 12N	16UN 16N
$2\frac{1}{16}$	—	—	—	—	—	2
$2\frac{1}{8}$	—	—	—	2	$2\frac{3}{64}$	$2\frac{1}{16}$
$2\frac{3}{16}$	—	—	—	—	—	$2\frac{1}{8}$
$2\frac{1}{4}$	$2\frac{1}{32}$	—	—	$2\frac{1}{8}$	$2\frac{11}{64}$	$2\frac{3}{16}$
$2\frac{5}{16}$	—	—	—	—	—	$2\frac{1}{4}$
$2\frac{3}{8}$	—	—	—	—	$2\frac{19}{64}$	$2\frac{5}{16}$
$2\frac{7}{16}$	—	—	—	—	—	$2\frac{3}{8}$
$2\frac{1}{2}$	$2\frac{1}{4}$	—	—	$2\frac{3}{8}$	$2\frac{27}{64}$	$2\frac{7}{16}$
$2\frac{5}{8}$	—	—	—	—	$2\frac{35}{64}$	$2\frac{9}{16}$
$2\frac{3}{4}$	$2\frac{1}{2}$	—	—	$2\frac{5}{8}$	$2\frac{43}{64}$	$2\frac{11}{16}$
$2\frac{7}{8}$	—	—	—	—	$2\frac{51}{64}$	$2\frac{13}{16}$
3	$2\frac{3}{4}$	—	—	$2\frac{7}{8}$	$2\frac{59}{64}$	$2\frac{15}{16}$
$3\frac{1}{8}$	—	—	—	—	$3\frac{3}{64}$	$3\frac{1}{16}$
$3\frac{1}{4}$	3	—	—	$3\frac{1}{8}$	$3\frac{11}{64}$	$3\frac{3}{16}$

TABLE 8 (Continued)
Tap Drills for Various Threads

Thread Nominal Size	Tap Drill					
	UNC NC	UNF NF	UNEF NEF	8UN 8N	12UN 12N	16UN 16N
$3\ \frac{3}{8}$	—	—	—	—	$3\ \frac{19}{64}$	$3\ \frac{5}{16}$
$3\ \frac{1}{2}$	$3\ \frac{1}{4}$	—	—	$3\ \frac{3}{8}$	$3\ \frac{27}{64}$	$3\ \frac{7}{16}$
$3\ \frac{5}{8}$	—	—	—	—	$3\ \frac{35}{64}$	$3\ \frac{9}{16}$
$3\ \frac{3}{4}$	$3\ \frac{1}{2}$	—	—	$3\ \frac{5}{8}$	$3\ \frac{43}{64}$	$3\ \frac{11}{16}$
$3\ \frac{7}{8}$	—	—	—	—	$3\ \frac{51}{64}$	$3\ \frac{13}{16}$
4	$3\ \frac{3}{4}$	—	—	$3\ \frac{7}{8}$	$3\ \frac{59}{64}$	$3\ \frac{15}{16}$
$4\ \frac{1}{4}$	—	—	—	$4\ \frac{1}{8}$	$4\ \frac{11}{64}$	$4\ \frac{3}{16}$
$4\ \frac{1}{2}$	—	—	—	$4\ \frac{3}{8}$	$4\ \frac{27}{64}$	$4\ \frac{7}{16}$
$4\ \frac{3}{4}$	—	—	—	$4\ \frac{5}{8}$	$4\ \frac{43}{64}$	$4\ \frac{11}{16}$
5	—	—	—	$4\ \frac{7}{8}$	$4\ \frac{59}{64}$	$4\ \frac{15}{16}$
$5\ \frac{1}{4}$	—	—	—	$5\ \frac{1}{8}$	$5\ \frac{11}{64}$	$5\ \frac{3}{16}$
$5\ \frac{1}{2}$	—	—	—	$5\ \frac{3}{8}$	$5\ \frac{27}{64}$	$5\ \frac{7}{16}$
$5\ \frac{3}{4}$	—	—	—	$5\ \frac{5}{8}$	$5\ \frac{43}{64}$	$5\ \frac{11}{16}$
6	—	—	—	$5\ \frac{7}{8}$	$5\ \frac{59}{64}$	$5\ \frac{15}{16}$

TABLE 9

Slotted Headless Set Screws

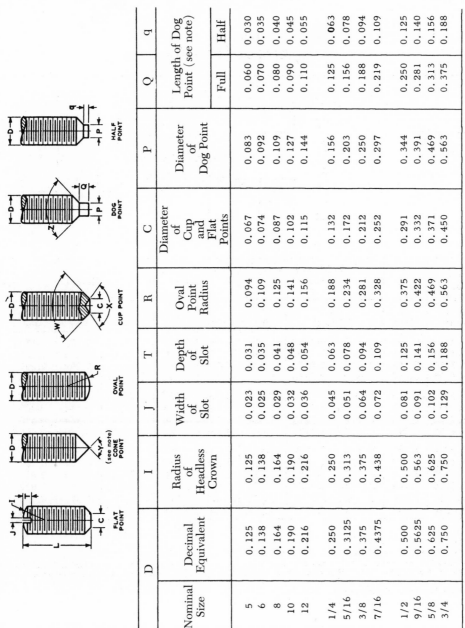

Nominal Size	D Decimal Equivalent	I Radius of Headless Crown	J Width of Slot	T Depth of Slot	R Oval Point Radius	C Diameter of Cup and Flat Points	P Diameter of Dog Point	Q Length of Dog Point (see note) Full	q Length of Dog Point (see note) Half
5	0.125	0.125	0.023	0.031	0.094	0.067	0.083	0.060	0.030
6	0.138	0.138	0.025	0.035	0.109	0.074	0.092	0.070	0.035
8	0.164	0.164	0.029	0.041	0.125	0.087	0.109	0.080	0.040
10	0.190	0.190	0.032	0.048	0.141	0.102	0.127	0.090	0.045
12	0.216	0.216	0.036	0.054	0.156	0.115	0.144	0.110	0.055
1/4	0.250	0.250	0.045	0.063	0.188	0.132	0.156	0.125	0.063
5/16	0.3125	0.313	0.051	0.078	0.234	0.172	0.203	0.156	0.078
3/8	0.375	0.375	0.064	0.094	0.281	0.212	0.250	0.188	0.094
7/16	0.4375	0.438	0.072	0.109	0.328	0.252	0.297	0.219	0.109
1/2	0.500	0.500	0.081	0.125	0.375	0.291	0.344	0.250	0.125
9/16	0.5625	0.563	0.091	0.141	0.422	0.332	0.391	0.281	0.140
5/8	0.625	0.625	0.102	0.156	0.469	0.371	0.469	0.313	0.156
3/4	0.750	0.750	0.129	0.188	0.563	0.450	0.563	0.375	0.188

Where usable length of thread is less than the nominal diameter, half-dog point shall be used.
When L (length of screw) equals nominal diameter or less, Y = 118 deg ± 2 deg; when L exceeds nominal diameter, Y = 90 deg ± 2 deg.
Point Angles. W = 80 deg to 90 deg; X = 118 deg. ± 5 deg; Z = 100 deg to 110 deg.
Thread shall be coarse or fine, Class 2A.
Extracted from ASA B18.6.2–1956.

TABLE 10
Regular Square Bolts and Nuts

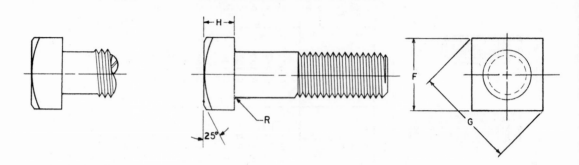

Nominal Size or Basic Major Diameter of Thread		Body Diam	Width Across Flats F			Width Across Corners G		Height H			Radius of Fillet R
		Max	Max (Basic)		Min	Max	Min	Nom	Max	Min	Max
1/4	0.2500	0.260	3/8	0.3750	0.362	0.530	0.498	11/64	0.188	0.156	0.031
5/16	0.3125	0.324	1/2	0.5000	0.484	0.707	0.665	13/64	0.220	0.186	0.031
3/8	0.3750	0.388	9/16	0.5625	0.544	0.795	0.747	1/4	0.268	0.232	0.031
7/16	0.4375	0.452	5/8	0.6250	0.603	0.884	0.828	19/64	0.316	0.278	0.031
1/2	0.5000	0.515	3/4	0.7500	0.725	1.061	0.995	21/64	0.348	0.308	0.031
5/8	0.6250	0.642	15/16	0.9375	0.906	1.326	1.244	27/64	0.444	0.400	0.062
3/4	0.7500	0.768	1 1/8	1.1250	1.088	1.591	1.494	1/2	0.524	0.476	0.062
7/8	0.8750	0.895	1 5/16	1.3125	1.269	1.856	1.742	19/32	0.620	0.568	0.062
1	1.0000	1.022	1 1/2	1.5000	1.450	2.121	1.991	21/32	0.684	0.628	0.093
1 1/8	1.1250	1.149	1 11/16	1.6875	1.631	2.386	2.239	3/4	0.780	0.720	0.093
1 1/4	1.2500	1.277	1 7/8	1.8750	1.812	2.652	2.489	27/32	0.876	0.812	0.093
1 3/8	1.3750	1.404	2 1/16	2.0625	1.994	2.917	2.738	29/32	0.940	0.872	0.093
1 1/2	1.5000	1.531	2 1/4	2.2500	2.175	3.182	2.986	1	1.036	0.964	0.093
1 5/8	1.6250	1.658	2 7/16	2.4375	2.356	3.447	3.235	1 3/32	1.132	1.056	0.125

All dimensions given in inches.

Bolt is not finished on any surface.

Minimum thread length shall be twice the diameter plus 1/4 in. for lengths up to and including 6 and twice the diameter plus 1/2 in. for lengths over 6. Bolts too short for the formula thread length shall be threaded as close to the head as practical.

Thread shall be coarse-thread series, class 2A.

Extracted from ASA B18.2—1960.

TABLE 10 (Continued)
Regular Square Bolts and Nuts

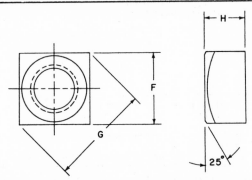

Nominal Size or Basic Major Diameter of Thread		Width Across Flats F			Width Across Corners G		Thickness H		
		Max (Basic)		Min	Max	Min	Nom	Max	Min
1/4	0.2500	7/16	0.4375	0.425	0.619	0.584	7/32	0.235	0.203
5/16	0.3125	9/16	0.5625	0.547	0.795	0.751	17/64	0.283	0.249
3/8	0.3750	5/8	0.6250	0.606	0.884	0.832	21/64	0.346	0.310
7/16	0.4375	3/4	0.7500	0.728	1.061	1.000	3/8	0.394	0.356
1/2	0.5000	13/16	0.8125	0.788	1.149	1.082	7/16	0.458	0.418
5/8	0.6250	1	1.0000	0.969	1.414	1.330	35/64	0.569	0.525
3/4	0.7500	1 1/8	1.1250	1.088	1.591	1.494	21/32	0.680	0.632
7/8	0.8750	1 5/16	1.3125	1.269	1.856	1.742	49/64	0.792	0.740
1	1.0000	1 1/2	1.5000	1.450	2.121	1.991	7/8	0.903	0.847
1 1/8	1.1250	1 11/16	1.6875	1.631	2.386	2.239	1	1.030	0.970
1 1/4	1.2500	1 7/8	1.8750	1.812	2.652	2.489	1 3/32	1.126	1.062
1 3/8	1.3750	2 1/16	2.0625	1.994	2.917	2.738	1 13/64	1.237	1.169
1 1/2	1.5000	2 1/4	2.2500	2.175	3.182	2.986	1 5/16	1.348	1.276

All dimensions given in inches.
Regular square nuts are not finished on any surface but are threaded.
Threads shall be coarse-thread series, class 2B.

TABLE 11
Regular Unfinished Hexagon Bolts and Nuts

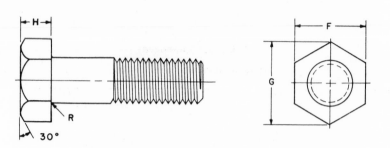

Nominal Size or Basic Major Diameter of Thread		Body Diam* Max	Width Across Flats F			Width Across Corners G		Height H			Radius of Fillet R
			Max (Basic)		Min	Max	Min	Nom	Max	Min	Max
1/4	0.2500	0.260	7/16	0.4375	0.425	0.505	0.484	11/64	0.188	0.150	0.031
5/16	0.3125	0.324	1/2	0.5000	0.484	0.577	0.552	7/32	0.235	0.195	0.031
3/8	0.3750	0.388	9/16	0.5625	0.544	0.650	0.620	1/4	0.268	0.226	0.031
7/16	0.4375	0.452	5/8	0.6250	0.603	0.722	0.687	19/64	0.316	0.272	0.031
1/2	0.5000	0.515	3/4	0.7500	0.725	0.866	0.826	11/32	0.364	0.302	0.031
5/8	0.6250	0.642	15/16	0.9375	0.906	1.083	1.033	27/64	0.444	0.378	0.062
3/4	0.7500	0.768	1 1/8	1.1250	1.088	1.299	1.240	1/2	0.524	0.455	0.062
7/8	0.8750	0.895	1 5/16	1.3125	1.269	1.516	1.447	37/64	0.604	0.531	0.062
1	1.0000	1.022	1 1/2	1.5000	1.450	1.732	1.653	43/64	0.700	0.591	0.093
1 1/8	1.1250	1.149	1 11/16	1.6875	1.631	1.949	1.859	3/4	0.780	0.658	0.093
1 1/4	1.2500	1.277	1 7/8	1.8750	1.812	2.165	2.066	27/32	0.876	0.749	0.093
1 3/8	1.3750	1.404	2 1/16	2.0625	1.994	2.382	2.273	29/32	0.940	0.810	0.093
1 1/2	1.5000	1.531	2 1/4	2.2500	2.175	2.598	2.480	1	1.036	0.902	0.093
1 3/4	1.7500	1.785	2 5/8	2.6250	2.538	3.031	2.893	1 5/32	1.196	1.054	0.125
2	2.0000	2.039	3	3.0000	2.900	3.464	3.306	1 11/32	1.388	1.175	0.125
2 1/4	2.2500	2.305	3 3/8	3.3750	3.262	3.897	3.719	1 1/2	1.548	1.327	0.188
2 1/2	2.5000	2.559	3 3/4	3.7500	3.625	4.330	4.133	1 21/32	1.708	1.479	0.188
2 3/4	2.7500	2.827	4 1/8	4.1250	3.988	4.763	4.546	1 13/16	1.869	1.632	0.188
3	3.0000	3.081	4 1/2	4.5000	4.350	5.196	4.959	2	2.060	1.815	0.188
3 1/4	3.2500	3.335	4 7/8	4.8750	4.712	5.629	5.372	2 3/16	2.251	1.936	0.188
3 1/2	3.5000	3.589	5 1/4	5.2500	5.075	6.062	5.786	2 5/16	2.380	2.057	0.188
3 3/4	3.7500	3.858	5 5/8	5.6250	5.437	6.495	6.198	2 1/2	2.572	2.241	0.188
4	4.0000	4.111	6	6.0000	5.800	6.928	6.612	2 11/16	2.764	2.424	0.188

All dimensions given in inches.

Bolt is not finished on any surface.

Minimum thread length shall be twice the diameter plus 1/4 in. for lengths up to and including 6 in. and twice the diameter plus 1/2 in. for lengths over 6 in. Bolts too short for the formula thread length shall be threaded as close to the head as practical.

Thread shall be coarse-thread series, class 2A.

*The dimensions of 1/4 to 5/8-in. size nuts are published for interim use during the change-over to the new standard

Extracted from ASA B18.2—1960.

TABLE 11 (Continued)
Regular Unfinished Hexagon Bolts and Nuts

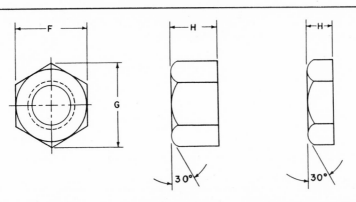

Nominal Size or Basic Major Diameter of Thread		Width Across Flats F			Width Across Corners G		Thickness Regular Nuts H			Thickness Regular Jam Nuts H		
		Max (Basic)		Min	Max	Min	Nom	Max	Min	Nom	Max	Min
1/4	0.2500	7/16	0.4375	0.425	0.505	0.484	7/32	0.235	0.203	5/32	0.172	0.140
5/16	0.3125	9/16	0.5625	0.547	0.650	0.624	17/64	0.283	0.249	3/16	0.204	0.170
3/8	0.3750	5/8	0.6250	0.606	0.722	0.691	21/64	0.346	0.310	7/32	0.237	0.201
7/16	0.4375	3/4	0.7500	0.728	0.866	0.830	3/8	0.394	0.356	1/4	0.269	0.231
1/2	0.5000	13/16	0.8125	0.788	0.938	0.898	7/16	0.458	0.418	5/16	0.332	0.292
9/16	0.5625	7/8	0.8750	0.847	1.010	0.966	1/2	0.521	0.479	11/32	0.365	0.323
5/8	0.6250	1	1.0000	0.969	1.155	1.104	35/64	0.569	0.525	3/8	0.397	0.353
3/4	0.7500	1 1/8	1.1250	1.088	1.299	1.240	21/32	0.680	0.632	7/16	0.462	0.414
7/8	0.8750	1 5/16	1.3125	1.269	1.516	1.447	49/64	0.792	0.740	1/2	0.526	0.474
1	1.0000	1 1/2	1.5000	1.450	1.732	1.653	7/8	0.903	0.847	9/16	0.590	0.534
1 1/8	1.1250	1 11/16	1.6875	1.631	1.949	1.859	1	1.030	0.970	5/8	0.655	0.595
1 1/4	1.2500	1 7/8	1.8750	1.812	2.165	2.066	1 3/32	1.126	1.062	3/4	0.782	0.718
1 3/8	1.3750	2 1/16	2.0625	1.994	2.382	2.273	1 13/64	1.237	1.169	13/16	0.846	0.778
1 1/2	1.5000	2 1/4	2.2500	2.175	2.598	2.480	1 5/16	1.348	1.276	7/8	0.911	0.839

All dimensions given in inches.

Nuts are not finished on any surface but are threaded.

Thread shall be coarse-thread series, class 2B tolerance.

TABLE 12
Regular Semifinished Hexagon Bolts and Nuts

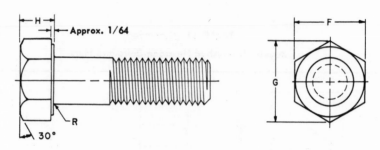

Nominal Size or Basic Major Diameter of Thread		Body Diam* Max	Width Across Flats F			Width Across Corners G		Height H			Radius of Fillet R	
			Max (Basic)		Min	Max	Min	Nom	Max	Min	Min	M.
1/4	0.2500	0.260	7/16	0.4375	0.425	0.505	0.484	5/32	0.163	0.150	0.009	0.0
5/16	0.3125	0.324	1/2	0.5000	0.484	0.577	0.552	13/64	0.211	0.195	0.009	0.0
3/8	0.3750	0.388	9/16	0.5625	0.544	0.650	0.620	15/64	0.243	0.226	0.009	0.0
7/16	0.4375	0.452	5/8	0.6250	0.603	0.722	0.687	9/32	0.291	0.272	0.009	0.0
1/2	0.5000	0.515	3/4	0.7500	0.725	0.866	0.826	5/16	0.323	0.302	0.009	0.0
5/8	0.6250	0.642	15/16	0.9375	0.906	1.083	1.033	25/64	0.403	0.378	0.021	0.00
3/4	0.7500	0.768	1 1/8	1.1250	1.088	1.299	1.240	15/32	0.483	0.455	0.021	0.00
7/8	0.8750	0.895	1 5/16	1.3125	1.269	1.516	1.447	35/64	0.563	0.531	0.031	0.00
1	1.0000	1.022	1 1/2	1.5000	1.450	1.732	1.653	39/64	0.627	0.591	0.062	0.0!
1 1/8	1.1250	1.149	1 11/16	1.6875	1.631	1.949	1.859	11/16	0.718	0.658	0.062	0.0!
1 1/4	1.2500	1.277	1 7/8	1.8750	1.812	2.165	2.066	25/32	0.813	0.749	0.062	0.09
1 3/8	1.3750	1.404	2 1/16	2.0625	1.994	2.382	2.273	27/32	0.878	0.810	0.062	0.09
1 1/2	1.5000	1.531	2 1/4	2.2500	2.175	2.598	2.480	15/16	0.974	0.902	0.062	0.0!
1 3/4	1.7500	1.785	2 5/8	2.6250	2.538	3.031	2.893	1 3/32	1.134	1.054	0.078	0.1:
2	2.0000	2.039	3	3.0000	2.900	3.464	3.306	1 7/32	1.263	1.175	0.078	0.1:
2 1/4	2.2500	2.305	3 3/8	3.3750	3.262	3.897	3.719	1 3/8	1.423	1.327	0.125	0.1:
2 1/2	2.5000	2.559	3 3/4	3.7500	3.625	4.330	4.133	1 11/32	1.583	1.479	0.125	0.1:
2 3/4	2.7500	2.827	4 1/8	4.1250	3.988	4.763	4.546	1 11/16	1.744	1.632	0.125	0.1:
3	3.0000	3.081	4 1/2	4.5000	4.350	5.196	4.959	1 7/8	1.935	1.815	0.125	0.1:
3 1/4	3.2500	3.335	4 7/8	4.8750	4.712	5.629	5.372	2	2.064	1.936	0.125	0.1:
3 1/2	3.5000	3.589	5 1/4	5.2500	5.075	6.062	5.786	2 1/8	2.193	2.057	0.125	0.1:
3 3/4	3.7500	3.858	5 5/8	5.6250	5.437	6.495	6.198	2 5/16	2.385	2.241	0.125	0.1:
4	4.0000	4.111	6	6.0000	5.800	6.928	6.612	2 1/2	2.576	2.424	0.125	0.1!

All dimensions given in inches.

Semifinished bolt is processed to produce a flat bearing surface under head only.

Minimum thread length shall be twice the diameter plus 1/4 in. for lengths up to and including 6 in.; twice the diameter plus 1/2 in. for lengths over 6 in. The tolerance shall be plus 3/16 in. or 2-1/2 threads, whichever is greater. On products that are too short for minimum thread lengths, the distance from the bearing surface of the head to the first complete thread shall not exceed the length of 2-1/2 threads, as measured with a ring thread gage, for sizes up to and including 1 in. and 3-1/2 threads for sizes larger than 1 in.

Thread shall be coarse-thread series, class 2A.

*This table is published for interim use during the change-over to the new standard.

Extracted from ASA B18.2—1960.

TABLE 12 (Continued)

Regular Semifinished Hexagon Bolts and Nuts

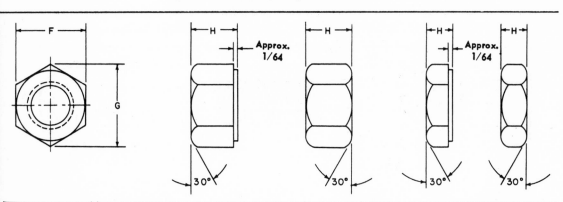

Nominal Size or Basic Major Diameter of Thread		Width Across Flats F			Width Across Corners G		Thickness Regular Nuts H			Thickness Regular Jam Nuts H		
		Max (Basic)		Min	Max	Min	Nom	Max	Min	Nom	Max	Min
1/4	0.2500	7/16	0.4375	0.425	0.505	0.485	13/64	0.219	0.187	9/64	0.157	0.125
5/16	0.3125	9/16	0.5625	0.547	0.650	0.624	1/4	0.267	0.233	11/64	0.189	0.155
3/8	0.3750	5/8	0.6250	0.606	0.722	0.691	5/16	0.330	0.294	13/64	0.221	0.185
7/16	0.4375	3/4	0.7500	0.728	0.866	0.830	23/64	0.378	0.340	15/64	0.253	0.215
1/2	0.5000	13/16	0.8125	0.788	0.938	0.898	27/64	0.442	0.402	19/64	0.317	0.277
9/16	0.5625	7/8	0.8750	0.847	1.010	0.966	31/64	0.505	0.463	21/64	0.349	0.307
5/8	0.6250	1	1.0000	0.969	1.155	1.104	17/32	0.553	0.509	23/64	0.381	0.337
3/4	0.7500	1 1/8	1.1250	1.088	1.299	1.240	41/64	0.665	0.617	27/64	0.446	0.398
7/8	0.8750	1 5/16	1.3125	1.269	1.516	1.447	3/4	0.776	0.724	31/64	0.510	0.458
1	1.0000	1 1/2	1.5000	1.450	1.732	1.653	55/64	0.887	0.831	35/64	0.575	0.519
1 1/8	1.1250	1 11/16	1.6875	1.631	1.949	1.859	31/32	0.999	0.939	39/64	0.639	0.579
1 1/4	1.2500	1 7/8	1.8750	1.812	2.165	2.066	1 1/16	1.094	1.030	23/32	0.751	0.687
1 3/8	1.3750	2 1/16	2.0625	1.994	2.382	2.273	1 11/64	1.206	1.138	25/32	0.815	0.747
1 1/2	1.5000	2 1/4	2.2500	2.175	2.598	2.480	1 9/32	1.317	1.245	27/32	0.880	0.808
1 5/8	1.6250	2 7/16	2.4375	2.356	2.815	2.686	1 25/64	1.429	1.353	29/32	0.944	0.868
1 3/4	1.7500	2 5/8	2.6250	2.538	3.031	2.893	1 1/2	1.540	1.460	31/32	1.009	0.929
1 7/8	1.8750	2 13/16	2.8125	2.719	3.248	3.100	1 39/64	1.651	1.567	1 1/32	1.073	0.989
2	2.0000	3	3.0000	2.900	3.464	3.306	1 23/32	1.763	1.675	1 3/32	1.138	1.050
2 1/4	2.2500	3 3/8	3.3750	3.262	3.897	3.719	1 59/64	1.970	1.874	1 13/64	1.251	1.155
2 1/2	2.5000	3 3/4	3.7500	3.625	4.330	4.133	2 9/64	2.193	2.089	1 29/64	1.505	1.401
2 3/4	2.7500	4 1/8	4.1250	3.988	4.763	4.546	2 23/64	2.415	2.303	1 37/64	1.634	1.522
3	3.0000	4 1/2	4.5000	4.350	5.196	4.959	2 37/64	2.638	2.518	1 45/64	1.763	1.643

All dimensions given in inches.

Semifinished nuts are finished on bearing surface and threaded.

Bearing surface shall be washer faced or with chamfered corners. Diameter of washer face and the diameter of circle of bearing surface of double chamfered nuts shall be the maximum width across flats within a tolerance of minus 5 per cent.

Thread may be coarse-, fine-, or 8-thread series; class 2B tolerance; unless otherwise specified coarse-thread series will be furnished.

TABLE 13
Regular Finished Hexagon Bolts and Nuts

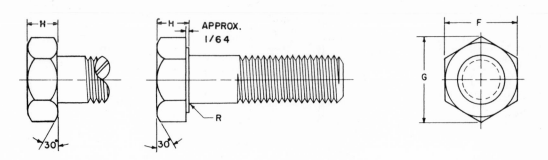

Nominal Size or Basic Major Diameter of Thread		Body Diameter Min (Maximum Equal to Nominal Size)	Width Across Flats F			Width Across Corners G		Height H				Radius of Fillet R	
				Max (Basic)	Min*	Max	Min	Nom	Max	Min		Max	Min
1/4	0.2500	0.2450	7/16	0.4375	0.428	0.505	0.488	5/32	0.163	0.150		**0.009**	0.023
5/16	0.3125	0.3065	1/2	0.5000	0.489	0.577	0.557	13/64	0.211	0.195		**0.009**	0.023
3/8	0.3750	0.3690	9/16	0.5625	0.551	0.650	0.628	15/64	0.243	0.226		**0.009**	0.023
7/16	0.4375	0.4305	5/8	0.6250	0.612	0.722	0.698	9/32	0.291	0.272		**0.009**	0.023
1/2	0.5000	0.4930	3/4	0.7500	0.736	0.866	0.840	5/16	0.323	0.302		**0.009**	0.023
9/16	0.5625	0.5545	13/16	0.8125	0.798	0.938	0.910	23/64	0.371	0.348		**0.021**	0.041
5/8	0.6250	0.6170	15/16	0.9375	0.922	1.083	1.051	25/64	0.403	0.378		**0.021**	0.041
3/4	0.7500	0.7410	1 1/8	1.1250	1.100	1.299	1.254	15/32	0.483	0.455		**0.021**	0.041
7/8	0.8750	0.8660	1 5/16	1.3125	1.285	1.516	1.465	35/64	0.563	0.531		**0.041**	0.062
1	1.0000	0.9900	1 1/2	1.5000	1.469	1.732	1.675	39/64	0.627	0.591		**0.062**	0.093
1 1/8	1.1250	1.1140	1 11/16	1.6875	1.631	1.949	1.859	11/16	0.718	0.658		**0.062**	0.093
1 1/4	1.2500	1.2390	1 7/8	1.8750	1.812	2.165	2.066	25/32	0.813	0.749		**0.062**	0.093
1 3/8	1.3750	1.3630	2 1/16	2.0625	1.994	2.382	2.273	27/32	0.878	0.810		**0.062**	0.093
1 1/2	1.5000	1.4880	2 1/4	2.2500	2.175	2.598	2.480	15/16	0.974	0.902		**0.062**	0.093
1 3/4	1.7500	1.7380	2 5/8	2.6250	2.538	3.031	2.893	1 3/32	1.134	1.054		**0.062**	0.093
2	2.0000	1.9880	3	3.0000	2.900	3.464	3.306	1 7/32	1.263	1.175		**0.062**	0.093
2 1/4	2.2500	2.2380	3 3/8	3.3750	3.262	3.897	3.719	1 3/8	1.423	1.327		**0.062**	0.093
2 1/2	2.5000	2.4880	3 3/4	3.7500	3.625	4.330	4.133	1 17/32	1.583	1.479		**0.062**	0.093
2 3/4	2.7500	2.7380	4 1/8	4.1250	3.988	4.763	4.546	1 11/16	1.744	1.632		**0.062**	0.093
3	3.0000	2.9880	4 1/2	4.5000	4.350	5.196	4.959	1 7/8	1.935	1.815		**0.062**	0.093

All dimensions given in inches.

BOLD TYPE INDICATES PRODUCTS UNIFIED DIMENSIONALLY WITH BRITISH AND CANADIAN STANDARDS.

"Finished" in the title refers to the quality of manufacture and the closeness of tolerance and does not indicate that surfaces are completely machined.

Minimum thread length shall be twice the diameter plus 1/4 in. for lengths up to and including 6 in.; twice the diameter plus 1/2 in. for lengths over 6 in. The tolerance shall be plus 3/16 in. or 2-1/2 threads, whichever is greater. On products that are too short for minimum thread lengths, the distance from the bearing surface of the head to the first complete thread shall not exceed the length of 2-1/2 threads, as measured with a ring thread gage, for sizes up to and including 1 in. and 3-1/2 threads for sizes larger than 1 in.

Threads shall be coarse-, fine-, or 8-thread series, class 2A.

Extracted from ASA B18.2—1960.

TABLE 13 (Continued)
Regular Finished Hexagon Bolts and Nuts

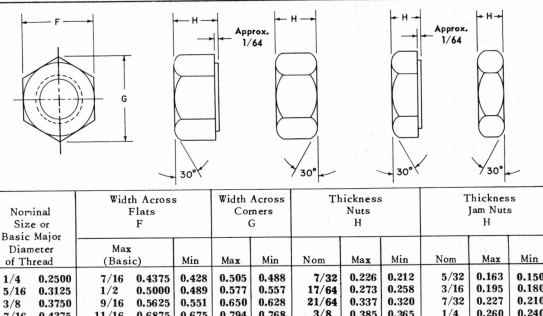

Nominal Size or Basic Major Diameter of Thread		Width Across Flats F			Width Across Corners G		Thickness Nuts H			Thickness Jam Nuts H		
		Max (Basic)		Min	Max	Min	Nom	Max	Min	Nom	Max	Min
1/4	0.2500	7/16	0.4375	0.428	0.505	0.488	7/32	0.226	0.212	5/32	0.163	0.150
5/16	0.3125	1/2	0.5000	0.489	0.577	0.557	17/64	0.273	0.258	3/16	0.195	0.180
3/8	0.3750	9/16	0.5625	0.551	0.650	0.628	21/64	0.337	0.320	7/32	0.227	0.210
7/16	0.4375	11/16	0.6875	0.675	0.794	0.768	3/8	0.385	0.365	1/4	0.260	0.240
1/2	0.5000	3/4	0.7500	0.736	0.866	0.840	7/16	0.448	0.427	5/16	0.323	0.302
9/16	0.5625	7/8	0.8750	0.861	1.010	0.982	31/64	0.496	0.473	5/16	0.324	0.301
5/8	0.6250	15/16	0.9375	0.922	1.083	1.051	35/64	0.559	0.535	3/8	0.387	0.363
3/4	0.7500	1 1/8	1.1250	1.088	1.299	1.240	41/64	0.665	0.617	27/64	0.446	0.398
7/8	0.8750	1 5/16	1.3125	1.269	1.516	1.447	3/4	0.776	0.724	31/64	0.510	0.458
1	1.0000	1 1/2	1.5000	1.450	1.732	1.653	55/64	0.887	0.831	35/64	0.575	0.519
1 1/8	1.1250	1 11/16	1.6875	1.631	1.949	1.859	31/32	0.999	0.939	39/64	0.639	0.579
1 1/4	1.2500	1 7/8	1.8750	1.812	2.165	2.066	1 1/16	1.094	1.030	23/32	0.751	0.687
1 3/8	1.3750	2 1/16	2.0625	1.994	2.382	2.273	1 11/64	1.206	1.138	25/32	0.815	0.747
1 1/2	1.5000	2 1/4	2.2500	2.175	2.598	2.480	1 9/32	1.317	1.245	27/32	0.880	0.808
1 3/4	1.7500	2 5/8	2.6250	2.538	3.031	2.893	1 1/2	1.540	1.460	31/32	1.009	0.929
2	2.0000	3	3.0000	2.900	3.464	3.306	1 23/32	1.763	1.675	1 3/32	1.138	1.050
2 1/4	2.2500	3 3/8	3.3750	3.262	3.897	3.719	1 59/64	1.970	1.874	1 13/64	1.251	1.155
2 1/2	2.5000	3 3/4	3.7500	3.625	4.330	4.133	2 9/64	2.193	2.089	1 29/64	1.505	1.401
2 3/4	2.7500	4 1/8	4.1250	3.988	4.763	4.546	2 23/64	2.415	2.303	1 37/64	1.634	1.522
3	3.0000	4 1/2	4.5000	4.350	5.196	4.959	2 37/64	2.638	2.518	1 45/64	1.763	1.643

All dimensions given in inches.
BOLD TYPE INDICATES PRODUCTS UNIFIED DIMENSIONALLY WITH BRITISH AND CANADIAN STANDARDS.
"Finished" in the title refers to the quality of manufacture and the closeness of tolerance and does not indicate that surfaces are completely machined.

Bearing surface shall be washer faced or with chamfered corners. Diameter of circle of bearing surface shall be the maximum width across flats within a tolerance of minus 5 per cent. Tapped hole shall be counter-sunk 1/64 in. over the major diameter of thread for nuts up to and including 1/2 in. and 1/32 in. over the major diameter of thread for nuts over 1/2 in. size.

Thread shall be coarse-, fine-, or 8-thread series; class 2B.

TABLE 14
Slotted Head Machine Screws

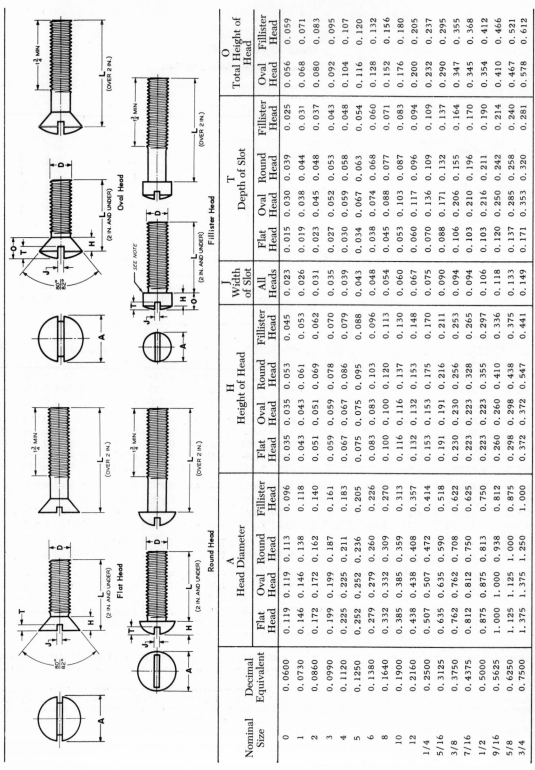

Nominal Size	Decimal Equivalent	A Head Diameter				H Height of Head				J Width of Slot	T Depth of Slot				O Total Height of Head	
		Flat Head	Oval Head	Round Head	Fillister Head	Flat Head	Oval Head	Round Head	Fillister Head	All Heads	Flat Head	Oval Head	Round Head	Fillister Head	Oval Head	Fillister Head
0	0.0600	0.119	0.119	0.113	0.096	0.035	0.035	0.053	0.045	0.023	0.015	0.030	0.039	0.025	0.056	0.059
1	0.0730	0.146	0.146	0.138	0.118	0.043	0.043	0.061	0.053	0.026	0.019	0.038	0.044	0.031	0.068	0.071
2	0.0860	0.172	0.172	0.162	0.140	0.051	0.051	0.069	0.062	0.031	0.023	0.045	0.048	0.037	0.080	0.083
3	0.0990	0.199	0.199	0.187	0.161	0.059	0.059	0.078	0.070	0.035	0.027	0.052	0.053	0.043	0.092	0.095
4	0.1120	0.225	0.225	0.211	0.183	0.067	0.067	0.086	0.079	0.039	0.030	0.059	0.058	0.048	0.104	0.107
5	0.1250	0.252	0.252	0.236	0.205	0.075	0.075	0.095	0.088	0.043	0.034	0.067	0.063	0.054	0.116	0.120
6	0.1380	0.279	0.279	0.260	0.226	0.083	0.083	0.103	0.096	0.048	0.038	0.074	0.068	0.060	0.128	0.132
8	0.1640	0.332	0.332	0.309	0.270	0.100	0.100	0.120	0.113	0.054	0.045	0.088	0.077	0.071	0.152	0.156
10	0.1900	0.385	0.385	0.359	0.313	0.116	0.116	0.137	0.130	0.060	0.053	0.103	0.087	0.083	0.176	0.180
12	0.2160	0.438	0.438	0.408	0.357	0.132	0.132	0.153	0.148	0.067	0.060	0.117	0.096	0.094	0.200	0.205
1/4	0.2500	0.507	0.507	0.472	0.414	0.153	0.153	0.175	0.170	0.075	0.070	0.136	0.109	0.109	0.232	0.237
5/16	0.3125	0.635	0.635	0.590	0.518	0.191	0.191	0.216	0.211	0.090	0.088	0.171	0.132	0.137	0.290	0.295
3/8	0.3750	0.762	0.762	0.708	0.622	0.230	0.230	0.256	0.253	0.094	0.106	0.206	0.155	0.164	0.347	0.355
7/16	0.4375	0.812	0.812	0.750	0.625	0.223	0.223	0.328	0.265	0.094	0.103	0.210	0.196	0.170	0.345	0.368
1/2	0.5000	0.875	0.875	0.813	0.750	0.223	0.223	0.355	0.297	0.106	0.103	0.216	0.211	0.190	0.354	0.412
9/16	0.5625	1.000	1.000	0.938	0.812	0.260	0.260	0.410	0.336	0.118	0.120	0.250	0.242	0.214	0.410	0.466
5/8	0.6250	1.125	1.125	1.000	0.875	0.298	0.298	0.438	0.375	0.133	0.137	0.285	0.258	0.240	0.467	0.521
3/4	0.7500	1.375	1.375	1.250	1.000	0.372	0.372	0.547	0.441	0.149	0.171	0.353	0.320	0.281	0.578	0.612

All dimensions are maximum values.   Threads are UNC or UNF. Class 2A.   Extracted from ASA B18.6.3—1962.

TABLE 15

Square and Hexagonal Machine Screw Nuts

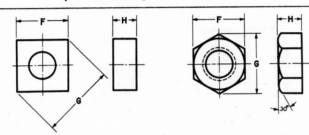

Diameter of Screw		F	G		H
		Width Across Flats	Width Across Corners°		Thickness
Nominal Size	Decimal Equivalent	Square and Hex.	Square	Hex.	Square and Hex.
0	0.0600	5/32	0.221	0.180	3/64
1	0.0730	5/32	0.221	0.180	3/64
2	0.0860	3/16	0.265	0.217	1/16
3	0.0990	3/16	0.265	0.217	1/16
4	0.1120	1/4	0.354	0.289	3/32
5	0.1250	5/16	0.442	0.361	7/64
6	0.1380	5/16	0.442	0.361	7/64
8	0.1640	11/32	0.486	0.397	1/8
10	0.1900	3/8	0.530	0.433	1/8
12	0.2160	7/16	0.619	0.505	5/32
1/4	0.2500	7/16	0.619	0.505	3/16
5/16	0.3125	9/16	0.795	0.650	7/32
3/8	0.3750	5/8	0.884	0.722	1/4

°Maximum value.
Threads for square nuts are UNC, Class 2B.
Threads for hexagon nuts are UNC or UNF, Class 2B.
Extracted from ASA B18.6.3—1962.

TABLE 16
Hexagon Head Cap Screws

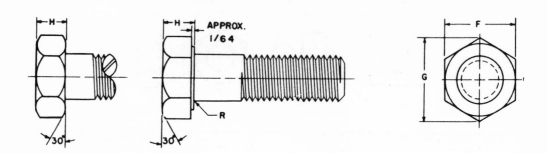

Nominal Size or Basic Major Diameter of Thread		Body Diam Min (Maximum Equal to Nom Size)	F Width Across Flats			G Width Across Corners		H Height			R Radius of Fillet	
			Max	(Basic)	Min	Max	Min	Nom	Max	Min	Max	Min
1/4	0.2500	0.2450	7/16	0.4375	0.428	0.505	0.488	5/32	0.163	0.150	0.023	0.009
5/16	0.3125	0.3065	1/2	0.5000	0.489	0.577	0.557	13/64	0.211	0.195	0.023	0.009
3/8	0.3750	0.3690	9/16	0.5625	0.551	0.650	0.628	15/64	0.243	0.226	0.023	0.009
7/16	0.4375	0.4305	5/8	0.6250	0.612	0.722	0.698	9/32	0.291	0.272	0.023	0.009
1/2	0.5000	0.4930	3/4	0.7500	0.736	0.866	0.840	5/16	0.323	0.302	0.023	0.009
9/16	0.5625	0.5545	13/16	0.8125	0.798	0.938	0.910	23/64	0.371	0.348	0.041	0.021
5/8	0.6250	0.6170	15/16	0.9375	0.922	1.083	1.051	25/64	0.403	0.378	0.041	0.021
3/4	0.7500	0.7410	1 1/8	1.1250	1.100	1.299	1.254	15/32	0.483	0.455	0.041	0.021
7/8	0.8750	0.8660	1 5/16	1.3125	1.285	1.516	1.465	35/64	0.563	0.531	0.062	0.041
1	1.0000	0.9900	1 1/2	1.5000	1.469	1.732	1.675	39/64	0.627	0.591	0.093	0.062
1 1/8	1.1250	1.1140	1 11/16	1.6875	1.631	1.949	1.859	11/16	0.718	0.658	0.093	0.062
1 1/4	1.2500	1.2390	1 7/8	1.8750	1.812	2.165	2.066	25/32	0.813	0.749	0.093	0.062
1 3/8	1.3750	1.3630	2 1/16	2.0625	1.994	2.382	2.273	27/32	0.878	0.810	0.093	0.062
1 1/2	1.5000	1.4880	2 1/4	2.2500	2.175	2.598	2.480	15/16	0.974	0.902	0.093	0.062

All dimensions given in inches.

BOLD TYPE INDICATES PRODUCTS UNIFIED DIMENSIONALLY WITH BRITISH AND CANADIAN STANDARDS.

Minimum thread length shall be twice the diameter plus ¼ in. for lengths up to and including 6 in.; twice the diameter plus ½ in. for lengths over 6 in. The tolerance shall be plus 3/16 in. or 2½ threads, whichever is greater. On products that are too short for minimum thread lengths the distance from the bearing surface of the head to the first complete thread shall not exceed the length of 2½ threads, as measured with a ring thread gage, for sizes up to and including 1 in. and 3½ threads for sizes larger than 1 in.

Threads shall be coarse, fine, or 8-thread series, class 2A.

Extracted from ASA B18.6.2—1956.

TABLE 17
Slotted Head Cap Screws

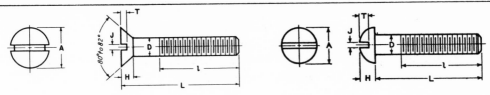

Flat Head   Round Head

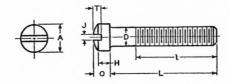

Fillister Head

Nominal Size	Width of Slot	Flat Head			Round Head			Fillister Head			
	J	A	H	T	A	H	T	A	H	T	O
$\frac{1}{4}$	0.075	0.500	0.140	0.068	0.437	0.191	0.117	0.375	0.172	0.097	0.216
$\frac{5}{16}$	0.084	0.625	0.177	0.086	0.562	0.245	0.151	0.437	0.203	0.115	0.253
$\frac{3}{8}$	0.094	0.750	0.210	0.103	0.625	0.273	0.168	0.562	0.250	0.142	0.314
$\frac{7}{16}$	0.094	0.8125	0.210	0.103	0.750	0.328	0.202	0.625	0.297	0.168	0.368
$\frac{1}{2}$	0.106	0.875	0.210	0.103	0.812	0.354	0.218	0.750	0.328	0.193	0.413
$\frac{9}{16}$	0.118	1.000	0.244	0.120	0.937	0.409	0.252	0.812	0.375	0.213	0.467
$\frac{5}{8}$	0.133	1.125	0.281	0.137	1.000	0.437	0.270	0.875	0.422	0.239	0.521
$\frac{3}{4}$	0.149	1.375	0.352	0.171	1.250	0.546	0.338	1.000	0.500	0.283	0.612
$\frac{7}{8}$	0.167	1.625	0.423	0.206				1.125	0.594	0.334	0.720
1	0.188	1.875	0.494	0.240				1.312	0.656	0.371	0.803
$1\frac{1}{8}$	0.196	2.062	0.529	0.257							
$1\frac{1}{4}$	0.211	2.312	0.600	0.291							
$1\frac{3}{8}$	0.226	2.562	0.665	0.326							
$1\frac{1}{2}$	0.258	2.812	0.742	0.360							

All dimensions are maximum values.
Threads are coarse, fine, or 8-thread series, Class 2A.
Minimum length of thread equals 2D plus ¼ inch.
Extracted from ASA B18.6.2–1956.

TABLE 18
Woodruff Keys[1]

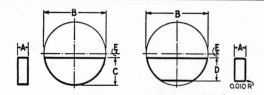

Key Number[2]	Nominal Key Size	Width of Key		Diam. of Key		Height of Key				Distance Below Center
		A		B		C		D		
	$A \times B$	Max.	Min.	Max.	Min.	Max.	Min.	Max.	Min.	E
204	1/16 × 1/2	0.0635	0.0625	0.500	0.490	0.203	0.198	0.194	0.188	3/64
304	3/32 × 1/2	0.0948	0.0938	0.500	0.490	0.203	0.198	0.194	0.188	3/64
305	3/32 × 5/8	0.0948	0.0938	0.625	0.615	0.250	0.245	0.240	0.234	1/16
404	1/8 × 1/2	0.1260	0.1250	0.500	0.490	0.203	0.198	0.194	0.188	3/64
405	1/8 × 5/8	0.1260	0.1250	0.625	0.615	0.250	0.245	0.240	0.234	1/16
406	1/8 × 3/4	0.1260	0.1250	0.750	0.740	0.313	0.308	0.303	0.297	1/16
505	5/32 × 5/8	0.1573	0.1563	0.625	0.615	0.250	0.245	0.240	0.234	1/16
506	5/32 × 3/4	0.1573	0.1563	0.750	0.740	0.313	0.308	0.303	0.297	1/16
507	5/32 × 7/8	0.1573	0.1563	0.875	0.865	0.375	0.370	0.365	0.359	1/16
606	3/16 × 3/4	0.1885	0.1875	0.750	0.740	0.313	0.308	0.303	0.297	1/16
607	3/16 × 7/8	0.1885	0.1875	0.875	0.865	0.375	0.370	0.365	0.359	1/16
608	3/16 × 1	0.1885	0.1875	1.000	0.990	0.438	0.433	0.428	0.422	1/16
609	3/16 × 1 1/8	0.1885	0.1875	1.125	1.115	0.484	0.479	0.475	0.469	5/64
807	1/4 × 7/8	0.2510	0.2500	0.875	0.865	0.375	0.370	0.365	0.359	1/16
808	1/4 × 1	0.2510	0.2500	1.000	0.990	0.438	0.433	0.428	0.422	1/16
809	1/4 × 1 1/8	0.2510	0.2500	1.125	1.115	0.484	0.479	0.475	0.469	5/64
810	1/4 × 1 1/4	0.2510	0.2500	1.250	1.240	0.547	0.542	0.537	0.531	5/64
811	1/4 × 1 3/8	0.2510	0.2500	1.375	1.365	0.594	0.589	0.584	0.578	3/32
812	1/4 × 1 1/2	0.2510	0.2500	1.500	1.490	0.641	0.636	0.631	0.625	7/64
1008	5/16 × 1	0.3135	0.3125	1.000	0.990	0.438	0.433	0.428	0.422	1/16
1009	5/16 × 1 1/8	0.3135	0.3125	1.125	1.115	0.484	0.479	0.475	0.469	5/64
1010	5/16 × 1 1/4	0.3135	0.3125	1.250	1.240	0.547	0.542	0.537	0.531	5/64
1011	5/16 × 1 3/8	0.3135	0.3125	1.375	1.365	0.594	0.589	0.584	0.578	3/32
1012	5/16 × 1 1/2	0.3135	0.3125	1.500	1.490	0.641	0.636	0.631	0.625	7/64
1210	3/8 × 1 1/4	0.3760	0.3750	1.250	1.240	0.547	0.542	0.537	0.531	5/64
1211	3/8 × 1 3/8	0.3760	0.3750	1.375	1.365	0.594	0.589	0.584	0.578	3/32
1212	3/8 × 1 1/2	0.3760	0.3750	1.500	1.490	0.641	0.636	0.631	0.625	7/64

[1] Woodruff Keys, Keyslots, and Cutters. ASA B17f—1930. (Reaffirmed 1955.)
[2] Key numbers indicate the nominal key dimensions. The last two digits give the nominal diameter (B) in eighths of an inch and the digits preceding the last two give the nominal width (A) in thirty-seconds of an inch. Thus, 204 indicates a key 2/32 × 4/8 or 1/16 × 1/2 inches; 1210 indicates a key 12/32 × 10/8 or 3/8 × 1 1/4 inches.

TABLE 19

Woodruff Keyseats and Keyways[1]

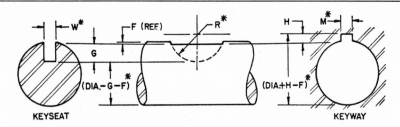

Recommended Shaft Dia.[2]	Key		Keyseat			Keyway				Values of "F"	
	No.	R Nom.	W Min.	W Max.	G Nom.	M Min.	M Max.	H Min.	H Max.	Dia. of Shaft by Width of Key	F
$\frac{5}{16}$-$\frac{3}{8}$	204	$\frac{1}{4}$	0.0615	0.0630	0.1668	0.0635	0.0655	0.0372	0.0422		
$\frac{7}{16}$-$\frac{1}{2}$	304	$\frac{1}{4}$	0.0928	0.0943	0.1511	0.0948	0.0968	0.0529	0.0579		
	305	$\frac{5}{16}$	0.0928	0.0943	0.1981	0.0948	0.0968	0.0529	0.0579		
$\frac{9}{16}$-$\frac{3}{4}$	404	$\frac{1}{4}$	0.1240	0.1255	0.1355	0.1260	0.1280	0.0685	0.0735		
	405	$\frac{5}{16}$	0.1240	0.1255	0.1825	0.1260	0.1280	0.0685	0.0735	$\frac{5}{16} \times \frac{1}{16}$	0.0032
	406	$\frac{3}{8}$	0.1240	0.1255	0.2455	0.1260	0.1280	0.0685	0.0735	$\frac{3}{8} \times \frac{1}{16}$	0.0026
										$\frac{7}{16} \times \frac{3}{32}$	0.0051
$\frac{13}{16}$-$1\frac{5}{16}$	505	$\frac{5}{16}$	0.1553	0.1568	0.1669	0.1573	0.1593	0.0841	0.0891	$\frac{1}{2} \times \frac{3}{32}$	0.0044
	506	$\frac{3}{8}$	0.1553	0.1568	0.2299	0.1573	0.1593	0.0841	0.0891		
	507	$\frac{7}{16}$	0.1553	0.1568	0.2919	0.1573	0.1593	0.0841	0.0891	$\frac{9}{16} \times \frac{1}{8}$	0.0070
										$\frac{5}{8} \times \frac{1}{8}$	0.0063
1-$1\frac{3}{16}$	606	$\frac{3}{8}$	0.1863	0.1880	0.2443	0.1885	0.1905	0.0997	0.1047	$\frac{11}{16} \times \frac{1}{8}$	0.0057
	607	$\frac{7}{16}$	0.1863	0.1880	0.2763	0.1885	0.1905	0.0997	0.1047	$\frac{3}{4} \times \frac{1}{8}$	0.0052
	608	$\frac{1}{2}$	0.1863	0.1880	0.3393	0.1885	0.1905	0.0997	0.1047		
	609	$\frac{9}{16}$	0.1863	0.1880	0.3853	0.1885	0.1905	0.0997	0.1047	$\frac{13}{16} \times \frac{5}{32}$	0.0076
										$\frac{7}{8} \times \frac{5}{32}$	0.0070
$1\frac{1}{4}$-$1\frac{3}{4}$	807	$\frac{7}{16}$	0.2487	0.2505	0.2450	0.2510	0.2530	0.1310	0.1360	$\frac{15}{16} \times \frac{5}{32}$	0.0066
	808	$\frac{1}{2}$	0.2487	0.2505	0.3080	0.2510	0.2530	0.1310	0.1360		
	809	$\frac{9}{16}$	0.2487	0.2505	0.3540	0.2510	0.2530	0.1310	0.1360	$1 \times \frac{3}{16}$	0.0089
	810	$\frac{5}{8}$	0.2487	0.2505	0.4170	0.2510	0.2530	0.1310	0.1360	$1\frac{1}{8} \times \frac{3}{16}$	0.0079
	811	$\frac{11}{16}$	0.2487	0.2505	0.4640	0.2510	0.2530	0.1310	0.1360	$1\frac{1}{4} \times \frac{3}{16}$	0.0071
	812	$\frac{3}{4}$	0.2487	0.2505	0.5110	0.2510	0.2530	0.1310	0.1360		
										$1\frac{3}{8} \times \frac{1}{4}$	0.0115
$1\frac{13}{16}$-$2\frac{1}{2}$	1008	$\frac{1}{2}$	0.3111	0.3130	0.2768	0.3135	0.3155	0.1622	0.1672	$1\frac{1}{2} \times \frac{1}{4}$	0.0105
	1009	$\frac{9}{16}$	0.3111	0.3130	0.3228	0.3135	0.3155	0.1622	0.1672	$1\frac{5}{8} \times \frac{1}{4}$	0.0097
	1010	$\frac{5}{8}$	0.3111	0.3130	0.3858	0.3135	0.3155	0.1622	0.1672	$1\frac{3}{4} \times \frac{1}{4}$	0.0090
	1011	$\frac{11}{16}$	0.3111	0.3130	0.4328	0.3135	0.3155	0.1622	0.1672		
	1012	$\frac{3}{4}$	0.3111	0.3130	0.4798	0.3135	0.3155	0.1622	0.1672	$1\frac{7}{8} \times \frac{5}{16}$	0.0131
										$2 \times \frac{5}{16}$	0.0123
	1210	$\frac{5}{8}$	0.3735	0.3755	0.3545	0.3760	0.3780	0.1935	0.1985	$2\frac{1}{4} \times \frac{5}{16}$	0.0109
	1211	$\frac{11}{16}$	0.3735	0.3755	0.4015	0.3760	0.3780	0.1935	0.1985	$2\frac{1}{2} \times \frac{5}{16}$	0.0098
	1212	$\frac{3}{4}$	0.3735	0.3755	0.4485	0.3760	0.3780	0.1935	0.1985		

* These dimensions are required on detail drawings.
[1] Courtesy, Douglas Aircraft Company, Inc.
[2] Supplied to table.

TABLE 20

Plain Parallel Stock Keys[1]

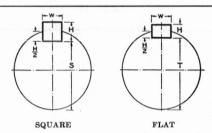

SQUARE   FLAT

Shaft Diameter	Square Key $W \times H$	Flat Key $W \times H$	Tolerance[2,3] on W and H (—)	Bottom of Keyseat to Opposite Side of Shaft	
				Square Key S	Flat Key T
$\frac{1}{2}$	$\frac{1}{8} \times \frac{1}{8}$	$\frac{1}{8} \times \frac{3}{32}$	0.0020	0.430	0.445
$\frac{9}{16}$	$\frac{1}{8} \times \frac{1}{8}$	$\frac{1}{8} \times \frac{3}{32}$	0.0020	0.493	0.509
$\frac{5}{8}$	$\frac{3}{16} \times \frac{3}{16}$	$\frac{3}{16} \times \frac{1}{8}$	0.0020	0.517	0.548
$\frac{11}{16}$	$\frac{3}{16} \times \frac{3}{16}$	$\frac{3}{16} \times \frac{1}{8}$	0.0020	0.581	0.612
$\frac{3}{4}$	$\frac{3}{16} \times \frac{3}{16}$	$\frac{3}{16} \times \frac{1}{8}$	0.0020	0.644	0.676
$\frac{13}{16}$	$\frac{3}{16} \times \frac{3}{16}$	$\frac{3}{16} \times \frac{1}{8}$	0.0020	0.708	0.739
$\frac{7}{8}$	$\frac{3}{16} \times \frac{3}{16}$	$\frac{3}{16} \times \frac{1}{8}$	0.0020	0.771	0.802
$\frac{15}{16}$	$\frac{1}{4} \times \frac{1}{4}$	$\frac{1}{4} \times \frac{3}{16}$	0.0020	0.796	0.827
1	$\frac{1}{4} \times \frac{1}{4}$	$\frac{1}{4} \times \frac{3}{16}$	0.0020	0.859	0.890
$1\frac{1}{16}$	$\frac{1}{4} \times \frac{1}{4}$	$\frac{1}{4} \times \frac{3}{16}$	0.0020	0.923	0.954
$1\frac{1}{8}$	$\frac{1}{4} \times \frac{1}{4}$	$\frac{1}{4} \times \frac{3}{16}$	0.0020	0.986	1.017
$1\frac{3}{16}$	$\frac{1}{4} \times \frac{1}{4}$	$\frac{1}{4} \times \frac{3}{16}$	0.0020	1.049	1.081
$1\frac{1}{4}$	$\frac{1}{4} \times \frac{1}{4}$	$\frac{1}{4} \times \frac{3}{16}$	0.0020	1.112	1.144
$1\frac{5}{16}$	$\frac{5}{16} \times \frac{5}{16}$	$\frac{5}{16} \times \frac{1}{4}$	0.0020	1.137	1.169
$1\frac{3}{8}$	$\frac{5}{16} \times \frac{5}{16}$	$\frac{5}{16} \times \frac{1}{4}$	0.0020	1.201	1.232
$1\frac{7}{16}$	$\frac{3}{8} \times \frac{3}{8}$	$\frac{3}{8} \times \frac{1}{4}$	0.0020	1.225	1.288
$1\frac{1}{2}$	$\frac{3}{8} \times \frac{3}{8}$	$\frac{3}{8} \times \frac{1}{4}$	0.0020	1.289	1.351
$1\frac{9}{16}$	$\frac{3}{8} \times \frac{3}{8}$	$\frac{3}{8} \times \frac{1}{4}$	0.0020	1.352	1.415
$1\frac{5}{8}$	$\frac{3}{8} \times \frac{3}{8}$	$\frac{3}{8} \times \frac{1}{4}$	0.0020	1.416	1.478
$1\frac{11}{16}$	$\frac{3}{8} \times \frac{3}{8}$	$\frac{3}{8} \times \frac{1}{4}$	0.0020	1.479	1.542
$1\frac{3}{4}$	$\frac{3}{8} \times \frac{3}{8}$	$\frac{3}{8} \times \frac{1}{4}$	0.0020	1.542	1.605
$1\frac{13}{16}$	$\frac{1}{2} \times \frac{1}{2}$	$\frac{1}{2} \times \frac{3}{8}$	0.0025	1.527	1.590
$1\frac{7}{8}$	$\frac{1}{2} \times \frac{1}{2}$	$\frac{1}{2} \times \frac{3}{8}$	0.0025	1.591	1.654
$1\frac{15}{16}$	$\frac{1}{2} \times \frac{1}{2}$	$\frac{1}{2} \times \frac{3}{8}$	0.0025	1.655	1.717
2	$\frac{1}{2} \times \frac{1}{2}$	$\frac{1}{2} \times \frac{3}{8}$	0.0025	1.718	1.781
$2\frac{1}{16}$	$\frac{1}{2} \times \frac{1}{2}$	$\frac{1}{2} \times \frac{3}{8}$	0.0025	1.782	1.843

[1] ASA B17.1–1934.

[2] Stock keys are applicable to the general run of work and the tolerances have been set accordingly. It is understood that these keys are to be cut from cold-finished stock and are to be used without machining. They are not intended to cover the finer applications where a closer fit may be required.

[3] These tolerances are *negative* and represent the maximum allowable variation *below* the exact nominal size. For example, the standard stock square key for a 2″ shaft has a maximum size of 0.500 × 0.500 inch and a minimum size of 0.4975 × 0.4975 inch.

TABLE 20 (Continued)

Plain Parallel Stock Keys

Shaft Diameter	Square Key $W \times H$	Flat Key $W \times H$	Tolerance[2,3] on W and H (−)	Bottom of Keyseat to Opposite Side of Shaft	
				Square Key S	Flat Key T
$2\frac{1}{8}$	$\frac{1}{2} \times \frac{1}{2}$	$\frac{1}{2} \times \frac{3}{8}$	0.0025	1.845	1.908
$2\frac{3}{16}$	$\frac{1}{2} \times \frac{1}{2}$	$\frac{1}{2} \times \frac{3}{8}$	0.0025	1.909	1.971
$2\frac{1}{4}$	$\frac{1}{2} \times \frac{1}{2}$	$\frac{1}{2} \times \frac{3}{8}$	0.0025	1.972	2.034
$2\frac{5}{16}$	$\frac{5}{8} \times \frac{5}{8}$	$\frac{5}{8} \times \frac{7}{16}$	0.0025	1.957	2.051
$2\frac{3}{8}$	$\frac{5}{8} \times \frac{5}{8}$	$\frac{5}{8} \times \frac{7}{16}$	0.0025	2.021	2.114
$2\frac{7}{16}$	$\frac{5}{8} \times \frac{5}{8}$	$\frac{5}{8} \times \frac{7}{16}$	0.0025	2.084	2.178
$2\frac{1}{2}$	$\frac{5}{8} \times \frac{5}{8}$	$\frac{5}{8} \times \frac{7}{16}$	0.0025	2.148	2.242
$2\frac{5}{8}$	$\frac{5}{8} \times \frac{5}{8}$	$\frac{5}{8} \times \frac{7}{16}$	0.0025	2.275	2.368
$2\frac{3}{4}$	$\frac{5}{8} \times \frac{5}{8}$	$\frac{5}{8} \times \frac{7}{16}$	0.0025	2.402	2.495
$2\frac{7}{8}$	$\frac{3}{4} \times \frac{3}{4}$	$\frac{3}{4} \times \frac{1}{2}$	0.0025	2.450	2.575
$2\frac{15}{16}$	$\frac{3}{4} \times \frac{3}{4}$	$\frac{3}{4} \times \frac{1}{2}$	0.0025	2.514	2.639
3	$\frac{3}{4} \times \frac{3}{4}$	$\frac{3}{4} \times \frac{1}{2}$	0.0025	2.577	2.702
$3\frac{1}{8}$	$\frac{3}{4} \times \frac{3}{4}$	$\frac{3}{4} \times \frac{1}{2}$	0.0025	2.704	2.829
$3\frac{1}{4}$	$\frac{3}{4} \times \frac{3}{4}$	$\frac{3}{4} \times \frac{1}{2}$	0.0025	2.831	2.956
$3\frac{3}{8}$	$\frac{7}{8} \times \frac{7}{8}$	$\frac{7}{8} \times \frac{5}{8}$	0.0030	2.880	3.005
$3\frac{7}{16}$	$\frac{7}{8} \times \frac{7}{8}$	$\frac{7}{8} \times \frac{5}{8}$	0.0030	2.944	3.069
$3\frac{1}{2}$	$\frac{7}{8} \times \frac{7}{8}$	$\frac{7}{8} \times \frac{5}{8}$	0.0030	3.007	3.132
$3\frac{5}{8}$	$\frac{7}{8} \times \frac{7}{8}$	$\frac{7}{8} \times \frac{5}{8}$	0.0030	3.140	3.259
$3\frac{3}{4}$	$\frac{7}{8} \times \frac{7}{8}$	$\frac{7}{8} \times \frac{5}{8}$	0.0030	3.261	3.386
$3\frac{7}{8}$	1×1	$1 \times \frac{3}{4}$	0.0030	3.309	3.434
$3\frac{15}{16}$	1×1	$1 \times \frac{3}{4}$	0.0030	3.373	3.498
4	1×1	$1 \times \frac{3}{4}$	0.0030	3.437	3.562
$4\frac{1}{4}$	1×1	$1 \times \frac{3}{4}$	0.0030	3.690	3.815
$4\frac{7}{16}$	1×1	$1 \times \frac{3}{4}$	0.0030	3.881	4.006
$4\frac{1}{2}$	1×1	$1 \times \frac{3}{4}$	0.0030	3.944	4.069
$4\frac{3}{4}$	$1\frac{1}{4} \times 1\frac{1}{4}$	$1\frac{1}{4} \times \frac{7}{8}$	0.0030	4.042	4.229
$4\frac{15}{16}$	$1\frac{1}{4} \times 1\frac{1}{4}$	$1\frac{1}{4} \times \frac{7}{8}$	0.0030	4.232	4.420
5	$1\frac{1}{4} \times 1\frac{1}{4}$	$1\frac{1}{4} \times \frac{7}{8}$	0.0030	4.296	4.483
$5\frac{1}{4}$	$1\frac{1}{4} \times 1\frac{1}{4}$	$1\frac{1}{4} \times \frac{7}{8}$	0.0030	4.550	4.733
$5\frac{7}{16}$	$1\frac{1}{4} \times 1\frac{1}{4}$	$1\frac{1}{4} \times \frac{7}{8}$	0.0030	4.740	4.927
$5\frac{1}{2}$	$1\frac{1}{4} \times 1\frac{1}{4}$	$1\frac{1}{4} \times \frac{7}{8}$	0.0030	4.803	4.991
$5\frac{3}{4}$	$1\frac{1}{2} \times 1\frac{1}{2}$	$1\frac{1}{2} \times 1$	0.0030	4.900	5.150
$5\frac{15}{16}$	$1\frac{1}{2} \times 1\frac{1}{2}$	$1\frac{1}{2} \times 1$	0.0030	5.091	5.341
6	$1\frac{1}{2} \times 1\frac{1}{2}$	$1\frac{1}{2} \times 1$	0.0030	5.155	5.405

[2] Stock keys are applicable to the general run of work and the tolerances have been set accordingly. It is understood that these keys are to be cut from cold-finished stock and are to be used without machining. They are not intended to cover the finer applications where a closer fit may be required.

[3] These tolerances are *negative* and represent the maximum allowable variation *below* the exact nominal size. For example, the standard stock square key for a 2″ shaft has a maximum size of 0.500 × 0.500 inch and a minimum size of 0.4975 × 0.4975 inch.

TABLE 21
Washers[1]

Nominal Size[2]	Plain Washers			Spring Lock Washers				
	Inside Dia.	Outside Dia.	Thickness ±.010	Inside Dia. (Min.)	Outside Dia. (Max.)		Thickness	
					Light	Extra Heavy	Light	Extra Heavy
#2 (0.086)	3/32	1/4	1/32	0.088	0.165	0.211	0.015	0.027
#4 (0.112)	1/8	5/16	1/32	0.115	0.202	0.256	0.020	0.034
#6 (0.138)	5/32	3/8	3/64	0.141	0.237	0.315	0.025	0.045
#8 (0.164)	3/16	7/16	3/64	0.168	0.280	0.378	0.031	0.057
#10 (0.190)	7/32	1/2	1/16	0.194	0.323	0.437	0.040	0.068
#12 (0.216)	1/4	9/16	1/16	0.221	0.364	0.500	0.047	0.080
1/4	9/32	5/8	1/16	0.255	0.489	0.539	0.047	0.084
5/16	11/32	11/16	1/16	0.319	0.575	0.627	0.056	0.108
3/8	13/32	13/16	1/16	0.382	0.678	0.746	0.070	0.123
7/16	15/32	15/16	1/16	0.446	0.780	0.844	0.085	0.143
1/2	17/32	1 1/16	3/32	0.509	0.877	0.945	0.099	0.162
9/16	19/32	1 3/16	3/32	0.573	0.975	1.049	0.113	0.182
5/8	21/32	1 5/16	3/32	0.636	1.082	1.164	0.126	0.202
11/16	23/32	1 3/8	3/32	0.700	1.178	1.266	0.138	0.221
3/4	13/16	1 1/2	1/8	0.763	1.277	1.369	0.153	0.241
7/8	15/16	1 3/4	1/8	0.890	1.470	1.586	0.179	0.285
1	1 1/16	2	1/8	1.017	1.656	1.810	0.202	0.330
1 1/8	1 3/16	2 1/4	1/8	1.144	1.837	2.031	0.224	0.375
1 1/4	1 5/16	2 1/2	5/32	1.271	2.012	2.244	0.244	0.417
1 3/8	1 7/16	2 3/4	5/32	1.398	2.183	2.453	0.264	0.458
1 1/2	1 9/16	3	5/32	1.525	2.352	2.654	0.282	0.496

[1] SAE Standard.
[2] Washer size for bolt or screw of same nominal size.

TABLE 22

Taper Pins[1]

Taper, ¼ inch per foot

No. of Taper Pin	Diameter F at Large End of Pin	Approx. Fractional Size F	Maximum Length L
00000	0.094	$\frac{3}{32}$	$\frac{3}{4}$
0000	0.109	$\frac{7}{64}$	$\frac{7}{8}$
000	0.125	$\frac{1}{8}$	1
00	0.141	$\frac{9}{64}$	$1\frac{1}{8}$
0	0.156	$\frac{5}{32}$	$1\frac{1}{4}$
1	0.172	$\frac{11}{64}$	$1\frac{1}{4}$
2	0.193	$\frac{3}{16}$	$1\frac{1}{2}$

No. of Taper Pin	Diameter F at Large End of Pin	Approx. Fractional Size F	Maximum Length L
3	0.219	$\frac{7}{32}$	$1\frac{3}{4}$
4	0.250	$\frac{1}{4}$	2
5	0.289	$\frac{19}{64}$	$2\frac{1}{4}$
6	0.341	$\frac{11}{32}$	3
7	0.409	$\frac{13}{32}$	$3\frac{3}{4}$
8	0.492	$\frac{1}{2}$	$4\frac{1}{2}$
9	0.591	$\frac{19}{32}$	$5\frac{1}{4}$
10	0.706	$\frac{23}{32}$	6
11	0.860	$\frac{55}{64}$	$7\frac{1}{4}$
12	1.032	$1\frac{1}{32}$	9
13	1.241	$1\frac{15}{64}$	11
14	1.523	$1\frac{33}{64}$	13

[1] Specify reamers for taper pins by giving taper pin number in the notation.

INDEX